AQA GCSE Mathematics

FOUNDATION TIER

Series Editor | Trevor Senior
Linear Course

Student Book

Contents

Contents

Introduction

Welcome to *Longman AQA GCSE Mathematics Linear Foundation Student Book and ActiveBook*. It has been written to cover all the skills and knowledge required for AQA's GCSE Mathematics Foundation Tier Specification.

The Student Book

Each chapter has a number of units to work through, with full explanations of each topic, numerous worked examples and plenty of exercises, followed by a Chapter Summary and chapter review questions.

Each unit is introduced by a 'Can you remember' box, which tells you what you need to know before you can tackle the unit. There is then a box highlighting the learning objectives for each unit.

The text and worked examples that follow have been written to support you through the subsequent exercises. In Exercise A you will practice the skills and knowledge required for that topic.

The further explanatory text and worked examples lead into Exercise B. Exercise B questions have been written to stretch you a bit further than Exercise A and will require you to use and apply the knowledge you have learnt from the unit. The questions in all exercises have been written to progress from easy to more difficult.

At the end of each chapter, there is a Chapter Summary which will help you remember all the key points and concepts you need to know from the chapter and tell you what you should be able to do for the exam.

Following the Chapter Summary is a Chapter Review which comprises further questions, all of which are exam-style questions and have been written by examiners for the new specifications. Like the questions in the exercise sections, these progress from easy to hard.

In the exercise sections and Chapter Reviews 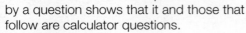 by a question shows that it and those that follow are non-calculator questions. by a question shows that it and those that follow are calculator questions.

The ActiveBook

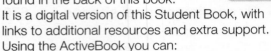

The ActiveBook CD-ROM is found in the back of this book. It is a digital version of this Student Book, with links to additional resources and extra support. Using the ActiveBook you can:

- See what vocabulary you will need to know for the unit
- Click on glossary words to see and hear their definitions
- Easily access and display answers to the questions in the exercise sections (these do not appear in the printed Student Book)
- Access a complete glossary for the whole book
- Practice exam questions and improve your exam technique with *Exam Tutor* model questions and answers. Each question that has an *Exam Tutor* icon beside it links to a worked solution with audio and visual annotation to guide you through it

Recommended specification
Pentium 3 500 Mhz processor
128MB RAM
8× speed CD-ROM
1GB free hard disc space
800 × 600 (or 1024 × 768) resolution screen at 16 bit colour
sound card, speakers or headphones

Windows 2000 or XP. This product has been designed for Windows 98, but will be unsupported in line with Microsoft's Product Life-Cycle policy.

Installation
Insert the CD. If you have autorun enabled the program should start within a few seconds. Follow on-screen instructions. Should you experience difficulty, please locate and review the readme file on the CD.

Technical support
If after reviewing the readme you are unable to resolve your problem, contact customer support:

- telephone 0870 6073777 (between 8.00 and 4.00)
- email schools.cd-romhelpdesk@pearson.com
- web http://centraal.uk.knowledgebox.com/kbase/

Working with numbers

1.1 Place value

CAN YOU REMEMBER

- How to multiply and divide whole numbers?
- The meaning of 'integer'?

IN THIS SECTION YOU WILL

- Write a number in words or figures.
- Work out the value of each digit in a whole number or a decimal.
- Multiply and divide any number by 10, 100, 1000 etc.

In the number 8074, the *digits* 8, 0, 7 and 4 have different values.
Write 8074 in a *place value* table:

Thousands	Hundreds	Tens	Units	.	tenths
8	0	7	4		

The column headings show the value of each digit.
- The value of the digit 8 is 8 thousands or 8000
- The value of the digit 7 is 7 tens or 70
- The value of the digit 4 is 4 units or 4

The number is made up of 8 thousands (8000), 7 tens (70) and 4 units (4).
In figures write 8074
In words write **eight thousand and seventy-four**.

A place value table includes a *decimal point*. This separates the integer part from the fraction part.

Write 3.56 in a place value table:

Thousands	Hundreds	Tens	Units	.	tenths	hundredths	thousandths
			3	.	5	6	

- The value of the digit 3 is 3 units or 3
- The value of the digit 5 is 5 tenths or 0.5
- The value of the digit 6 is 6 hundredths or 0.06

The number has an integer part and a fraction part.
It is made up of 3 units (3), 5 tenths (.5) and 6 hundredths (.06).
In figures write 3.56
In words write **three point five six**.

Example 1

Write the numbers in a place value table under the correct column headings.
a   491   b   40 753   c   73.48   d   5 412 968.2

Solution 1

	Millions	Hundred thousands	Ten thousands	Thousands	Hundreds	Tens	Units	.	tenths	hundredths	thousandths
a					4	9	1				
b			4	0	7	5	3				
c						7	3	.	4	8	
d	5	4	1	2	9	6	8	.	2		

Example 2

Write the following numbers in words.
a   802   b   1006   c   23 049

Solution 2

Write the numbers in a place value table:

	Ten thousands	Thousands	Hundreds	Tens	Units
a			8	0	2
b		1	0	0	6
c	2	3	0	4	9

a   eight hundred and two
b   one thousand and six
c   twenty-three thousand and forty-nine

Example 3

Write the following numbers in figures.
a   two hundred and three
b   five thousand and eighty-one
c   eight hundred and fifty thousand one hundred and four

Solution 3

(Write the numbers under the column headings.)

a 203   b 5081   c 850 104

	Hundred thousands	Ten thousands	Thousands	Hundreds	Tens	Units
a				2	0	3
b			5	0	8	1
c	8	5	0	1	0	4

Exercise A

1 Copy the place value table from Example 1. Write the following numbers in the correct columns.

  a 104   b 2095   c 3768   d 20 026
  e 507.1   f 389.02   g 1076.043   h 3804.59

2 Write the following numbers in words.

  a 367   b 409   c 2041   d 500 000
  e 238 147   f 630 129   g 1 000 000   h 4 650 012

3 Write the following numbers in figures.

  a four hundred and eight
  b two hundred and sixty
  c one thousand two hundred and thirty-four
  d nine thousand and sixty-seven
  e twenty-three thousand two hundred and ninety-one
  f five hundred and thirty-four thousand eight hundred and sixty-nine
  g four million six hundred thousand two hundred and thirteen
  h nine million one hundred and eighty-four thousand three hundred and ninety-five

4 Work out the value of each of the following.
Write each answer in i figures ii words.

  a 36×91 b 143×102 c $9870 \div 42$ d $409\,785 \div 51$
  e $723\,627 \div 27$ f $9\,840\,000 \div 328$ g $245 \times 362 \times 35$

To multiply by 10 move the digits one column to the left.
For example $17 \times 10 = 170$

Hundreds	Tens	Units
	1	7
1	7	0

The zero in the units column shows there are no units.
It keeps the other digits in their correct place value columns.

To multiply by 100 move the digits two columns to the left and so on.
For example 8.21 × 100 = 821

Hundreds	Tens	Units	.	tenths	hundredths
		8	.	2	1
8	2	1			

To divide by 10 move the digits one column to the right.
For example 46 ÷ 10 = 4.6

Tens	Units	.	tenths
4	6		
	4	.	6

To divide by 100 move the digits two columns to the right and so on.
For example 1230 ÷ 100 = 12.3

Thousands	Hundreds	Tens	Units	.	tenths
1	2	3	0		
		1	2	.	3

Example 4

Work out each of the following.
Write down in words the value of the digit 8 in the answer.
a   3814 × 100   b   23 681 × 10   c   6184 ÷ 10

Solution 4

a   To multiply by 100, the digits move two places to the left.

Hundred thousands	Ten thousands	Thousands	Hundreds	Tens	Units
		3	8	1	4
3	8	1	4	0	0

3814 × 100 = 381 400
The value of the digit 8 is eighty thousand.

b   To multiply by 10, the digits move one place to the left.

Hundred thousands	Ten thousands	Thousands	Hundreds	Tens	Units
	2	3	6	8	1
2	3	6	8	1	0

23 681 × 10 = 236 810
The value of the digit 8 is eight hundred.

c To divide by 10, the digits move one place to the right.

Thousands	Hundreds	Tens	Units	.	tenths
6	1	8	4		
	6	1	8	.	4

$6184 \div 10 = 618.4$
The value of the digit 8 is eight units or eight.

Exercise B

Work out each of the following.
Write down the value of the digit 3 in the answer.

1 834×10 **2** 1203×1000 **3** $437 \div 100$

4 $34\,065 \times 100$ **5** $9173 \div 10$ **6** $25\,139 \div 1000$

7 25.873×10 **8** $13.427 \div 100$ **9** $0.034 \div 10$

Work out each of the following.
Write down the value of the digit 3 in the answer.

10 $0.3471 \times 1\,000\,000$ **11** $3\,047\,296 \div 100\,000$

12 $0.005\,346 \times 10\,000$ **13** $376\,428 \div 10\,000\,000$

1.2 Number lines

CAN YOU REMEMBER

- How to sort whole numbers from smallest to biggest?
- How to answer questions such as: Which number is 35 more than 27?
- How to answer questions such as: Which number is 14 less than 88?

IN THIS SECTION YOU WILL

- Use a number line to add and subtract numbers.
- Use a number line to sort whole numbers into order.
- Use a number line to answer questions such as: Which number is halfway between 23 and 31?

Number lines can be used to sort numbers from smallest to biggest.

Number lines can be used to add and subtract by breaking down the number into easier chunks.

For example, to add 34, add 30 and then add 4
To add move to the right.

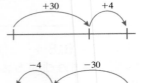

For example, to subtract 34, subtract 30 and then 4
To subtract move to the left.

Example 1

Use a number line to work out the number that is 36 more than 15

Solution 1

36 more than 15 is the same as 15 + 36
15 + 36 = 15 + 30 + 6

Draw a number line starting at 15
Jump 30, then 6

15 + 36 = 51

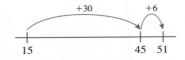

Example 2

Fill in the missing values on the number line.

Solution 2

There are 4 steps between 50 and 70

70 − 50 = 20
4 steps = 20
1 step = 20 ÷ 4 = 5

Labelling in steps of 5 gives

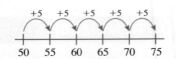

Exercise A

1 Copy the number lines and label the numbers shown by the arrows.

a 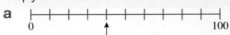   **b**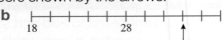

c 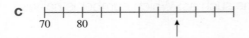   **d**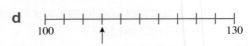

2 Put each list of numbers in order of size starting with the smallest.

a	4	17	13	9	2	20	
b	18	12	5	26	21	17	
c	36	42	26	23	74	32	33	68
d	102	98	117	86	134	106	101	99

3 From each list of numbers write down the biggest and the smallest number.

a 1024   2104   4102   1042   4021   4012
b Six million   Six thousand   Six hundred thousand   Sixty thousand
c 50301   10305   30501   10503   30105   50103
d 34615   35416   36145   36541   35641

4 Draw number lines and use them to find the answers to each of the following.
Show clearly how you worked out your answers.
  a The number that is 25 more than 42
  b The number that is 12 less than 100
  c The number that is exactly halfway between 40 and 70
  d The even number that is bigger than 56 and less than 59

5 Work out each of the following using a number line labelled from 0 to 100
in steps of 10
Check your answers using a calculator.
  a $37 + 56$ **b** $19 + 45$
  c $83 - 45$ **d** $87 - 39$
  e 17×5 (*Hint* 5 steps of 17)   **f** 7×14

Example 3

Work out the number that is exactly halfway between 18 and 42

Solution 3

Method 1
The *difference* between 18 and 42 is $42 - 18 = 24$
Half of $24 = 12$

Halfway between 18 and 42 is 12 more than 18
$18 + 12 = 30$

Method 2
To find the number halfway between two numbers:
add the numbers together and *divide* the answer by 2

The number that is halfway between 18 and 42 $= \dfrac{18 + 42}{2} = \dfrac{60}{2} = 30$

Exercise B

1 Work out the number that is exactly halfway between each of the following pairs of numbers.

   a 10 and 30   **b** 140 and 150   **c** 86 and 90

   d 14 and 24   **e** 25 and 31   **f** 74 and 86

2 Find the missing number for each of the following.

   a 42 is exactly halfway between 30 and .....

   b 18 is exactly halfway between 14 and .....

   c 30 is exactly halfway between ..... and 48

   d 71 is exactly halfway between ..... and 90

   e 29 is exactly halfway between 11 and .....

   f 63 is exactly halfway between 45 and .....

3 Work out the number that is exactly halfway between each of the following pairs of numbers.

   a 82 and 104   **b** 114 and 200   **c** 43 and 97

   d 8 and 162   **e** 29 and 91   **f** 55 and 101

4 Find the missing number for each of the following.

   a 118 is exactly halfway between 52 and .....

   b 340 is exactly halfway between 200 and .....

   c 152 is exactly halfway between .... and 237

   d 681 is exactly halfway between .... and 900

   e 192 is exactly halfway between 101 and .....

   f 483 is exactly halfway between 241 and .....

1.3 Everyday arithmetic

CAN YOU REMEMBER

- The multiplication table up to 10×10?
- The meaning of 'sum', 'total', 'difference'?
- How to solve number problems in everyday life, for example, about money?

IN THIS SECTION YOU WILL

- Learn some quick methods for calculating mentally.
- Work out complements of 100, e.g. $100 - 34$
- Use adding on as a method of subtracting.
- Solve money problems with and without a calculator.

Here are some ways of simplifying calculations without using a calculator.

To add a 'near 10', add the multiple of 10 and then add or subtract the difference.

Add 9	Add 10 then subtract 1
Add 99	Add 100 then subtract 1
Add 90	Add 100 then subtract 10
Add 48	Add 50 then subtract 2
Add 42	Add 40 then add 2

To subtract a 'near 10', subtract the multiple of 10 and then add or subtract the difference.

Subtract 49	Subtract 50 then add 1
Subtract 63	Subtract 60 then subtract 3
Subtract 101	Subtract 100 then subtract 1

To *multiply* by a 'near 10', multiply by the multiple of 10 and then add or subtract the difference.

99×8	$100 \times 8 - 1 \times 8$ $= 800 - 8 = 792$

To work out subtractions, start with the smaller number and add on till you reach the bigger one. This is sometimes called shopkeeper's addition.

The bill is £5.86. What is the change from £10?	Start with £5.86 Add on 4p to make £5.90 Add on 10p to make £6 Add on £4 to make £10 £10 − £5.86 = £4.14	$\left.\right\}$ 4p + 10p + £4 = £4.14
100 − 34	Start at 34 Add on 6 to make 40 Add on 60 to make 100 100 − 34 = 66	$\left.\right\}$ 6 + 60 = 66

Example 1

Work out
a $23 + 90$ b $37 + 49$ c $117 + 42$

Solution 1

a $23 + 100 - 10 = 113$ b $37 + 50 - 1 = 86$ c $117 + 40 + 2 = 159$

Example 2

Work out
a   £1.99 × 7   b   £1.48 × 4

Solution 2

a   £2 × 7 − 1p × 7 = £14 − 7p
              = £13.93

b   £1.50 × 4 − 2p × 4 = £6 − 8p
                  = £5.92

Exercise A

1 Work out
   a 54 + 42   **b** 19 + 29   **c** 90 + 99   **d** 120 + 80 + 55
   e 45 + 35   **f** 82 + 99 + 99   **g** 55 + 25 + 72   **h** 12 + 24 + 36

2 Work out
   a 100 − 43   **b** 100 − 24   **c** 100 − 96   **d** 100 − 37
   e 50 − 26   **f** 180 − 94   **g** 360 − 255   **h** 360 − 190

3 Work out
   a 96 − 43   **b** 108 − 31   **c** 110 − 94   **d** 156 − 34
   e 62 − 28   **f** 109 − 93   **g** 305 − 145   **h** 407 − 206

4 Work out
   a 7 × 9   **b** 8 × 6   **c** 4 × 9   **d** 6 × 6
   e 5 × 7   **f** 10 × 12   **g** 6 × 9   **h** 7 × 8

5 Work out
   a 49 ÷ 7   **b** 54 ÷ 6   **c** 70 ÷ 10   **d** 81 ÷ 9
   e 56 ÷ 7   **f** 42 ÷ 6   **g** 36 ÷ 9   **h** 64 ÷ 8

6 Work out
   a £1.99 × 5   **b** 6 × £2.99   **c** £8.54 + £1.99   **d** £3.36 − 99p
   e £2.34 + 99p   **f** £2.49 × 8   **g** £8.99 + £2.99   **h** £10 − £3.49

7 From the list of numbers
   2   5   13   25   28   43   65   80
   write down
   a two numbers with a sum of 38   **b** two numbers with a sum of 70
   c two numbers with a difference of 3   **d** two numbers with a difference of 15

8 From the list of numbers
   4   14   24   34   44   54   64   74
   write down
   a two numbers greater than 36 and less than 60
   b two numbers greater than 23 and less than 70
   c two numbers with a sum of 78
   d two numbers with a difference of 70

9 Use your calculator to work out
   a £84.90 + £23.60   **b** £29.37 + £91.04
   c £2.37 + £1.87 + £3.65   **d** £15.43 + £18.62 + £34.20
   e £4.20 + 87p

10 Use your calculator to work out
   a £30 − £24.21   **b** £100 − £91.23
   c £20 − £16.46   **d** £5 − 64p

Example 3

Dravid is paid £6.40 per hour.

a One day he works for $5\frac{1}{2}$ hours. How much is he paid?

b On another day he is paid £19.20. How many hours did he work?

Solution 3

a Working for 5 hours pays £6.40 × 5 = £32

Working for $\frac{1}{2}$ an hour pays £6.40 ÷ 2 = £3.20

Total pay = £32 + £3.20 = £35.20

b One hour pays £6.40

Number of hours worked = £19.20 ÷ £6.40 = 3 hours

Example 4

Hayley is paid £10 for attending a meeting.
She is also paid £15 for every 30 minutes that she attends.

How much is she paid for attending a meeting for 2 hours?

Solution 4

In 2 hours there are four 30-minute periods.

She is paid £10 + 4 × £15 = £10 + £60 = £70

Example 5

Complete the shopping bill.

	£	Pence
3 colas @ £1.99		
2 choco bars @ 42p		
4 ices @ 37p		
Total		

Solution 5

3 × £1.99 = £5.97

2 × 42p = 84p

4 × 37p = £1.48

Completing the bill and totalling:

	£	Pence
3 colas @ £1.99	5	97
2 choco bars @ 42p		84
4 ices @ 37p	1	48
Total	8	29

Exercise B

1   Complete the following bills.

a

	£	Pence
3 loaves @ 60p		
2 buns @ £1.10		
4 cakes @ £1.20		
Total		

b

	£	Pence
3 fish @ £2		
2 large fries @ £1.20		
4 sausages @ 80p		
Total		

c

	£	Pence
4 candles @ 50p		
1 hose @ £5.60		
2 plugs @ 45p		
Total		

d

	£	Pence
6 toys @ £1.99		
2 books @ £4.99		
Total		

2   A cleaner charges £3.50 per room plus a fixed charge of £5
   a   How much does he charge altogether to clean three rooms?
   b   How much does he charge altogether to clean five rooms?
   c   If the charge is £40, how many rooms has he cleaned?

3   A phone company charges £12.50 per month rental and then 5p per minute for calls.
   a   What is the **total** cost of making 300 minutes of calls in a month?
   b   What is the **total** cost of making 500 minutes of calls in a month?
   c   The **total** charges for a month are £17.50
       How many minutes of calls were used?

4   Shirts cost £10.50 each.
   a   A man buys three shirts. How much change does he receive from £40?
   b   His change is given using the smallest possible number of notes and coins.
       How is the change given?

5   The cash price of a television is £550
   The credit price is £120 deposit and then £50 per month for 12 months.

   How much cheaper is it to pay by cash than to pay on credit?

6   A burger costs 99p. Fries cost £1.15
   Matthew buys two burgers and some bags of fries.
   The total cost is £6.58
   How many bags of fries did Matthew buy?

7 A bottle of water costs £1.70. A glass of water costs 80p
The water in a bottle is enough to fill six glasses.
How much cheaper is it to buy a bottle of water than six glasses of water?

8 Jon goes shopping.
    a Work out his total bill.
    b Jon pays with a £20 note.
       How much change does he get?

Item	Price (£)
Bread	0.78
Cheese	2.31
Chocolate	3.27
Butter	0.87
Fruit juice	2.00
Total	

9 A man works for 7 hours and 30 minutes. He is paid £6.80 per hour.
How much does he earn?

10 A woman works for 8 hours. She is paid £58.80
    a How much does she earn per hour?
    b How much would she earn if she worked for $5\frac{1}{2}$ hours?

1.4 Negative numbers

CAN YOU REMEMBER

- How to sort numbers into order, from smallest to biggest?
- How to use a number line?

IN THIS SECTION YOU WILL

- Sort negative numbers into order, from smallest to biggest.
- Add and subtract using negative numbers.

The number lines show both
positive numbers, for example +2,
and *negative numbers*, for example −3

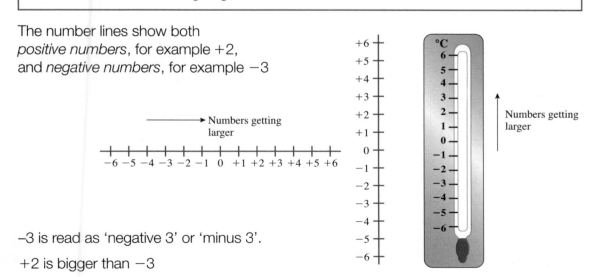

−3 is read as 'negative 3' or 'minus 3'.

+2 is bigger than −3

Example 1

The diagram shows a thermometer.
a   Which temperature is warmer, $-2\,°C$ or $+3\,°C$?
b   What is the difference between the temperatures?

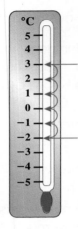

Solution 1

a $+3\,°C$ is higher up the temperature scale than $-2\,°C$,
   so $+3\,°C$ is warmer than $-2\,°C$.
b   Counting up from $-2\,°C$, the difference between
   the temperatures is $5\,°C$.

Exercise A

1   For each pair, which number is bigger? You may use a number line to help you.
   a -5 or $+3$ b -4 or 0 c $+7$ or -1 d $+3$ or -3
   e -7 or -3 f -1 or -5 g 0 or -6 h -2 or -8

2   Work out the difference between the pairs of numbers in question **1**.

3   For each pair of numbers in question **1**:
     i mark the numbers on a number line
    ii work out the number that is exactly halfway between them.

4   Put each set of numbers in order of size, starting with the smallest.
   a   5   7 -2 1 -6
   b   4 -4 -3 2   6
   c   12 -3 0   2 -7
   d -2 -5 -4 1   3
   e -7 -3 2   6   0
   f -4 -3 -8 -7 -1
   g -9 0 -6 -2 -8
   h   5 -4 4 -5 -3

5   Work out
   a $27 - 84$ b $-84 + 27$
   c $-80 - 4 + 20 + 7$ d $20 + 7 - 4 - 80$

6   Work out
   a $-35 - 48$ b $-48 - 35$
   c $-40 - 30 - 5 - 8$ d $-30 - 40 - 8 - 5$

7   Work out
   a $-34 + 18$ b $165 - 192$ c $138 - 264$ d $-271 + 204$
   e $-86 - 94$ f $-169 - 183$ g $-468 + 321$ h $-1234 + 4321$

Example 2

The table shows the temperatures in different places in England at midnight one night in November.

Town or City	Temperature (°C)
Bristol	+4
Ipswich	0
London	+6
Manchester	−3
Newcastle	−5
York	−1

a Which place is the warmest?
b Which place is the coldest?
c How much warmer is Bristol than York?
Twelve hours later the temperature in each place is 5° higher.
d Write down the new temperatures.

Solution 2

Town or City	Temperature (°C)
Bristol	+9
Ipswich	+5
London	+11
Manchester	+2
Newcastle	0
York	+4

a +6 is the biggest number, so London is the warmest.
b −5 is the smallest number, so Newcastle is the coldest.
c The difference in temperature between Bristol and York is 5°
d Add 5° to each temperature.

Exercise B

1 The tables show the temperatures in different cities on one day.
For each table a, b and c
  i Which place is the warmest?
  ii Which place is the coldest?
  iii Write the names of the places in order of temperature, starting with the coldest.
  iv Later that day the temperature in each place is 3° lower.
    Write down the new temperatures.

a

City	Temperature (°C)
London	−2
Paris	+1
Rome	+6
Dublin	−4
Berlin	−5

b

City	Temperature (°C)
New York	−3
Salt Lake City	+1
Montreal	−6
Los Angeles	+19

2 The table shows the height of places above or below sea level.

Place	Height
Lake Assal, Africa	156 m below sea level
Lake Eyre, Australia	12 m below sea level
Death Valley, USA	86 m below sea level
Mont Blanc, France/Italy	4800 m above sea level
Mount Everest, Nepal/China	8850 m above sea level

a Which place is the highest?

b Which place is the lowest?

c What is the difference in height between

    i Lake Assal and Lake Eyre   **ii** Mount Everest and Lake Assal

   iii Death Valley and Mont Blanc   **iv** Lake Eyre and Mont Blanc?

1.5 Reading information from a table

CAN YOU REMEMBER

- How to convert between a '12 hour clock' time and a '24 hour clock' time?
- How to find the time taken for a journey by counting on?
- How to calculate using money?

IN THIS SECTION YOU WILL

- Learn how to read and interpret information from tables and charts.
- Read timetables.
- Use information from tables and charts to solve problems.

This Eurostar timetable shows train times from London (Waterloo) between 0800 and 1200

LONDON	**08.12**	**08.39**	**09.09**	**09.39**	**09.42**	**10.12**	**10.39**	**10.42**	**11.39**
Ashford	–	09.30	09.59	10.31	10.40	–	–	–	–
Calais	–	–	–	–	–	–	–	–	–
Lille	–	11.29	–	–	–	–	–	13.24	14.21
BRUSSELS	–	**12.10**	–	–	–	–	–	**14.05**	–
PARIS	**11.47**		**12.53**	–	–	**13.53**	**14.17**		**15.23**
Disneyland				13.29	–				
Moutiers					**17.47**				
Aime la Plagne					**18.05**				
Bourg St. Maurice					**18.20**				

Check these facts from the timetable:

None of the trains stops at Calais.

The first train to arrive at Paris departs from London at 0812

The 1042 from London goes to Brussels.

Only one train goes to Disneyland.

It is important to read tables carefully and to state units, e.g. for distances or prices.

Example 1

Look again at the Eurostar timetable.
a What time does the first train to Brussels depart from London?
b How long does the 0942 from London take to reach Ashford?
c What time does the 0942 from London arrive at Bourg St. Maurice?

Solution 1

a The first arrival in Brussels is at 1210. This train departs from London at 0839
b The 0942 from London arrives at Ashford at 1040
  0942 to 1042 = 1 hour = 60 minutes, so 0942 to 1040 is 60 − 2 = 58 minutes
  It takes 58 minutes from London to Ashford.
c It arrives at Bourg St. Maurice at 1820

Exercise A

1 Here is another part of the Eurostar timetable from London (Waterloo).

LONDON	12.09	12.39	13.09	13.41	14.09	14.42	15.11	16.12	16.39	17.09
Ashford	12.59	13.30	–	–	14.59	–	–	–	17.30	17.59
Calais	14.31	–	–	–	–	–	17.26	–	–	19.31
Lille	–	15.29	–	16.21	–	17.21	–	–	19.29	–
BRUSSELS	–	16.10	–	–	–	18.02	–	–	20.10	–
PARIS	15.59		16.47	17.23	17.53		18.53	19.47		20.59

a How many trains stop at Lille?
b At what time does the 1709 from London arrive in Paris?
c Imran wants to arrive in Paris before 5 pm.
  Which train should he catch from London?
d Marie arrives in Paris at 1853. What time did she leave Calais?

2 Here is a fare table.

Price shown in £	Maintown to Wardville				Maintown to Beeville			
	Standard		First		Standard		First	
	Single	Return	Single	Return	Single	Return	Single	Return
Standard	149	298			125	250		
Leisure		119		299		115		
Leisure Day Trip		99		179		95		170
Senior		99				95		
Youth	70	119			60	115		
Passholder	50	100	90	180	40	80	75	150
Child	25	50	50	100	22	44	40	80

How much does it cost for
a a standard return ticket from Maintown to Wardville?
b a single ticket for a youth from Maintown to Beeville?
c a return first-class ticket for a child from Maintown to Beeville?
d a senior return ticket from Maintown to Beeville?

3 Here is a fare table for a bus route.
The fare from the hospital to the town centre is 60p.

Bus station				
80p	Town centre			
£1.35	60p	Hospital		
£1.60	£1.15	90p	School	
£1.95	£1.40	£1.10	85p	Railway station

a How much is the fare
   i from the town centre to the railway station?
  ii from the bus station to the school?
 iii from the hospital to the school?
  iv from the hospital to the railway station?

b Mr and Mrs Jones travel from the bus station to the hospital.
Mr Jones pays with a £5 note. How much change does he receive?

4 Here is a bus timetable for a circular route.

City Centre Shuttle   Free Bus Service

Monday to Saturday (except Bank Holidays)

Emmanuel Street, Stop J	**0900**	**0915**	**0930**	**0945**	**1000**	Then	**1700**
Fair Street (for Grafton Centre)	0902	0917	0932	0947	1002	every	1702
Jesus Lane	0904	0919	0934	0949	1004	15	1704
St. John's College	0905	0920	0935	0950	1005	minutes	1705
Senate House (for Market)	0906	0921	0936	0951	1006	until	1706
Corpus Christi College	0908	0923	0938	0953	1008		1708
Emmanuel Street, Stop J	**0913**	**0928**	**0943**	**0958**	**1013**		**1713**

a How long does the bus take to complete the route?

b At 0920, Tariq is waiting at Fair Street for a bus to Corpus Christi College.
What time should he arrive?

c At what time does the 1245 bus from Emmanuel Street arrive at the Senate House?

d How many times does the bus complete the route during one day?

Exercise B

1 Look again at this fares table.

Bus station				
80p	Town centre			
£1.35	60p	Hospital		
£1.60	£1.15	90p	School	
£1.95	£1.40	£1.10	85p	Railway station

This table shows the number of tickets sold on a journey.

Bus station				
14	Town centre			
7	4	Hospital		
16	8	0	School	
6	3	2	0	Railway station

a   Which was the most popular journey?

b   How many passengers travelled from the bus station to the railway station?

c   Calculate the cost of 14 tickets at 80p each.

d   Copy and complete the table for the total cost of the tickets for each journey.

Bus station				
	Town centre			
	£2.40	Hospital		
		£0	School	
£11.70		£2.20	£0	Railway station

e   Use the results in the table to calculate the total of the fares paid.

2   The table shows part of a TV guide.

a   How long is the Cartoon special?

b   How long is Football final scores?

c   Apart from football, there are two programmes which are on twice. What are they?

d   'It's a laugh!' is 50 minutes long. At what time does it finish?

e   The programme before Cartoon special was 25 minutes long. At what time did it start?

08:10	Cartoon special
08:35	The Terriers
09:00	Home improvements
11:00	Music charts
12:00	News
12:10	Football
13:00	Cricket update
13:10	Rugby
13:15	Darts
15:45	Football half-time scores
15:50	Darts
16:30	Football final scores
17:10	News
17:25	It's a laugh!

3   The table shows the distances (in kilometres) between some French towns and cities.

a   How far is it from Calais to Rouen?

b   How much further is it from Paris to Rouen than from Le Mans to Tours?

c   Which places are furthest apart?

Calais				
423	Le Mans			
290	206	Paris		
216	205	133	Rouen	
530	85	238	272	Tours

d   Explain why the distance from Calais to Paris is not the same as the distance from Calais to Rouen added to the distance from Rouen to Paris.

1.6 Rounding

CAN YOU REMEMBER

- How to read a scale accurately?
- How to carry out simple calculations involving whole numbers?

IN THIS SECTION YOU WILL

- Round numbers to the nearest 10, 100, 1000
- Round numbers to the nearest *whole number* (integer).
- Round numbers to up to three *decimal places*.
- Round numbers to one *significant figure*.

Sometimes an exact value is not needed. *Rounding* gives an approximate value.

In Geography, a population is given to the nearest thousand.

The population of Grassville is 186 000.

In Science, the percentages of oxygen and nitrogen in the air are given to the nearest whole number.

Air is 78% nitrogen.

In Food Technology, recipes give quantities to the nearest 10 grams.

Fairy cakes
100 g self-raising flour
50 g margarine
50 g sugar
1 egg
1 tablespoon milk

Usually it is sensible to round the answer to a calculation.
Write down the exact result of any calculation before rounding to an approximate answer.

Example 1

Round the number 321.574
a to the nearest whole number **b** to the nearest 10
c to one decimal place **d** to one significant figure.

Solution 1

a The number is between the whole numbers 321 and 322 but the digit 5 shows it is nearer to 322

Answer = 322

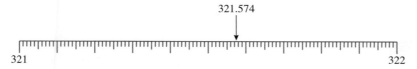

b The number is between the multiples of ten, 320 and 330, but is nearer to 320

Answer = 320

c Rounding to one decimal place means rounding to the nearest tenth.
The number is between 321.5 and 321.6 but the digit 7 in the hundredths column shows it is nearer to 321.6

Answer = 321.6

d The most significant figure is the 3. This has the value 300. So for this number rounding to one significant figure means rounding to the nearest hundred.
When a number is rounded to one significant figure it has only one figure apart from zeros.
The number is between 300 and 400 but the digit 2 in the tens column shows that it is closer to 300

Answer = 300

Example 2

a   Round the number 45 to the nearest 10
b   Round the number 2.5 to the nearest whole number.

Solution 2

a   45 is exactly halfway between the multiples of ten, 40 and 50.
The rule is to round up.
Answer = 50
b   2.5 is exactly halfway between 2 and 3. Rounding up gives
Answer = 3

Example 3

Use a calculator to work out 8.67 × 3.41
a   Write down the full calculator display.
b   Write the answer to one decimal place.

Solution 3

a   29.5647
b   The number is between 29.5 and 29.6 but
because there are six hundredths it is nearer to 29.6
Answer = 29.6

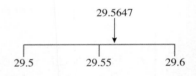

Exercise A

1   Round the following numbers to the nearest 10

a	84	**b**	28	**c**	42	**d**	37
e	65	**f**	695	**g**	206	**h**	196

2   Round the following numbers to the nearest 100

a	172	**b**	579	**c**	427	**d**	643
e	350	**f**	4249	**g**	3990	**h**	4006

3   Round the following numbers to the nearest 1000

a	2654	**b**	3999	**c**	7129	**d**	5050
e	4996	**f**	14 567	**g**	12 505	**h**	11 995

4   Round the following numbers to the nearest
i 10   **ii** 100   **iii** 1000

a	1523	**b**	2682	**c**	6361	**d**	7586
e	3538	**f**	5217	**g**	8924	**h**	9023

5 Round the following numbers to the nearest whole number.

a	7.4	**b**	6.1	**c**	3.6	**d**	4.7
e	8.6	**f**	10.32	**g**	12.63	**h**	17.45

6 Round the following numbers to one decimal place.

a	7.85	**b**	6.24	**c**	5.91	**d**	8.47
e	5.791	**f**	6.025	**g**	9.093	**h**	15.472

7 Round the following numbers to two decimal places.

a	10.615	**b**	3.698	**c**	4.297	**d**	5.711
e	6.8312	**f**	10.134	**g**	93.7654	**h**	100.3651

8 Round the following numbers to
i one decimal place   **ii** two decimal places   **iii** three decimal places.

a	2.3175	**b**	13.8691	**c**	7.4512	**d**	98.7255
e	100.0836	**f**	23.7465	**g**	18.4129	**h**	43.0085

9 Round the following numbers to one significant figure.

a	27	**b**	83	**c**	16	**d**	88
e	243	**f**	871	**g**	915	**h**	184
i	22.6	**j**	64.9	**k**	184.7	**l**	0.54
m	0.26	**n**	0.75	**o**	0.034	**p**	0.012

10 Use a calculator to work out each calculation.
  i Write down the full calculator display.
  ii Write the answer to one decimal place.

a	3.1×4.25	**b**	6.14×2.33	**c**	8.7×9.61	**d**	14.3×7.2
e	17.4×109.6	**f**	$83 \div 24$	**g**	$71.5 \div 0.34$	**h**	$175 \div 13.6$

Example 4

Look at the measuring cylinders.
What is the volume of water in each
cylinder to the nearest 10 ml?

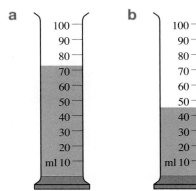

Solution 4

a The water level is approximately 72 ml.
  To the nearest 10, the answer is 70 ml
  as it is closer to 70 ml than 80 ml.
b The water level is approximately 45 ml.
  To the nearest 10, the answer is 50 ml.

Use rounded numbers to estimate the answer to a calculation.

Example 5

By writing each number to one significant figure estimate the value of 98×3.8

Solution 5

98 written to one significant figure is 100. 3.8 written to one significant figure is 4

98×3.8 is approximately $100 \times 4 = 400$

Exercise B

1   Look at each weighing scale and estimate the mass to
   i the nearest 10 grams
   ii the nearest 100 grams.

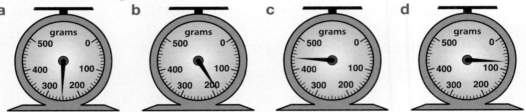

a   **b**   **c**   **d**

2   A piece of rope is measured as 168.3 cm.
   How long is the rope
   a   to the nearest 10 cm?   **b**   to the nearest 100 cm?

3   The attendance at a concert is 1945. The organisers claim that nearly 2000
   attended while the police claim that over 1900 attended.
   Who is more accurate? Explain your answer.

4   Match the cards in groups of three to make correct statements.
   One has been done for you.

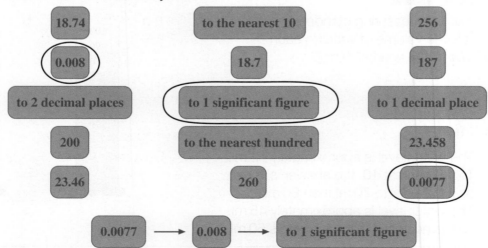

5 Estimate the value of each of the following.
In each case write down the numbers you have used.
   a 19.7×3.1 **b** 31.4×9.9 **c** 196×6.02 **d** 59.2×2.13
   e 20.4×8.1 **f** 78.9×10.4 **g** $19.9 \div 3.86$ **h** $48.2 \div 4.95$

6 You are given that $32 \times 47 = 1504$
Write down the answer to 3.2×4.7

7 **a** Jack says that $18.2 \times 15.7 = 285$ to the nearest whole number.
Is he correct? Explain your answer.
   b Jill says that $18.2 \times 15.7 = 285.7$ to one decimal place. Is she correct?
Explain your answer.

8 Use a calculator to work out each calculation.
   i Write down the full calculator display.
   ii Write the answer to one decimal place.

   a $3.75 + 2.0182$ **b** $\dfrac{4.1 \times 3.2}{5.7}$ **c** $\dfrac{19}{18 + 22}$ **d** $\dfrac{7.4}{3.6 + 2.7}$

9 Use approximations to make estimates to check your answers to question **8**.

Chapter summary

■ To write a number in words, write it in a place value table under the correct column headings.
For example 4096.21

Thousands	Hundreds	Tens	Units	.	tenths	hundredths	thousandths
			3	.	5	6	

To multiply by 10 move the digits one column to the left.
To multiply by 100 move the digits two columns to the left, and so on.
To divide by 10 move the digits one column to the right.
To divide by 100 move the digits two columns to the right, and so on.

■ To help add and subtract numbers use a number line.

■ To find a number that is halfway between two numbers:
(1)   work out the difference between the two numbers
(2)   add half of this difference to the smaller number.

■ Another way of finding a number that is halfway between two numbers is:
add the numbers together and divide the answer by 2

■ There is a quick method for adding numbers that are close to a multiple of 10 or 100 like 9, 39, 90 and 290
For example: $36 + 29 = 36 + 30 - 1 = 66 - 1 = 65$

■ Multiplying numbers that are close to a multiple of 10 or 100 can also be done using a similar approach.
For example: $99 \times 7 = 100 \times 7 - 1 \times 7 = 700 - 7 = 693$

■ Adding on can be used to subtract.

■ Remember to use correct notation for money, for example £3.21 not £3.21p.

■ When putting numbers into order it is helpful to use a number line.

■ The difference between a negative number and a positive number can be found using a number line.
For example, the difference between
-4 and $+5$ is $4 + 5 = 9$

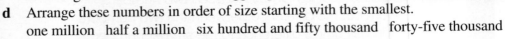

■ Numbers can be rounded in different ways,
e.g. to the nearest whole number, to two decimal places, to one significant figure.

■ When rounding numbers
if the last digit is less than 5, round down
if the last digit is 5 or more, round up.
For example, 2.5 to the nearest whole number rounds to 3

■ Write down the exact result of a calculation from the calculator display before rounding to an approximate answer.

■ To work out an estimate of a calculation, round the numbers in the calculation to one significant figure.

Chapter review

1 a Write seven million in figures.
  b Write four thousand and sixty-seven in figures.

2 a i Write 8342 in words. **ii** Write 8342 to the nearest 1000.
  b From this list of numbers
    2   21   27   39   49   68   81
    write down
      i two numbers which have a sum of 70
      ii two numbers which have a difference of 10

3 a Write the number 3621 in words.
  b Write 8576 to the nearest hundred.
  c Here are four number cards.
    Rearrange the cards to make the biggest possible number.   3 6 8 5
  d Arrange these numbers in order of size starting with the smallest.
    one million   half a million   six hundred and fifty thousand   forty-five thousand
  e What is the value of the digit 6 in the number 75 620?

4 The number of spectators at a football match is 14 376
  a Write the number 14 376 in words.
  b In the number 14 376, write down the value of
      i the figure 7   **ii** the figure 4

c One quarter of all the spectators are season ticket holders.
How many spectators are season ticket holders?

d Write 14 376 to the nearest 100

5 On 1 January, the midday temperature in Glasgow was $-3\,°C$. On the same day, the midday temperature in London was $7\,°C$ higher than it was in Glasgow. The midday temperature in Aviemore was $9\,°C$ lower than it was in Glasgow.
Find, giving your answers in $°C$,
a the midday temperature in London **b** the midday temperature in Aviemore.

6 Here is a bus route and a fares table.
a How much is the bus fare from the University to Crookes? Give your answer in £.
b Meia travels to Sheffield from Broomhill.
She pays with a £5 note.
How much change does she receive from a £5 note? Give your answer in £.
c A child pays 45p for any journey. What is the total cost for an adult and two children to travel from Broomhill to Crookes? Give your answer in £.

Sheffield				
86p	University			
£1.20	57p	Hospital		
£1.56	£1.15	65p	Broomhill	
£1.85	£1.45	£1.04	55p	Crookes

7 Write the number 6273
a to the nearest 10 **b** to the nearest 100.

8 The populations of three towns are given below.
Bogton 13 637 **Cogton** 9794 **Dogton** 11 207
a Write the number 13 637 to the nearest thousand.
b Put the towns in order of their population, with the smallest first.

9 a Write seven thousand three hundred and sixty-four in figures.
b The number in part **a** is divided by 100.
What is the value of the digit seven in the answer?
c Write 28 637 to the nearest 100
d Write 28 637 to the nearest 1000

10 a Copy and complete the shopping bill for Ben.
b The shop gives Ben one discount point for every £2 spent.
How many discount points is Ben given?
c Ben buys nine pens at 56 pence each.
He pays with a £10 note.
How much change does he receive? Give your answer in £.

	£	p
Apples 3 kg at £1.20 per kg		
Bananas 2 kg at £1.65 per kg		
3 bottles of cola at £0.85 each		
Total		

Angles in shapes

2.1 Angles

IN THIS SECTION YOU WILL

- Learn the difference between *acute*, *obtuse* and *reflex* angles.
- Practise estimating the size of angles.
- Practise measuring angles.

An angle is a measure of turn. One full turn measures 360°.

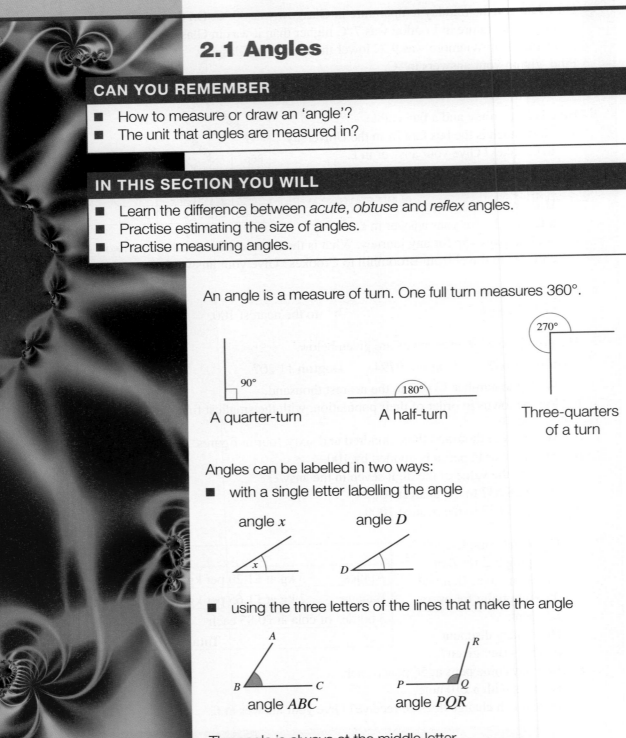

A quarter-turn   A half-turn   Three-quarters of a turn

Angles can be labelled in two ways:

- with a single letter labelling the angle

angle x angle D

- using the three letters of the lines that make the angle

angle ABC angle PQR

The angle is always at the middle letter.

An angle between 0° and 90° is an *acute angle*.

An angle of exactly 90° is a *right angle*.

A right angle is marked with a small square

An angle between 90° and 180° is an *obtuse angle*.

An angle between 180° and 360° is a *reflex angle*.

Example 1

State whether each of the following angles are acute, obtuse or reflex.

a 125°   **b** 234°   **c** 47°   **d** 352°

Solution 1

a 125° is obtuse (greater than 90° but less than 180°)
b 234° is reflex (greater than 180° but less than 360°)
c 47° is acute (less than 90°)
d 352° is reflex (greater than 180° but less than 360°)

Example 2

Draw an angle of 70°

Solution 2

Draw a line.
Position the centre of a protractor on
one end of the line.
Mark a dot at 70°
(Remember that 70° is an acute angle
so your angle must be smaller than a
right angle.)

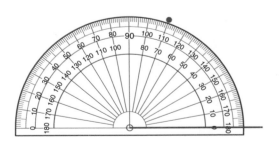

Join the end of the line to the dot.

70°

Exercise A

1 Draw a table like this:

Acute	Obtuse	Reflex

Write each of the following angles in the table under the correct heading.

a 117°	**b** 196°	**c** 84°	**d** 5°	**e** 242°
f 100°	**g** 45°	**h** 93°	**i** 182°	**j** 270°
k 76°	**l** 312°	**m** 29°	**n** 177°	**o** 123°

2 For each of these angles:
  i name the angle using letters
  ii write down whether the angle is acute, obtuse or a right angle
  iii measure the angle.

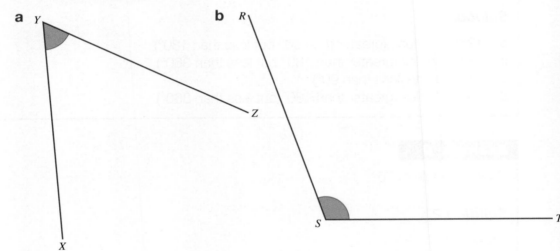

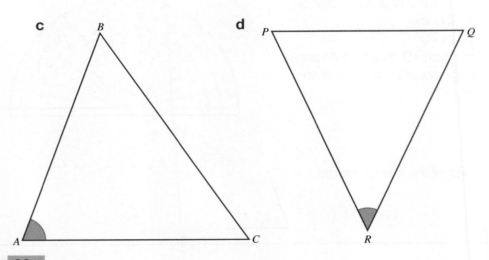

3 Draw these angles accurately:

    a 50°   **b** 110°   **c** 140°   **d** 30°

    e 80°   **f** 75°   **g** 125°   **h** 42°

    i 157°   **j** 132°

Example 3

For the following marked angle:

a state whether it is acute, obtuse or reflex

b estimate the size of the angle

c measure the angle accurately.

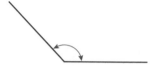

Solution 3

a This angle is obtuse.

b An obtuse angle is between 90° and 180°
The angle is not quite halfway between 90°
and 180° so not quite 135°
Estimate 130°

c Using a protractor, the angle measures 132°

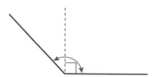

Exercise B

For each of the following marked angles:

a state whether the angle is acute, obtuse or reflex

b estimate the size of the angle

c measure the angle accurately.

1

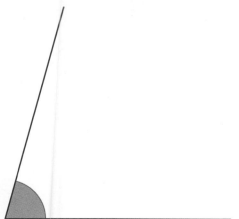

2

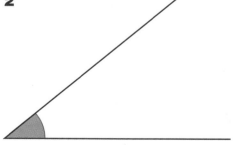

3

4

5

6

7

8

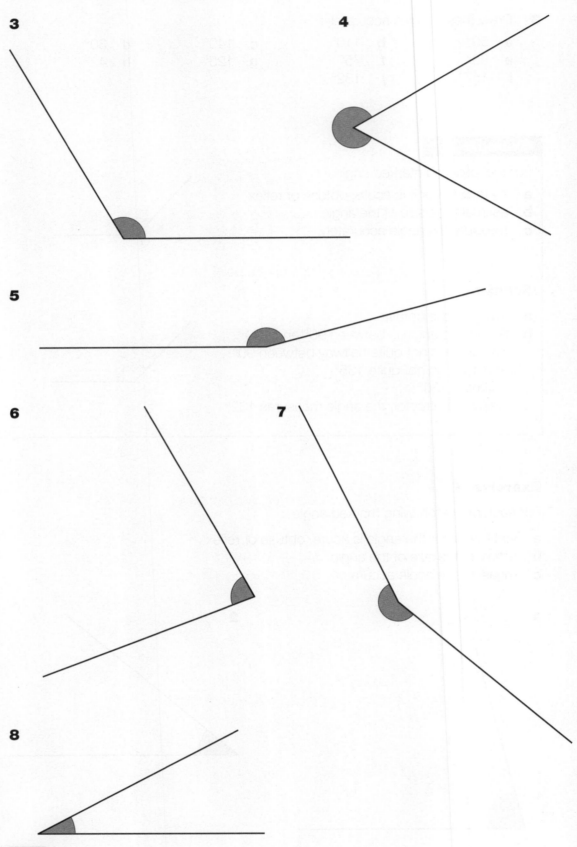

2.2 Angles and straight lines

CAN YOU REMEMBER

- That there are 360° in a full circle?
- That there are 180° in a half-circle?
- That a quarter-turn measures 90°?

IN THIS SECTION YOU WILL

- Learn about *angles at a point*.
- Understand the properties of angles and straight lines.
- Learn about *perpendicular* lines.

This diagram shows three angles meeting at a point.

Drawing a curve round each angle forms a complete circle.
There are 360° in a complete circle.
So angles at a point add up to 360° and $x + y + z = 360°$

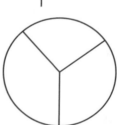

This diagram shows two angles meeting on a straight line.

Drawing a curve round each angle forms half a circle.
So angles on a straight line must total 180° and $a + b = 180°$

If a straight line is divided into two equal angles
they must both be 90°

$180 ÷ 2 = 90$

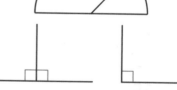

Two lines meeting at right angles are called *perpendicular lines*.
AB is perpendicular to *CD*.

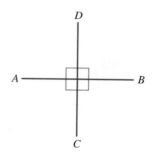

Example 1

Calculate the value of angles x and y.

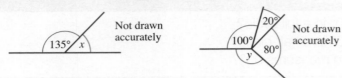

Not drawn accurately

Solution 1

a $x = 180° - 135°$ (angles on a straight line add up to 180°)
   so $x = 45°$

b $100° + 20° + 80° = 200°$

   $y = 360° - 200°$ (angles at a point add up to 360°)
   so $y = 160°$

Exercise A

The diagrams are not drawn accurately.
Calculate the missing angles:

1
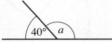

2

3
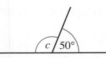

4
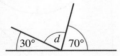

5

6
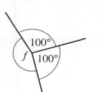

7
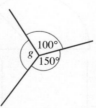

8

9
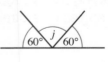

10
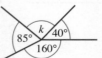

11

12

13
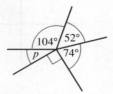

14
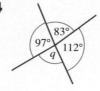

15

16

17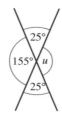

18

When two lines *intersect*, they form four angles:
a is vertically opposite c
b is vertically opposite d

Vertically opposite angles are equal.

$$a = c$$
$$b = d$$

Example 2

Work out the size of angles x, y and z,
giving reasons for your answers.

Solution 2

Angle $x = 180° - 108° = 72°$ (angles on a straight line add up to 180°)

y is vertically opposite x z is vertically opposite 108°
So angle $y = 72°$ So angle $z = 108°$

Exercise B

Calculate the size of all the angles marked with letters.
The diagrams are not drawn accurately.

1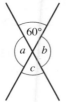

2

3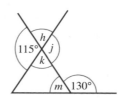

4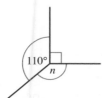

5

6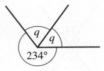

7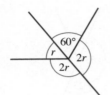

8

9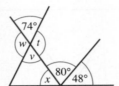

10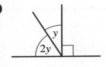

2.3 Angles in triangles

CAN YOU REMEMBER

- That a right angle measures 90°?
- That angles on a straight line add up to 180°?

IN THIS SECTION YOU WILL

- Learn the names of types of triangles.
- Learn how to calculate angles in triangles.
- Learn about interior and exterior angles in triangles.
- Understand a proof about the exterior angle of any triangle.

There are three main types of triangle.

Equilateral triangle

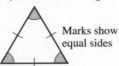
Marks show equal sides

Three equal sides
Three equal angles,
each 60°

Isosceles triangle

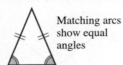
Matching arcs show equal angles

Two equal sides
Two equal angles
The equal angles are
opposite the equal sides.

Scalene triangle

No equal sides
No equal angles

Any triangle with a right angle is called a *right-angled triangle*.

Right-angled scalene triangle   Right-angled isosceles triangle

Example 1

For each of the following triangles write down whether they are scalene, isosceles, equilateral or right-angled.

Give reasons for your answers.

a

b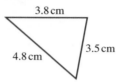

c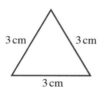

d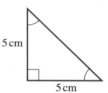

Solution 1

a Isosceles (two equal angles, so two equal sides)
b Scalene (all sides different lengths)
c Equilateral (three equal sides, so three equal angles)
d Right-angled isosceles (right angle, and two equal sides)

Exercise A

For the following triangles write down whether they are scalene, isosceles, equilateral or right-angled.

Give reasons for your answers.

1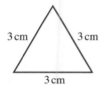

2

3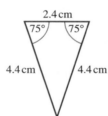

4

5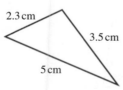

6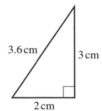

7

8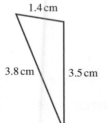

9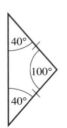

10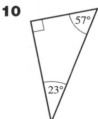

The three angles in an equilateral triangle each measure 60°
Adding these together gives a total of 180°
This is also the total of the angles in **any** type of triangle.

The sum of the angles of a triangle is 180°

$$a + b + c = 180°$$

Look at the triangles in Exercise A.
If the three angles are given, check that they add up to 180°

When the side of a triangle is extended it
forms an *exterior* angle.

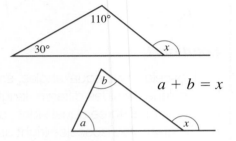

The exterior angle is always equal to the
sum of the opposite *interior* angles
(the opposite two angles inside the triangle).

$$a + b = x$$

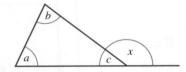

To prove this is true:

Label the third angle of the triangle c.

$a + b + c = 180°$ (angles in a triangle total 180°)
$\quad x + c = 180°$ (angles on a straight line total 180°)
So $a + b = x$

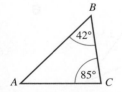

Example 2

In a triangle, angle $ABC = 42°$ and angle $BCA = 85°$

What is the size of the third angle?

Solution 2

First sketch a diagram.

Third angle $= 180° - (42° + 85°)$
$\qquad\qquad\quad = 180° - 127°$
$\qquad\qquad\quad = 53°$

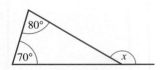

Example 3

Find the size of angle x.

Solution 3

$x = 70° + 80°$ (the exterior angle is the sum of the opposite interior angles)
$x = 150°$

Exercise B

The diagrams in this exercise are not drawn accurately.

1 In each part find the size of the third angle and identify the type of triangle.

a 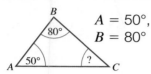 $A = 50°$, $B = 80°$

b 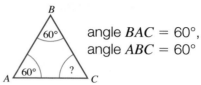 angle $BAC = 60°$, angle $ABC = 60°$

c 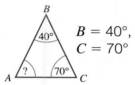 $B = 40°$, $C = 70°$

d 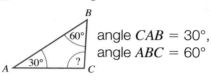 angle $CAB = 30°$, angle $ABC = 60°$

e 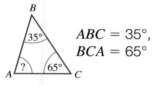 $ABC = 35°$, $BCA = 65°$

f 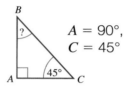 $A = 90°$, $C = 45°$

2 Find the size of angle x.

a

b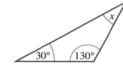

c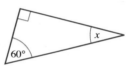

d

e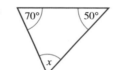

f

g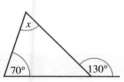

h

i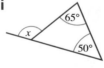

j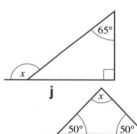

3 Find the size of the angles marked with letters.

a

b

c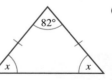

d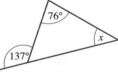

e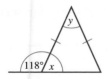

f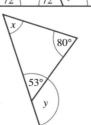

g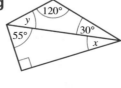

h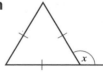

4 *ABC* is a triangle.
  D is a point on *AC* such that *AB* = *BD*.

  Work out the value of the angles
  marked with letters.

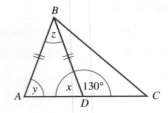

5

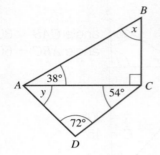

  a Work out the value of *x*.
  b Work out the value of *y*.
  c Does *AD* = *AC*?
     Give a reason for your answer.

6 a Work out the size of
    i angle *x*   **ii** angle *y*   **iii** angle *z*
  b What type of triangle is *ABD*?
     Give a reason for your answer.

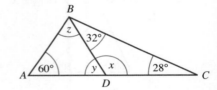

2.4 Constructing triangles

CAN YOU REMEMBER

- How to draw straight lines of given length accurately?
- How to use compasses?
- How to use a protractor to draw an angle?

IN THIS SECTION YOU WILL

- Learn how to draw triangles accurately using a ruler and protractor.
- Learn how to construct triangles accurately using a straight edge (ruler) and compasses.

A *construction* is an accurate drawing.
To construct a triangle where one or more angles are given, use a ruler and protractor.

Draw a sketch first, unless the question includes one. Mark on all the information given.

Example 1

Draw a triangle ABC with $AB = 8$ cm, $BC = 6$ cm and angle $B = 40°$

Solution 1

Rough sketch:

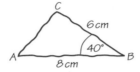

Step 1: Draw the longest side AB 8 cm long.
Make sure there is plenty of space for the rest of the triangle.

Step 2: Use a protractor as shown to measure the angle of 40° at B.

Diagrams not
drawn accurately

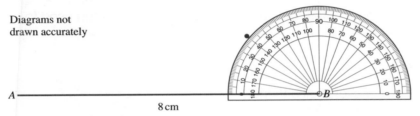

Step 3: Draw in the line through B, making sure
that it is longer than the required length.

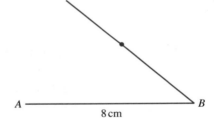

Step 4: Use a ruler to measure 6 cm from B.

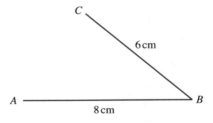

Step 5: Complete the diagram by joining the
vertices A and C with a straight line.
Label the sides and angle given.

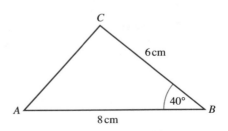

Example 2

Here is a rough sketch of a triangle.
Use a ruler and protractor to make
an accurate drawing of this triangle.

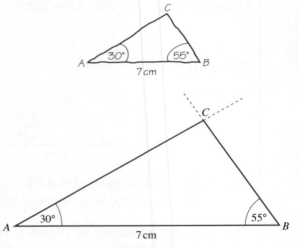

Solution 2

Step 1: Draw the line *AB* 7 cm long.

Step 2: Use a protractor to measure an
angle of 30° at *A*. Draw a line.

Step 3: Use a protractor to measure an
angle of 55° at *B*. Draw a line.

Step 4: The point where these two lines
cross is the third *vertex* of the
triangle. Add the labels.

Leave in the construction lines above C, to show the method used to draw the triangle.

Exercise A

1 Ben draws a sketch of a triangle.
Make an accurate drawing of
Ben's triangle.

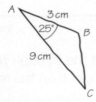

2 Use a ruler and protractor to draw the following triangles:
   a Triangle *PQR* where *PQ* = 10 cm, *PR* = 7 cm and angle *P* = 70°
   b Triangle *DEF* where *DE* = 8 cm, *EF* = 5 cm and angle *E* = 40°
   c Triangle *XYZ* where *XY* = 7 cm, *XZ* = 6 cm and angle *X* = 105°

3 A sketch of triangle *XYZ* is shown.
Make an accurate drawing of triangle *XYZ*.

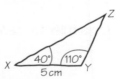

4 Use a ruler and protractor to draw the following triangles:
   a Triangle *ABC* where *BC* = 6 cm, angle *B* = 80° and angle *C* = 25°
   b Triangle *PQR* where *PQ* = 8 cm, angle *P* = 45° and angle *Q* = 60°
   c Triangle *LMN* where *MN* = 5 cm, angle *M* = 100° and angle *N* = 20°

5 Draw these triangles accurately using the information given in each diagram.
   a   **b**   **c**   **d**

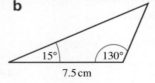
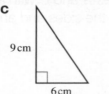
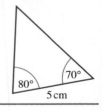

To construct a triangle where only lengths are given, use a ruler and a pair of compasses.

Example 3

Construct the triangle ABC where $AB = 6$ cm, $AC = 4.5$ cm and $BC = 3$ cm.

Solution 3

Sketch the triangle first.

Step 1: Draw AB 6 cm long.

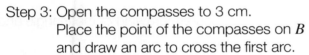

Step 2: Open the compasses to 4.5 cm.
Place the point of the compasses
on A and draw an arc.

All the points on the arc are 4.5 cm
from A.

Step 3: Open the compasses to 3 cm.
Place the point of the compasses on B
and draw an arc to cross the first arc.

All the points on this arc are 3 cm from B.

The point where the two arcs cross
is 4.5 cm from A and 3 cm from B.
It is C, the third *vertex* of the triangle.

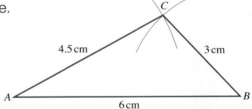

Step 4: Join AC and BC to complete the triangle.
Label vertex C and the lengths.

Leave in the construction arcs, to
show the method used to draw
the triangle.

Exercise B

1 Using a ruler and compasses, construct the following triangles:
   a Triangle ABC with $AB = 5$ cm, $BC = 6$ cm and $AC = 7$ cm
   b Triangle DEF with $DE = 5$ cm, $EF = 4.7$ cm and $DF = 3.5$ cm

2 Use a ruler and compasses to construct the following equilateral triangles:
   a Side length 7 cm
   b Side length 5.5 cm
   c Side length 6.3 cm

3 Triangle *PQR* has side *PQ* of length 7.4 cm, angle *PQR* of 75° and side *QR* of length 5.2 cm.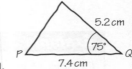
   a Use a ruler and protractor to make an accurate drawing of triangle *PQR*.
   b Measure and write down the length of *PR* on your drawing.
   c Write down the size of angle *PRQ*.

4 Use a ruler and protractor to draw a triangle with two sides of 4.2 cm where the angle between these two sides is 56°

5 Use a ruler and compasses to construct an isosceles triangle with a base of 8.4 cm and equal sides of 5 cm.

6 Triangle *PQR* has side *PQ* = 5 cm, angle *QPR* = 60° and angle *PQR* = 60°
   a Make an accurate drawing of this triangle.
   b Calculate the size of angle *PRQ* and check your answer by measurement.
   c What name is given to this type of triangle?

7 An isosceles triangle has two equal sides of 6.5 cm and two equal angles of 50°
   a Draw a sketch of this triangle.
   b Use a ruler and protractor to make an accurate drawing of the triangle and write down the length of the third side.

Chapter summary

■ There are
  ■ 360° in a full turn
  ■ 180° in a half-turn
  ■ 90° in a quarter-turn

■ An angle between 0° and 90° is an *acute angle*.

■ An angle of exactly 90° is a *right angle*.

  A right angle is marked with a small square

■ An angle between 90° and 180° is an *obtuse angle*.

■ An angle between 180° and 360° is a *reflex angle*.

■ Angles at a point total 360°
  $x + y + z = 360°$

- Angles on a straight line total 180°
  $a + b = 180°$

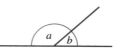

- *Perpendicular lines* meet at right angles.

  Lines AB and CD are perpendicular.

- When two lines intersect the vertically opposite angles are equal.
  $a = c$
  $b = d$

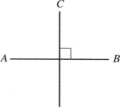

- An *equilateral* triangle has all three sides equal. The three angles each measure 60°

- An *isosceles* triangle has two sides of equal length and two equal angles.

- A *scalene* triangle has three sides of different lengths and three angles of different sizes.

- A *right-angled triangle* has an angle of 90°

- The three angles in any triangle always add up to 180°

- The *exterior* angle of a triangle is equal to the sum of the two opposite *interior* angles.

- To construct a triangle where one or more angles are given, use a ruler and protractor.

- To construct a triangle where only lengths are given, use a ruler and compasses.

- Leave construction arcs and lines in the diagram to show the method used to draw the triangle.

Chapter review

1 Here is a list of angles.
  20°   37°   90°   100°   146°   190°   298°
  From the list, write down an angle which is
  a obtuse   **b** reflex.

2 The diagram shows triangle ABC.
  Angle ABC is a right angle and angle $BCA = 36°$
  Work out the value of x.
  Give a reason for your answer.

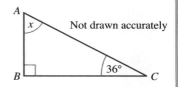

3 In triangle *ABC*, the side *AB* is 6 cm.
Angle *A* = 50° and angle *B* = 100°

Make an accurate drawing of the triangle.

4 In the diagram:
angle *ABC* = 110°
angle *DBC* = 27°
   a What type of angle is *ABC*?
   b What type of angle is *DBC*?
   c Work out the size of angle *ABD*.

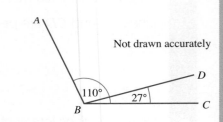

Not drawn accurately

5 *ABC* is a triangle and *BD* is a straight line.
   a Calculate the size of the angle marked *x*.
   Give a reason for your answer.
   b Calculate the size of the angle marked *y*.
   Give a reason for your answer.

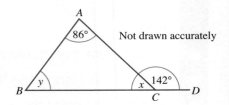

Not drawn accurately

6 Make an accurate drawing of this triangle.

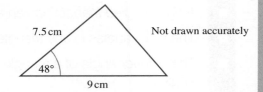

Not drawn accurately

7 **a** The diagram shows three angles
   on a straight line *AB*.
   Work out the value of *x*.

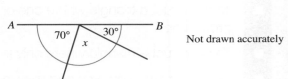

Not drawn accurately

   b The diagram shows three angles
   meeting at a point.
   Work out the value of *y*.

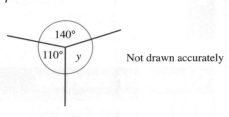

Not drawn accurately

   c The diagram shows a triangle.
   Work out the value of *z*.

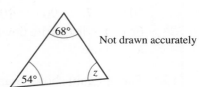

Not drawn accurately

8 In triangle *ABC*, angle *A* = 100°, *AB* = 6 cm and *AC* = 5 cm.
Make an accurate drawing of the triangle.

9 *ABC* is a right-angled triangle.
Angle *A* = 39°

Work out the size of angle *C*.

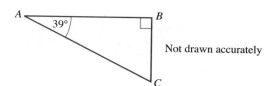

Not drawn accurately

10 a Which of the angles
      45°   60°   90°   135°   180°   240°
   i is an obtuse angle?
   ii is a reflex angle?

b *ABCD* is a rectangle.
   Find
   i the value of *a*
   ii the value of *b*.

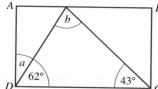

Not drawn accurately

3

Powers and roots

3.1 Square numbers

CAN YOU REMEMBER

- The meaning of the phrase 'to square a number'?
- The multiplication tables up to 10×10?

IN THIS SECTION YOU WILL

- Identify *square numbers* up to 10×10
- Reinforce your knowledge of square numbers.
- Learn to use the square button on your calculator.

Square numbers can be represented as square patterns of dots.

$1 \times 1 = 1$ $2 \times 2 = 4$ $3 \times 3 = 9$ $4 \times 4 = 16$

To square a number multiply it by itself. For example, $5 \times 5 = 25$
5×5 can be written as 5^2.

A *square number* is a whole number squared.
For example, $25 = 5 \times 5 = 5^2$ is a square number.

Example 1

Use a calculator to work out 23^2

Solution 1

Method 1
Enter the number 23 and use the 'square' key.

Make sure you know how to use the square key on your own calculator.

Answer = 529

Method 2
Work out 23×23

Answer = 529

Exercise A

1 Write down the square of:

a 8	**b** 5	**c** 9	**d** 1
e 10	**f** 7	**g** 6	**h** 4

2 Write down all the square numbers from each list.

a 3	8	17	25	42	64	81	99
b 4	9	18	26	43	65	82	100
c 7	16	24	49	60	81	90	96
d 1	10	16	36	50	64	88	100

3 Match the multiplication cards to the square number cards.

4 Use a calculator to work out:

a 15^2	**b** 11^2	**c** 13^2	**d** 12^2
e 41^2	**f** 73^2	**g** 24^2	**h** 18^2

5 Use a calculator to square each of the following decimals:

a 4.3^2	**b** 6.2^2	**c** 12.5^2	**d** 8.4^2
e 7.6^2	**f** 9.1^2	**g** 11.8^2	**h** 52.2^2

6 **a** Work out the answers to each part. Write down what you notice.

    i 12^2 **ii** 120^2 **iii** 1200^2

  b Work out the answers to each part. Write down what you notice.

    i 7^2 **ii** 0.7^2 **iii** 0.07^2

Example 2

Write down two square numbers with
a a sum of 61   **b** a difference of 5   **c** units digit 6

Solution 2

a $25 + 36 = 61$ **b** $9 - 4 = 5$ **c** 16 and 36 have units digit 6

Exercise B

1 Write down two square numbers with a sum of

a 181	**b** 113	**c** 5	**d** 145
e 53	**f** 85	**g** 130	**h** 25

2 Write down two square numbers with a difference of

a 7	**b** 17	**c** 11	**d** 19
e 80	**f** 55	**g** 33	**h** 60

3 Write down two square numbers

   a greater than 50 and less than 100   **b** with units digit 9

   c with units digit 4   **d** greater than 4×5 but less than 6×7

4 **a** Work out $8^2 - 7^2$ **b** Work out $8 + 7$

   c Comment on your answers to parts **a** and **b**.

5 **a** Work out $9^2 - 8^2$ **b** Work out $9 + 8$

   c Comment on your answers to parts **a** and **b**.

6 **a** Work out $10^2 - 9^2$ **b** Work out $10 + 9$

   c Comment on your answers to parts **a** and **b**.

7 **a** Work out the answers to each line of the pattern. $1 + 3$

   b Use the pattern of your answers to write $1 + 3 + 5$

      down the answer to $1 + 3 + 5 + 7 + 9$ $1 + 3 + 5 + 7$

   c **i** Write down the first five square numbers.

      ii Compare your answers to parts **a** and **b** with your answers to part **c i**.
          What do you notice?

     iii Write down the sum of the first 10 odd numbers.

8 **a** Show that the difference between 5^2 and 4^2 is 3^2

   b Use a calculator to find another example where the difference between two square numbers is a square number.

3.2 Square roots

CAN YOU REMEMBER

- The square numbers up to 100?
- How to write numbers to one decimal place?

IN THIS SECTION YOU WILL

- Learn the meaning of the term 'square root'.
- Identify the square roots of square numbers up to 100
- Use the square root button on your calculator.

The opposite of squaring a number is finding its *square root*.

For example, $5^2 = 5 \times 5 = 25$, so the square root of 25 is 5

The symbol for square root is $\sqrt{\ }$.

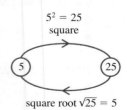

Example 1

a Without using a calculator, work out

  i $\sqrt{81}$ **ii** $\sqrt{36}$

b Use a calculator to work out

  i $\sqrt{5.29}$ **ii** $\sqrt{2.25}$

Solution 1

a **i** $\sqrt{81} = 9$ because $9 \times 9 = 81$

  ii $\sqrt{36} = 6$ because $6 \times 6 = 36$

b **i** $\sqrt{5.29} = 2.3$

  ii $\sqrt{2.25} = 1.5$

Make sure you know how to work out square roots on your own calculator.

Exercise A

1 Copy and complete:

  a $\sqrt{9} = 3$ because ..... × ..... = 9

  c $\sqrt{64} = ...$ because ..... × ..... = ...

  b $\sqrt{1} = 1$ because ..... × ..... = ...

  d $\sqrt{.....} = 7$ because ..... × ..... = ...

2 Without using a calculator work out:

  a $\sqrt{100}$ **b** $\sqrt{16}$ **c** $\sqrt{4}$ **d** $\sqrt{1}$

  e $\sqrt{25}$ **f** $\sqrt{64}$ **g** $\sqrt{49}$ **h** $\sqrt{36}$

3 These cards match in pairs.
Match the square root cards to
the answer cards.

4 These cards match in pairs.
Match the square root cards to
the answer cards.
One has been done for you.

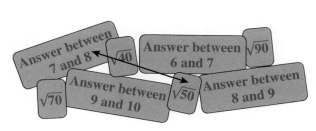

5 Use a calculator to work out each square root.

  i Write down the full calculator display.

  ii Write the answer to one decimal place.

  a $\sqrt{84}$ **b** $\sqrt{43}$ **c** $\sqrt{97}$ **d** $\sqrt{50}$

  e $\sqrt{250}$ **f** $\sqrt{104}$ **g** $\sqrt{124}$ **h** $\sqrt{1000}$

6 For each set:
Work out the square and square root.
Put the three values in order, starting with the smallest.

  a 6.5 $\sqrt{41}$ 2.5^2

  c 7.5 $\sqrt{56}$ 2.7^2

  b 10 3.2^2 $\sqrt{99}$

  d 7.5 $\sqrt{57}$ 2.8^2

Example 2

Which is the greater, $\sqrt{50}$ or 7? Show your working.

Solution 2

$7^2 = 7 \times 7 = 49$
$\sqrt{49} = 7$, so $\sqrt{50}$ is greater than 7

Example 3

Without using a calculator work out:

a $\sqrt{64}$ **b** $\sqrt{6400}$ **c** $\sqrt{640\,000}$

Solution 3

a $\sqrt{64} = 8$ **b** $\sqrt{6400} = \sqrt{64 \times 100}$ **c** $\sqrt{640\,000} = \sqrt{64 \times 100 \times 100}$

$$= \sqrt{64} \times \sqrt{100} \qquad\qquad = \sqrt{64} \times \sqrt{100} \times \sqrt{100}$$
$$= 8 \times 10 \qquad\qquad\qquad = 8 \times 10 \times 10$$
$$= 80 \qquad\qquad\qquad\qquad = 800$$

Exercise B

1 Which is the greater? Show your working.

     a $\sqrt{40}$ or 6   **b** $\sqrt{60}$ or 8   **c** $\sqrt{80}$ or 9   **d** $\sqrt{70}$ or 8

2 Without using a calculator work out:

     a $\sqrt{81}$ **b** $\sqrt{8100}$ **c** $\sqrt{810\,000}$

3 Without using a calculator work out:

     a $\sqrt{25}$ **b** $\sqrt{2500}$ **c** $\sqrt{250\,000}$

4 Without using a calculator work out:

     a $\sqrt{36}$ **b** $\sqrt{3600}$ **c** $\sqrt{360\,000}$

5 Without using a calculator work out:

     a $\sqrt{100}$ **b** $\sqrt{10\,000}$ **c** $\sqrt{1\,000\,000}$

6 Use your calculator to work out:

     a $\sqrt{11.56}$ **b** $\sqrt{11.56} + \sqrt{27.04}$ **c** $\dfrac{\sqrt{11.56}}{\sqrt{2.89}}$

     d $\dfrac{\sqrt{27.04}}{\sqrt{1.69}}$ **e** $\sqrt{\dfrac{40.96}{10.24}}$ **f** $\sqrt{1.21} \times \sqrt{100}$

7 Use your calculator to work out:

a $\sqrt{39.69} - \sqrt{38.44}$ **b** $\sqrt{2209} + 9^2$ **c** $\sqrt{249.64} - \sqrt{94.09} + \sqrt{1.3225}$

d $\dfrac{\sqrt{1156} + 19^2}{\sqrt{25}}$ **e** $\sqrt{\dfrac{65.61}{7.29}} - \sqrt{\dfrac{2.56}{0.16}}$ **f** $\sqrt{201.64} \div \sqrt{50.41}$

3.3 Powers

CAN YOU REMEMBER

- How to write simple number patterns?
- Multiplications up to 10×10?

IN THIS SECTION YOU WILL

- Work out *powers of numbers*, e.g. 2^4
- Understand the meaning of the word '*cube*'.
- Learn the cubes of 1, 2, 3, 4, 5 and 10
- Use the power button on a calculator.

The square of 5 is written 5^2
In this example, 5 is called the *base number* and 2 is called the *power*.

The *cube* of a number is the number multiplied by itself three times.
For example, the cube of 2 is $2 \times 2 \times 2 = 8$. The cube of 2 is written 2^3

Here are some numbers and their cubes to remember.

$$1^3 = 1 \times 1 \times 1 = 1 \qquad\qquad 4^3 = 4 \times 4 \times 4 = 64$$
$$2^3 = 2 \times 2 \times 2 = 8 \qquad\qquad 5^3 = 5 \times 5 \times 5 = 125$$
$$3^3 = 3 \times 3 \times 3 = 27 \qquad\qquad 10^3 = 10 \times 10 \times 10 = 1000$$

Square and cube are special names for numbers raised to the powers 2 and 3
2^2 is '2 squared'. 2^3 is '2 cubed'.

Powers can be greater than 3, but these do not have special names.
For example, 2^4 is '2 to the power 4' 4^5 is '4 to the power 5'.

The power gives the number of times the *base number* is multiplied by itself.

For example, $2^4 = \underbrace{2 \times 2 \times 2 \times 2}_{4 \text{ times}} = 16$

A number to the power 1 is the number itself. For example, $5^1 = 5$

Make sure you know how to work out powers using the power key on your own calculator.

Example 1

Work out the value of:

a 2^6 **b** 5^4

Solution 1

a $2^6 = 2 \times 2 \times 2 \times 2 \times 2 \times 2$
      $= 64$

b $5^4 = 5 \times 5 \times 5 \times 5$
      $= 625$

Exercise A

1 Work out the value of:

  a 2^5 **b** 3^3 **c** 4^2 **d** 5^2 **e** 4^3

  f 10^3 **g** 2^7 **h** 10^4 **i** 2^6 **j** 3^2

2 These cards match in pairs.
Match the power cards to
the answer cards.

3 Here is a pattern of powers of 10. Copy and complete the pattern.

  10   10^2 10^3 10^4 10^5 10^6 10^7

  10   100   1000   ...   .

4 Here is a pattern of powers of 2. Copy and complete the pattern.

  2   2^2 2^3 2^4 2^5 2^6 2^7

  2   4   8   ...   .

5 Here is a pattern of powers of 3. Copy and complete the pattern.

  3   3^2 3^3 3^4

  3   ...   .

6 Here is a pattern of powers of 5. Copy and complete the pattern.

  5   5^2 5^3 5^4

    625

7 Use the power button on a calculator to work out the value of:

  a 8^3 **b** 7^4 **c** 5^5 **d** 6^5 **e** 9^3

  f 2^{10} **g** 11^4 **h** 4^8 **i** 8^5 **j** 7^6

8 These cards match in pairs.
Use a calculator to help you
match the power cards to
the answer cards.

9 Use the power button on a calculator to help you work out which is greater:

    a 4^3 or 7^2 **b** 9^3 or 5^4 **c** 2^{10} or 10^3

    d 6^3 or 4^5 **e** 17^2 or 2^8 **f** 13^3 or 31^2

Example 2

Work out the value of $6^2 \times 2^3$

Solution 2

$$6^2 \times 2^3 = 6 \times 6 \times 2 \times 2 \times 2$$
$$= 36 \times 8$$
$$= 288$$

Exercise B

1 Work out the value of:

    a $2^5 \times 3$ **b** $3^3 \times 2$ **c** $3^2 \times 2^2$ **d** $5^3 \times 2^3$ **e** $10^4 \times 5^3$

2 By working out the values, write the following in order of size, starting with the smallest:

    a 2^5 3^2 4^3 5^2 **b** 1^{10} 10^1 2^2 3^3

    c 6^2 4^3 2^5 3^4 **d** 4^2 15^1 3^3 5^2

3 Work out the difference between 2^5 and 5^2

4 Work out the sum of 2^6 and 6^2

5 Write down the value of 176^1

6 Write down the cube numbers from this list:

    24   27   33   64   67   100   125

7 Which numbers in this list are equal?

    4^3 8^2 2^6 64^1

8 Use your calculator to work out:

    a 2×6^3 **b** 8×4^2 **c** $5^2 \times 4^3$ **d** $2^5 \times 3^7$ **e** $10^3 \div 5^2$

    f $8^4 \div 16^2$ **g** $27^2 \div 3^5$ **h** $12^3 \div 4^2$ **i** $9^4 \div 3^8$

9 Use your calculator to work out:

    a $8^4 + 6^4$ **b** $9^3 + 7^3$ **c** $2^{10} + 10^3$ **d** $5^5 + 4^6$

    e $7^3 - 5^3$ **f** $2^{12} - 4^4$ **g** $13^3 - 12^3$

10 Investigate powers of 2 on your calculator 2^1, 2^2 and so on.

    What happens to the calculator display as the powers become very large?

Chapter summary

- A square number is a whole number multiplied by itself.
  For example, 25 is a square number because $5 \times 5 = 25$
- 5^2 is shorthand for 5×5
- The opposite of squaring a number is finding its square root.
  The symbol for square root is $\sqrt{\ }$.
- 3^5 (3 to the power 5) is shorthand for $3 \times 3 \times 3 \times 3 \times 3$
  - In this example 3 is the base and 5 is the power.
- The power gives the number of times the base is multiplied by itself.
- Square and cube are special words for numbers raised to the powers 2 and 3

Chapter review

1 Write down the values of: **a** 5^2 **b** $\sqrt{64}$

2 **a** Write down the square root of 81   **b** Write down the value of 10^3

3 **a** Write down the square of 9   **b** Work out the value of $9^2 + \sqrt{16}$

4 Which is greater: 5^3 or 10^2? Show your working.

5 Here is a number pattern.

Line 1:	1	= 1
Line 2:	$1 + 3$	= 4
Line 3:	$1 + 3 + 5$	= 9
Line 4:	$1 + 3 + 5 + 7$	= 16
Line 5:	$1 + 3 + 5 + 7 + 9$	= 25
Line 6:	....	= .....

a Copy and complete line 6
b What is the special name given to numbers in the sequence 1, 4, 9, 16, 25, ...?
c Line 4 adds up to 16
What does line 9 add up to?
d Which line adds up to 121?

6 Roger worked out: $5^2 - 2^2 = 25 - 4 = 21$
He then said 'The difference between any two square numbers is always an odd number.' By means of an example, show that Roger is wrong.

7 Here is a list of numbers:
1   2   3   4   5   6   7   8   9   10   11   12
a Write down all the square numbers in the list.
b Write down two numbers that multiply together to give 24
c Which number in this list is one quarter of 32?

8 **a** Work out 4.3^2 **b** Work out the cube of 5

9 **a** Calculate $\sqrt{10.89}$ **b** Calculate $\sqrt{10.89} + 2.8^2$

10 Calculate $2.6^2 + 3^3$

Collecting data

4.1 Tally charts

A researcher records the number of red cars she sees.

Each time she sees a red car she draws a mark | called a *tally* on her *tally chart*. To make the tallies easier to count she groups them in 5s: ||||| or *five-bar gates*.

The total number of tallies is the *frequency* of red cars.

Example 1

Sandra picks sweets one at a time from a large bag.
She records the colour of each sweet she picks as:

Red (R)   Green (G)   Yellow (Y)   Pink (P)   Brown (B)

Her results are:

R	B	R	Y	P	R	G	R	B	Y
B	P	P	R	R	Y	R	Y	Y	G

Tally her results.

Solution 1

Work along the list of results, making a tally mark for each colour. Count up the tallies and write the totals in the frequency column.

Colour	Tally	Frequency
Red (R)	||||| ||	7
Green (G)	||	2
Yellow (Y)	|||||	5
Pink (P)	|||	3
Brown (B)	|||	3

Exercise A

1 Nina throws a fair dice and records the following scores:

3	6	5	2	3	4	6	1	4	2
5	6	3	3	2	6	1	4	6	3

Complete the tally chart for her results.

Score	Tally	Frequency
1		
2		
3		
4		
5		
6		

2 A bus driver records whether passengers are adults (A) or children (C).
The results are:

A	A	C	C	C	A	A	A	C	A
C	A	A	A	A	C	C	A	A	C
A	A	A	C	C	A	A	A	A	C
A	A	C	C	C	C	C	A	A	A

Complete the tally chart.

Passenger	Tally	Frequency
Adult (A)		
Child (C)		

3 Jasmine records each bird that she sees in her garden on one winter's day.
She records the birds as: Robin (R)   Sparrow (S)   Thrush (T)   Blackbird (B)

Her results are:

S	T	B	T	S	S	S	R	T	B	S	S	T	R	S
S	B	S	S	S	S	R	S	S	S	B	B	T	S	T

Complete the tally chart.

Bird	Tally	Frequency
Robin (R)		
Sparrow (S)		
Thrush (T)		
Blackbird (B)		

4 Jarnail asks his friends to name their favourite sport. He records their favourites as:

Football (F) Rugby (R) Tennis (T) Golf (G) Other (O)

His results are:

| F | F | R | R | R | G | F | T | O | T |
| R | F | G | G | F | F | F | R | R | O |

Complete the full chart.

Favourite sport	Tally	Frequency
Football (F)		
Rugby (R)		

5 John asks his friends how many DVDs they watched in the past month.
Their replies are:

| 2 | 0 | 4 | 1 | 2 | 1 | 3 | 4 | 2 | 0 | 3 | 5 | 0 | 1 | 1 |
| 5 | 2 | 3 | 3 | 1 | 5 | 3 | 2 | 5 | 0 | 0 | 1 | 1 | 2 | 1 |

Complete the chart.

Number of DVDs	Tally	Frequency
0		
1		

6 Aimee records the type of person she sees in TV adverts as:

Man (M) Woman (W) Boy (B) Girl (G)

Her results are:

M	W	M	W	M	M	W
W	B	G	W	W	W	M
M	B	B	B	W	G	W
G	M	W	W	W	W	M
B	W	M	W	B	G	B
W	W	M	G			

Complete the chart.

Person	Tally	Frequency
Man (M)		
Woman (W)		
Boy (B)		
Girl (G)		

7 Mia spins this spinner 50 times.

Her scores are:

3	2	3	1	4	3	4	2	3	1
1	1	2	3	4	1	2	3	2	3
2	1	1	4	2	4	2	2	3	4
2	3	1	3	3	2	3	1	4	2
1	3	2	3	1	2	4	4	2	1

Complete the chart.

Score	Tally	Frequency
1		
2		

8 Oliver notes the weather each day for 30 days.
Copy and complete his chart.

Weather	Tally	Frequency
Sunny	卌 卌	
Cloudy		11
Raining	卌 II	
Windy		2

9 Mrs Shaw records the number of students absent from her class each day for one month.
Copy and complete her chart.

Number of pupils absent	Tally	Frequency
0	卌 II	
1		4
2		3
3	卌 I	

10 David counts the number of letters he receives each weekday for a few months.
Some of the data is in the chart.

Number of letters	Tally	Frequency
0	卌 III	
1	卌 卌 卌	
2	卌 卌 卌 卌 I	
3	卌 卌 卌 卌 卌 III	
4	卌 卌	
5	III	
6	I	

The rest of David's data is:

3	2	4	2	1	0	3	3	3	2	4	6	1
1	2	3	3	2	2	5	0	3	1	4	2	

a Copy David's chart. Add the tallies for the rest of his data.
b Complete the frequency column.
c For how many days did David collect data?

Tally charts can be used to find out information.

Example 2

A police officer collects data on the number of people in each car leaving a service station. His results are:

Number of people in car	Tally	Frequency
1	ЖГ ЖГ ЖГ ЖГ |||	23
2	ЖГ ЖГ ЖГ ЖГ		21
3	ЖГ ЖГ |||	13
4	ЖГ ||	7
5	ЖГ		6

a How many cars have only two people in them?

b How many cars does he see in total?

c What is the most common number of people in a car?

Solution 2

a 21 cars have two people.

b Total number of cars = number with one person + number with two people, and so on: $23 + 21 + 13 + 7 + 6 = 70$

c The highest frequency is 23, for one person in a car.
One person is the most common.

A tally chart is sometimes called an *observation sheet* or *data collection sheet*.

To design a data collection sheet or observation sheet:
- think of the possible answers
- draw a table with a row for each possible answer.

For example, for an observation sheet for data about the number of pets kept by 20 people you need columns for number of pets, tally and frequency.

Some people have no pets, some have one or two.
A few people may have lots.
Instead of having a row for every possible number, make the last class *open-ended*.

Class intervals are used when there are a large number of different data values.
The classes must not overlap. For example, if both classes 1–5 and 5–10 were included, where would the result '5' be tallied?

Number of pets
0
1
2
3
4
5
6 or more

Example 3

Casey measures the lengths of 30 worms to
the nearest centimetre (cm).
Here is her data:

5	8	2	12	7	18	17	5	13	22
31	6	13	17	9	1	12	27	20	16
19	6	2	34	12	9	7	8	16	4

a Make a tally chart for these results.
b Which group has the most worms in it?

Solution 3

a The first worm is 5 cm so tally
it in the 1–5 class.
The next worm is 8 cm, so
tally it in the 6–10 class,
and so on.

b The 6–10 cm group has the
most worms.

Length of worm (cm)	Tally	Frequency
1–5	⅋⅋⅋ I	6
6–10	⅋⅋⅋ III	8
11–15	⅋⅋⅋	5
16–20	⅋⅋⅋ II	7
21–25	I	1
26–30	I	1
31–35	II	2

Exercise B

1 Every day Eugene counts how many apples have fallen off his apple tree.
His data for one month is:

| 3 | 1 | 4 | 2 | 0 | 5 | 2 | 13 | 3 | 2 | 2 | 3 | 0 | 0 | 8 |
| 3 | 1 | 2 | 5 | 3 | 1 | 4 | 3 | 9 | 10 | 2 | 3 | 0 | 1 | 8 |

Copy and complete the tally chart.

Number of apples	Tally	Frequency
0		
1		
2		
3		
4		
5 or more		

2 Design a tally chart to record the number of letters that arrive at your house every day.
Invent data for 20 days and write it in your chart.

3 The amount of time Peter spends on the internet each day is shown below.

15	35	22	65	15	18	33	75	34	41
12	45	19	55	23	25	32	55	90	67
23	5	13	10	28	32	65	83	42	11

Time (minutes)
0–10
11–20
21–30
31–60
61–90

   a Copy and complete the tally chart.
   b Which class interval is the most common?

4 A travel company records how many foreign holidays each customer has one year. The results are:

| 3 | 1 | 2 | 0 | 1 | 2 | 3 | 2 | 2 | 2 | 1 | 0 | 0 | 1 | 3 |
| 3 | 3 | 4 | 1 | 2 | 1 | 2 | 1 | 0 | 2 | 1 | 0 | 0 | 2 | 3 |

   a Design and complete a tally chart to show this data.
   b What was the most common number of foreign holidays?

5 Design an observation sheet with class intervals to record the number of cars queuing at a set of traffic lights.

6 Design a data collection sheet to record people's opinions of a new chocolate bar called 'Choco'.
   Invent the first 20 responses people might give and tally them in your chart.

7 The distances, in miles, that 30 employees travel to work are:

12	8	5	4	19	24	13	3	2	1
42	1	2	4	1	18	14	16	2	4
16	11	21	8	7	4	2	1	1	5

   a Design and complete a tally chart to summarise this information.
      Use class intervals 1–10, 11–20, 21–30, 31–40, 41–50
   b Which class interval is the most common?
   c How many employees travel more than 20 miles to work?

8 Sasha makes 24 telephone calls. The lengths of the calls (in minutes) are:

| 12 | 3 | 45 | 18 | 9 | 13 | 43 | 14 | 9 | 24 | 21 | 7 |
| 21 | 18 | 30 | 7 | 2 | 18 | 24 | 42 | 23 | 18 | 31 | 19 |

   a Design and complete a tally chart to show this data.
      Use class intervals 0–9, 10–19, 20–29, 30–39 and 40–49
   b Which class interval is the most common?

9 Nadia recorded the lottery numbers for several weeks:

6	13	25	26	32	48
2	24	28	32	39	49
21	22	35	39	43	45
11	20	30	42	47	48

1	3	9	13	40	43
12	23	32	33	34	43
4	11	13	32	40	46
6	15	17	21	24	38

a Design and complete a tally chart to show this data.
   Use class intervals 1–9, 10–19, …

b How many numbers under 40 were drawn?

10 Copy this incomplete tally chart. Use the information below to complete it.

Scores of a cricket team over 100 innings:

Runs scored	Tally	Frequency
0–99	ⅢⅠ I	6
100–199		
200–299		
300–399		
400–599		

- 100–199 runs were scored twice as often as 0–99 runs.
- 200–299 runs were scored three times as often as 100–199 runs.
- 300–399 runs and 400–599 runs were scored the same number of times as each other.

4.2 Pictograms

CAN YOU REMEMBER

- How to count up in twos?
- How to read a key?

IN THIS SECTION YOU WILL

- Learn how to draw pictograms.
- Interpret information from pictograms.

A *pictogram* is a diagram that shows data clearly using pictures or symbols.

Pictograms need a *key* to show what a symbol represents. Key: 🧍 = two people.

It is important to draw the symbols all the same size and in line with symbols above and below.

For fractions of the quantity, use fractions of the symbol: ⌇ = one person.

Example 1

The pictogram shows the number of CDs owned by four of Sally's friends.

a How many CDs does Helen have?

b Which of Sally's friends has the most CDs?

c How many more CDs than Nadia does Emma have?

d Sally has 30 CDs. Draw the symbols to show this.

Key: 🔘 represents 10 CDs.

Joan	🔘 🔘 🔘 🔘 🔘
Nadia	🔘
Helen	🔘 🔘 🔘 🔘
Emma	🔘 🔘

Solution 1

a Helen has $3 \times 10 + \frac{1}{2} \times 10 = 30 + 5 = 35$ CDs.

b Joan has the most CDs.

c Emma has $2 \times 10 = 20$ CDs. Nadia has $1 \times 10 = 10$ CDs.
So Emma has $20 - 10 = 10$ more CDs than Nadia.
Or Emma has 10 more because she has one extra symbol in her row.

d 🔘 🔘 🔘

Exercise A

1 Copy and complete the pictogram for the following data.

Favourite milkshake	Number of people
Strawberry	6
Raspberry	4
Vanilla	8
Chocolate	10

Key: 🥤 represents two people.

Strawberry	🥤 🥤 🥤
Raspberry	🥤 🥤
Vanilla	
Chocolate	

2 Copy and complete the pictogram for the following data.

Use the symbol  to represent two DVDs.

Name	Number of DVDs owned
Tim	7
Jamila	4
Sayeed	5
Sharon	9

Tim	🔘 🔘 🔘 🔘
Jamila	🔘 🔘
Sayeed	
Sharon	

3 Draw a pictogram to represent this data.

Use the symbol 😞 to represent two pupils.

Day	Number of pupils in detention
Monday	2
Tuesday	4
Wednesday	5
Thursday	3
Friday	1

4 The number of landline telephones in each house on a street is shown below.

4	3	2	1	3	1	2	4	2	2	2	4
3	3	1	5	2	3	4	3	5	2	2	1

a Draw a pictogram to represent the data.

Use the symbol 🏠 to represent two houses.

b What is the greatest number of telephones in a house?

c What is the most common number of telephones in a house?

5 The numbers of computers in different classrooms in a school are:

4	3	6	7	2	1
0	0	3	5	2	2
1	5	4	0	0	6
2	7	3	6	8	9
0	1	8	3	2	4

a Copy and complete the pictogram to represent this data.

b What is the greatest number of computers in a classroom?

c What is the most common number of computers in a classroom?

Key: 💻 represents two classrooms.

Number of computers	
0	💻 💻 💻
1–2	💻 💻 💻 💻
3–4	
5–6	
7 or more	

6 The numbers of people arriving late at an airport for five flights are:

Flight	Number of people arriving late
A	2
B	4
C	5
D	11
E	7

a Draw a pictogram to represent this data.

Use the symbol 🧍 to represent two people.

b What is the greatest number of people arriving late?

c What is the total number of people arriving late?

Pictograms can be used to compare data.

Example 2

Steve asks his friends to choose their favourite game from a list. Their replies are:

Football	Tennis	Football	Hockey	Netball	Football
Hockey	Netball	Netball	Football	Football	Tennis
Hockey	Football	Hockey	Football	Netball	Hockey

a Complete a tally chart for this data.

b Draw a pictogram to show these results.

Use the symbol ⊗ to represent two replies.

c Which game was the most popular?

d How many more people chose football than tennis?

Solution 2

a

Game	Tally	Frequency
Football	⊬ |||	7
Tennis	||	2
Hockey	⊬	5
Netball	||||	4

b

Football	⊗ ⊗ ⊗ ◖
Tennis	⊗
Hockey	⊗ ⊗ ◖
Netball	⊗ ⊗

c Football.

d Football has $2\frac{1}{2}$ more symbols than tennis.

$2\frac{1}{2}$ symbols represent five people.

Five more people chose football than tennis.

Exercise B

1 Peter records the number of burgers he sells each day for one week:

Day	Number of burgers sold
Monday	20
Tuesday	25
Wednesday	35
Thursday	15
Friday	10
Saturday	20
Sunday	30

a Draw a pictogram to represent this data.
Use the symbol ⬭ to represent five burgers.

b Which day does Peter sell most burgers?

c How many burgers does Peter sell in total in the week?

2 Jayne records the number of letters she receives each day for one week:
a Draw a pictogram to represent this data. Use the symbol to represent four letters.
b Which day does Jayne receive most letters?
c How many letters does Jayne receive in total?

Day	Number of letters
Monday	8
Tuesday	10
Wednesday	6
Thursday	2
Friday	14

3 A bank records the numbers of customers queuing at midday on 28 Fridays.
a Draw a pictogram to represent this data. Use the symbol ⊕ to represent two days.
b On how many Fridays were three customers queuing at midday?
c Which is the most common number of customers queuing?
d On how many Fridays were more than two customers queuing?

Number of customers queuing	Frequency (number of Fridays)
0	4
1	2
2	3
3	7
4	8
5	4
6	3

4 Zak has an ice cream van. He records the number of cornets he sells each day.
a Draw a pictogram for this data. Use the symbol ▽ to represent four cornets.
b Which day did Zak sell most cornets?
c How many cornets did Zak sell altogether in the week?

Day	Number of cornets sold
Monday	10
Tuesday	12
Wednesday	8
Thursday	6
Friday	4
Saturday	14
Sunday	22

5 A driving test centre records the number of people who pass and fail in one week. The results are shown in the table:
a Draw a pictogram to show the number of people who pass the driving test each day. Use the symbol ⚊ to represent four people.
b How many more people failed the driving test than passed on Tuesday?
c In total, how many more people failed the driving test than passed that week?

Day	Number who pass	Number who fail
Monday	10	10
Tuesday	6	14
Wednesday	4	16
Thursday	2	18
Friday	12	8

6 Salem the dog loves digging up bones. His owner keeps a record of how many bones Salem digs up every day. The results for last week are shown in the table.

Day	Number of bones
Monday	4
Tuesday	6
Wednesday	3
Thursday	7
Friday	1
Saturday	10
Sunday	5

    a Draw a pictogram to show the number of bones Salem dug up each day last week.
       You must design your own symbol. Give the pictogram a key.

    b How many bones did Salem dig up in total last week?

4.3 Bar charts

CAN YOU REMEMBER

- The meaning of the word 'frequency'?
- How to draw a numbered axis?

IN THIS SECTION YOU WILL

- Draw 'bar charts' to show data.
- Interpret information from a bar chart.

A tester in a factory records the colours of sweets in a packet. She draws a *bar chart* to show the data.

A bar chart is a *frequency diagram*.
It shows the number (or frequency) of each item.

It is important that:

- The bar chart has a title.
- The *axes* are labelled.
- The *scale* for the frequency axis is numbered in equal steps, starting at zero.
- The bars are all equal in width.
- There are gaps between the bars.

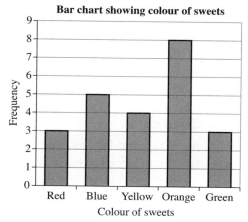

The heights of the bars show how many sweets of each colour there are in the packet.

Example 1

The students in a class choose
their favourite drink.

The results are shown in the table.

Draw a bar chart to represent
this information.

Favourite drink	Number of students
Milk	12
Cola	7
Orange juice	10
Lemonade	3

Solution 1

The frequency axis must start from zero.
The highest frequency is 12, so draw the
axis long enough to show this.

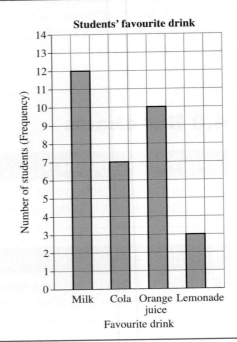

Example 2

The horizontal bar chart shows the shoe
size of a number of students.

a   Which is the most common shoe size?

b   How many students have a shoe size larger
than 6?

c   How many more students have size 7 shoes
than size 6?

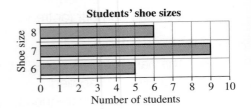

Solution 2

a   7 has the longest bar. The most common shoe size is 7

b   9 students have shoe size 7. 6 students have shoe size 8
So 9 + 6 = 15 students have shoe size larger than 6

c   9 students have shoe size 7. 5 students have shoe size 6
So 9 − 5 = 4 more students have size 7 shoes than size 6

Exercise A

1 Draw a bar chart to show the following data.

Favourite type of meal	Frequency
Hot food	8
Salad	5
Sandwiches	10

2 Draw a bar chart to show this data.

Colour of car	Frequency
Red	25
Blue	14
Silver	8
Other	30

3 A shop records the numbers and sizes of T-shirts it sells in one week.
The bar chart shows the results.
  a How many small T-shirts are sold?
  b Which size of T-shirt sells the most?
  c How many T-shirts are sold in total?

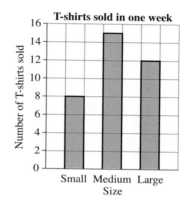

4 In a quiz each person was asked five questions.
The number of answers each person got right was recorded.
The bar chart shows the results.
  a How many people gave only one correct answer?
  b How many people gave four correct answers?
  c How many people gave three or more correct answers?
  d Every person gave at least one correct answer.
    How many people took part in the quiz?

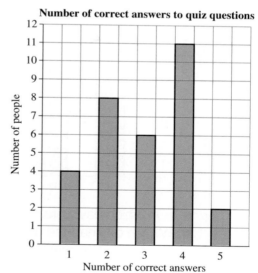

5 An ice cream stall records the numbers of ice creams sold in one day.

Draw a bar chart to show this information.

	Number sold
Lollipops	24
Wafers	15
Tubs	8
Cornets	28

6 Jono keeps a tally of the number of goals scored by four players in his football team. The results are:

Player	Tally
Jono	卌 卌 卌 卌
Trevor	卌 卌 卌 卌 I
Ali	卌 卌
Neil	卌 IIII

a Work out the frequency for each player.
b Who scored the most goals?
c Draw a bar chart to show these results.
d How many goals did these four players score in total?

7 The bar chart shows the number of pupils absent from Tall Trees High School each day in one week.

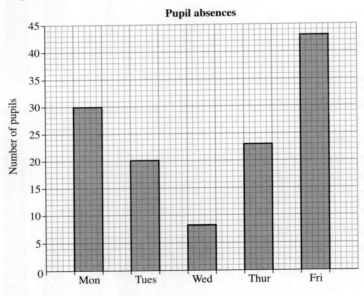

a On which day were exactly 30 pupils absent?
b Which day had the greatest number of pupils absent?
c On which two days was the difference between the numbers of pupils absent equal to 15?
d How many absences were there altogether that week?

Dual bar charts

A *dual bar chart* represents two sets of data on the same chart.
A key identifies each set of data.

A dual bar chart makes it easier to compare two sets of data.

Example 3

The dual bar chart shows the numbers of boys and girls in each of Mr Junior's lessons during one day.

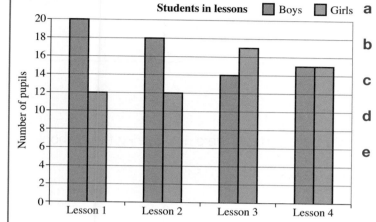

a How many boys were in Lesson 1?
b How many girls were in Lesson 1?
c Which lesson had the same number of boys as girls?
d How many students were there altogether in Lesson 3?
e Which lesson had the most students?

Solution 3

a For boys, read the purple bar: 20   **b** Blue bar: 12
c Look for the lesson with boys' and girls' bars the same height: Lesson 4 (15 boys and 15 girls).
d 14 boys + 17 girls = 31 students altogether.
e Lesson 1 had 20 + 12 = 32   Lesson 2 had 18 + 12 = 30
Lesson 3 had 14 + 17 = 31   Lesson 4 had 15 + 15 = 30
Lesson 1 had the most students.

Example 4 has the same data as Example 3, presented in a different way. Decide which is easiest to use for each part **a–e**.

Component bar chart

A *component bar chart* shows two or more sets of data in each bar.
A key identifies the data sets.

Example 4

The component bar chart shows the number of boys and girls in each of Mr. Junior's lessons during one day.
a How many boys were in Lesson 1?
b How many girls were in Lesson 1?
c Which lesson had the same number of boys as girls?
d How many students were there altogether in Lesson 3?
e Which lesson had the most students?

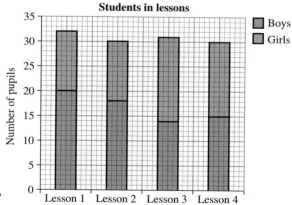

Solution 4

a In Lesson 1, the purple part of the bar is from 0 to 20: 20 boys.

b The blue part of the bar is from 20 to 32. 32 − 20 = 12: 12 girls.

c Look for the bar that is divided exactly in half: Lesson 4 (15 boys and 15 girls).

d The bar for Lesson 3 has height 31: 31 students.

e The tallest bar: Lesson 1

Exercise B

1 A school recorded how many boys and girls were not wearing their school tie one day.
The dual bar chart shows the results.

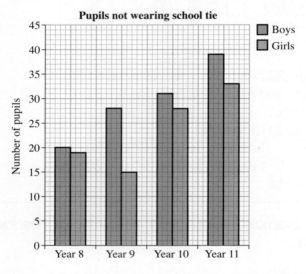

a How many girls in Year 8 were not wearing their school tie?

b Which school year had the biggest difference between the number of boys and girls not wearing their school ties?

c How many boys altogether were not wearing their school tie?

d How many pupils from Years 10 and 11 were not wearing their school tie?

2 The number of caravans and tents on a site on four Saturdays is shown below.

	1st Saturday	2nd Saturday	3rd Saturday	4th Saturday
Caravans	12	15	22	18
Tents	8	10	15	12

a Draw a dual bar chart to show these results.

b How many more caravans than tents were there altogether?

3   The component bar chart shows the costs of gas and electricity each quarter for a small flat.

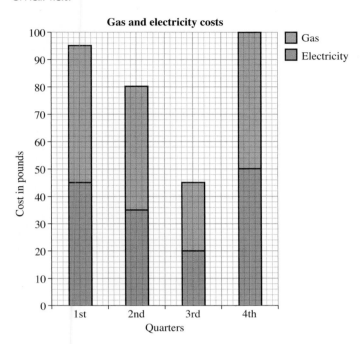

Gas and electricity costs

- **a**   What was the cost for electricity in the first quarter?
- **b**   What was the total cost for gas and electricity in the first quarter?
- **c**   What was the cost of the gas in the third quarter?
- **d**   Calculate the total cost of the electricity over the four quarters.
- **e**   Give a possible reason for the costs being so low in the third quarter.

4   The total numbers of home and away fans at United's last five home matches are given in the table.
The values are rounded to the nearest 1000

Fans/match	Match 1	Match 2	Match 3	Match 4	Match 5
Home fans	31 000	35 000	26 000	15 000	30 000
Away fans	4000	8000	3000	1000	2000

- **a**   Draw a component bar chart to show this data.
  Label the frequency axis from 0 to 45 000 in steps of 5000
- **b**   Which match had the greatest difference between the numbers of home and away fans?
- **c**   How many away fans were there in total at the five matches?
- **d**   One match was played in really bad weather.
  Which one do you think it was?

5 Mario recorded the numbers of fish and sausages he sold at his fish and chip shop over five days.

The component bar chart shows the data.

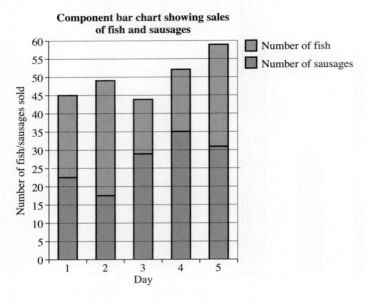

a How many fish were sold on day 2?

b How many sausages were sold on day 5?

c Which did Mario sell more of — fish or sausages?

6 Mr Aziz gave his class of 15 boys and 15 girls six spellings to learn for a test.

The dual bar chart shows the results for boys and girls in the spelling test.

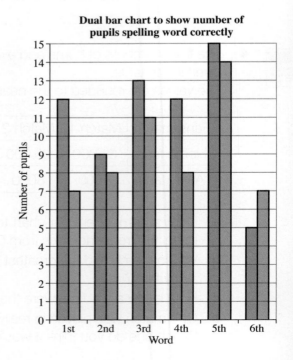

a What is missing from the dual bar chart?

b 12 girls spelled the first word correctly.
How many boys did the same?

c How many correct spellings did the girls get in total?

d How many wrong spellings did the boys get in total?

e Draw a component bar chart for the same data.

Chapter summary

- Tally charts are used for recording data.
- Tallies are grouped in 5s using *five bar gates* |||| .
- The *frequency* is the total number of tallies for each class.
- When there are a large number of data values it may help to group the classes. For example, group 1, 2, 3, 4 and 5 into a class interval 1–5
- Class intervals must not overlap.
- Pictograms use pictures or symbols to show data.
- A pictogram needs a key to show how many items each symbol represents.
- The symbols must all be the same size.
- A fraction of a picture can be used to show fractions of a quantity.
- A bar chart is a frequency diagram that shows the numbers of each item.
  - A bar chart must have a title.
  - The axes must be labelled.
  - The scale for the frequency axis is numbered in equal steps.
  - The bars are drawn carefully with a ruler.
  - The bars are all equal in width.
  - There are gaps between the bars.
- A dual bar chart shows two sets of data in pairs of bars next to each other.
- A component bar chart shows two sets of data in single bars of two colours.
- Dual bar charts and component bar charts need a key to identify each part.

Chapter review

1 The pictogram shows the number of DVDs owned by each of four friends.

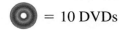 = 10 DVDs

  a Who owns the most DVDs?
  b How many more DVDs does Megan own than Ruth?

Megan	◉ ◉
Ruth	◉ ◖
Rachel	◉ ◉ ◉ ◖
Dina	◉

2   Ameet asks his friends what their favourite colour is. His results are as follows:

blue	red	green	blue	green	red	yellow	blue	green
green	red	yellow	green	blue	blue	red	red	green
blue	yellow	blue	red	blue	green	green	green	blue
green	blue	blue	yellow	blue				

a   Copy and complete the chart.

Colour	Tally	Frequency
Blue		
Green		
Red		
Yellow		

b   How many friends did Ameet ask altogether?

c   Copy and complete the pictogram to show Ameet's results.

Use the symbol � to represent four friends.

Blue	
Green	
Red	
Yellow	

3   The pictogram shows the number of cars sold each month by a garage.

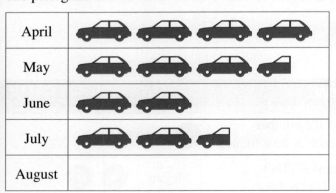

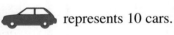 represents 10 cars.

35 cars were sold in August.

a   In which month was the smallest number of cars sold?

b   How many cars were sold in
   i April   **ii** July?

c   Draw the correct number of symbols to show the number of cars sold in August.

d   Calculate the total number of cars sold in the five months.

4 The diagram shows the maximum and minimum temperatures, in °C, for one day in June in five cities.

a Which two cities have the same minimum temperature?

b Work out the difference between the maximum and minimum temperature in
  i Rome ii Helsinki

c Owen says the maximum temperature is always about double the minimum temperature for each city.
Give an example to show that Owen is wrong.
Give a reason for your choice.

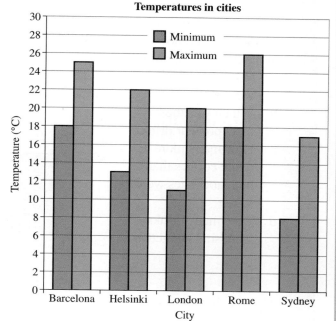

Temperatures in cities

5 Tom wants to find out how students travel to school.

a Design an observation sheet for Tom to record the data.

b Complete the observation sheet by inventing data for 20 students.

6 The distances, to the nearest mile, that 20 people travel to work are shown below.

18	3	1	2	17	10	8	9	25	37
3	4	15	16	11	34	22	7	8	6

a Copy and complete the chart.

b How many people travel between 21 and 30 miles to work?

Distance (miles)	Tally	Frequency
1–10		
11–20		
21–30		
31–40		

7 Sally has a café. She keeps a tally of the sandwiches sold in one day.

a Copy and complete the chart.

b Draw a bar chart for this data.

c How many sandwiches were sold altogether?

Item	Tally	Frequency
Cheese	ЖЖ ЖЖ ЖЖ ЖЖ	
Chicken	ЖЖ ЖЖ ЖЖ II	
Egg	ЖЖ IIII	
Salad	ЖЖ ЖЖ IIII	

8 The number of drinks sold at a vending machine during a day is shown in the bar chart opposite.

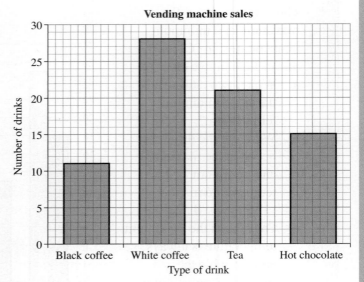

a How many teas were sold?

b Which was the most popular drink?

c How many more white coffees than hot chocolates were sold?

d How many drinks were sold altogether?

9 The dual bar chart shows the maximum temperatures in England and Greece over four months.

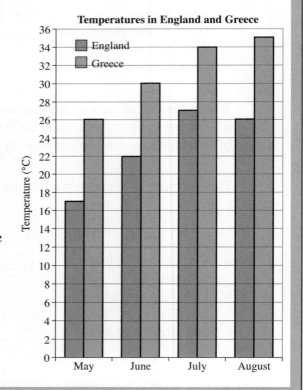

a What was the maximum temperature in Greece in July?

b Which of these months had the highest temperature in England?

c What was the difference in maximum temperature between England and Greece in May?

d Which of these months shows the smallest difference in temperature between England and Greece?

e Ben says: 'The graph shows me that the maximum temperature each month for the whole year is never below 25 °C.'
Is he correct?
Give a reason for your answer.

Operations

5.1 Multiplication and division of negative numbers

CAN YOU REMEMBER

- How to add and subtract positive and negative numbers?
- The multiplication table up to 10×10?
- Mental methods for carrying out quick calculations?

IN THIS SECTION YOU WILL

- Learn the rules for multiplying and dividing by negative numbers.
- Reinforce skills in multiplying and dividing.

The multiplication table can be extended to show negative numbers.

×	4	3	2	1	0	−1	−2	−3	−4
4	16	12	8	4	0	−4	−8	−12	−16
3	12	9	6	3	0	−3	−6	−9	−12
2	8	6	4	2	0	−2	−4	−6	−8
1	4	3	2	1	0	−1	−2	−3	−4
0	0	0	0	0	0	0	0	0	0
−1	−4	−3	−2	−1	0	1	2	3	4
−2	−8	−6	−4	−2	0	2	4	6	8
−3	−12	−9	−6	−3	0	3	6	9	12
−4	−16	−12	−8	−4	0	4	8	12	16

The extended multiplication table can be used to work out the rules for multiplying or dividing by negative numbers.

Rules for multiplying

×	+	−
+	+	−
−	−	+

For example
$$+3 \times +4 = +12$$
$$+2 \times -3 = -6$$
$$-1 \times +4 = -4$$
$$-4 \times -2 = +8$$

Rules for dividing

÷	+	−
+	+	−
−	−	+

For example
$$+12 \div +3 = +4$$
$$-6 \div +2 = -3$$
$$+8 \div -4 = -2$$
$$-4 \div -1 = +4$$

Example 1

Use the rules above or the multiplication table to work out:

a -3×4 **b** $3 \div -1$ **c** -3×0 **d** $0 \div 2$

e -5×8 **f** -6×-4 **g** $-10 \div 5$ **h** $-30 \div -6$

Solution 1

a $-3 \times +4$
$- \times + = -$ and $3 \times 4 = 12$
so $-3 \times 4 = -12$

b $+ \div - = -$ and $3 \div 1 = 3$
so $3 \div -1 = -3$

c Any number multiplied by zero $= 0$
so $-3 \times 0 = 0$

d Zero divided by any number $= 0$
so $0 \div 2 = 0$

e $-5 \times 8 = -5 \times +8$
$- \times + = -$ and $5 \times 8 = 40$
so $-5 \times 8 = -40$

f -6×-4
$- \times - = +$ and $6 \times 4 = 24$
so $-6 \times -4 = 24$

g $-10 \div 5 = -10 \div +5$
$- \div + = -$ and $10 \div 5 = 2$
so $-10 \div 5 = -2$

h $-30 \div -6$
$- \div - = +$ and $30 \div 6 = 5$
so $-30 \div -6 = 5$

Exercise A

1 Copy and complete the multiplication tables.

a

×	1	3	5	7
2			10	
4		12		
6	6			

b

×	4	2	0	−2
3	12			
0			0	
−3		−6		

c

×	10	−4	−3
7		−28	
1	10		
−5			15

d

×	9	−7	3
−8	−72		
−9		63	
6			18

2 Copy and complete the division tables.

a

		First number		
	÷	20	12	8
Second	2			$8 \div 2 = 4$
number	4		$12 \div 4 = 3$	

b

		First number		
	÷	0	10	−15
Second	5	0		
number	−5			3

c

		First number		
	÷	24	−18	−30
Second	2		−9	
number	−6	−4		

d

		First number		
	÷	64	−16	40
Second	−8			−5
number	2	32		

3 Work out:

a 6×-7	**b** -2×-4	**c** 7×-8	**d** -3×-5
e -8×8	**f** -10×4	**g** -6×-9	**h** 9×-5

4 Work out:

a $24 \div -3$	**b** $-18 \div -6$	**c** $72 \div -8$	**d** $-100 \div -10$
e $-36 \div 9$	**f** $-64 \div 8$	**g** $-42 \div -7$	**h** $35 \div -5$

5 Use a calculator to work out:

a 12×-7	**b** -15×-6	**c** 16×-9	**d** -24×-5
e -18×8	**f** -22×11	**g** -17×-14	**h** 9×-19

6 Use a calculator to work out:

a $96 \div -8$	**b** $-180 \div -12$	**c** $126 \div -21$	**d** $-144 \div -9$
e $-360 \div 45$	**f** $-315 \div 15$	**g** $-84 \div -12$	**h** $720 \div -18$

Example 2

Work out:

a $-2 \times 3 \times -4$ **b** $\dfrac{-8 \times 2}{-4}$ **c** $(-2)^3$ **d** $(-5)^2$

Solution 2

a $-2 \times 3 \times -4 = -2 \times +3 \times -4$

$$\underbrace{- \times + \times -}$$

$$= \quad - \quad \times - = +$$

and $2 \times 3 \times 4 = 24$

so $-2 \times 3 \times -4 = 24$

b $\dfrac{-8 \times 2}{-4} = \dfrac{-8 \times +2}{-4}$

$$\dfrac{- \times +}{-} = \dfrac{-}{-} = +$$

and $\dfrac{8 \times 2}{4} = \dfrac{16}{4} = 4$

so $\dfrac{-8 \times 2}{-4} = 4$

c $(-2)^3 = -2 \times -2 \times -2$

$$\underbrace{- \times - \times -}$$

$$= \quad + \quad \times - = -$$

and $2 \times 2 \times 2 = 8$

so $(-2)^3 = -8$

d $(-5)^2 = -5 \times -5$

$- \times - = +$

and $5 \times 5 = 25$

so $(-5)^2 = 25$

Exercise B

1 Work out:

a $3 \times 4 \times -5$	**b** $-1 \times 6 \times -2$	**c** $-4 \times -2 \times 3$
d $\dfrac{-10 \times -3}{-5}$	**e** $\dfrac{-8 \times 10}{-2 \times -5}$	**f** $(-3)^3$
g $(-1)^3$	**h** $(-5)^2$	**i** $(-4)^2$

2 Match the calculations with the answers.

$$\boxed{-3 \times -8} \quad \boxed{-24} \quad \boxed{-6 \times -3} \quad \boxed{24} \quad \boxed{6 \times -4} \quad \boxed{-18}$$

$$\boxed{24 \times 0} \quad \boxed{18} \quad \boxed{9 \times -2} \quad \boxed{0}$$

3 Explain why -2×-3 is greater than 3×-2

4 Which has the greater value: $-18 \div -2$ or $-81 \div 9$?
Explain your answer.

5 Work out:
  a 20×30 **b** -40×30 **c** 60×-40 **d** 200×-50

6 You are given that $124 \times 36 = 4464$. Write down the value of each of the following and then check your answers using a calculator.
  a 124×-36 **b** -124×-36 **c** $-4464 \div 36$ **d** $4464 \div -124$

7 Copy and complete the following.
  a $135 \times \ldots\ldots = -945$ **b** $\ldots\ldots \times -68 = -1836$
  c $936 \div \ldots\ldots = -26$ **d** $-3075 \div \ldots\ldots = 75$

8 Work out:
  a -8×-4 **b** $\dfrac{-8 \times -4}{-2}$ **c** 7×-9 **d** $\dfrac{7 \times -9}{-3}$

5.2 Number machines

CAN YOU REMEMBER

- How to add and subtract positive and negative numbers?
- How to multiply and divide positive and negative numbers?
- Mental methods for carrying out quick calculations?

IN THIS SECTION YOU WILL

- Understand how to use a number machine for basic calculations.
- Learn the meaning of the terms 'input' and 'output'.
- Reinforce your skills in adding, subtracting, multiplying and dividing.

The diagram shows a number machine.

This number machine has:

Input → (6) → [Add 5] → (11) Output

- *input* value 6. This is the starting number that is put into the machine.
- instruction box 'add 5'. This gives the instruction to add 5 to the input value.
- *output* value 11. This is the result of adding 5 to the input value, 6

Number machines can have more than one instruction box.

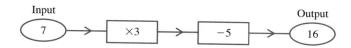

Example 1

Here is a number machine.

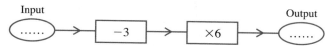

a Calculate the output if the input is 10

b Calculate the output if the input is 2

Solution 1

a

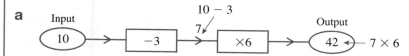

b

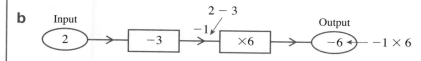

Exercise A

1 Copy and complete the table for this number machine.

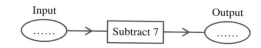

Input	9	12	26	100	4	0	−3	−11
Output								

2 Copy and complete the table for this number machine.

Input	4	7	9	20	0	11	80	300
Output								

3 Copy and complete the table for this number machine.

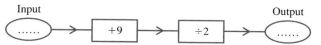

Input	1	5	11	0	6	10	−1	−4
Output								

4 Make an input/output table for this number machine.
Use inputs 4, 7, 11, 20, 100, 3, 0, 2

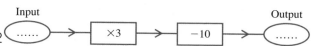

5 Make an input/output table for this number machine. Use inputs 8, 19, 27, 56, 107, 925, 1728, 2008

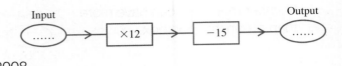

6 Make an input/output table for this number machine. Use inputs 12, 24, 80, 138, 175, 297, 3762, 10 029

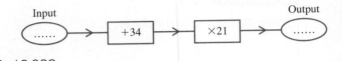

Exercise B

1 Copy and complete the table for this number machine.

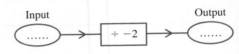

Input	6	5	9	0	−2	−7	−5	−11
Output								

2 Make an input/output table for this number machine. Use inputs 4, 12, 18, 0, −10, −8, −24, −200

3 Make an input/output table for this number machine. Use inputs 2, 11, 17, −1, −7, −10, −22, −28

4 Make an input/output table for this number machine. Use inputs 3, 6, 10, 0, −4, −8, −1, −10

5 Make an input/output table for this number machine. Use inputs 1, 0, −1, 2

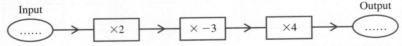

6 Make an input/output table for this number machine. Use inputs 5, 11, 15, 61, 106, 0, −47, −72

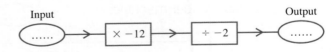

7 Make an input/output table for this number machine. Use inputs 54, 72, 186, 0, −48, −144, −3600, −666

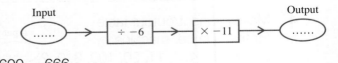

8 Here are three instruction boxes and a number machine. In each part put the instruction boxes into the correct order to make the number machine work.

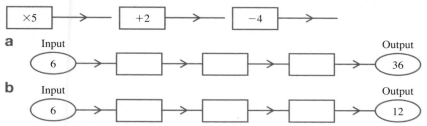

a

Input 6 → ☐ → ☐ → ☐ → Output 36

b

Input 6 → ☐ → ☐ → ☐ → Output 12

9 a Copy and complete the instruction boxes to make the number machine work.

Input 8 → $+ \ldots$ → $\times \ldots$ → $- \ldots$ → Output 26

b Find a different set of instruction boxes that work in part **a**.

5.3 Inverse number machines

CAN YOU REMEMBER

- The multiplication table up to 10×10 and corresponding divisions?
- The meaning of 'square', 'square root', 'cube' and 'operation'?

IN THIS SECTION YOU WILL

- Learn which operations are inverses of each other and how to use an inverse number machine.
- Reinforce your skills in adding, subtracting, multiplying and dividing.
- Reinforce your skills in finding the square, square root and cube of a number.
- Learn how to find the cube root of a number.

An *operation* is a rule for processing a number. The *inverse* operation 'undoes' the operation.

The table shows some operations and their inverses.

Every number machine has an inverse number machine.

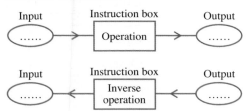

Operation	Inverse operation
Add	Subtract
Subtract	Add
Multiply	Divide
Divide	Multiply
Square	Square root
Square root	Square
Cube	Cube root
Cube root	Cube

When the output is known, the inverse operation can be used to work out the input.

Example 1

Here is a number machine.
a Calculate the output when the input is 6
b Calculate the input when the output is 18

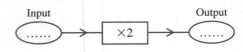

Solution 1

a The input is 6
6 × 2 = 12
The output is 12

b The output is 18
The inverse number machine is

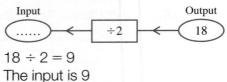

18 ÷ 2 = 9
The input is 9

Exercise A

1 Here is a number machine.
  a Work out the output when the input is 6
  b Draw the inverse number machine.
  c Work out the input when the output is 45

2 Here is a number machine.
  a Work out the output when the input is 7
  b Draw the inverse number machine.
  c Work out the input when the output is 39

3 Here is a number machine.
  a Work out the output when the input is 4
  b Draw the inverse number machine.
  c Work out the input when the output is 3

For questions **4–11**, copy and complete the table using the number machine given.

4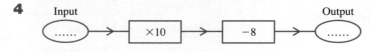

Input	15	
Output		22

5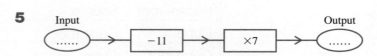

Input	8	
Output		35

6

Input	27	
Output		4

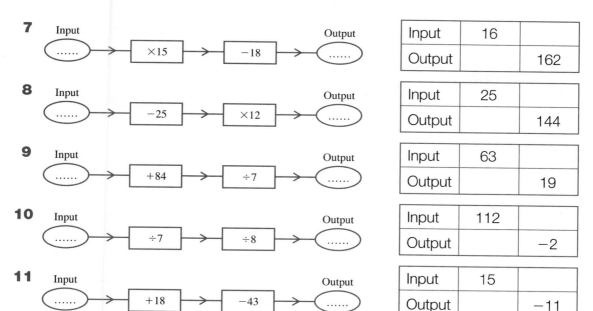

7 Input ...... → ×15 → −18 → Output ......

Input	16	
Output		162

8 Input ...... → −25 → ×12 → Output ......

Input	25	
Output		144

9 Input ...... → +84 → ÷7 → Output ......

Input	63	
Output		19

10 Input ...... → ÷7 → ÷8 → Output ......

Input	112	
Output		−2

11 Input ...... → +18 → −43 → Output ......

Input	15	
Output		−11

Example 2

Here is a number machine.
a Calculate the output when the input is 4
b Calculate the input when the output is 30

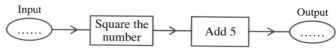

Input ...... → Square the number → Add 5 → Output ......

Solution 2

a The input is 4
Squaring gives $4^2 = 16$
Adding 5 gives
$16 + 5 = 21$
The output is 21

b The inverse number machine is

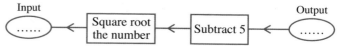

Input ...... ← Square root the number ← Subtract 5 ← Output ......

The output is 30
Subtracting 5 gives $30 − 5 = 25$
Taking the square root of 25 gives 5
The input is 5

Exercise B

1 Here is a number machine.
  a Work out the output when the input is 8
  b Work out the input when the output is 5

Input ...... → Square the number → +5 → Output ......

2 Here is a number machine.
  a Work out the output when the input is 5
  b Work out the input when the output is 17

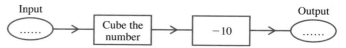

Input ...... → Cube the number → −10 → Output ......

3 Matt thinks of a number. He multiplies it by 2 and then subtracts 11
His answer is 3
   a Draw a number machine for this calculation.
   b Draw the inverse number machine.
   c Use the inverse number machine to find the number that Matt was thinking of.

4 Viki thinks of a number. She squares it and then divides it by 4
Her answer is 9
Use number machines to work out her number.

5 Efe says that the inverse of doubling a number and then adding 1 is halving the
number and subtracting 1
Show that he is wrong.

6 Here is a number machine.

Richard says, 'Here is the
inverse number machine.'

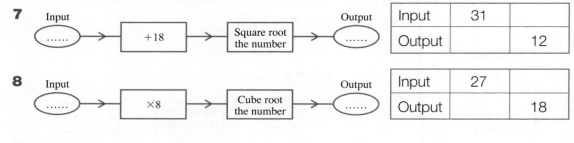

Explain why Richard is not correct.

For questions **7–9**, copy and complete the table for the number machine given.

7

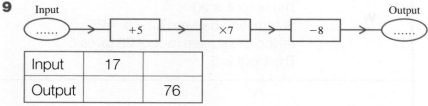

Input	31	
Output		12

8

Input	27	
Output		18

9

Input	17	
Output		76

10 Rebecca thinks of a number. She cubes it and then squares the answer.
Her final answer is 64. What number did she think of?

11 Serge thinks of a number. He squares it and then finds the cube root.
His answer is 25. What was the number?

12 Sarah thinks of a number. She doubles it and then subtracts 10
David doubles Sarah's answer and subtracts 10. His answer is 170
What was the number that Sarah thought of?

5.4 Order of operations

CAN YOU REMEMBER

- How to add, subtract, multiply and divide integers?
- How to square and cube a number?
- How to work out simple powers, e.g. 2^5?

IN THIS SECTION YOU WILL

- Carry out calculations in the correct order.
- Use brackets in calculations.
- Use BODMAS or BIDMAS.
- Consolidate your skills in addition, subtraction, multiplication and division.
- Consolidate your knowledge of square numbers and cube numbers.

BODMAS and BIDMAS are ways of remembering the correct order to carry out operations:

B	**B**rackets	Work out calculations inside brackets first
O or I	**O**thers or **I**ndices	Powers, squares, cubes, square roots, cube roots
D	**D**ivision	In any order
M	**M**ultiplication	
A	**A**ddition	In any order
S	**S**ubtraction	

For the calculation $2 + 3 \times 4$

In BOD**M**AS, **M** comes before **A**.
So the multiplication 3×4 is carried out first.

$$2 + 3 \times 4$$

$$= 2 + 12 = 14$$

Example 1

Work out each of the following.

a $4 \times 1 + (5 - 3)$ **b** $2 + 3^2 - 7$ **c** $\frac{1}{2}$ of $6 + 4$

Solution 1

a

$$4 \times 1 + (5 - 3)$$

Work out the **b**racket	$= 4 \times 1 + 2$	BODMAS/BIDMAS
Work out the **m**ultiplication	$= 4 + 2$	BODMAS/BIDMAS
Work out the **a**ddition	$= 6$	BODMAS/BIDMAS

b

	$2 + 3^2 - 7$	
Work out the square (index or other)	$= 2 + 9 - 7$	BODMAS/BIDMAS
Work out the addition	$= 11 - 7$	BODMAS/BIDMAS
Work out the subtraction	$= 4$	BODMAS/BIDMAS

c

	$\frac{1}{2}$ of $6 + 4$	
Replace 'of' with a multiplication sign	$= \frac{1}{2} \times 6 + 4$	
Work out the multiplication	$= 3 + 4$	BODMAS/BIDMAS
Work out the addition	$= 7$	BODMAS/BIDMAS

Example 2

Use a scientific calculator to work out
$35 - 24 \times 17$

Solution 2

$35 - 24 \times 17$
To complete the calculation in one step it is helpful to insert brackets around the part to be carried out first.
$35 - 24 \times 17 = 35 - (24 \times 17)$
Put the calculation into the calculator using the brackets keys.
Make sure you know how to enter brackets on your own calculator.
Answer $= -373$

Exercise A

1 Work out the following. Show each step of your working.
  a $7 + 3 \times 8$ **b** $5 + 2 \times 4$ **c** $8 - 7 \times 1$ **d** $15 - 2 \times 5$
  e $11 \times 6 - 2$ **f** $5 \times 4 + 7$ **g** $8 \times 5 - 3$ **h** $5 \times 9 + 6$

2 Work out the following. Show each step of your working.
  a $10 + 6 \div 2$ **b** $25 - 20 \div 5$ **c** $18 + 6 \div 6$ **d** $32 - 12 \div 4$
  e $45 \div 5 + 4$ **f** $72 \div 9 - 8$ **g** $100 \div 10 + 10$ **h** $63 \div 9 - 7$

3 Work out the following. Show each step of your working.
  a $(3 + 2) + 4 \times 6$ **b** $(9 - 4) - 1 \times 5$ **c** $(10 + 3) + 25 \div 5$
  d $(12 - 4) - 32 \div 8$ **e** $10 \times 3 + 5 \times 7$ **f** $9 \times 6 + 64 \div 8$
  g $6 \times 6 - 35 \div 7$ **h** $3 \times (12 - 4) + 10$

4 Work out the following. Show each step of your working.

a $3^2 + (5 - 1) \div 4$ **b** $14 - (8 - 6)^3 + 5$ **c** $5 - (7 - 4)^2 \div 3$

d $24 \div (18 - 12) + 9$ **e** $15 \div (25 \div 5)$ **f** $(27 + 18) \div (27 - 18)$

g $(81 \div 9) \times (9 - 6)$ **h** $(100 - 52) \div (30 - 24)$

5 Work out the following. Show each step of your working.

a $\frac{1}{2}$ of 4^2 **b** $\frac{1}{3}$ of 3^3 **c** $\frac{1}{4}$ of $(32 + 32) \div 8$

d $\frac{1}{5}$ of $(3^2 + 4^2)$ **e** $\frac{1}{10}$ of $(24 + 26) \div 5$ **f** $\frac{1}{4} \times (3 + 1)^2$

g $\frac{1}{2}$ of $\left(\frac{1}{2} \text{ of } 4^2\right)$ **h** $\frac{1}{2}$ of $\left(\frac{1}{2} \text{ of } 4\right)^2$

6 Use a scientific calculator to work out the following.

a $19 + 14 \times 12$ **b** $16 + 32 \times 11$ **c** $26 - 25 \times 24$

d $82 - 34 \times 9$ **e** $18 + 104 \div 26$ **f** $46 - 2414 \div 71$

g $99 + 34 \div 136$ **h** $320 - 736 \div 32$

7 Use a scientific calculator to work out the following.

a $(68 + 10 + 42) \div (4 \times 15)$ **b** $(24 \times 7) - (18 \times 5)$

c $(48 \times 3) + (16 \times 9)$ **d** $7^3 \div (6 \times 8 + 1)$

e $(99 + 22) - (125 - 36)$ **f** $(103 - 34) \times (84 - 67)$

g $(108 + 37) \times (24 \times 11)$ **h** $187^2 \div (86 - 75)$

8 Use a scientific calculator to work out the following.

a $13^2 + (127 - 43) \div 12$ **b** $2049 - (18 - 4)^3 + 60$

c $435 - (17.7 - 4.2)^2 \div 5$ **d** $267 \div (117 - 28) + 92$

e $\frac{1}{5}$ of $(15^2 + 20^2)$ **f** $\frac{1}{10}$ of $(224 + 326) \div 5$

g $\frac{1}{4} \times (83 + 17)^2$ **h** $\frac{1}{2}$ of $\left(\frac{1}{2} \text{ of } 24^2\right)$

Example 3

Insert brackets into this calculation to make it correct. $2 + 7 \times 3 + 8 = 79$

Solution 3

Try brackets around $2 + 7$

$(2 + 7) \times 3 + 8 = 9 \times 3 + 8$

$\qquad\qquad = 27 + 8 = 35$

This is not the correct answer, so the brackets are in the wrong place.

Try brackets around $3 + 8$

$2 + 7 \times (3 + 8) = 2 + 7 \times 11$

$\qquad\qquad = 2 + 77 = 79$

This is the correct answer, so the brackets are in the right place.

In a division calculation, the division line can be replaced with brackets.

For example $\dfrac{9 + 3 \times 5}{8 - 1 \times 2}$ can be written as $(9 + 3 \times 5) \div (8 - 1 \times 2)$.

To make sure you do the calculations in the correct order, write a division calculation using brackets first.

Example 4

Work out $\dfrac{9 + 3 \times 5}{8 - 1 \times 2}$

Solution 4

Write using brackets	$(9 + 3 \times 5) \div (8 - 1 \times 2)$	
Work out the numerator bracket	$9 + 3 \times 5$ $= 9 + 15 = 24$	**B**ODMAS/**B**IDMAS
Work out the denominator bracket	$8 - 1 \times 2$ $= 8 - 2 = 6$	**B**ODMAS/**B**IDMAS
Work out the **d**ivision numerator ÷ denominator	$24 \div 6 = 4$	BO**D**MAS/**B**IDMAS

Exercise B

1 Copy each calculation and insert **one** pair of brackets to make it correct.

    a $2 + 7 - 4 \times 3 + 1 = 12$ **b** $2 + 7 - 4 \times 3 + 1 = -2$

    c $2 + 7 - 4 \times 3 + 1 = 16$ **d** $2 + 7 - 4 \times 3 + 1 = -7$

    e $11 - 6 + 2 \times 5 - 3 = 9$ **f** $11 - 6 + 2 \times 5 - 3 = -32$

    g $11 - 6 + 2 \times 5 - 3 = 32$ **h** $11 - 6 + 2 \times 5 - 3 = -2$

2 Copy each calculation and insert **two** pairs of brackets to make it correct.

    a $8 - 9 - 7 \times 3 \div 1 + 2 = 6$ **b** $8 - 9 - 7 \times 3 \div 1 + 2 = -20$

    c $8 - 9 - 7 \times 3 \div 1 + 2 = -24$ **d** $1 + 2 \times 3 + 4 - 5 \times 6 = 3$

    e $1 + 2 \times 3 + 4 - 5 \times 6 = -9$ **f** $1 + 2 \times 3 + 4 - 5 \times 6 = 36$

    g $1 + 2 \times 3 + 4 - 5 \times 6 = -5$

3 Work out:

    a $\dfrac{18 + 9}{3 + 6}$ **b** $\dfrac{35 - 7}{2 + 2}$ **c** $\dfrac{1 + 2 \times 3}{8 - 1 \times 1}$

    d $\dfrac{8 + 6 \times 4}{10 - 3 \times 3}$ **e** $\dfrac{1 + 5 \times 6 + 4}{8 - 1}$ **f** $\dfrac{4 - 1 \times 3 + 4}{3 + 1 \times 2}$

    g $\dfrac{3 \times 6 - 4 \times 2}{2 + 1 \times 3}$ **h** $\dfrac{(2 + 3) \times (4 + 7)}{3 \times 2 + 5}$

4 Work out the difference between $2 + 3 \times 4$ and $(2 + 3) \times 4$

5 a By working out the correct answer, explain why $8 + 7 \times 6$ is not equal to 90

    b Copy $8 + 7 \times 6 = 90$ and insert brackets to make the calculation correct.

6 Tom and Sam use their calculators to work out $5 + 6 \times 9$

    They press the following buttons.   

    Tom's calculator gives 99. Sam's calculator gives 59

    Which calculator gives the correct answer? Explain why this happens.

7 Work out:

a $\dfrac{18.3 + 3.7}{1.1 + 0.9}$

b $\dfrac{76.3 - 17.1}{2.5 - 0.5}$

c $\dfrac{4.8 + 2.1 \times 3.3}{21 - 9.27}$

d $\dfrac{8.4 + 12.2}{24.8 \div 6.2}$

e $\dfrac{19.1 + 43.7}{0.4}$

f $\dfrac{36.9}{40 + 6.125}$

g $\dfrac{12.5 - 6.35}{0.2 + 0.3}$

h $\dfrac{\sqrt{7.84}}{3.16 + 4.25}$

i $\dfrac{\sqrt{26.2}}{8.74 - 3.10}$

8 Which is the greater:
$9.1 + 11.6 \times 6.4$ or $(9.1 + 11.6) \times 6.4$?
Show your working.

3.4 divided by 1.7 plus 1.7 equals 3.7

9 Belinda says that $\dfrac{3.4}{1.7 + 1.7}$ is equal to 3.7
Is she correct?
Explain your answer.

10 a In a game of Target, Sara has the digits 2, 3, 4 and 5 to make the target number 44
Each digit must be used once. She can use any operations.
Show how she can do this.
Write your answer as a calculation that can be input into a calculator in one sequence.

b Repeat part **a** for a target number of 45
c Repeat part **a** for a target number of 49
d What other target numbers can be made with the digits 2, 3, 4 and 5?

Chapter summary

■ The rules for multiplying or dividing positive and negative numbers are:

× or ÷	+	−
+	+	−
−	−	+

$+5 \times -2 = -10$ $-10 \div 5 = -2$

$-2 \times -9 = +18$ $-42 \div -6 = +7$

■ A number machine has:
  ■ An input value.
  ■ Instruction boxes.
  ■ An output value.

Input: 10 → ×2 → −4 → Output: 16

■ An *operation* is a rule for processing a number.

■ The *inverse* operation 'undoes' the operation.

Operation	Inverse operation
Add	Subtract
Subtract	Add
Multiply	Divide
Divide	Multiply
Square	Square root
Square root	Square
Cube	Cube root
Cube root	Cube

■ Every number machine has an inverse number machine.

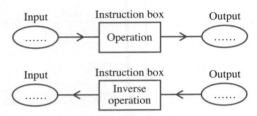

■ BODMAS and BIDMAS are ways of remembering the correct order to carry out operations.

■
B	**B**rackets	Work out calculations inside brackets first
O or **I**	**O**thers or **I**ndices	Powers, squares, cubes, square roots, cube roots
D	**D**ivision	In any order
M	**M**ultiplication	
A	**A**ddition	In any order
S	**S**ubtraction	

Chapter review

1 Write down the values of
  a 3×-8 **b** $-35 \div -5$ **c** $6 \times -7 + -1 \times -4$

2 **a** Work out $14 - (9 - 3)$
   b Put brackets in each of these calculations to make them correct.
      i $14 - 5 - 3 = 12$ **ii** $2 + 6 \times 3 = 20$ **iii** $30 \div 7 - 4 = 10$

3 Work out $1.4 \times 10 + 0.6 \times 100$

4 Sadie thinks of a number.
She multiplies it by 3 and then takes away 9. The answer is 27
What was the number?

5 When you input a number into a number machine, the machine subtracts 6 from the number and then divides the result by 3

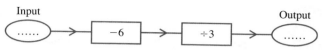

 a The input is 15. What is the output?   **b** The output is 7. What is the input?

6 a This is a number machine.

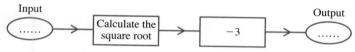

  i You start with 25. What is the output?
  ii You start with 36. What is the output?

 b This is a different number machine.

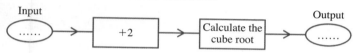

  i You start with 25. What is the output?
  ii You start with 6. What is the output?

7 Here is a number machine. Copy the table and use the number machine to complete it.

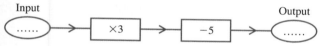

Input	2	
Output	1	25

8 Use your calculator to work out $\dfrac{86.3 + 29.4}{47.1 - 25.6}$

 a Write down your full calculator display.
 b Give your answer to 2 significant figures.

9 a Work out 5.1^2
 b Calculate $\dfrac{11.4}{3.7 \times 2.1}$
  i Write down your full calculator display.
  ii Write your answer to 1 decimal place.

10 a Work out 4.3^2 **b** Work out the cube of 5
 c Work out $4 \div 0.9^2$
  i Write down the full calculator display.
  ii Give your answer to the nearest whole number.
 d Calculate $\dfrac{8.1}{6.8 - 1.4}$

11 Use your calculator to find the value of $\dfrac{\sqrt{8.75}}{9.37 + 6.48}$

Introducing algebra

6.1 Using letter symbols

CAN YOU REMEMBER

■ That letter symbols, for example x, are used to represent numbers?
■ That there is a simple connection between multiplying and adding?

IN THIS SECTION YOU WILL

■ Start to use letter symbols to represent numbers in different situations.
■ Learn that multiplication signs are not needed with letter symbols.
■ Identify when a letter symbol represents any number and when it represents an unknown number.

The area of a rectangle can be worked out using this *word formula*:
Area equals length multiplied by width.

The formula can also be written using *letter symbols*, $A = l \times w$
The formula describes the relationship between the quantities.
When letter symbols are multiplied together, leave out the multiplication sign. So the formula is $A = lw$

Length (l)

Width (w)

Addition and multiplication are linked.
$3 + 3 + 3 + 3 = 4$ lots of $3 = 4 \times 3$

$x + x + x + x + x = 5$ lots of $x = 5 \times x = 5x$

Example 1

a Check that $4 + 4 + 4 + 5 + 5$ equals $3 \times 4 + 2 \times 5$
b Write $a + a + a + a + b + b + b$ in a shorter form.

Solution 1

a $4 + 4 + 4 + 5 + 5 = 22$ $3 \times 4 + 2 \times 5 = 12 + 10 = 22$
(multiplication before addition)
So $4 + 4 + 4 + 5 + 5 = 3 \times 4 + 2 \times 5$
b $a + a + a + a + b + b + b = 4 \times a + 3 \times b = 4a + 3b$

Example 2

Write down a formula for the perimeter, P, of a rectangle of length l and width w.

Solution 2

$P = l + l + w + w$

$P = 2 \times l + 2 \times w$

$P = 2l + 2w$

Length (l)

Width (w)

Exercise A

1 **a** Match pairs of expressions with the same value.

| $7 + 7 + 7 + 7$ | $5 + 5$ | $3 + 3 + 3 + 3 + 3$ | $2 + 2 + 2 + 3 + 3$ |

| 3×4 | $3 \times 2 + 2 \times 3$ | $4 + 4 + 4$ | $4 + 7 + 7 + 7$ |

| 4×7 | $4 + 3 \times 7$ | 5×3 | 2×5 |

b Match sets of three expressions with the same value.

| $x + x + x + x$ | $2x$ | $x + x$ | $2 \times x$ |

| $2 \times x + 3 \times y$ | $x + 4y$ | $x + x + y + y + y$ |

| $x + y + y + y + y$ | $x + 4 \times y$ | $4 \times x$ | $2x + 3y$ | $4x$ |

2 $2x$ means $2 \times x$ $2xy$ means $2 \times x \times y$
    27 means $20 + 7$ 356 means $300 + 50 + 6$
  a **i** What does $5y$ mean?   **ii** What does 54 mean?
  b **i** What does $8n$ mean?   **ii** What does 82 mean?
  c **i** What does xyz mean?   **ii** What does 234 mean?

3 Write each of these **with** the multiplication symbol ($\times$) inserted.
  a $2a + 3b$ **b** $5x + 2y + 3z$ **c** abc
  d $ab + bc + de$ **e** $2x + 32$ **f** $235a + 27b + 42$

4 Copy and complete this table.

a	$x + x + x$	$3x$
b	$x + x + x + x + x$	
c		$4b$
d	$a + a + a + b + b$	$3a + 2b$
e	$x + x + y + y + y + y$	
f	$m + m + m + m + m + n$	
g	$x + x + y + z + z + z$	
h		$2p + 3q + r$
i	$a + a + b + b + b + b + c + c + c$	
j		$5x + 2y + z$

5 Write each of these **without** the multiplication symbol ($\times$).

a $\quad 2 \times x$ b $\quad 2 \times x + 25$ c $\quad 5 \times x + 2 \times y$

d $\quad 5 \times a + 2 \times b + 7$ e $\quad 3 \times x + 5 \times y + 7 \times z$

6 Write a formula for the perimeter (P) of each shape.
Give your formula in its simplest form.

a   b 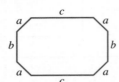   c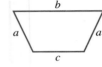

7 Look at this number machine.

a   What is the output number when the input number is 4?

b   What is the input number when the output number is 10?

c   Copy and complete the word formula.
Output number = ... + ...

d   Use the letter symbols x for the input number and y for the output number to complete this formula. .... = ... + ...

For questions **8–10** repeat question **7** for the number machines given.

8

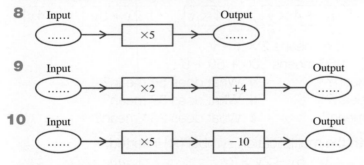

9

10

Sometimes a letter symbol is used to represent **any** number.

The formula for this number machine is $y = x + 4$.
x can represent any number and y is always 4 more than x.

For example
when $x = 1$, $y = 1 + 4 = 5$ when $x = 6$, $y = 6 + 4 = 10$

Sometimes a letter symbol represents a particular unknown number.

   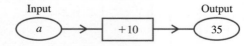

z represents the number 12
because $14 - 2 = 12$

a represents the number 25
because $25 + 10 = 35$

Example 3

Rewrite the following word formula using letter symbols of your choice.
State clearly what each letter symbol represents.

> The distance a car travels in miles on a journey equals its average speed in miles per hour multiplied by the time that the journey takes in hours.

Solution 3

For example: $d = s \times t = st$ d is the distance travelled in miles.
s is the average speed in miles per hour. t is the time taken in hours.

Example 4

Tom has x coins.
- a Bill has three more coins than Tom.
     How many coins does Bill have?
- b Sally has twice as many coins as Tom.
     How many coins does Sally have?
- c Do you know the actual number of coins that Tom, Bill and Sally have?

Solution 4

- a Bill has three more coins than x coins or $x + 3$ coins.
- b Twice as many means $\times 2$. Sally has $2 \times x$ or $2x$ coins.
- c No. x could represent any number.

Exercise B

1 Rewrite the following using letter symbols of your choice.
State clearly what each letter symbol represents.
- a Pay equals hourly rate multiplied by the number of hours worked.
- b Pay equals hourly rate multiplied by the number of hours worked, plus weekly bonus.
- c The volume of a box equals its length multiplied by its width multiplied by its height.

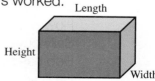

2 a Write a formula for y in terms of x for this number machine.

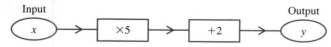

b Do x and y in the formula stand for different pairs of values or one particular pair of unknown values? Explain your answer.

3 In each of the following, do the letter symbols have one value or could they have lots of values? In each case give a reason for your answer.

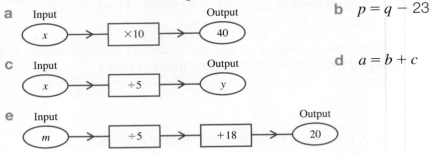

b $p = q - 23$

d $a = b + c$

4 Work out the values of x and y for these number machines.

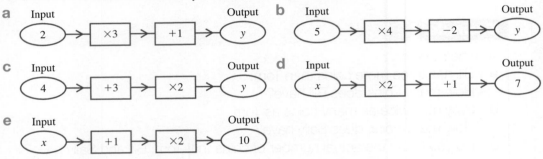

5 A shop sells marbles in boxes. There are m marbles in each box.

   a Tim has five marbles. He buys one box of marbles.
How many marbles does he have?

   b There are two marbles missing from the box that Adil buys.
How many marbles does Adil buy?

   c Jimmy buys three boxes of marbles. How many marbles does Jimmy buy?

   d Do you know the actual number of marbles that Tim, Adil and Jimmy have?
Explain your answer.

6 Packets of sweets each contain n sweets.

   a Joti buys one packet and eats three of the sweets.
How many sweets does he have left?

   b Sally buys three packets of sweets. How many sweets does she have?

   c Bob has seven sweets left in a packet he bought yesterday.
He buys another packet. How many sweets does Bob have altogether?

7 This formula gives the total cost, in pence, of m packets of mints and b bars of chocolate.

$T = 20m + 30b$

   a How could you use the formula to work out the cost of one packet of mints?

   b What is the cost of one bar of chocolate?

8 Abdul writes four connected number facts.

$2 + 3 = 5$ $3 + 2 = 5$ $5 - 2 = 3$ $5 - 3 = 2$

a Write down four connected number facts starting with $4 + 7 = 11$

b Write down four connected number facts for $a + 5 = 9$
Does a represent **any** number or does it have a value you know?

c Write down four connected number facts for $a + b = 10$
Do a and b represent **any** numbers or do they have values you know?

d Write down four connected number facts for $a + b = c$
Do a, b and c represent **any** numbers or do they have values you know?

6.2 Writing expressions and formulae

CAN YOU REMEMBER

■ The meaning of 'square' and 'cube'?
■ The order of operations for number calculations?

IN THIS SECTION YOU WILL

■ Extend what you know about using letter symbols and start to learn about terms, expressions and formulae.
■ Learn that division signs are **not** needed with letter symbols.
■ Learn how to write formulae and expressions, including those involving brackets, squares and cubes.

$3 + 4$, $x + 2y$ and $3a^2 + 5$ are all examples of mathematical *expressions*.

An expression does **not** have an '$=$' sign.

Expressions are made up of *terms*.
For example, in the expression $x + 2y$ both x and $2y$ are terms.

Algebraic expressions involving division use a horizontal division line.

For example $x \div 2$ is written $\dfrac{x}{2}$ $3 \times y \div 5$ is written $\dfrac{3y}{5}$

Algebraic expressions often include brackets.
For example $3(x + 2)$ means $3 \times (x + 2)$

$(x + 2) \div 5$ is written $\dfrac{x + 2}{5}$

In this case the division line acts like a bracket.
Calculations above or below the division line must be done first.

The order of operations for number calculations is given by BODMAS or BIDMAS (see page 91).

The same order applies to algebraic expressions.

103

Example 1

Draw number machines for these expressions

a $5x + 2$ b $4(y - 3)$ c $\dfrac{x}{5} - 2$ d $\dfrac{x + 2}{5}$

Solution 1

a $5x + 2$ First multiply x by 5
Then add 2

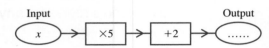

b $4(y - 3)$ Start with the expression in the brackets.
So first subtract 3 from y
Then multiply by 4

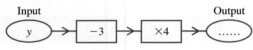

c $\dfrac{x}{5} - 2$ First divide x by 5
Then subtract 2

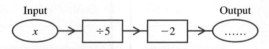

d $\dfrac{x + 2}{5}$ Start with the expression above the division line.
So first add 2 to x
Then divide by 5

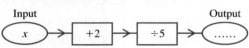

A *formula* describes a relationship between quantities so it must have an '=' sign.

Example 2

a   Sally, Ben and Amit share n sweets equally between them.
Write a formula for s, the number of sweets they each receive.

b   Dan has four boxes each containing x sunflower seeds.
Ricky has five more sunflower seeds than Dan.
Write an expression for the number of sunflower seeds that Ricky has.

Solution 2

a n sweets are shared equally between three people.

So each person receives $n \div 3$ or $\dfrac{n}{3}$ sweets. The formula is $s = \dfrac{n}{3}$

b $4x + 5$ sunflower seeds

Exercise A

1 Copy and complete these tables.

	Expression	Meaning
a	$x + 3$	
b		Subtract 3 from p
c	$3x$	Multiply x by 3
d	$5y$	
e		Multiply b by 7
f	$\dfrac{x}{3}$	
g		Divide a by 4
h	$3(x + 6)$	Add 6 to x and then multiply by 3
i	$2(y - 3)$	

	Expression	Meaning
j	$2y - 3$	
k		Multiply z by 4 and then add 3
l	$\dfrac{x}{2} + 7$	Divide x by 2 and then add 7
m		Subtract 7 from n and then divide by 2
n	$\dfrac{a}{5} - 1$	
o	$\dfrac{b + 4}{5}$	

2 Copy and complete these tables.

a	$8a$	$8 \times a$	b	$\dfrac{a}{3}$	$a \div 3$	c		$7 \times a$
d	$\dfrac{a}{b}$		e	$2x + \dfrac{3}{y}$	$2 \times x + 3 \div y$	f	$2(x + 5)$	
g		$y \div 5 + 2$	h	$\dfrac{y + 5}{2}$		i		$(p - 5) \div 3$
j	$a(b + c)$		k		$(a + b) \div c$			

3 Match an expression in Set A with a statement in Set B.

Set A $\quad$ $ab + c$ $\qquad$ $\dfrac{a}{b} + c$ $\qquad$ $\dfrac{a + b}{c}$ $\qquad$ $\dfrac{b + c}{a}$ $\qquad$ $a(b + c)$ $\qquad$ $c(a + b)$

Set B

Multiply a by b and then add c	Add a to b and then divide by c	Add b to c and then divide by a
Add b to c and then multiply by a	Add a to b and then multiply by c	Divide a by b and then add c

4 Here are some algebra cards. $\quad$ $2x + 1$ $\quad$ $\dfrac{x}{2} + 1$ $\quad$ $x \div 2 + 1$ $\quad$ $\dfrac{x + 1}{2}$

$x + \dfrac{1}{2}$ $\quad$ $2(x + 1)$ $\quad$ $(x + 1) \div 2$ $\quad$ $x + 1 + x + 1$ $\quad$ $x + 1 \div 2$ $\quad$ $2 \times x + 1$

a Does each of these cards show an expression or a formula?

b Match the pairs that mean the same.

5 Write a formula for the output, y, for each of these number machines.

a

Input — x → $\times 4$ → $+6$ → Output y

b

Input — x → $+6$ → $\times 4$ → Output y

c

Input — x → $\div 4$ → $+6$ → Output y

d

Input — x → $+6$ → $\div 4$ → Output y

6 Draw a number machine showing the output y for the input x for each formula.

  a $y = 2(x - 3)$ **b** $y = 2x - 3$ **c** $y = \dfrac{x}{2} + 3$ **d** $y = \dfrac{x + 3}{2}$

7 There are 28 students in Miss Smith's class.
Miss Smith splits the class into g groups.
Write an expression for the number of students in each group.

8 John has two bags each containing x sweets.
Tim has five more sweets than John.
  a Write an expression for the number of sweets that John has.
  b Write an expression for the number of sweets that Tim has.

9 Shona gets £5 a week pocket money.
She also earns £x a week from a paper round.
  a Write an expression for how much Shona gets each week.
  b Write an expression for how much Shona gets in 10 weeks.

10 Karim writes down four connected number facts.

  $2 \times 3 = 6$ $3 \times 2 = 6$ $\frac{6}{2} = 3$ $\frac{6}{3} = 2$

  a Write four connected number facts for $5a = 10$
  Does a represent any number or does it have a value you know?
  b Write four connected number facts for $ab = 20$
  Do a and b represent any numbers or do they have values you know?
  c Write four connected number facts for $ab = c$.
  Do a, b and c represent any numbers or do they have values you know?

Here is a list of square numbers
$$1 = 1 \times 1 = 1^2$$
$$4 = 2 \times 2 = 2^2$$
$$9 = 3 \times 3 = 3^2$$
$$16 = 4 \times 4 = 4^2$$

Here is a list of cube numbers
$$1 = 1 \times 1 \times 1 = 1^3$$
$$8 = 2 \times 2 \times 2 = 2^3$$
$$27 = 3 \times 3 \times 3 = 3^3$$
$$64 = 4 \times 4 \times 4 = 4^3$$

Any number, x, squared can be written as $x \times x$ or, in shorthand, x^2.
Similarly any number, x, cubed can be written as $x \times x \times x$ or, in shorthand, x^3.

Algebraic expressions can involve squares or cubes.
$5x^2$ means $5 \times x^2$ or $5 \times x \times x$ $x^3 - 5$ means $x \times x \times x - 5$
$(x + 2)^2$ means $(x + 2) \times (x + 2)$

Follow BODMAS/BIDMAS and work out squares and cubes after brackets or calculations above/below the division line.

Example 3

Draw number machines for these expressions

a $x^2 + 5$ **b** $(y - 1)^2$ **c** $5x^3$ **d** $\dfrac{x^2}{5} + 3$

Solution 3

a $x^2 + 5$ First square.
Then add 5

b $(y - 1)^2$ Start with the expression in the brackets.
So first subtract 1 from y
Then square.

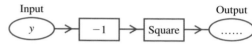

c $5x^3$ First cube.
Then multiply by 5

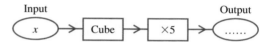

d $\dfrac{x^2}{5} + 3$ First square.
Then divide by 5
Then add 3

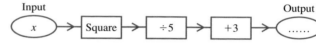

Example 4

For each number machine, write an expression for the output y.

Solution 4

a The number machine says: 'Cube and then add 2'. So the expression is $x^3 + 2$
b The number machine says: 'Add 5 to x and then square'.
So the expression is $(x + 5)^2$. The brackets are needed because the addition is done first.

Example 5

Tom has three red boxes with x coins in each and five blue boxes with y coins in each.

a Write an expression for the total number of coins in the red boxes.
b Write an expression for the total number of coins in the blue boxes.
c Write a formula for C, the total number of coins in all the boxes.
d Tom tips out all the coins and then shares them equally between the eight boxes.
Write an expression for the number of coins in each box.

Solution 5

a $3 \times x$ or $3x$ coins in the red boxes.

b $5 \times y$ or $5y$ coins in the blue boxes.

c Adding the expressions gives $C = 3x + 5y$

d Sharing the total equally between eight boxes gives $\dfrac{3x + 5y}{8}$ in each box.

Exercise B

1 Write a formula for the output y for each of these number machines.

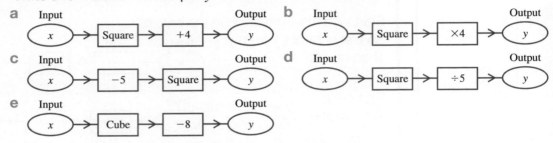

2 A maths class looks at this number machine.
Derek is asked to write down a formula for
the output from this machine.
He writes down $x + 7 \times 2$
Derek has made two mistakes.
What are they? Correct his work.

3 James says that the expressions $a(b + c)$ and $ab + c$ are the same.
Explain why he is wrong.

4 Penny buys two bags of sweets.
There are m sweets in one of the bags and n sweets in the other.
  a How many sweets does Penny have altogether?
  b Penny eats three of the sweets. How many sweets does Penny have left?

5 Bill has five shelves each containing c CDs.
  a How many CDs does Bill have altogether?
  b Bill gives ten CDs to a friend. How many CDs does Bill have now?

6

  a Write an expression for the cost, in pence, of x kg of apples.
  b Write an expression for the cost, in pence, of y kg of pears.
  c Write an expression for the total cost in pence of x kg of apples and y kg of pears.

7 **a** Rubbers cost 18p each. How much does Dilip pay for x rubbers?
   b Pens cost n pence each. Rulers cost m pence each.
     Write down the total cost of four pens and one ruler.

8 Ranjit shares n sweets between herself and x friends.
   She puts the sweets in bags.
   a How many bags does she need?
   b How many sweets are in each bag?

6.3 Simplifying expressions

CAN YOU REMEMBER

- How to multiply and divide single-digit numbers?
- How to add and subtract negative numbers?

IN THIS SECTION YOU WILL

- Find out about 'like terms'.
- Learn how to simplify expressions by adding and subtracting like terms.
- Learn how to simplify expressions by multiplying and dividing terms.

In the expression $7p + 3q + 2p$ there are two different letter symbols, p and q.
The terms $7p$ and $2p$ are called *like terms*.
They both contain the same letter p, which represents the **same** number.
The terms $7p$ and $3q$ are **not** like terms because q represents a **different** number from p.

Expressions that contain like terms can be written in a shorter form.

This is called *simplifying*.

Simplifying expressions with like terms is similar to simplifying numerical expressions.

For example

Number: $2 \times 3 + 5 \times 3$
     $(3 + 3) + (3 + 3 + 3 + 3 + 3)$
     7×3

Algebra: $2x + 5x$
     $(x + x) + (x + x + x + x + x)$
     $7x$

- Terms (or numbers) can be added in any order.
- The $+$ or $-$ sign before a term belongs to that term.

Number: $(2 \times 3) + (5 \times 4) + (7 \times 3) - (2 \times 4)$
     $(2 \times 3) + (7 \times 3) + (5 \times 4) - (2 \times 4)$
     $9 \times 3 + 3 \times 4$

Algebra: $2x + 5y + 7x - 2y$
     $2x + 7x + 5y - 2y$
     $9x + 3y$

Example 1

Simplify each of these expressions.

a $x + x + x - x - x + y + y - y$ $\qquad$ b $7x + x + 9$ $\qquad$ c $5x + 4y - y + 7x$

Solution 1

a $x + \cancel{x} + \cancel{x} - \cancel{x} - \cancel{x} + y + \cancel{y} - \cancel{y}$
   $= x + y$
b $8x + 9$

c $5x + 4y - y + 7x$
   $= 5x + 7x + 4y - y$
   $= 12x + 3y$

Expressions can also be simplified using multiplication.
Multiply numbers and letter symbols separately.

Example 2

Simplify each of these expressions.

a $3x \times 5$ $\qquad\qquad$ b $3x \times 5y$ $\qquad\qquad$ c $3x \times 5x$

Solution 2

a $3x \times 5 = 3 \times 5 \times x = 15x$ $\qquad$ b $3x \times 5y = 3 \times 5 \times x \times y = 15xy$
c $3x \times 5x = 3 \times 5 \times x \times x = 15x^2$

Exercise A

1   Show by calculation that the following are correct:
   a $3 \times 4 + 5 \times 4 = 8 \times 4$ b $2 \times 6 + 3 \times 6 = 5 \times 6$ c $7 \times 5 - 3 \times 5 = 4 \times 5$
   d $3 \times 5 + 4 \times 2 + 4 \times 5 + 5 \times 2 = 7 \times 5 + 9 \times 2$
   e $8 \times 4 + 5 \times 3 - 3 \times 4 + 2 \times 3 = 5 \times 4 + 7 \times 3$

2   What numbers should replace the $\square$ and the $\bigcirc$ in the following?
   Do a calculation to work out that your answers are correct.
   a $2 \times 3 + 4 \times 3 = \square \times 3$ $\qquad\qquad$ b $3 \times 5 + \square \times 5 = 7 \times 5$
   c $8 \times 4 - 2 \times 4 = \square \times 4$ $\qquad\qquad$ d $\square \times 2 - 3 \times 2 = 6 \times 2$
   e $3 \times 4 + 4 \times 7 + 5 \times 4 + 3 \times 7 = \square \times 4 + \bigcirc \times 7$
   f $8 \times 9 + 2 \times 7 + 3 \times 7 - 7 \times 9 = \square \times 9 + \bigcirc \times 7$
   g $6 \times 5 + 3 \times 3 + 4 \times 3 - 4 \times 5 = \square \times 5 + \bigcirc \times 3$
   h $8 \times 2 + 6 \times 8 - 2 \times 8 - 3 \times 2 = \square \times 2 + \bigcirc \times 8$
   i $9 \times 3 + 6 \times 6 - 3 \times 6 - 4 \times 3 = \square \times 3 + \bigcirc \times 6$

3   Simplify:
   a $a + a + a$ $\qquad\qquad\qquad\qquad$ b $b + b + b + b + b$
   c $x + x + x + x + x + x + y + y + y$ $\qquad$ d $y + y + y + y - y - y - y$
   e $x + x + x - x + y + y - y$ $\qquad\qquad$ f $a + a + a + a + b + b + b + c + c$
   g $a + a + a - a + b + b - b + c$ $\qquad\qquad$ h $p + p + p + p + q + q + q + r + r$

4 Simplify each of the following expressions:

a $2x + 5x$

b $3n + n$

c $7g + 2g + g$

d $5a - 3a$

e $3b - b + 4b$

f $7x + 2x - 3x$

g $2p + 5p - 4p$

h $3y + 5y - 7y$

i $7c - 4c - 3c$

j $3a + 8a - 2a - 5a$

5 In the lists below **expression A** matches **simplified expression f**.
Match the other expressions with their simplified expressions.

Expression

A $2x + 3x + 4$

B $x + 2 + 4x + 1$

C $5x + 9y + x - 7y$

D $2x + 6y + x - 2y$

E $x + 4y + x - y - 2x$

F $2x + 6 - x - 5$

G $2x - 4 - 2x + 9$

H $7x - 6 - 2x + 8$

I $4x + 2y - x - 2y$

J $6x + 6y - 2y + 3x$

Simplified expression

a $3x + 4y$

b $x + 1$

c $3x$

d 5

e $5x + 3$

f $5x + 4$

g $9x + 4y$

h $6x + 2y$

i $3y$

j $5x + 2$

6 In an addition wall, to find the number in each cell add the numbers in the two cells below it. For example:

```
        3 + 5 = 8
    1 + 2 = 3   2 + 3 = 5
      1        2        3
```

Copy and complete each addition wall. Write the expression in the top cell as simply as possible.

a

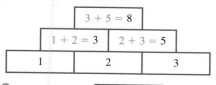

b

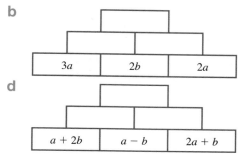

c

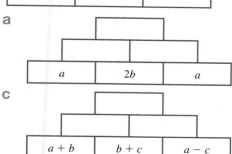

d

7 Simplify:

a $2 \times 3 \times a$

b $2 \times 3 \times b \times b$

c $2 \times 3 \times c \times c \times c$

d $2 \times d \times 4$

e $2 \times e \times 4 \times e$

f $2 \times f \times 4 \times f \times f$

g $g \times 4 \times g \times 4 \times g$

h $h \times 5 \times 3 \times h$

i $7 \times j \times j \times 3 \times j$

8 Simplify:

a $2x \times 3$

b $2x \times 3x$

c $3x \times 2x^2$

d $2x \times 5y$

e $2x \times 3x \times 4x$

f $2x \times x^2$

g $2x^3 \times 4$

h $5x \times 3x$

Simplifying expressions may give negative terms.

Example 3

a   Simplify $5x + 2y - 3x - 5y$ b   Simplify $4x - 3y - 7x - 6y$

Solution 3

a $5x + 2y - 3x - 5y = 5x - 3x + 2y - 5y = 2x - 3y$
b $4x - 3y - 7x - 6y = 4x - 7x - 3y - 6y = -3x - 9y$

Expressions involving division can also be simplified.
Divide numbers and letter symbols separately.

Example 4

a   Simplify $10a \div 5$ b   Simplify $10b \div b$

Solution 4

a $10a \div 5 = \dfrac{10 \times a}{5} = \dfrac{10}{5} \times a = 10 \div 5 \times a = 2a$

b $10b \div b = \dfrac{10 \times b}{b} = 10 \times \dfrac{\cancel{b}^{1}}{\cancel{b}_{1}} = 10 \times 1 = 10$

Exercise B

1   Simplify each of these expressions:

    a $2x - 5x$ b $a - 5a$
    c $2m + 2 - m - 5$ d $2x - 6y + 3x + 2y$
    e $-4a - a$ f $-5x - x$
    g $-6x - 2y + 3y - 2x$ h $2p - 4 - 4p - 2$
    i $-7a + 2a + 2b - 8b$ j $x - 4y + 3x - y - 2x + 2y$

2   Simplify each of the following:

    a $6a \div 3$ b $6a \div a$ c $\dfrac{12x}{6}$ d $\dfrac{12x}{x}$

    e $\dfrac{12x}{6x}$ f $20a \div 5$ g $20a \div 5a$ h $20a \div 4a$

3   Simplify each of the following:

    a $3a + 4a - 2a$ b $3a - 4b + 5a + 2b$ c $5a \times 3b$ d $\dfrac{18a}{9a}$

4   Match these expressions.

$-x - 2y + 4x$	$7x - 3y + 5y - 4x$	$2x - 3y$	$-2x + 4y + 5x - 2y$
$3x + 2y$	$4x + y - 3y - x$	$-x - 2y + 3x - y$	$x - 4y + x + y$

5 a Write an expression for the perimeter of each of these shapes.
Give each expression in its simplest form.

i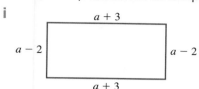

ii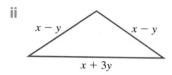

b This rectangle has a perimeter of $8x - 2$
Find the lengths and widths of three more
rectangles that have a perimeter of $8x - 2$

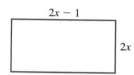

6 a Write down an expression for the area of each of these rectangles.
Write each answer in its simplest form.

i 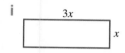   **ii**    **iii**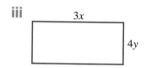

b This rectangle has an area of $12x$
Find the lengths and widths of three more
rectangles that have an area of $12x$

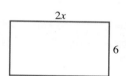

7 In an addition wall, to find the number in each
cell add the numbers in the two cells below it.
Copy and complete this addition wall.

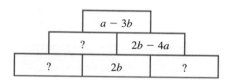

8 The diagram shows an **L** shape with dimensions as shown.

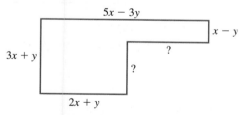

Work out expressions for the missing lengths.

9 Write an expression for the area of this triangle.
Give your answer in its simplest form.

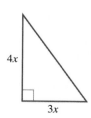

10 a Copy and complete each of these addition squares.

+	$x + 2y$	$3x + 4y$
$3x - 2y$		$6x + 2y$
$x - y$		

+	$3r + 2s$	$r - 4s$
$3r - s$		
	$3r + 5s$	

b Copy and complete each of these multiplication squares.

×	x	$3y$
x		
$2y$		

×	$3a$	$4b$
$2b$		
	$9a^2$	

×	$3b$	
$2b$		$8ab$
	$9b^2$	

6.4 Substitution

CAN YOU REMEMBER

- How to add, subtract, multiply and divide with both positive and negative numbers?
- The order of operations in number calculations?

IN THIS SECTION YOU WILL

- Learn how to work out the value of expressions after substituting numbers for letter symbols.

In an algebraic expression the letter symbols represent numbers.
When the values of the letter symbols are known the value of the expression can be worked out. This is called *substitution*.

For example, to substitute $x = 2$ into the term $5x$
Step 1: Write the term with the multiplication symbol. $5x = 5 \times x$
Step 2: Replace the letter symbol x with the value given. $5 \times x = 5 \times 2$
Step 3: Work out the value of the expression. $5 \times 2 = 10$

Follow the order of operations.

Example 1

Work out the value of the following expressions when $x = 4$ and $y = 5$

a $2x$

b $\dfrac{x}{2}$

c $x + 2y$

Solution 1

a $\quad 2x = 2 \times x$
When $x = 4 \quad 2 \times x = 2 \times 4 = 8$

b $\quad \dfrac{x}{2}$ means $x \div 2$
When $x = 4 \quad x \div 2 = 4 \div 2 = 2$

c $\quad x + 2y = x + 2 \times y$
When $x = 4$ and $y = 5$
$x + 2 \times y = 4 + 2 \times 5 = 4 + 10 = 14$ (multiplication before addition)

Exercise A

1 Work out the values of the following expressions when $a = 2$, $b = 5$ and $c = 7$

   a $\quad a + b$ **b** $\quad b + c$ **c** $\quad b - a$

   d $\quad a + b - c$ **e** $\quad b + c - a$ **f** $\quad c - b + a$

2 Work out the values of the following expressions when $x = 5$, $y = 3$ and $z = 7$

   a $\quad 2x$ **b** $\quad 5y$ **c** $\quad 7z$

   d $\quad 12x$ **e** $\quad 8y$ **f** $\quad 9z$

3 Work out the values of the following expressions when $p = 4$, $q = 5$ and $r = 8$

   a $\quad pq$ **b** $\quad pr$ **c** $\quad 2pr$

   d $\quad 5pq$ **e** $\quad pqr$ **f** $\quad 2pqr$

4 Work out the values of the following expressions when $p = 2$, $q = 4$ and $r = 20$

   a $\quad \dfrac{12}{p}$ **b** $\quad \dfrac{12}{q}$ **c** $\quad \dfrac{r}{4}$ **d** $\quad \dfrac{r}{p}$ **e** $\quad \dfrac{r}{q}$

5 Work out the values of the following expressions when $l = 4$, $m = 10$ and $n = 5$

   a $\quad 2l + 4$ **b** $\quad 3m - 1$ **c** $\quad 6 + 5n$ **d** $\quad \dfrac{m}{2} + 5$

   e $\quad \dfrac{20}{l} + 8$ **f** $\quad 7 - \dfrac{15}{n}$ **g** $\quad 3l + 4n$ **h** $\quad 5m - 2n$

   i $\quad lm + 6n$ **j** $\quad 2mn - 3l$ **k** $\quad \dfrac{30}{m} + \dfrac{32}{l}$ **l** $\quad 3l + \dfrac{m}{5}$

Use the rules for calculating with negative numbers when substituting negative values into an expression.

Example 2

Calculate the value of each of these expressions when $x = 5$ and $y = -3$

   a $\quad 2(x + 3)$ **b** $\quad xy$ **c** $\quad \dfrac{x + y}{2}$ **d** $\quad 2x - y$ **e** $\quad 3x^2$

Solution 2

a $2(x + 3) = 2 \times (x + 3)$
When $x = 5$ $2 \times (x + 3) = 2 \times (5 + 3) = 2 \times 8 = 16$ (brackets first)

b $xy = x \times y$
When $x = 5$ and $y = -3$
$x \times y = 5 \times -3 = -15$ (positive $\times$ negative = negative)

c $\dfrac{x + y}{2} = \dfrac{5 + -3}{2}$

$\dfrac{5 + -3}{2} = \dfrac{2}{2} = 1$ (calculation above the division line first)

d $2x - y = 2 \times x - y$
$2 \times x - y = 2 \times 5 - -3 = 2 \times 5 + 3 = 10 + 3 = 13$
(subtracting a negative is the same as adding a positive)

e $3x^2 = 3 \times x^2 = 3 \times 5^2 = 3 \times 25 = 75$ (square before multiplying)

Exercise B

1 Jane says that when $x = 5$ the expression $3x$ equals 35
Explain why Jane is wrong.

2 Calculate the value of each of these expressions when $a = 2$, $b = 3$ and $c = 9$

a $a + b - c$ **b** $5b$ **c** $\dfrac{c}{3}$

d $5a + 2b - 2c$ **e** $2(b - 9)$ **f** $\dfrac{b - 9}{2}$

3 The number machine shows how to
calculate the value of the expression
$5x + 2$ when $x = 2$

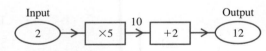

Use number machines to calculate the value of the following expressions.
a $3p - 4$ when $p = 5$ **b** $3(p - 4)$ when $p = 5$
c $2t + 5$ when $t = 4$ **d** $2(t + 5)$ when $t = 4$
e $3n + 9$ when $n = -2$ **f** $3(n + 9)$ when $n = -2$
g $3(5m - 4)$ when $m = 2$ **h** $2(4q + 3)$ when $q = -2$

4 Calculate the value of each of these expressions when $x = 8$ and $y = -4$
a $x + y$ **b** $x - y$ **c** $3y$ **d** $2x + 3y$

e $2(x + y)$ **f** $\dfrac{x - y}{3}$ **g** $3(2 - x)$ **h** $3(2 - y)$

5 Peter and Jade work out the value of $5(x + 5)$ when $x = -2$
Peter gets -5 and Jade gets 15.
Who is right? What has one of them done wrong?

6 Work out the value of the following expressions when $p = 5$, $q = 2$ and $r = 8$

a $\quad p^2$ b $\quad q^3$ c $\quad p^2 + q^2$ d $\quad 2p^2$ e $\quad 4q^2$

f $\quad 2r^2$ g $\quad 3q^3$ h $\quad \dfrac{r^2}{4}$ i $\quad \dfrac{q^3}{2}$ j $\quad \dfrac{p^2 - 5}{2}$

7 Jim was given the values -5, 5, -2, 2 and 1 to substitute into some expressions. This is what he got for each expression.

$$a^2 + b^2 = 29 \qquad\qquad 2a + 3b = 4$$

$$2(a + c) = 12 \qquad\qquad \frac{d + 11}{3} = 2$$

$$d + e = -3$$

What are the values of a, b, c, d and e?

8 Use $a = 12.6$, $b = 23.4$ and $c = 0.6$ to work out:

a $\quad \dfrac{ab}{c}$ b $\quad a + bc$ c $\quad \dfrac{a^2}{c} - b$ d $\quad \dfrac{(a + b)}{c}$ e $\quad \dfrac{(b - a)}{2c}$

Chapter summary

- In algebra letter symbols are used to represent numbers.
- Letter symbols follow the same rules as arithmetic.
  $$x + x + x + x = 4 \times x = 4x \qquad 3y + 4y = 7y \qquad n \times n = n^2$$
- When using letter symbols:
  - Leave out the multiplication symbol. $5 \times x$ as $5x$
  - Use a division line instead of the division symbol. $5 \div x$ as $\dfrac{5}{x}$
- Sometimes letter symbols are used to represent any number.
  For example, when $x + y = 100$, x and y can take any values as long as x and y add up to 100
- Sometimes letter symbols represent just one number.
  For example, when $x + 40 = 100$, x must have the value 60
- A formula is a rule for working out one quantity from other quantities.
  A formula uses either words or letter symbols and must have an '=' sign.
- An algebraic expression includes terms. Terms can have letter symbols, numbers or both.
  For example, the expression $3x + 2$ has terms $3x$ and 2
  An expression does **not** have an '=' sign.
- The order of operations for calculating with number also applies to algebraic expressions.
- Like terms are terms with the same letter symbol. x and $2x$ are like terms.
  To simplify an expression, add or subtract the like terms.
- Expressions can be simplified by multiplication and division.
- Substitution means replacing letter symbols with numbers and working out the resulting calculation.

Chapter review

1 Aisha buys q apples at 18 pence each.
  a Write down an expression for the total cost in terms of q.
  b She now buys r pears at 22 pence each.
     Write down an expression for the total cost of the apples and pears.

2 **a** Find the value of $4x + 3y$
       i when $x = 3$ and $y = 6$ **ii** when $x = 5$ and $y = -3$
    b Find the value of $a^2 + b^3$ when $a = 5$ and $b = 2$

3 **a** Simplify the following:
       i $2p + 3p + p$ **ii** $3x - 2x + x$ **iii** $4x + 5y - 3x + 4y$
    b A pencil costs x pence and a rubber costs y pence.
       i How much do four pencils cost?
       ii What is the total cost of a pencil and a rubber?
       Ten rulers cost y pence.
       iii What is the cost of one ruler?

4 **a** Work out the value of $6a + 4b$ when $a = 7$ and $b = 3$
    b Simplify the expression $2c + 6d + 4c - 8c$
    c Find the value of $3x + y^3$ when $x = -2$ and $y = 2$
    d Find the value of $u^2 - v^2$ when $u = 5$ and $v = 3$

5 Boris has six bags containing x marbles each and five loose marbles.

He shares them out equally between three friends.
  a How many marbles does each friend get?
  b How many marbles are left over?

6 **a** Simplify $5x + 3y - 2x + 4y$
    b Find the value of $5p + 2q$ when $p = 4$ and $q = -7$
    c Find the value of $\dfrac{a - b}{4}$ when $a = 10$ and $b = -2$

7 Sam is x years old.
  a Paul is 5 years younger than Sam.
     Write an expression, in terms of x, for Paul's age.
  b Barry is 9 years older than Sam.
     Write an expression, in terms of x, for Barry's age.
  c Tim is double Sam's age.
     Write an expression, in terms of x, for Tim's age.
  d Emma is a half of Barry's age.
     Write an expression, in terms of x, for Emma's age.

8 The length of the rectangle is $3x$ cm.
The width of the rectangle is 5 cm.

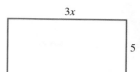

   a Write down an expression for the perimeter of the rectangle.
   b Write down an expression for the area of the rectangle. Give your answer in its simplest form.

9 If $a = -6$ and $b = 14$, find the value of:

   a $3a + b$ **b** $b^2 + a^2$ **c** $\dfrac{a}{(a - b)}$

10 Use $p = 18.8$, $q = 37.2$ and $r = 0.4$ to work out:

   a $p + \dfrac{q}{r}$ **b** $\dfrac{p + q}{r}$

11 Write an expression, in terms of x, for the outputs from each of these number machines.

   a

   b
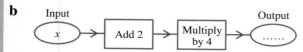

Multiples, factors and primes

7.1 Multiplying and dividing

CAN YOU REMEMBER

- The multiplication table up to 10×10?
- The meaning of 'product'?

IN THIS SECTION YOU WILL

- Practise multiplication and division using written methods and using a calculator.
- Use multiplication to solve problems in everyday situations.
- Learn how to check your answers to multiplications using the units digit.

One fact from the multiplication tables gives three more related facts.

For example:

$3 \times 8 = 24$ $24 \div 3 = 8$

$8 \times 3 = 24$ $24 \div 8 = 3$

To multiply larger numbers without a calculator, use the grid method or a column method.

Example 1

Work out 23×41 using

a the grid method   **b** the column method

Solution 1

a

$\times$	**20**	**3**	
40	*800*	*120*	$800 + 120 = 920$
1	*20*	*3*	$20 + 3 = 23$
	$800 + 20 = 820$	$120 + 3 = 123$	$820 + 123 = 943$

$$\begin{array}{r} 920 \\ + \quad 23 \\ \hline \end{array}$$

b

$$\begin{array}{r} 2\ 3 \\ \times \quad 4\ 1 \\ \hline 2\ 3 \\ 9^1 2\ 0 \\ \hline 9\ 4\ 3 \\ \hline \end{array}$$
   (23×1)
(23×40)
$(23 + 920)$

Example 2

A school hall has 32 rows of chairs. There are 24 chairs in each row.
640 people attend a meeting.

How many empty chairs are there at the meeting?

Solution 2

The number of chairs is 32 × 24 = 768
The number of empty chairs = 768 − 640 = 128 chairs

Exercise A

1 Work out:
    a 2 × 7   **b** 3 × 9   **c** 7 × 4   **d** 8 × 5   **e** 6 × 9
    f 8 × 7   **g** 7 × 10   **h** 9 × 4   **i** 5 × 7   **j** 8 × 9

2 Work out:
    a 14 × 8   **b** 18 × 7   **c** 32 × 5   **d** 16 × 6
    e 253 × 4   **f** 184 × 9   **g** 217 × 7   **h** 442 × 6

3 Work out:
    a 35 × 12   **b** 24 × 15   **c** 14 × 18   **d** 52 × 21
    e 56 × 38   **f** 112 × 14   **g** 238 × 26   **h** 413 × 62

4 Work out:
    a 42 ÷ 6   **b** 35 ÷ 7   **c** 30 ÷ 5   **d** 48 ÷ 8
    e 56 ÷ 7   **f** 70 ÷ 10   **g** 63 ÷ 7   **h** 72 ÷ 9

5 **a** The product of two whole numbers is 20
      Write down all the possible pairs of numbers.
  b The product of two whole numbers is 56
      Write down **one** possible pair of numbers.

6 **a** Use a calculator to work out 26 × 84
  b Copy and complete: **i** ...... ÷ 84 = 26   **ii** ...... ÷ 26 = 84

7 **a** Use a calculator to work out 174 × 23
  b Copy and complete: **i** ...... ÷ 174 = 23   **ii** ...... ÷ 23 = 174

8 4512 ÷ 96 = 47
  Copy and complete: **a** ...... × 96 = 4512   **b** 4512 ÷ ...... = 47
  Check your answers using a calculator.

9 $1820 \div 65 = 28$
Copy and complete: **a** $28 \times \ldots = 1820$ **b** $1820 \div \ldots = 65$
Check your answers using a calculator.

10 A farmer has 3500 sheep. Their average weight is 68 kg.
What is the total weight of all the sheep?

To check the answer to a multiplication, check whether the units digit is correct.
Use simple estimation to check if the answer is roughly correct.

Example 3

a Explain how you know that 234×18 is **not equal** to 4214
b Use estimation to show that 29.3×2.9 is **not equal** to 849.7

Solution 3

a Multiplying the units digits of each number: $4 \times 8 = 32$
So the answer must have units digit 2
So 4214 is not correct. (The correct answer is 4212)
b 29.3 is approximately 30 and 2.9 is approximately 3
So 29.3×2.9 is approximately $30 \times 3 = 90$
So 849.7 is not correct. (The correct answer is 84.97)

Exercise B

1 For each part, write down the units digit of the answer.
You do not need to do the whole calculation.
    a 35×73 **b** 46×91 **c** 39×67 **d** 82×37
    e 15×70 **f** 94×35 **g** 145×27 **h** 268×83

2 Match the calculations with their answers.

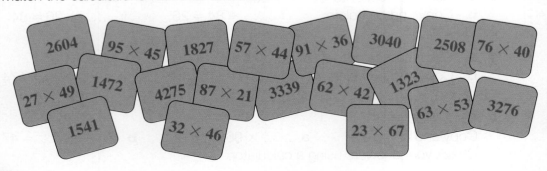

2604 95×45 1827 57×44 91×36 3040   2508 76×40

27×49 1472   4275 87×21 3339 62×42 1323 63×53 3276

1541 32×46 23×67

3 Match the calculations with their answers.

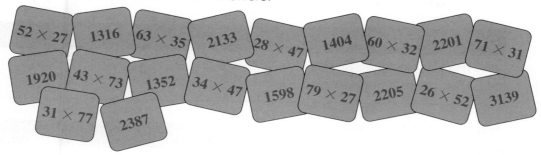

52×27 1316 63×35 2133 28×47 1404 60×32 2201 71×31

1920 43×73 1352 34×47 1598 79×27 2205 26×52 3139

31×77 2387

4 a Amas picks three *consecutive numbers* 22, 23 and 24
He says that 23×23 is greater than 22×24
Is he correct? Explain your answer.
b Viki says that this always works for three consecutive numbers.
As an example, she says that for 16, 17 and 18, 17×17 is greater
than 16×18. Is her example correct?
c Test Viki's idea using other sets of consecutive numbers. What do you notice?

5 12, 14 and 16 are three numbers with a difference of 2
Work out the values of 12×16 and 14^2
a What is the difference of your answers?
b Investigate other sets of three numbers with a difference of 2
What do you notice?

6 a Repeat question **5** using three numbers with a difference of 3, for example 21,
24 and 27
b Use your answers to questions **4**, **5** and **6a** to predict what happens for three
numbers with a difference of 4

7 A first-class carriage has 120 seats. A second-class carriage has 132 seats.
A train has four first-class carriages and twelve second-class carriages.
How many seats are there altogether?

8 Harriet says that $77 \times 38 = 2962$. She is wrong.
Explain how you can tell that she is wrong.
Use a calculator to work out the correct answer.

9 470 people tour a castle.
One guide can take 18 people on the tour.
a How many tours are needed in total?
b Each person pays £6.50 for the tour.
How much do the 470 people pay altogether?

10 Every month a woman buys £180 of premium bonds.
The limit for premium bonds is £30 000 per person.
How many months will it take her to reach the limit?

7.2 Factors

CAN YOU REMEMBER

■ The tests for divisibility by 2, 3, 4, 5, 6, 8 and 9?
■ The square numbers up to 100?

IN THIS SECTION YOU WILL

■ Learn the meaning of the term 'factor'.
■ Identify factors of a number from lists.
■ Work out all the factors of a number.

A *factor* of a number divides exactly into that number.
Factors of a number can be found from multiplication or division facts for that number.

Every number has at least two factors: 1 and the number itself.

Example 1

Find the factors of 18

Solution 1

1 and the number itself are always factors.
1 and 18 are factors of 18 because $1 \times 18 = 18$ and $18 \div 1 = 18$
2 and 9 are factors of 18 because $2 \times 9 = 18$ and $18 \div 2 = 9$
3 and 6 are factors of 18 because $3 \times 6 = 18$ and $18 \div 3 = 6$

18 is not divisible by any other number.
So the factors of 18 are 1, 2, 3, 6, 9 and 18

Example 2

Here is a list of numbers:

  1   5   20   24   30

Which numbers in the list are factors of 100?

Solution 2

1 is a factor of every number.
$100 \div 5 = 20$. The answer is a whole number so 5 is a factor of 100
20 is also a factor of 100 since $5 \times 20 = 100$
$100 \div 24$ is not a whole number so 24 is **not** a factor of 100
$100 \div 30$ is not a whole number so 30 is **not** a factor of 100

Exercise A

1 Find the factors of:

   a 8   **b** 10   **c** 12   **d** 15

   e 16   **f** 20   **g** 24   **h** 25

2 Here is a list of numbers:

   1   2   3   4   5   10   20   25   40

   Which numbers in the list are factors of:

   a 5   **b** 20   **c** 35   **d** 40?

3 Here is a list of numbers:

   5   6   7   8   9   10   11   12

   Which numbers in the list are factors of:

   a 45   **b** 50   **c** 55   **d** 60?

4 Find the factors of:

   a 30   **b** 42   **c** 45   **d** 48

   e 60   **f** 72   **g** 81   **h** 96

5 Here is a list of numbers:

   1   5   8   10   12   15   20   30

   Which numbers in the list are factors of:

   a 72   **b** 80   **c** 108   **d** 120?

6 Here is a list of numbers:

   6   8   12   16   20   24   25   30   36

   Which numbers in the list are factors of:

   a 96   **b** 144   **c** 200   **d** 300?

Exercise B

1 Write down a number that is:

   a even and a factor of 10

   b odd and a factor of 10

   c a square number and a factor of 50

   d a number with a units digit of 6 and a factor of 32

2 Write down a number that is:

   a even and a factor of 12

   b odd and a factor of 12

   c a square number and a factor of 18

   d a number with a units digit of 5 and a factor of 30

3 Write down two factors of 20 that:
  a have a sum of 15
  b have a difference of 3
  c are both even
  d are both odd.

4 Write down two factors of 24 that:
  a have a sum of 20
  b have a difference of 7
  c are both even
  d are both odd.

5 Use a calculator to find a factor of 384 that is:
  a greater than 30 and less than 35
  b a square number
  c a different square number
  d odd.

6 Use a calculator to find a factor of 405 that is:
  a greater than 10 and less than 20
  b greater than 100 and less than 150
  c a square number
  d a different square number.

7 Use a calculator to find a number that is a factor of both:
  a 51 and 85
  b 39 and 104
  c 46 and 161
  d 116 and 145

8 Fred says 5 is a factor of 28. Explain why he is wrong.

9 Work out the sum of all the factors of 20

10 Find the two factors of 506 that have a difference of 1

7.3 Multiples

CAN YOU REMEMBER

- Multiplication tables up to 10×10?

IN THIS SECTION YOU WILL

- Learn the meaning of the term 'multiple'.
- Identify multiples of a number from lists.
- Work out a set of multiples for a given number.
- Appreciate the difference between a multiple and a factor.

Multiples of a number are all the members of that number's multiplication table.
For example, the multiples of 4 are the answers to $1 \times 4, 2 \times 4, 3 \times 4, 4 \times 4, 5 \times 4, \ldots$
The multiples of 4 are 4, 8, 12, 16, 20, ...

There are an *infinite* number of multiples of any number.

Example 1

Which numbers in this list are multiples of 6?

1   2   3   6   12   18   20

Solution 1

The numbers from the list that are in the 6 times table are 6, 12 and 18
These are the first three multiples of 6

Example 2

Write down the fifth multiple of 7

Solution 2

The fifth multiple of 7 is $5 \times 7 = 35$
(The first multiple is 1×7, the second multiple is 2×7 and so on.)

Exercise A

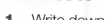

1 Write down the first five multiples of:
    a 2   **b** 3   **c** 4   **d** 5   **e** 6   **f** 8   **g** 9   **h** 10

2 Here is a list of numbers:
    1   2   3   4   5   10   20   25   40
    Which numbers in the list are multiples of:
    a 2   **b** 5   **c** 10   **d** 20?

3 Here is a list of numbers:
    8   12   16   20   24   28   32   36
    Which numbers in the list are multiples of:
    a 4   **b** 8   **c** 12   **d** 16?

4 **a** Write down the fourth multiple of 6
    b Write down the sixth multiple of 4
    c What do you notice?

5 Write down the first five multiples of:
    a 14   **b** 17   **c** 26   **d** 34

6 Here is a list of numbers:
    24   32   38   42   56   60   72
    Which numbers in the list are multiples of:
    a 16   **b** 18   **c** 20   **d** 28?

7 Here is a list of numbers:

90   91   92   93   94   95   96

Which numbers in the list are multiples of:

a 15   **b** 16   **c** 18   **d** 19?

8 322 is a multiple of 23. Use a calculator to show that this is true.

Example 3

Work out the smallest number that is a multiple of both 12 and 15

Solution 3

The first few multiples of 12 are   12, 24, 36, 48, **60**, 72, 84, 96, 108, 120, ...
The first few multiples of 15 are   15, 30, 45, **60**, 75, 90, 105, 120, ...
Comparing the lists:
The smallest number that is a multiple of both 12 and 15 is 60

Exercise B

1 Write down a number that is:
   a even and a multiple of 3   **b** even and a multiple of 7
   c a square number and a multiple of 50
   d a number with a units digit of 6 and a multiple of 12

2 Write down a number that is:
   a even and a multiple of 5   **b** even and a multiple of 11
   c a square number and a multiple of 8
   d a number with a units digit of 3 and a multiple of 7

3 Write down:
   a two multiples of 7 that have a sum of 35
   b two multiples of 8 that have a sum of 24
   c two multiples of 9 that have a sum of 36
   d two multiples of 10 that have a sum of 90

4 Write down two multiples of 4 that:
   a have a difference of 12 and a sum of 20
   b have a difference of 8 and a sum of 56
   c have a difference of 4 and a sum of 36
   d have a difference of 12 and a sum of 76

5 Ben says 2 is a factor of 6
   Sarah says 2 is a multiple of 6
   Who is correct? Explain your answer.

6 Use a calculator to find a multiple of 16 that is:
    a greater than 120 and less than 130   **b** greater than 220 and less than 230
    c also a multiple of 14   **d** also a multiple of 18

7 Use a calculator to find a multiple of 12 that is:
    a greater than 100 and less than 110   **b** greater than 200 and less than 205
    c also a multiple of 11   **d** also a multiple of 15

8 Use a calculator to find a number that is a multiple of both:
    a 8 and 15   **b** 7 and 16   **c** 9 and 21   **d** 11 and 24

9 Samina says that 84 is a multiple of 12. Is she correct? Explain your answer.

10 Here is a list of numbers:
    7   11   14   21   22   28   44   56
    Copy and complete each statement, using numbers from the list.
    a 28 is a factor of .... and ....   **b** 22 is a multiple of .... and ....

11 Write down:
    a the first five multiples of 8   **b** the first five multiples of 6
    c a number that is a multiple of both 6 and 8
    d a number that is a multiple of both 10 and 12

7.4 Prime numbers

CAN YOU REMEMBER

- The meaning of 'factor' and 'multiple'?
- The tests for divisibility?
- The multiplication tables up to 10 × 10?
- Powers of 2?

IN THIS SECTION YOU WILL

- Learn the meaning of the term 'prime number'.
- Identify prime numbers from lists.
- Identify and use prime factors of a number.

A *prime number* is a number that has only two factors. The factors of a prime number are 1 and the number itself. 1 is not a prime number as it only has one factor.

The first ten prime numbers are 2, 3, 5, 7, 11, 13, 17, 19, 23 and 29
The only even prime number is the number 2

Example 1

Find all the prime numbers in this list.

1   2   5   8   11   31   34

Solution 1

1 is not a prime number as it only has one factor.
The factors of 2 are 1 and 2   The factors of 5 are 1 and 5
The factors of 8 are 1, 2, 4 and 8   The factors of 11 are 1 and 11
The factors of 31 are 1 and 31   The factors of 34 are 1, 2, 17 and 34

The prime numbers in the list are 2, 5, 11 and 31

Example 2

Jack says that the number 579 is prime.
Use divisibility tests to show that he is wrong.

Solution 2

Try factors 2, 3, 4, etc., starting with the smallest.
Try 2: 579 is odd, so 2 is not a factor.
Try 3, using the divisibility test for 3: Add the digits $5 + 7 + 9 = 21$
$21 \div 3 = 7$. The sum of the digits is divisible by 3
So 579 is divisible by 3 and is not prime.

A *prime factor* of a number is a factor that is also a prime number.
For example, the factors of 10 are 1, 2, 5 and 10
2 and 5 are the prime factors of 10

To show that a number is not prime, find a factor other than 1 or the number itself.

Example 3

a   Use a calculator to show that 4897 has a factor of 59
b   Write down the prime factors of 4897

Solution 3

a $4897 \div 59 = 83$
    The answer is a whole number
    so 59 is a factor of 4897

b   Both 59 and 83 are prime numbers because:
    The only factors of 59 are 1 and 59
    The only factors of 83 are 1 and 83
    Prime factors of 4897 are 59 and 83

Exercise A

1 Draw a 10 × 10 square. Write in the numbers 1 to 10 on the top row, 11 to 20 on the second row etc. until all the squares have a number in them.
Shade the number 1 in one colour.
Shade the multiples of 2, apart from 2, in another colour.
Shade the multiples of 3, apart from 3, in another colour
and so on.
The numbers left unshaded should be the 25 prime numbers less than 100

2 From each list, write down the prime numbers.

a	4	7	11	17	24	30
b	3	5	9	12	19	22
c	2	4	6	13	17	29
d	5	6	11	18	23	34

3 Decide whether each of the following numbers is prime.

a	113	**b**	137	**c**	147	**d**	163
e	167	**f**	207	**g**	211	**h**	425

4 Use a calculator to show that each of the following numbers is **not** prime.

a	221	**b**	209	**c**	161	**d**	141	**e**	629	**f**	1001

5 **a** Use a calculator to show that 713 has a factor of 23
   b Write down the prime factors of 713

Example 4

Work out the prime factors of 18

Solution 4

The factors of 18 are 1, 2, 3, 6, 9 and 18
The factors of 18 that are also prime are 2 and 3
So 2 and 3 are the prime factors of 18

Exercise B

1 Write down a prime number that is also:

a	a factor of 9	**b**	a factor of 25	**c**	a factor of 49

2 Explain why a square number can never be prime.

3 Work out the prime factors of:

a	21	**b**	28	**c**	35	**d**	42

4 Aristotle says that the sum of two prime numbers is always an even number.
Give an example to show that he is wrong.

5 The sum of the prime numbers 7 and 29 is 36, a square number.
    a Find two other prime numbers that add together to give 36
    b Find two prime numbers that add together to give 9
    c Show that each square number from 4 to 100 can be expressed as the sum of
        two prime numbers.

6 Write down a prime number that is also:
    a a factor of 121   **b** a factor of 169   **c** a factor of 289

7 Work out the prime factors of:
    a 48   **b** 60   **c** 72   **d** 90

8 Here is a list of numbers:
    2   6   13   17   18   27
    Which of these numbers are:
    a multiples of 3   **b** factors of 108   **c** prime numbers?

Chapter summary

- One fact from the multiplication table gives three more related facts.
  For example, $3 \times 2 = 6$ gives $2 \times 3 = 6$, $6 \div 3 = 2$ and $6 \div 2 = 3$
- There are two ways of multiplying large numbers without a calculator.
  The grid method:

×	**30**	**6**	
10	*300*	*60*	*300 + 60 = 360*
8	*240*	*48*	*240 + 48 = 288*
			360
			+ 288
	300 + 240 = 540	*60 + 48 = 108*	**540 + 108 = 648**

- The column method:

$$\begin{array}{r} 3\ 6 \\ \times \underline{\quad 1\ 8} \\ 2\ 8^48 \\ \underline{3\ 6\ 0} \\ \underline{6\ 4\ 8} \end{array}$$

      (36×8)
      (36×10)
      $(288 + 360)$

- Check the accuracy of a multiplication using the units digits.
  Use simple estimation to check if the answer is roughly correct.
- A *factor* of a number divides exactly into that number.
- Factors of a number can be found from multiplication for division facts.

- Every number has at least two factors: 1 and the number itself.
- Multiples of a number are all the members of that number's multiplication table. All numbers have an infinite number of multiples.
- A prime number has only two factors, 1 and itself.
- The first few prime numbers are 2, 3, 5, 7, 11, 13, 17, ...
- Prime factors are factors that are also prime numbers.

Chapter review

1 Work out:

  a $514 - 135$ **b** 46×17 **c** $510 \div 15$

2 Work out 124×25

3 Which of the numbers

   3   8   12   27   39   44   49

  a   is a multiple of 6   **b**   is a factor of 9
  c   is a prime number   **d**   is a square number?

4 Work out:

  a 4.2×10 **b** 4.2×50 **c** 341×25 **d** 4^3

5 **a**   Which of the following numbers is not a factor of 36?

    6   9   12   18   24

  b   Which of the following numbers is not a multiple of 9?

    18   45   56   72   108

6 From the following list of numbers

   6   13   16   18   21   27   36   40

  write down:

  a   a cube number   **b**   a prime number   **c**   a power of 2

7 From the list of numbers

   6   7   19   24   35   37   42

  write down:

  a   the factors of 48   **b**   a multiple of 5   **c**   a prime number.

8 **a**   Find all the factors of 24
  b   Write down the factors of 24 which are also factors of 40

9 Find a multiple of 8 which is also a multiple of 12

10 Tom says: 'When you square a whole number you **always** get an odd number.'
Give an example to show that Tom is wrong.

Measures

8.1 Metric units

CAN YOU REMEMBER

- The units used in the metric system:
  - length – metres, centimetres, etc.
  - mass – grams, kilograms
  - capacity – litres, etc?
- How to multiply by 10, 100 and 1000?

IN THIS SECTION YOU WILL

- Convert between metric units, e.g. centimetres and metres, grams and kilograms, centilitres and litres.
- Carry out calculations using metric units.

This table shows the common metric units and their relationships.

Length	Mass
1 kilometre (km) = 1000 metres (m) 1 metre (m) = 100 centimetres (cm) 1 metre (m) = 1000 millimetres (mm) 1 centimetre (cm) = 10 millimetres (mm)	1 kilogram (kg) = 1000 grams (g) 1 tonne (t) = 1000 kilograms (kg)
	Capacity
	1 litre (l) = 100 centilitres (cl) 1 litre (l) = 1000 millilitres (ml) 1 cubic metre (m³) = 1000 litres (l)

To change a measurement to a smaller metric unit, multiply by 10, 100 or 1000

Example 1

Convert
a 4 metres to centimetres
b 3.5 kilograms to grams.

Solution 1

a 1 metre = 100 centimetres
   To convert metres to
   centimetres multiply by 100
   4 m = 4 × 100 cm = 400 cm
   4 m = 400 cm

b 1 kilogram = 1000 grams
   To convert kilograms to grams
   multiply by 1000
   3.5 kg = 3.5 × 1000 g = 3500 g
   3.5 kg = 3500 g

To change a measurement to a larger metric unit, divide by 10, 100 or 1000

Example 2

Change
a   47 millimetres to centimetres   b   1500 millilitres to litres.

Solution 2

a   10 millimetres = 1 centimetre   b   1000 millilitres = 1 litre
    To convert mm to cm divide by 10   To convert ml to l divide by 1000
    47 mm = 47 ÷ 10 = 4.7 cm   1500 ml = 1500 ÷ 1000 = 1.5 litres
    47 mm = 4.7 cm   1500 ml = 1.5 l

To compare measurements, they need to be in the same units.

Example 3

Write these lengths in order of size, smallest first.

60 cm,   0.3 m,   420 mm,   1.2 m,   105 cm

Solution 3

Converting each length to centimetres gives:

60 cm   0.3 m = 0.3 × 100 = 30 cm   420 mm = 420 ÷ 10 = 42 cm
1.2 m = 1.2 × 100 = 120 cm   105 cm

Writing the lengths in cm in order: 30 cm,   42 cm,   60 cm, 105 cm, 120 cm

Rewriting these using the original
units gives: 0.3 m,   420 mm, 60 cm, 105 cm, 1.2 m

Exercise A

1 Convert each of the following into centimetres.
   a   60 mm   b   3.5 m   c   15 m   d   45 mm   e   120 mm
   f   2.4 m   g   7.5 m   h   95 mm   i   0.4 m

2 Convert each of the following into grams.
   a   3 kg   b   4.2 kg   c   0.5 kg
   d   1.5 kg   e   2.75 kg   f   5.4 kg

3 Convert each of the following into litres.
   a   3000 ml   b   1500 ml   c   25 000 ml
   d   4200 ml   e   800 ml   f   7500 ml

4 Convert each of the following into millimetres.

a 36 cm	**b** 1.4 m	**c** 150 cm	**d** 0.3 m	**e** 225 cm
f 87 cm	**g** 2.6 m	**h** 46 cm	**i** 4.2 cm	

5 Write these measures in order of size, smallest first.
   a 0.8 m, 150 cm, 3700 mm, 450 mm
   b 1500 g, 3.2 kg, 0.3 kg, 450 g
   c 2 m³, 3500 *l*, 500 000 ml
   d 385 cm, 2.6 m, 0.4 km, 295 m, 75 cm

6 Convert each of the following into kilometres.

a 3628 m	**b** 147.5 m	**c** 7291 m	**d** 51 225 m
e 840 m	**f** 2348 m	**g** 345 m	**h** 5840 m

7 Convert each of the following into litres.

a 3420 ml	**b** 12 530 ml	**c** 463 ml	**d** 260 ml
e 76 809 ml	**f** 320 ml	**g** 4575 ml	**h** 6776 ml

8 Convert each of the following into metres.

a 472 mm	**b** 1.41 km	**c** 7845 cm	**d** 2.57 km
e 649 cm	**f** 228 mm	**g** 1456 mm	**h** 235 cm

9 Convert each of the following into kilograms.

a 3.6 tonnes	**b** 31 850 g	**c** 167 g	**d** 986 g
e 4381 g	**f** 2.14 tonnes	**g** 5945 g	**h** 1050 g

10 Write these measures in order of size, smallest first.
   a 386 m, 45 637 cm, 15.3 m, 0.04 km, 2120 cm
   b 517 g, 0.48 kg, 175 g, 0.02 kg, 39.84 g
   c 0.42 *l*, 1207 ml, 282 ml, 1.4 *l*, 600 ml

To add or subtract measurements, they need to be in the same units.

Example 4

Add together 140 cm and 5.4 m. Give your answer in metres.

Solution 4

To convert 140 cm to metres divide by 100   140 cm = 140 ÷ 100 = 1.4 m
Adding: 1.4 m + 5.4 m = 6.8 m

Example 5

Frozen vegetables are packed in bags.
Each full bag weighs 450 g.
How many kilograms of vegetables are needed
to fill 150 of these bags?

Solution 5

For 150 bags, 150 × 450 g of vegetables are
needed.
150 × 450 g = 67 500 g

To convert grams to kilograms divide by 1000
67 500 g = 67 500 ÷ 1000 = 67.5 kg
67.5 kg of vegetables are needed.

Exercise B

1 Add together 50 cm, 350 mm and 25 cm. Give your answer in centimetres.

2 Subtract 350 g from 2 kg. Give your answer in   **a** grams   **b** kilograms.

3 How many 10 millilitre doses of medicine can you pour from a 1 litre bottle?

4 Which statement is true?
   ■ 3500 cm is greater than 3.5 m.
   ■ 3500 cm is equal to 3.5 m.
   ■ 3500 cm is less than 3.5 m.
   Show your working.

5 A greengrocer has 50 kg of
   strawberries.
   He sells 40 kg and gives away 600 g.
   How many kilograms of strawberries
   does he have left?

6 Which statement is true?
   ■ 2800 ml is greater than 2.8 *l*.
   ■ 2800 ml is equal to 2.8 *l*.
   ■ 2800 ml is less than 2.8 *l*.
   Show your working.

7 Add together 1.1 kg, 850 g, 300 g
   and 0.4 kg.
   Give your answer in kilograms.

8 Which statement is true?
   ■ 1800 mm is greater than 18 cm.
   ■ 1800 mm is equal to 18 cm.
   ■ 1800 mm is less than 18 cm.
   Show your working.

9 A joiner needs 20 lengths of wood,
   each 240 cm long.
   Calculate the total length of wood
   needed.
   Give your answer in metres.

10 Butter is packed in 250 g tubs.
   How many tubs can be filled
   from 50 kg of butter?

11 A piece of material is 2.3 m long.
Lengths of 112 cm and 54 cm are cut from it.
What length, in metres, is left?

12 A bottle contains 1.8 litres of milk.
1456 ml of this milk is used. How many millilitres are left?

13 A gardener wants to cut pieces of string which are 28 cm long
from a 5 m ball of string.
  a How many 28 cm lengths can he cut from this ball?
  b How much string will be left over?

8.2 Metric and imperial measures

CAN YOU REMEMBER

- The units used in the imperial system:
    length – miles, yards, feet, inches   mass – pounds, ounces
    capacity – pints, gallons?
- The units used in the metric system:
    length – kilometres, metres, centimetres, millimetres   mass – kilograms, grams
    capacity – litres, millilitres?

IN THIS SECTION YOU WILL

- Convert between metric and imperial units, e.g. kilometres and miles, centimetres
  and inches or feet, kilograms and pounds, litres and pints or gallons.
- Compare metric and imperial quantities.

To convert metric units to imperial units, or vice versa, use the approximate conversions
shown in the tables.

Learn these conversions.

Length		Mass		Capacity	
Metric	Imperial	Metric	Imperial	Metric	Imperial
30 cm	1 foot	1 kg	2.2 pounds	1 litre	1.75 pints
8 km	5 miles			4.5 litres	1 gallon

Know how to use these conversions.

Length		Mass	
Metric	Imperial	Metric	Imperial
2.5 cm	1 inch	25 g	1 ounce
1 m	39 inches		

Example 1

Convert the following imperial units to the metric unit stated.

a   7 inches to centimetres   **b**   20 miles to kilometres

Solution 1

a   1 inch = 2.5 cm
        To convert inches to centimetres multiply by 2.5
        7 inches = 7 × 2.5 cm = 17.5 cm

b   5 miles = 8 km

Method 1	**Method 2**
Dividing both sides by 5 gives	Look at how many lots of 5 miles
1 mile = 8 km ÷ 5 = 1.6 km	make up the total miles.
To convert miles to kilometres	5 miles = 8 km
multiply by 1.6	20 miles = 4 × 5 miles
20 miles = 20 × 1.6 km = 32 km	20 miles = 4 × 8 km = 32 km

Example 2

Convert the following metric measurements to the imperial unit stated.

a   7 kg to pounds   **b**   3 litres to pints

Solution 2

a   1 kilogram = 2.2 pounds
        To convert kilograms to pounds
        multiply by 2.2
        7 kg = 7 × 2.2 pounds = 15.4 pounds

b   1 litre = 1.75 pints
        To convert litres to pints
        multiply by 1.75
        3 litres = 3 × 1.75 pints = 5.25 pints

Exercise A

1   Use the conversion 2.5 cm = 1 inch to convert the following to centimetres.

   a   4 inches   **b**   10 inches   **c**   8 inches
   d   20 inches   **e**   2 feet   **f**   5 feet
   g   6 feet   **h**   10 feet

2   Use the conversion 25 g = 1 ounce to convert the following to grams.

   a   2 ounces   **b**   4 ounces   **c**   8 ounces
   d   10 ounces   **e**   20 ounces   **f**   100 ounces

3   Convert the following to miles.

   a   16 km   **b**   40 km   **c**   80 km
   d   32 km   **e**   88 km   **f**   800 km

4   Convert the following to litres.

   a   2 gallons   **b**   10 gallons   **c**   20 gallons   **d**   100 gallons

5   Use the conversion 2.5 cm = 1 inch to convert the following to inches.

a 15 cm	**b** 35 cm	**c** 60 cm
d 117.5 cm	**e** 22.5 cm	**f** 55 cm

6   Convert the following to pounds.

a 4 kg	**b** 15.5 kg	**c** 2.8 kg
d 25 kg	**e** 38 kg	**f** 0.6 kg

7   Convert the following to pints.

a 4 litres	**b** 10 litres	**c** 12 litres
d 15.2 litres	**e** 3.6 litres	**f** 80 litres

8   Convert the following to kilometres.

a 7.5 miles	**b** 22 miles	**c** 45 miles
d 3 miles	**e** 120 miles	**f** 95 miles

To compare measurements, they need to be in the same units.

Example 3

Joanne is 156 cm tall. Sarah is 5 feet and 4 inches tall.
Calculate who is taller.

Solution 3

Change 5 feet and 4 inches to centimetres.
5 feet = 5 × 30 cm = 150 cm   4 inches = 4 × 2.5 cm = 10 cm
Adding gives 150 cm + 10 cm = 160 cm
Sarah is 160 cm tall.
Joanne is 156 cm tall, so Sarah is taller.

Exercise B

1 How many pints of milk are there in a 2 litre bottle?

2 The distance from Middlesbrough
to Newcastle is 50 miles.
How many kilometres is this?

3 Robert is exactly 5 feet tall.
Estimate his height in centimetres.

4 A petrol tank holds 10 gallons of petrol when full.
The tank is half full. Estimate, to the nearest litre,
the number of litres of petrol in the tank.

5 Jill cuts four pieces of ribbon, each 6 inches long, from a roll of ribbon.
Estimate how many centimetres of ribbon she has cut from the roll.

6 In a house there are two water tanks.
Tank A holds 25 gallons of water.
Tank B holds 108 litres of water.
Which water tank holds the most water?
Show your working.

7 Janine has a photograph which measures 18 cm by 15 cm.
She wants to put it in a frame which measures 10 inches by 8 inches.
Will the photograph fit in the frame?
Show your working.

8 A newborn baby weighs 3.5 kg.
What is the baby's weight in pounds?

9 Candice is baking a cake.
She needs to weigh 6 ounces of flour but
only has metric measures on her scales.
How many grams of flour must she weigh?

10 Ian travels 12 miles to work.
Javed travels 20 km to work.
Ian says that he travels further than Javed.
Is he correct?
Show your working.

8.3 Everyday use of imperial and metric units

CAN YOU REMEMBER

- How to convert between metric measures of length, mass and capacity?
- How to convert between metric and imperial measures for length, mass and capacity?
- How to write times using am and pm?

IN THIS SECTION YOU WILL

- Choose the correct units to use for everyday measures.
- Make estimates of a range of measures.
- Read scales on a range of measuring instruments.

Measures such as length, mass, capacity, time and temperature need to be given in sensible units. For example:

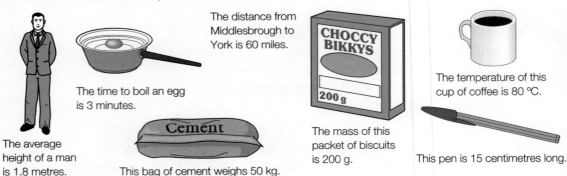

The distance from Middlesbrough to York is 60 miles.

The time to boil an egg is 3 minutes.

The temperature of this cup of coffee is 80 °C.

The average height of a man is 1.8 metres.

This bag of cement weighs 50 kg.

The mass of this packet of biscuits is 200 g.

This pen is 15 centimetres long.

To read measures from scales, work out what each division on the scales represents.

Example 1

Write down the readings on the following scales.

a

35 cm 40

b

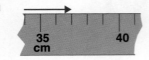

c

Solution 1

a There are 5 spaces between 35 and 40 so each space represents 1 cm.
The arrow is two spaces after 35
So the reading is 37 cm.

b There are 10 spaces between 8 and 9 so each space represents $\frac{1}{10}$ or 0.1 units.
The arrow is two spaces after 8 so the reading is 8.2 units.

c There are 10 spaces between 200 and 300
$100 \div 10 = 10$, so each space represents 10 ml.
The arrow is four spaces after 200
4×10 ml $= 40$ ml
So the reading is 240 ml.

Exercise A

1 Write down the most suitable metric unit for measuring:
  a the weight of an elephant
  b the length of a worm
  c the height of the London Eye
  d the amount of water needed to fill a bucket
  e the mass of a sack of carrots
  f the time taken to walk 30 kilometres.

2 Write down the most suitable imperial unit for measuring:
  a the weight of a 20 pence coin
  b the length of a pencil
  c the capacity of the fuel tank of a car
  d the time it takes to run 1 mile
  e the height of a tree
  f the amount of milk in a carton.

3 Write down the readings on each of these scales.

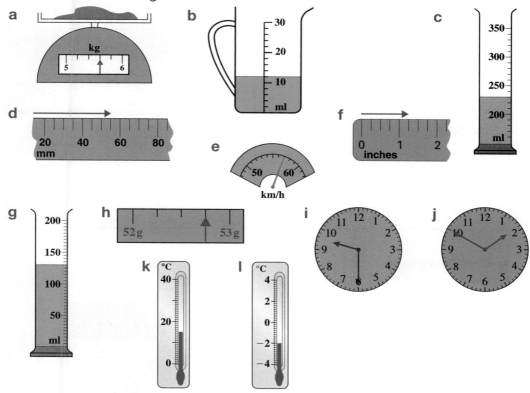

4 Copy each of these diagrams and mark the given value with an arrow.

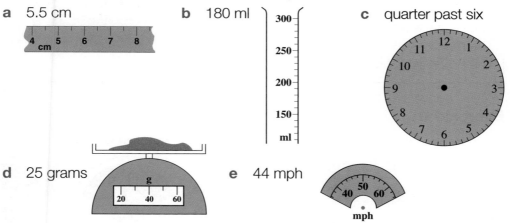

a 5.5 cm

b 180 ml

c quarter past six

d 25 grams

e 44 mph

5 For each of the following lines:

  a Estimate the length of the line in centimetres.

  b Measure the length of the line in centimetres.

  c Calculate the difference between your estimate and the actual length of each line.

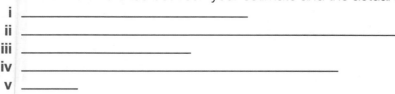

    i _____

   ii _____

  iii _____

  iv _____

   v _____

Example 2

Work out the difference in readings on these two scales.

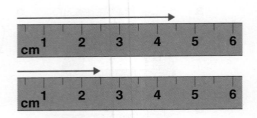

Solution 2

The first scale shows a reading of 4.5 cm.
The second scale shows a reading of 2.5 cm.
4.5 − 2.5 = 2
The difference in the readings is 2 cm.

Example 3

This man is 1.8 m tall.
Estimate the height of the house.

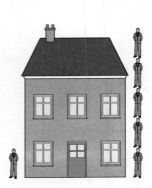

Solution 3

The house is about 5 times taller than the man.
The man is 1.8 m tall. 1.8 m × 5 = 9 m
The house is approximately 9 m tall.

Exercise B

1   Calculate the difference in the readings on each of these scales.

a

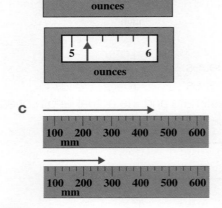

b

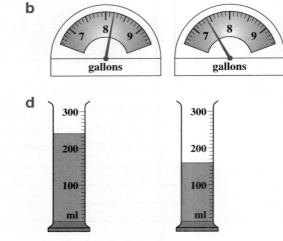

c

d

2 The speedometer shows the speed of a car travelling along a road.

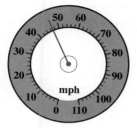

The speed limit for the road is 50 mph. What is the difference between the speed limit and the speed the car is travelling?

3 The diagram shows a boy who is 5 feet tall standing by a tree.

Estimate the height of the tree:
a in feet **b** in metres.

4

12 noon   6 pm

These two thermometers show the temperature in Toronto one day in August. By how much did the temperature drop between 12 noon and 6 pm?

5 The speedometer shows the speed of a lorry in miles per hour.
The speed limit on the road is 80 kilometres per hour.
Is the lorry travelling faster than the speed limit?
Use the conversion 5 miles per hour = 8 km per hour.
Show your working.

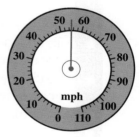

6 The car fuel gauges show the amount of fuel in a car before and after a journey.

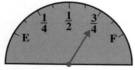 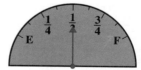

The car's fuel tank holds 8 gallons. Calculate the amount of fuel used on the journey.

7 Jenny is baking a cake.
She weighs some flour on her scales, which measure in grams.
The recipe says that she needs 6 ounces of flour for her cake.
Has Jenny weighed enough flour?
Use the conversion 1 ounce = 25 grams.
Show your working.

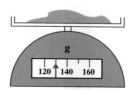

8 One kilogram of ham costs £3.60
John buys 250 g of ham.
How much does John pay?

9 Bridget leaves home at 7.50 am one morning to travel to work. She arrives at work at 8.37 am. How long did it take Bridget to travel to work?

10 Grapes are sold at £2.75 per kilogram. Calculate the cost of 1 pound of grapes. Use the conversion 1 kilogram = 2.2 pounds

Chapter summary

Length	Mass
1 kilometre (km) = 1000 metres (m) 1 metre (m) = 100 centimetres (cm) 1 metre (m) = 1000 millimetres (mm) 1 centimetre (cm) = 10 millimetres (mm)	1 kilogram (kg) = 1000 grams (g) 1 tonne (t) = 1000 kilograms (kg)
	Capacity
	1 litre (*l*) = 100 centilitres (cl) 1 litre (*l*) = 1000 millilitres (ml) 1 cubic metre (m³) = 1000 litres (*l*)

- To change a measurement to a smaller metric unit, multiply by 10, 100 or 1000 For example, 67 cm = 67 × 10 = 670 mm.
- To change a measurement to a larger metric unit, divide by 10, 100 or 1000 For example, 1200 g = 1200 ÷ 1000 = 1.2 kg.
- To compare measurements, they need to be in the same units.
- To add or subtract measurements, they need to be in the same units.
- To convert metric units to imperial units, or vice versa, use the approximate conversions shown in the table. Learn the conversions in red.

Length		Mass		Capacity	
Metric	**Imperial**	**Metric**	**Imperial**	**Metric**	**Imperial**
2.5 cm	1 inch	25 g	1 ounce	**1 litre**	**1.75 pints**
30 cm	**1 foot**	**1 kg**	**2.2 pounds**	**4.5 litres**	**1 gallon**
1 m	39 inches				
8 km	**5 miles**				

- Measures such as length, mass, capacity, time and temperature need to be given in sensible units.
- To read measures from scales, work out what each division on the scales represents.

Chapter review

1 Write down the value indicated by the pointer in each of these scales.

a

b

c

2 One kilogram of cheese costs £4.80. Anita buys 500 g of cheese.
How much does Anita pay?

3 The speed limit on motorways is 70 miles per hour.
The speedometer shows the speed of a lorry.

a How much slower than the speed limit is the lorry travelling?
b Convert 60 mph to kilometres per hour.
c Convert 80 km/h to miles per hour.

4 This scale shows pints and litres.

a How much liquid does the jug contain?
Give your answer in pints.
b Use the scale to estimate how many pints there are in 1 litre.
c Estimate the number of litres in 6 pints.

5 Javed swims 60 lengths of a swimming pool every day.
The swimming pool is 20 metres long.

a How far does Javed swim each day?
b What is this distance in kilometres?

6 How many files, each 2.5 cm thick,
will fit on a shelf 1.2 m wide?

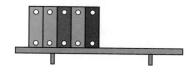

7 How many pounds are approximately equivalent to 6 kilograms?

8 Mrs Johnson is weighing a bag of potatoes on her kitchen scales.
a How much does the bag of potatoes weigh?
b Change this weight into pounds.
Give your answer to the nearest pound.
c Mrs Johnson is using a recipe that needs 1.5 pounds of potatoes.
What is this weight in kilograms? Give your answer to 1 d.p.

9 A newborn baby weighs 4.5 kilograms.
a Change 4.5 kg to grams.   **b** Change 4.5 kg to pounds.
Use the conversion 1 kilogram = 2.2 pounds.

10 Ellen drives 85 miles one day. Joe drives 140 kilometres on the same day.
Ellen says that she drove further than Joe. Is she correct? Show your working.

9.1 Solving by inspection and working backwards

CAN YOU REMEMBER

- How to show algebraic expressions using number machines?
- Which operations are inverses of each other?
- The order of operations for number and algebra?

IN THIS SECTION YOU WILL

- Learn the meaning of the term 'equation'.
- Learn some simple methods of solving equations.

An *equation* includes an equals sign; for example $5x - 3 = 7$
In an equation only **one** value of the letter symbol works in the equation. This value is called the *solution* of the equation.
Finding the solution of an equation is called *solving*.

Solving by inspection Look at the equation and spot the solution.

Solving by working backwards

Step 1: Draw the number machine for the equation.

Step 2: Work backwards through the number machine using the *inverse operations*:

Example 1

Solve the following equations **by inspection**.

a $w + 3 = 12$ b $x - 2 = 10$ c $3y = 15$ d $\dfrac{z}{4} = 2$

Solution 1

a $w + 3 = 12$ b $x - 2 = 10$ c $\quad 3y = 15$ d $\quad \dfrac{z}{4} = 2$
  $\ 9 + 3 = 12$ $\ 12 - 2 = 10$ $\ 3 \times 5 = 15$ $\quad \dfrac{8}{4} = 2$
So $\ w = 9$ So $\ x = 12$ So $\ y = 5$ So $\ z = 8$

Example 2

Solve these equations by **working backwards**.

a $6p = 18$ b $\dfrac{q}{4} = 9$ c $4r + 3 = 19$ d $\dfrac{s}{2} - 4 = 5$

Solution 2

a
Input		Output
p	×6	18

Input		Output
3	÷6	18

So $p = 3$

b
Input		Output
q	÷4	9

Input		Output
36	×4	9

So $q = 36$

c
Input		4r		Output
r	×4		+3	19

Input		16		Output
4	÷4		−3	19

So $r = 4$

d
Input		$\frac{s}{2}$		Output
s	÷2		−4	5

Input		9		Output
18	×2		+4	5

So $s = 18$

Exercise A

1   What numbers must be put in the boxes to make each equation true?

a $\Box + 3 = 5$ b $\Box - 5 = 2$ c $12 - \Box = 7$

d $3 \times \Box = 21$ e $\Box \div 4 = 5$ f $30 \div \Box = 10$

g $12 \times \Box = 36$ h $36 \div \Box = 3$

2   Write down the solutions to these equations.

a $w + 4 = 12$ b $x + 8 = 24$ c $y + 12 = 20$
d $30 = z + 7$ e $a - 2 = 6$ f $b - 8 = 4$
g $c - 12 = 9$ h $26 = d - 5$ i $8 + p = 8$
j $q - 12 = 0$ k $r + 24 = 25$ l $r - 24 = 25$

3   Solve these equations by inspection.

a $5w = 10$ b $3x = 12$ c $9y = 27$ d $24 = 6z$

e $\dfrac{a}{3} = 2$ f $\dfrac{b}{8} = 4$ g $\dfrac{c}{6} = 8$ h $20 = \dfrac{d}{4}$

i $6p = 42$ j $42 = \dfrac{q}{6}$ k $8r = 48$ l $48 = \dfrac{s}{6}$

4 What numbers must be put in the boxes to make each equation true?

a $\boxed{} \times 2 + 1 = 7$ b $12 - 3 \times \boxed{} = 6$

c $8 + 5 \times \boxed{} = 18$ d $\boxed{} \div 2 + 1 = 6$

e $4 \times \boxed{} - 3 = 5$ f $12 \div \boxed{} - 1 = 2$

g $7 \times \boxed{} + 8 = 50$ h $5 - 8 \div \boxed{} = 1$

i $18 - 4 \times \boxed{} = 6$ j $20 \div \boxed{} - 3 = 2$

5 Work backwards to find the input number for each of these number machines.

a Input · ? → ×4 → Output · 24 b Input · ? → +6 → Output · 9

c Input · ? → −2 → Output · 6 d Input · ? → ÷5 → Output · 8

e Input · ? → ×3 → ? → +2 → Output · 38

f Input · ? → ÷4 → ? → +7 → Output · 12

g Input · ? → ×8 → ? → −7 → Output · 25

h Input · ? → ÷6 → ? → +11 → Output · 15

6 Draw number machines for each equation.
Solve the equation by working backwards.

a $x + 14 = 21$ b $p - 9 = 11$ c $5a = 35$ d $\dfrac{n}{6} = 3$

e $3y - 9 = 3$ f $4t + 3 = 27$ g $7q - 2 = 5$ h $\dfrac{x}{5} + 1 = 3$

i $\dfrac{s}{4} - 1 = 2$ j $\dfrac{x}{5} + 3 = 7$ k $\dfrac{q}{2} - 9 = 1$ l $\dfrac{n}{4} + 4 = 7$

7 What was my number in each of these 'think of a number' problems?
 a I think of a number, add 7 and get 12
 b I think of a number, subtract 12 and get 18
 c I think of a number, multiply it by 2 and then add 5. I get 21
 d I think of a number, divide it by 5 and then subtract 3. I get 17
 e I think of a number, add 7 and then divide by 3. I get 25

Example 3

Solve each of these equations by working backwards.

a $4v = -20$ b $w + 7 = 5$ c $-4z + 26 = 14$

Solution 3

a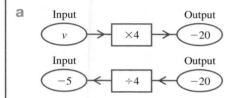

So $v = -5$ (negative ÷ positive = negative)

b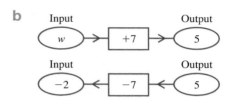

So $w = -2$

c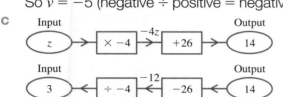

So $z = 3$ (negative ÷ negative = positive)

Exercise B

1 Work backwards to find the input number for each of these number machines.

a    b

c    d

e 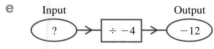   f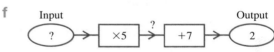

g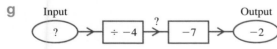

2 Solve the following equations.

  a $p + 9 = 5$ b $q + 9 = -5$ c $r - 9 = -5$ d $s - 2 = -1$

  e $t + 2 = 17$ f $u + 2 = -17$ g $v - 2 = -17$ h $w - 12 = -3$

  i $x + 11 = 6$ j $y - 11 = -6$

3 Solve the following equations.

  a $2p = -8$ b $3q = -6$ c $-4r = -12$ d $\dfrac{u}{4} = -5$

  e $\dfrac{-v}{5} = -1$ f $-12w = -36$ g $-10x = 60$ h $\dfrac{y}{8} = -2$

4   Solve the following equations by working backwards.

  a $3p + 17 = 11$ **b** $-3q - 9 = -15$ **c** $\dfrac{r}{2} + 7 = 5$

  d $\dfrac{s}{2} - 4 = -1$ **e** $5t + 12 = 2$ **f** $3u + 2 = -16$

  g $\dfrac{v}{4} - 2 = -7$ **h** $\dfrac{-w}{5} - 1 = -3$ **i** $-5x + 21 = 6$

  j $8y - 14 = -6$ **k** $\dfrac{z}{3} + 3 = -7$ **l** $\dfrac{n}{10} - 2 = -3$

5   What was my number in each of these 'think of a number' problems?
  a   I think of a number, add 14 and get 7
  b   I think of a number, subtract 12 and get -6
  c   I think of a number, multiply it by 2 and then add 7. I get 3
  d   I think of a number, divide it by 5 and then subtract 5. I get -2
  e   I think of a number, subtract 7 and then divide by -3. I get 2

6 $ax + b = c$ is an equation. a, b and c are whole numbers.
  For example, $a = 2$, $b = 3$ and $c = 13$ gives the equation $2x + 3 = 13$
  The solution of the equation $2x + 3 = 13$ is $x = 5$
  a   Find three more sets of values of a, b and c that give an equation with solution $x = 5$
  b   Find some equations with solution $x = 2$
  c   Find some equations with solution $x = -2$

7   Solve each of these equations by working backwards.

  a $14q = 308$ **b** $\dfrac{r}{23} = 36$ **c** $13s + 243 = 399$

  d $25t - 23 = 2002$ **e** $346 + \dfrac{u}{19} = 593$ **f** $\dfrac{v}{32} - 23 = 969$

  g $27 + 63w = 783$ **h** $12.1x - 15.85 = 183.8$

  i $2.4y + 8.96 = 14.96$ **j** $\dfrac{v}{2.2} + 152 = 374$

9.2 The balance method

CAN YOU REMEMBER

  ■   How to solve basic equations by inspection and by working backwards?
  ■   How to substitute values into expressions?

IN THIS SECTION YOU WILL

  ■   Learn how to solve simple equations using the balance method.
  ■   Learn how to check that your solutions are correct.

Tom puts some **unknown** equal weights and some 100 g weights on a pair of scales.

The scales balance.

Tom takes two 100 g weights **from both sides** of the balance.

The scales still balance.

Tom divides the weights by 2 **on both sides** of the balance.

The scales still balance.

This shows that the unknown weight is 300 g. The two sides of an equation are equal to each other, so they are balanced.

Doing the same thing to both sides of an equation keeps the two sides balanced. This idea can be used to solve equations.

Doing any of the following keeps an equation balanced:
- **add the same number** to both sides
- **subtract the same number** from both sides
- **multiply** both sides by **the same number**
- **divide** both sides by **the same number**.

These can be used to change an equation to a simpler equation that is still true. The inverses of the operations in the equation must be used in the correct order.

For example:
The scales show the equation $5x - 7 = 33$
Because $5x - 7$ and 33 are equal,
the scales balance.

The inverse of $- 7$ is $+ 7$
So add 7 to both sides of the equation.
This gives the equation $5x = 40$

$5x$ means $5 \times x$
The inverse of $\times$ by 5 is $\div$ by 5
So divide both sides of the equation by 5
This gives the solution $x = 8$

The solution of an equation should always be **checked**.
Do this by substituting the solution into the original equation.
When $x = 8$, $5x - 7 = 5 \times 8 - 7 = 40 - 7 = 33$
So when $x = 8$, $5x - 7 = 33$. So the solution $x = 8$ is correct.

Example 1

Solve each of these equations using the balance method.
Check your solutions by substituting your value into the original equation.

a $w + 7 = 11$ b $x - 7 = 11$ c $6y = 42$ d $\dfrac{z}{4} = 3$

Solution 1

a $w + 7 = 11$

Subtract 7 from both sides $w + 7 - \mathbf{7} = 11 - \mathbf{7}$
$$w = 4$$

Substitute $w = 4$ in the original equation to **check** the solution.
$$4 + 7 = 11 \checkmark \qquad \text{So } w = 4 \text{ is correct.}$$

b $x - 7 = 11$

Add 7 to both sides $x - 7 + \mathbf{7} = 11 + \mathbf{7}$
$$x = 18$$

Check $18 - 7 = 11 \checkmark \qquad \text{So } x = 18 \text{ is correct.}$

c $6y = 42$

Divide both sides by 6 $6y \div \mathbf{6} = 42 \div \mathbf{6}$
$$y = 7$$

Check $6 \times 7 = 42 \checkmark \qquad \text{So } y = 7 \text{ is correct.}$

d $\dfrac{z}{4} = 3$

Multiply both sides by 4 $\dfrac{z \times {}^1\!\cancel{4}}{{}^1\cancel{4}} = 3 \times \mathbf{4}$

$$z = 12$$

Check $12 \div 4 = 3 \checkmark \qquad \text{So } z = 12 \text{ is correct.}$

Example 2

Solve each of these equations using the balance method.

a $3a + 7 = 13$ b $\dfrac{b}{5} - 4 = 2$

Solution 2

a $3a + 7 = 13$

Subtract 7 from both sides $3a + 7 - \mathbf{7} = 13 - \mathbf{7}$
$$3a = 6$$

Divide both sides **by 3** $3a \div \mathbf{3} = 6 \div \mathbf{3}$
$$a = 2$$

Check $3 \times 2 + 7 = 6 + 7 = 13 \checkmark$

(Multiplication is done before addition.)

So $a = 2$ is correct.

b $\quad \dfrac{b}{5} - 4 = 2$

Add 4 to both sides $\qquad \dfrac{b}{5} - 4 + 4 = 2 + 4$

$$\dfrac{b}{5} = 6$$

Multiply both sides by 5 $\qquad \dfrac{b \times \cancel{1}5}{\cancel{1}5} = 6 \times 5$

$$b = 30$$

Check $\qquad\qquad 30 \div 5 - 4 = 6 - 4 = 2 \checkmark$

(Division is done before subtraction.)

So $b = 30$ is correct.

Exercise A

1 Sajid has some unknown weights labelled a, b, c, d and e, some 10 g and some 20 g weights.

He finds that the following combinations of weights balance.

a

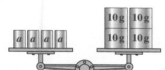

b

c

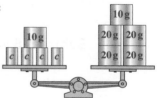

d

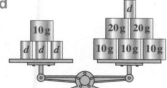

e

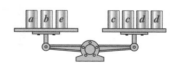

Work out the value of each unknown weight using the balance method.
Show your method clearly.

2 Solve the following equations using the balance method.
Show your method clearly.

a $w + 5 = 12$	**b** $x + 7 = 19$	**c** $42 = z + 9$	**d** $p - 4 = 7$
e $q - 11 = 1$	**f** $s - 8 = 17$	**g** $t + 33 = 48$	**h** $u - 27 = 38$

3 Solve the following equations using the balance method.
Show your method clearly.

a $2q = 62$	**b** $5r = 30$	**c** $\dfrac{s}{2} = 12$	**d** $\dfrac{t}{9} = 5$
e $7u = 56$	**f** $11v = 66$	**g** $\dfrac{w}{6} = 8$	**h** $\dfrac{x}{8} = 6$

4 Solve the following equations using the balance method. Show your method clearly.

a $3p + 2 = 14$ b $8q - 3 = 13$ c $\dfrac{r}{4} + 9 = 11$ d $\dfrac{s}{5} - 7 = 2$

e $7t + 5 = 61$ f $4u - 11 = 29$ g $\dfrac{v}{4} + 9 = 11$ h $\dfrac{w}{4} - 9 = 11$

i $4x + 11 = 51$ j $4y - 11 = 49$

5 Solve the following equations. Show your method clearly.

a $q + 284 = 428$ b $r - 367 = 229$ c $1.21s = 66.55$

d $\dfrac{t}{0.8} = 25$ e $25x + 168 = 1068$ f $19y - 146 = 595$

g $\dfrac{v}{4} + 296 = 363$ h $\dfrac{w}{6} - 235 = 506$ i $0.18x + 1.26 = 5.31$

Example 4

Solve each of these equations using the balance method. Show your method clearly.

a $u + 8 = 2$ b $\dfrac{z}{5} - 1 = -16$

Solution 4

a $u + 8 = 2$

Subtract 8 from both sides $u + 8 - 8 = 2 - 8$
                                                    $u = -6$

Check $-6 + 8 = 2$ ✓   So $u = -6$ is correct.

b $\dfrac{z}{5} - 1 = -16$

Add 1 to both sides $\dfrac{z}{5} - 1 + 1 = -16 + 1$

                                               $\dfrac{z}{5} = -15$

Multiply both sides **by 5** $\dfrac{z \times \cancel{5}^{1}}{\cancel{5}_{1}} = -15 \times 5$

                                               $z = -75$

Check $-75 \div 5 - 1 = -15 - 1 = -16$ ✓
                                 (Division is done before subtraction.)
                                                          So $z = -75$ is correct.

Exercise B

1 Solve the following equations using the balance method.
   Show your method clearly.

a $p + 9 = 5$ b $q + 5 = -9$ c $r - 5 = -9$ d $s - 8 = -2$
e $t + 21 = 1$ f $u + 21 = -1$ g $v - 21 = -1$ h $v - 1 = -21$
i $x + 33 = 18$ j $x - 33 = -18$

2 Solve the following equations using the balance method. Show your method clearly.

a $4r = -16$ b $-4s = -16$ c $\dfrac{t}{-} = -6$ d $\dfrac{u}{9} = -2$

e $10v = -40$ f $-10w = -40$ g $\dfrac{x}{-} = -1$ h $\dfrac{y}{5} = -8$

3 Solve the following equations using the balance method. Show your method clearly.

a $4p + 4 = 0$ b $4q - 4 = -8$ c $4r + 8 = -4$ d $\dfrac{s}{2} + 12 = 2$

e $\dfrac{t}{2} - 12 = -2$ f $\dfrac{u}{6} + 16 = 14$ g $-5v - 2 = -7$ h $5w - 2 = -7$

i $-3x + 2 = -7$ j $\dfrac{z}{8} + 12 = 9$

4 **a** The scales opposite balance. What is the weight marked x?

  b Sam and Delia share 5 bags of sweets
     and 12 extra sweets like this:

  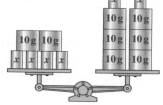

Sam and Delia have the same number of sweets.
How many sweets are in a bag?

  c Ranjit thinks of a number, multiplies it by 3 and adds 7
     Jenny thinks of the same number, multiplies it by 2 and adds 12
     Ranjit and Jenny get the same answer.
     What number did Ranjit and Jenny both think of?

5 Solve the following equations using the balance method. Show your method clearly.

  a $4p + 24 = 242$ b $12q + 145 = 367$ c $8r - 128 = -24$
  d $16s - 8 = 34$ e $2.5t - 0.2 = 7.8$ f $20u - 2 = 72$
  g $1.6x + 2.4 = 29.6$ h $35t - 120 = 2.5$

Chapter summary

- An equation contains terms and an equals sign.
  Only one value of the letter symbol works in the equation.
  This value is called the *solution*.
  Finding the solution is called *solving*.

- Equations may be solved **by inspection** or by **working backwards**.
  When working backwards, use inverse operations.
  The inverse of + is −   The inverse of − is +
  The inverse of × is ÷   The inverse of ÷ is ×

- Equations may be written in words.

Equations can be solved using the **balance method**.
Doing any of the following to **both sides** of the equation keeps the equation balanced:

- add the same number
- subtract the same number
- multiply by the same number
- divide by the same number.

Use the inverse of the operations in the equation.

To **check** the solution of an equation substitute the solution into the equation and make sure it works.

Chapter review

1 Solve the equations.

  a $4x = 12$ **b** $y + 5 = 12$ **c** $5z - 7 = 8$

2 In the table opposite w, x, y and z represent different numbers.
The total of each row is given at the side of the table.
Find the values of w, x, y and z.

32	w	w	w	w
29	w	w	w	x
24	w	w	x	y
22	w	x	y	z

3 Solve the equations:

  a $x - 3 = 8$ **b** $3x + 10 = 70$ **c** $3x + 2 = 14 - x$

4   **a** Solve the equation $5x = 35$ **b** Solve the equation $x - 7 = 35$

5 Solve these equations: **a** $5r + 2 = 17$ **b** $\dfrac{x}{3} = 9$

6 Solve the equations: **a** $\dfrac{20}{x} = 5$ **b** $\dfrac{y}{3} + 4 = 10$

7 Solve the equations.

  a $4w = -20$ **b** $x + 7 = 5$ **c** $5y - 4 = -39$ **d** $3z + 42 = 15$

8   **a** Esther thinks of a number. She multiplies it by 4 and then adds 2
      The answer is 14. What was the number?

  b Harry thinks of a number. He multiplies it by 3 and then takes away 7
      The answer is 29. What was the number?

9 Lucy says to Ben:

Think of a number, take away 4, multiply by 3 and then add 5. Now tell me your answer.

Ben's answer is 26
What number does Ben think of?

10 Solve the equations.

  a $22a = 269.5$ **b** $1.8x + 1.72 = 10$ **c** $44 - 5y = -262$

Fractions, decimals and percentages 1

10.1 Conversion of fractions, decimals and percentages

CAN YOU REMEMBER

- How to shade a fraction or percentage of a shape?
- How to identify a fraction or percentage of a shape?
- That percentage means 'out of 100', for example 5% means 5 out of 100 or $\frac{5}{100}$?

IN THIS SECTION YOU WILL

- Revise shading fractions and percentages of shapes.
- Revise identifying fractions or percentages of shapes.
- Convert frequently used fractions to decimals and percentages.
- Convert frequently used decimals and percentages to fractions.

Fractions, decimals and percentages are different ways of representing parts of a shape or quantity.

For example, $\frac{1}{2} = 0.5 = 50\%$.

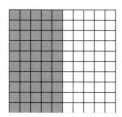

In this shape there are 100 squares. 50 out of the 100 squares are shaded. This is 50%.

Learn the fractions, decimals and percentages in this table.

Fraction	Decimal	Percentage	Fraction	Decimal	Percentage
$\frac{1}{2}$	0.5	50%	$\frac{1}{5}$	0.2	20%
$\frac{1}{4}$	0.25	25%	$\frac{1}{100}$	0.01	1%
$\frac{3}{4}$	0.75	75%	$\frac{1}{3}$	0.333...	33.3...%
$\frac{1}{10}$	0.1	10%	$\frac{1}{8}$	0.125	12.5%

The denominator of a fraction is the number of equal parts a quantity is divided into.
The numerator is the number of parts needed.

Example 1

Shade $\frac{1}{4}$ of the rectangle.

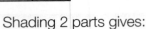

Solution 1

The rectangle is divided into 8 **equal** parts.
$\frac{1}{4}$ of 8 parts is 2 parts.
$\frac{1}{4}$ of 8 = 2

Shading 2 parts gives:

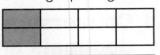

or

It does not matter which two parts are shaded.

Example 2

The hexagon is divided into 6 equal parts.
What fraction of the hexagon is shaded?

Solution 2

Each shaded part is $\frac{1}{6}$ of the hexagon.
5 parts out of the 6 equal parts are shaded.
The fraction shaded is $\frac{5}{6}$.

Example 3

Here is a square divided into 100 equal parts.
a   What fraction of the square is shaded?
b   Write the fraction shaded as a decimal.
c   What percentage of the square is shaded?
d   Complete: $\frac{4}{10} = 0. * = **\%$.

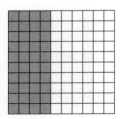

Solution 3

a   Each column is $\frac{1}{10}$
    4 columns are shaded so $\frac{4}{10}$

b $\frac{4}{10} = 4$ tenths $= 0.4$

c   Each square is $\frac{1}{100}$ or 1%.
    40 squares are shaded so $\frac{40}{100}$ or 40% is shaded.

d $\frac{4}{10} = 0.4 = 40\%$.

Exercise A

1   For each shape write down the fraction shaded.

a

b

c

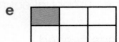

d

e

f

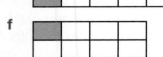

2 Look at each rectangle and work out:
  i the fraction shaded
  ii the fraction unshaded
  iii the percentage shaded
  iv the percentage unshaded

a   **b**   **c**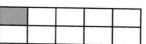

d 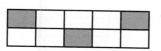 **e** 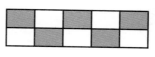 **f**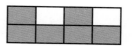

g 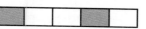 **h**

3 In each part copy the diagram. Shade the fraction required.

a **i** Shade $\frac{1}{3}$ of the hexagon.
   ii Copy and complete:
   $\frac{1}{3} = \ldots\ldots\% = 0.333\ldots$

b **i** Shade $\frac{1}{2}$ of the rectangle.
   ii Copy and complete:
   $\frac{1}{2} = \ldots\ldots\% = 0.5$

c **i** Shade $\frac{1}{4}$ of the square.
   ii Copy and complete:
   $\frac{1}{4} = \ldots\ldots\% = \ldots\ldots$

d **i** Shade $\frac{3}{4}$ of the triangle.
   ii Copy and complete:
   $\frac{3}{4} = \ldots\ldots\% = \ldots\ldots$

e **i** Shade $\frac{1}{5}$ of the pentagon.
   ii Copy and complete:
   $\frac{1}{5} = \ldots\ldots\% = \ldots\ldots$

f **i** Shade $\frac{2}{5}$ of the decagon.
   ii Copy and complete:
   $\frac{2}{5} = \ldots\ldots\% = \ldots\ldots$

g **i** Shade $\frac{3}{5}$ of the circle.
   ii Copy and complete:
   $\frac{3}{5} = \ldots\ldots\% = \ldots\ldots$

h **i** Shade $\frac{2}{3}$ of the circle.
   ii Copy and complete:
   $\frac{2}{3} = \ldots\ldots\% = \ldots\ldots$

4 In each part copy the diagram. Shade the required percentage.

a **i** Shade 25% of the octagon.
   ii Copy and complete:

$$25\% = \frac{\square}{\square} = 0.25$$

b **i** Shade 50% of the rectangle.
   ii Copy and complete:

$$50\% = \frac{\square}{\square} = \ldots\ldots$$

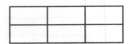

c **i** Shade 75% of the square.
   ii Copy and complete:

$$75\% = \frac{\square}{\square} = \ldots\ldots$$

d **i** Shade 100% of the triangle.
   ii Copy and complete:

$$\ldots\ldots\% = 1 \text{ whole one}$$

e **i** Shade 20% of the pentagon.
   ii Copy and complete:

$$20\% = \frac{\square}{\square} = \ldots\ldots$$

f **i** Shade 70% of the decagon.
   ii Copy and complete:

$$70\% = \frac{\square}{\square} = \ldots\ldots$$

g **i** Shade 80% of the circle.
   ii Copy and complete:

$$80\% = \frac{\square}{\square} = \ldots\ldots$$

h **i** Shade 30% of the circle.
   ii Copy and complete:

$$30\% = \frac{\square}{\square} = \ldots\ldots$$

Exercise B

1 Copy and complete the table.

Fraction	Decimal	Percentage	Fraction	Decimal	Percentage
$\frac{1}{10}$			$\frac{1}{5}$		
	0.3		$\frac{2}{5}$		
		70%		0.6	
$\frac{1}{2}$					80%
	0.25		$\frac{1}{3}$		
		75%		0.666…	

2 Match up the cards that are equal.

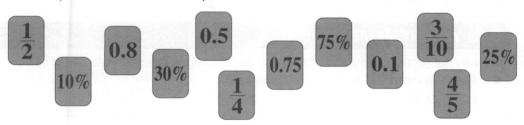

3 Match up the cards that are equal.

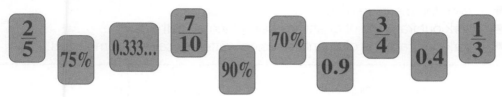

4 What fraction of a turn does the minute hand turn through between:

    a 2.15 pm and 2.30 pm
    b 3.30 pm and 3.50 pm
    c 11.00 am and 11.05 am
    d 5.40 pm and 5.50 pm
    e 7.25 am and 7.55 am
    f 9.05 am and 9.30 am
    g 1.25 pm and 1.35 pm
    h 2.55 am and 3.10 am

5 A man is facing North. He turns to face West.
    a How many degrees does he turn through?
    b Write the answer to part **a** as a fraction of a whole turn.
    c He continues to turn in the same
       direction until he faces North again.
       i How many degrees does he
        turn through?
       ii Write the answer to part **i** as
        a fraction of a whole turn.

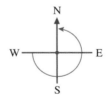
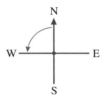

6 A woman is facing South. She turns to face South-East.
    a How many degrees does she turn through?
    b Write the answer to part **a** as a fraction of a whole turn.
    c She continues to turn in the same
       direction until she faces South again.
       i How many degrees does she
        turn through?
       ii Write the answer to part **i** as
        a fraction of a whole turn.

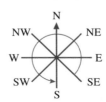
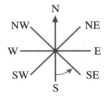

10.2 Fraction of a quantity

CAN YOU REMEMBER

- Mental strategies for division, such as 'halving is the same as dividing by 2'?
- That the word 'of' can mean 'multiply'?
  For example, 2 sets of 3 is the same as 2×3

IN THIS SECTION YOU WILL

- Learn the meaning of the term 'unit fraction'.
- Work out fractions of quantities using mental methods.
- Work out fractions of quantities using written or calculator methods.

A *unit fraction* is a fraction with *numerator* 1, for example $\frac{1}{5}$, $\frac{1}{4}$ or $\frac{1}{3}$

The *denominator* is the number of equal parts a quantity is divided into.

To find $\frac{1}{5}$ of £20, divide £20 into five equal parts. $£20 \div 5 = £4$

$\frac{3}{5}$ is 3 lots of $\frac{1}{5}$

so $\frac{3}{5}$ of £20 is 3 lots of £4

$\frac{1}{5}$ of £20 = £20 ÷ 5 = £4

$\frac{3}{5}$ of £20 = £4 × 3 = £12

£4.00 £4.00 £4.00 £4.00 £4.00

Example 1

Work out:
a $\frac{1}{4}$ of 60

b $\frac{2}{3}$ of 42

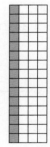

Solution 1

a To find $\frac{1}{4}$ of 60, divide 60 into four equal parts.
$60 \div 4 = 15$
So $\frac{1}{4}$ of 60 = 15

b To find $\frac{1}{3}$ of 42, divide 42 into three equal parts.
$42 \div 3 = 14$
So $\frac{1}{3}$ of 42 = 14
$\frac{2}{3}$ of 42 is 2 lots of 14 = 14 × 2 = 28

Exercise A

1 Re-write each of the following as divisions. Then write down the answer.
An example has been done for you.
$\frac{1}{2}$ of £40 = £40 ÷ 2 = £20

a $\frac{1}{2}$ of £30
b $\frac{1}{3}$ of 60 grams
c $\frac{1}{4}$ of 100 cm
d $\frac{1}{10}$ of £15
e $\frac{1}{5}$ of 20 kg
f $\frac{1}{8}$ of 24 metres
g $\frac{1}{100}$ of 500 miles
h $\frac{1}{10}$ of 45 feet

2   Work out:
    a one fifth of 35   **b** one third of 18   **c** one eighth of 40
    d one quarter of 60   **e** one tenth of 70   **f** one hundredth of 8000
    g one quarter of 84   **h** one third of 96

3   Work out:
    a $\frac{2}{3}$ of £9   **b** $\frac{3}{4}$ of 40 mm   **c** $\frac{2}{5}$ of 15 metres
    d $\frac{3}{10}$ of 20p   **e** $\frac{4}{5}$ of 30 grams   **f** $\frac{7}{8}$ of 16 feet
    g $\frac{7}{100}$ of 200 miles **h** $\frac{9}{10}$ of 50 km

4   Work out:
    a two fifths of 15   **b** two thirds of 27   **c** three eighths of 80
    d three quarters of 60 **e** seven tenths of 40   **f** nine hundredths of 300
    g three quarters of 28 **h** two thirds of 36

5   Use a calculator to work out:
    a $\frac{1}{2}$ of £98   **b** $\frac{1}{3}$ of 84 grams   **c** $\frac{1}{4}$ of 416 cm
    d $\frac{1}{10}$ of £275.40   **e** $\frac{1}{5}$ of 95 kg   **f** $\frac{1}{8}$ of 328 metres
    g $\frac{1}{100}$ of £127   **h** $\frac{1}{10}$ of £832.50

6   Work out:
    a one fifth of 75   **b** one third of 108
    c one eighth of 96   **d** one quarter of 148
    e one tenth of 96.5   **f** one hundredth of 187.06
    g one quarter of 94   **h** one third of 207

7   Work out:
    a $\frac{2}{3}$ of £18.57   **b** $\frac{3}{4}$ of 144 mm   **c** $\frac{2}{5}$ of 85 metres
    d $\frac{3}{10}$ of £1.60   **e** $\frac{4}{5}$ of 65 grams   **f** $\frac{7}{8}$ of 472 feet
    g $\frac{7}{100}$ of 1400 miles **h** $\frac{9}{10}$ of 520 km

8   Work out:
    a two fifths of 125   **b** two thirds of 363
    c three eighths of 120   **d** three quarters of 360
    e seven tenths of 180   **f** nine one hundredths of 7500
    g three quarters of 4600   **h** two thirds of 2520

Example 2

There are 300 workers in a factory. Two thirds are male.
How many are female?

Solution 2

Method 1	**Method 2**
The number of males is	The fraction of females is one third.
$\frac{2}{3}$ of 300 = 300 ÷ 3 × 2 = 200	$\frac{1}{3}$ of 300 = 100
The number of females is 300 − 200 = 100	The number of females is 100

Exercise B

1 Marbles are packed in different-sized bags.
   In each bag, one quarter of the marbles are red and the rest are blue.
   How many red marbles are there in a bag of:
   a 20 marbles   **b** 36 marbles   **c** 60 marbles?

2 A chain of shops finds that two fifths of their stock is out of date.
   For each shop, how many stock items are **not** out of date?
   a Shop A: 500 stock items   **b** Shop B: 1000 stock items
   c Shop C: 3000 stock items

3 A jug is full of water. It holds 70 cl when full.
   How much water is left in the jug after pouring out:
   a half of the water   **b** three tenths of the water   **c** two sevenths of the water?

4 A wheelie bin has a capacity of 120 litres.
   How many litres of empty space are there when it is:
   a two thirds full   **b** three quarters full   **c** nine tenths full?

5 Which is the greater: one quarter of 50 or one third of 45?
   Show your working.

6 A chocolate bar has 72 squares.
   How many squares are left after breaking off:
   a two thirds of the pieces   **b** three eighths of the pieces
   c four ninths of the pieces?

7 A library has 8400 books altogether.
   How many books are left in the library if:
   a one tenth are loaned out   **b** two fifths are loaned out
   c one eighth are loaned out?

8 A builder's skip holds 30 cubic metres when full.
   How many cubic metres of rubbish are in the skip
   when it is:
   a four fifths full
   b three quarters full
   c five sixths empty?

9 Which is the greater: four ninths of 729 or five sixths of 426?
Show your working.

10 Which is the greater: four sevenths of 98 or seven eighths of 40?
Show your working.

10.3 Percentage of a quantity

CAN YOU REMEMBER

- How to work out simple percentages, for example 50%, 25%?
- How to simplify a fraction by cancelling?
- How to multiply and divide decimals by 10, 100, and so on?

IN THIS SECTION YOU WILL

- Reinforce your knowledge of percentages and their equivalent fractions.
- Use mental methods to work out a percentage of a quantity.
- Use written methods to calculate harder percentage problems.

Percentage means number of parts per 100 The symbol % means per cent or 'out of 100'. For example 1% means $\frac{1}{100}$ and 60% means $\frac{60}{100}$

Finding a percentage of a quantity is exactly the same as finding a fraction of a quantity.

Finding 25% is the same as finding $\frac{1}{4}$ of the quantity.

$10\% = \frac{10}{100} = \frac{1}{10}$ so finding 10% is the same as finding $\frac{1}{10}$ of a quantity.

Finding 30% is the same as finding 3 lots of 10%. $30\% = 3 \times 10\%$

$5\% = \frac{1}{2}$ of 10% $20\% = 2 \times 10\%$ $75\% = 3 \times 25\%$

Example 1

Find   **a** 20% of 90   **b** 15% of £160   **c** 5% of 41.8

Solution 1

a 10% of $90 = \frac{1}{10}$ of $90 = 90 \div 10 = 9$
$20\% = 2 \times 10\%$
So 20% of $90 = 2 \times 9 = 18$

c 10% of $41.8 = 41.8 \div 10 = 4.18$
$5\% = \frac{1}{2}$ of 10%
So 5% of $41.8 = 4.18 \div 2 = 2.09$

b $15\% = 10\% + 5\%$
10% of £160 = £160 $\div$ 10 = £16
$5\% = \frac{1}{2}$ of 10%
So 5% of £160 = £16 $\div$ 2 = £8
15% of £160 = 10% of £160 + 5% of £160 = £16 + £8 = £24

Exercise A

1 Write down 10% of each of the following:

a	60	**b**	130	**c**	45	**d**	175	**e**	78
f	62	**g**	8400	**h**	7.6	**i**	2.5	**j**	6.7
k	0.75	**l**	0.04						

2 For each of the following, work out:
  i 10%   **ii** 5%   **iii** 20%   **iv** 15%

a	80	**b**	190	**c**	56	**d**	108	**e**	92	**f**	280
g	5000	**h**	8.4	**i**	1.2	**j**	18.8	**k**	0.6	**l**	0.08

3 For each of the following, work out:
  i 50%   **ii** 25%   **iii** 75%

a	100	**b**	400	**c**	80	**d**	24	**e**	16	**f**	44
g	12 000	**h**	8.4	**i**	10.8	**j**	3.2	**k**	22	**l**	3

4 Copy and complete the table.

100%	10%	5%	50%	25%	75%	15%	35%	200%
40		2					14	
90	9				67.5			180
32			16			4.8		
600				150				

5 Work out:

a	15% of £60	**b**	25% of 12 kg	**c**	30% of 24 litres
d	90% of 200 g	**e**	2.5% of £12.80	**f**	1% of $2400
g	5% of €180	**h**	75% of 360 degrees		

Example 2

Find   **a** 18% of 45   **b** 3.2% of £68

Solution 2

a **Method 1**
$1\% = \frac{1}{100}$
1% of 45 $= \frac{1}{100}$ of 45 $= 45 \div 100 = 0.45$
$18\% = 18 \times 1\%$
So 18% of 45 $= 18 \times 0.45 = 8.1$

Method 2
$18\% = \frac{18}{100}$
18% of 45 $= \frac{18}{100} \times 45$
$= 18 \div 100 \times 45$
$= 8.1$

b 1% of £68 $= \frac{1}{100}$ of £68 $=$ £68 $\div 100 =$ £0.68
3.2% of £68 $= 3.2 \times 0.68 =$ £2.176

Exercise B

1 Annie attempts 20 questions. She answers 10% incorrectly.
How many questions does she answer incorrectly?

2 There are 60 people on a bus. 90% of them are pensioners.
How many are not pensioners?

3 A train travels 200 miles. It is full for 25% of the journey.
How many miles does it travel when full?

4 There are 500 fish in a pond. 10% are trout.
How many of the fish are **not** trout?

5 In a school of 1500 students, 20% are in Year 11.
How many students are in Year 11?

6 Work out:
a 18% of 50	**b** 6% of 32	**c** 12% of 48
d 17% of 90	**e** 14% of 56	**f** 28% of 72
g 82% of 96	**h** 16% of 320	**i** 17.5% of 180

7 Work out:
a 24% of £32	**b** 11% of 7.5 tonnes	**c** 23% of 250 metres
d 26% of 70 litres	**e** 3% of 18.5 kg	**f** 34% of £95
g 14% of $560	**h** 17.5% of £52	**i** 17.5% of £32.40

8 A washing machine normally costs £340. In a sale there is 15% off.
How much is the saving, in pounds?

9 A car is priced at £6500 in January. In February the price is increased by 6%.
How much is the price increase, in pounds?

10 Here are the test results for three students:

Amrita: 32   Bob: 20   Chris: 12

Their target for the next test is to increase their marks by 12%.
For each student, work out the least number of extra marks they need to get.
(Remember, marks are only given in whole numbers.)

11 Work out:
a 2.9% of 50	**b** 4.1% of 32	**c** 1.2% of 48
d 5.6% of 90	**e** 7.5% of 56	**f** 18.9% of 72
g 7.4% of 96	**h** 87.5% of 320	**i** 17.5% of 180

12 Work out:
a 2.4% of £60	**b** 3.2% of 45 tonnes	**c** 25.5% of 150 metres
d 2.6% of 1.5 litres	**e** 4.1% of 19.5 kg	**f** 8.9% of £5000
g 1.4% of €350	**h** 17.5% of £52.64	**i** 17.5% of £40.80

10.4 Ordering decimals, fractions and percentages

CAN YOU REMEMBER

- How to sort whole numbers into order of size?
- How to write numbers in a place value table?
- How to write a fraction as a decimal, for example $\frac{1}{10} = 0.1$, $\frac{1}{4} = 0.25$?
- What is meant by 'significant figure'?

IN THIS SECTION YOU WILL

- Convert fractions into decimals using a calculator.
- Convert percentages into decimals.
- Sort fractions, decimals and percentages into order of size.
- Learn the meaning of 'recurring decimal'.

The numbers in the place value table are written in order of size, from biggest to smallest. This is called *descending order*.

Thousands	Hundreds	Tens	Units	.	tenths	hundredths	thousandths
2	5	6	1				
	2	5	6	.	1		
		2	5	.	6	1	
			2	.	5	6	1
			0	.	2	5	6

In each number, the first *significant* digit is 2
The first significant figure has the largest value in that number.
To work out which number is the largest, compare the first significant figures.
For example, in 2561 the 2 has value 2000. In 256.1 the 2 has value 200
So 2561 is larger than 256.1

When numbers are written in order of size from smallest to biggest this is called *ascending order*.

Example 1

Write the following numbers in ascending order:

2.41   2.14   4.21   4.12   1.24   1.42

Solution 1

Step 1:   The first significant figure is the **units** digit.
Write the numbers in ascending order of their **units** digits.
1.24,   **1**.42,   **2**.41,   **2**.14,   **4**.21,   **4**.12

Step 2: For numbers with the same units digit, compare the **tenths** digits.
Comparing 1.24 and 1.42: the smallest is 1.**2**4
Comparing 2.41 and 2.14: the smallest is 2.**1**4
Comparing 4.21 and 4.12: the smallest is 4.**1**2

So the numbers in ascending order are:
1.24   1.42   2.14   2.41   4.12   4.21

The fraction $\frac{3}{8}$ can be converted to a decimal using a calculator.

$\frac{3}{8} = 3 \div 8 = 0.375$

So $\frac{3}{8}$ is the same as 0.375

Example 2

Convert each of the following fractions into decimals.
Write the fractions in descending order.

$\frac{3}{4}$ $\frac{4}{5}$ $\frac{5}{8}$ $\frac{5}{9}$

Solution 2

$\frac{3}{4} = 3 \div 4 = 0.75$ $\frac{4}{5} = 4 \div 5 = 0.8$ $\frac{5}{8} = 5 \div 8 = 0.625$ $\frac{5}{9} = 5 \div 9 = 0.555...$

The decimals in descending order are: 0.8   0.75   0.625   0.555...

So the fractions written in descending order are: $\frac{4}{5}$ $\frac{3}{4}$ $\frac{5}{8}$ $\frac{5}{9}$

In the decimal for $\frac{5}{9}$, 0.555... is a *recurring decimal*.

For a recurring decimal, write down just the first 3 or 4 digits and then three dots ... to show it continues.

Another way of showing a recurring decimal is with a dot over the repeating digit. For example, write 0.555... as 0.$\dot{5}$

Exercise A

1 Sort the following lists of decimals into ascending order.

a 2.5	2.03	2.53	2.05	2.35	
b 6.42	6.24	6.042	6.402	6.204	
c 7.15	7.051	7.501	7.510	7.015	
d 10.02	10.2	12.0	1.02	2.01	
e 0.378	0.873	0.387	0.837	0.783	0.738
f 15.2	12.05	12.52	15.02	12.005	15.002
g 23.6	26.3	23.06	26.03	32.6	32.06
h 0.031	0.13	0.301	0.103		

2　Sort the following lists of decimals into descending order.

a	6.4	6.03	6.34	6.43	6.04	
b	9.17	7.91	7.19	9.71	9.701	
c	0.483	8.43	4.83	3.48	3.84	0.843
d	0.012	0.021	0.102	0.201	0.21	0.12
e	6.423	6.243	6.342	6.234	6.4023	6.0324
f	23.04	24.30	20.34	2.043	24.03	20.43
g	9.256	9.526	9.65	9.52	9.062	
h	0.176	0.167	0.017	0.061	0.107	

3　Sort the following lists of percentages into ascending order.

a	98.1%	89.1%	91.8%	81.9%	
b	20.3%	30.2%	32%	23%	
c	18.12%	12.82%	18.21%	12.81%	
d	36.0%	30.06%	36.03%	30.6%	
e	18%	17.99%	18.01%	18.10%	
f	46.37%	73.64%	43.67%	46.73%	
g	25.78%	27.8%	27.08%	28.52%	25.87%
h	100.2%	102%	101.2%	102.1%	100.12%

4　Sort the following lists of percentages into descending order.

a	53.65%	56.35%	55.36%	55.63%	
b	2.93%	29.3%	2.39%	23.9%	
c	2.16%	12.6%	2.61%	16.2%	
d	38.47%	37.84%	43.87%	34.78%	
e	21.76%	26.17%	21.67%	26.71%	
f	52.3%	35.2%	53.2%	32.5%	
g	17.4%	17.04%	14.7%	14.07%	14.77%
h	81.6%	86.1%	86.16%	81.61%	86.61%

5　Convert the following fractions into decimals.
Write the fractions in ascending order.

a $\frac{1}{5}$　$\frac{1}{4}$　$\frac{3}{8}$　$\frac{3}{20}$　　**b** $\frac{1}{2}$　$\frac{5}{8}$　$\frac{3}{5}$　$\frac{2}{3}$　　**c** $\frac{9}{10}$　$\frac{7}{12}$　$\frac{5}{6}$　$\frac{6}{10}$

d $\frac{2}{9}$　$\frac{4}{7}$　$\frac{7}{9}$　$\frac{8}{11}$　　**e** $\frac{3}{10}$　$\frac{7}{15}$　$\frac{1}{2}$　$\frac{9}{20}$

6　Convert the following fractions into decimals.
Write the fractions in descending order.

a $\frac{1}{4}$　$\frac{2}{5}$　$\frac{3}{10}$　$\frac{7}{20}$　　**b** $\frac{1}{3}$　$\frac{2}{5}$　$\frac{1}{2}$　$\frac{4}{15}$　　**c** $\frac{19}{20}$　$\frac{11}{12}$　$\frac{5}{6}$　$\frac{9}{10}$

d $\frac{1}{6}$　$\frac{2}{9}$　$\frac{1}{7}$　$\frac{3}{11}$　　**e** $\frac{7}{10}$　$\frac{13}{20}$　$\frac{11}{15}$　$\frac{2}{3}$

% means *per cent* or 'out of one hundred'.

For example, 35% = $\frac{35}{100}$　　35 ÷ 100 = 0.35, so as a decimal 35% = 0.35

8% = $\frac{8}{100}$ = 8 ÷ 100 = 0.08, so as a decimal 8% = 0.08

14.2% means 14.2 out of 100 or 14.2 ÷ 100 = 0.142

To order a mixture of fractions, decimals and percentages one method is to convert all the values to decimals.

Example 3

Write the following in ascending order:

$\frac{3}{4}$ 0.7   72%

Solution 3

$\frac{3}{4} = 0.75$ 72% = 0.72

Writing the decimals in order gives: 0.7   0.72   0.75

The original values in order are   0.7   72% $\frac{3}{4}$

Exercise B

1 Write the following in ascending order.

   a $\frac{1}{4}$ 0.2   30%
   b $\frac{1}{2}$ 52%   0.48

   c $\frac{3}{10}$ 33%   0.333
   d $\frac{3}{4}$ 76%   0.755

   e $\frac{4}{5}$ 45%   4.5
   f $\frac{9}{10}$ 9.1%   0.89

2 Write the following in descending order.

   a $\frac{1}{2}$ 0.6   48%
   b $\frac{1}{5}$ 0.5   22%

   c $\frac{7}{10}$ 0.75   73%
   d $\frac{3}{4}$ 0.34   7.5%

   e $\frac{1}{3}$ 0.3   33%
   f $\frac{2}{3}$ 0.66   67%

3 Which is bigger, $\frac{2}{5}$ or 35%?
   Show your working.

4 Which is smaller, $\frac{1}{3}$ or 0.3?
   Show your working.

5 Write the following in ascending order.

   a $\frac{2}{9}$ 0.22   22.2%
   b $\frac{3}{7}$ 42%   4.2

   c $\frac{3}{11}$ 27%   0.28
   d $\frac{4}{15}$ 28%   0.27

   e $\frac{4}{9}$ 45%   0.5
   f $\frac{6}{11}$ 54%   0.53

6 Write the following in descending order.

   a $\frac{1}{3}$ 0.4   30%
   b $\frac{2}{3}$ 0.6   70%

   c $\frac{7}{9}$ 0.76   74%
   d $\frac{3}{13}$ 0.23   20%

   e $\frac{4}{7}$ 0.58   60%
   f $\frac{6}{17}$ 0.3   35%

7 Which is bigger, $\frac{7}{8}$ or 75%?
   Show your working.

8 Which is smaller, $\frac{5}{6}$ or 0.8?
   Show your working.

9 Which is closest to $\frac{1}{4}$: 0.23 or 26%?

10 Which is closest to $\frac{2}{3}$: $\frac{1}{2}$ or $\frac{5}{6}$ or neither?

10.5 Equivalent fractions

CAN YOU REMEMBER

- The meaning of 'numerator' and 'denominator'?
- How to cancel a fraction?

IN THIS SECTION YOU WILL

- Learn the meaning of the term 'common denominator'.
- Learn the meaning of the term 'equivalent fraction'.
- Learn how to compare the size of fractions.

Equivalent fractions have the same value

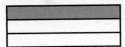

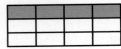

$\frac{1}{3}$ is the same as $\frac{4}{12}$

$\frac{1}{3}$ and $\frac{4}{12}$ are equivalent fractions.

$$\frac{1}{3} = \frac{1 \times 4}{3 \times 4} = \frac{4}{12}$$

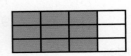

$\frac{3}{4}$ is the same as $\frac{9}{12}$

$\frac{3}{4}$ and $\frac{9}{12}$ are equivalent fractions.

$$\frac{3}{4} = \frac{3 \times 3}{4 \times 3} = \frac{9}{12}$$

When two fractions have the same denominator it is called a *common denominator*.

For example, $\frac{4}{12}$ and $\frac{9}{12}$ have common denominator 12. To compare two fractions with different denominators, convert them to fractions with a common denominator. The common denominator can be any multiple of both denominators. To keep the calculations simple, use the smallest number that is a multiple of both denominators.

Example 1

Write the fractions $\frac{3}{4}$ and $\frac{2}{3}$ with a common denominator.
State which is the smaller.

Solution 1

Method 1
Write out the multiples of the fractions until you find two with the same denominator.

$\frac{3}{4} = \frac{6}{8} = \frac{9}{12} = \dots$

$\frac{2}{3} = \frac{4}{6} = \frac{6}{9} = \frac{8}{12} = \dots$

So $\frac{3}{4} = \frac{9}{12}$ and $\frac{2}{3} = \frac{8}{12}$

$\frac{8}{12}$ is smaller than $\frac{9}{12}$, so $\frac{2}{3}$ is smaller than $\frac{3}{4}$

Method 2

The smallest number that is a multiple of both 3 and 4 is 12

Rewriting $\frac{3}{4}$ with denominator 12 gives $\frac{3 \times 3}{4 \times 3} = \frac{9}{12}$

Rewriting $\frac{2}{3}$ with denominator 12 gives $\frac{2 \times 4}{3 \times 4} = \frac{8}{12}$

So $\frac{2}{3}\left(= \frac{8}{12}\right)$ is smaller than $\frac{3}{4}\left(= \frac{9}{12}\right)$

Exercise A

1 Copy and complete the following:

a $\frac{1}{2} = \frac{\square}{4} = \frac{3}{\square}$ **b** $\frac{1}{3} = \frac{\square}{6} = \frac{\square}{9}$ **c** $\frac{1}{5} = \frac{2}{\square} = \frac{\square}{15}$

d $\frac{1}{7} = \frac{\square}{14} = \frac{3}{\square}$ **e** $\frac{1}{4} = \frac{2}{\square} = \frac{\square}{12}$ **f** $\frac{1}{10} = \frac{\square}{20} = \frac{3}{\square}$

g $\frac{1}{6} = \frac{\square}{12} = \frac{3}{\square}$ **h** $\frac{1}{9} = \frac{2}{\square} = \frac{\square}{27}$

2 For each pair of fractions, write down the smallest number that is a multiple of both denominators. The first one has been done for you.

a $\frac{1}{2}$ and $\frac{1}{3}$: smallest multiple of both denominators = 6

b $\frac{1}{3}$ and $\frac{1}{4}$ **c** $\frac{1}{6}$ and $\frac{1}{4}$ **d** $\frac{1}{5}$ and $\frac{1}{3}$ **e** $\frac{1}{10}$ and $\frac{1}{2}$

f $\frac{1}{3}$ and $\frac{1}{10}$ **g** $\frac{1}{7}$ and $\frac{1}{2}$ **h** $\frac{1}{4}$ and $\frac{1}{8}$

3 Write each set of fractions with a common denominator.

a $\frac{1}{2}$ $\frac{1}{3}$ $\frac{1}{5}$ **b** $\frac{1}{3}$ $\frac{1}{5}$ $\frac{1}{10}$ **c** $\frac{1}{6}$ $\frac{1}{8}$ $\frac{1}{4}$

d $\frac{1}{3}$ $\frac{1}{4}$ $\frac{1}{5}$ **e** $\frac{1}{2}$ $\frac{1}{7}$ $\frac{1}{3}$ **f** $\frac{1}{5}$ $\frac{1}{2}$ $\frac{1}{8}$

g $\frac{1}{2}$ $\frac{1}{3}$ $\frac{1}{4}$ $\frac{1}{5}$ **h** $\frac{1}{4}$ $\frac{1}{5}$ $\frac{1}{10}$ $\frac{1}{20}$

4 a Write each pair of fractions with a common denominator.
State which is the bigger in each pair.

i $\frac{1}{2}$ or $\frac{1}{5}$ **ii** $\frac{1}{4}$ or $\frac{1}{3}$ **iii** $\frac{1}{8}$ or $\frac{1}{6}$ **iv** $\frac{1}{5}$ or $\frac{1}{9}$

b Compare the denominators in part **a**.
What do you notice about the bigger fraction?

5 Sort each set of fractions into order, from smallest to biggest.

a $\frac{1}{2}$ $\frac{1}{6}$ $\frac{1}{5}$ $\frac{1}{9}$ **b** $\frac{1}{3}$ $\frac{1}{9}$ $\frac{1}{8}$ $\frac{1}{4}$

c $\frac{1}{10}$ $\frac{1}{5}$ $\frac{1}{7}$ $\frac{1}{4}$ **d** $\frac{1}{6}$ $\frac{1}{2}$ $\frac{1}{8}$ $\frac{1}{3}$

6 Match up the pairs of equivalent fractions in each box.

a

| $\frac{1}{2}$ | | $\frac{5}{15}$ | $\frac{27}{54}$ |
| | $\frac{1}{3}$ | | |

b

| $\frac{1}{2}$ | $\frac{1}{7}$ | $\frac{9}{18}$ |
| | | $\frac{6}{42}$ | |

c

| $\frac{1}{8}$ | | $\frac{7}{56}$ | $\frac{3}{21}$ |
| | $\frac{1}{7}$ | | |

7 Here is a multiplication table:

Copy and complete the following.
Use the multiplication table to help.

×	5	6	7	8	9
2	10	12	14	16	18
3	15	18	21	24	27

a $\dfrac{2}{3} = \dfrac{18}{\square}$ **b** $\dfrac{2}{3} = \dfrac{\square}{21}$ **c** $\dfrac{2}{3} = \dfrac{16}{\square}$ **d** $\dfrac{2}{3} = \dfrac{\square}{18}$

8 a Copy and complete the multiplication table opposite.

   b Write down five fractions that are equivalent to $\frac{5}{7}$
   Use the table to help.

×	12	14	19	23	32
5					
7					

Example 2

Which of these fractions are greater than $\frac{2}{3}$?

$\frac{2}{5}$ $\frac{3}{4}$ $\frac{7}{12}$ $\frac{13}{20}$

Solution 2

Find a common denominator.
List some multiples of 3, 4, 5, 12 and 20:
3, 6, 9, 12, 15, 18, 21, 24, 27, 30, 33, 36, 39, 42, 45, 48, 51, 54, 57, **60**, ...
5, 10, 15, 20, 25, 30, 35, 40, 45, 50, 55, **60**, ...
4, 8, 12, 16, 20, 24, 28, 32, 36, 40, 44, 48, 52, 56, **60**, ...
12, 24, 36, 48, **60**, ...
20, 40, **60**, ...
The smallest number that is a multiple of 3, 4, 5, 12 and 20 is 60

Convert each fraction to an equivalent fraction with a denominator of 60

$3 \times 20 = 60$, so multiply the numerator and the denominator of $\frac{2}{3}$ by 20:

$$\frac{2}{3} = \frac{2 \times 20}{3 \times 20} = \frac{40}{60} \qquad \frac{2}{5} = \frac{2 \times 12}{5 \times 12} = \frac{24}{60}$$

Converting the other fractions in the same way gives:

$$\frac{3}{4} = \frac{3 \times 15}{4 \times 15} = \frac{45}{60} \qquad \frac{7}{12} = \frac{7 \times 5}{12 \times 5} = \frac{35}{60} \qquad \frac{13}{20} = \frac{13 \times 3}{20 \times 3} = \frac{39}{60}$$

The fractions and their equivalents are:

$\frac{2}{3}$	$\frac{2}{5}$	$\frac{3}{4}$	$\frac{7}{12}$	$\frac{13}{20}$
↓	↓	↓	↓	↓
$\frac{40}{60}$	$\frac{24}{60}$	$\frac{45}{60}$	$\frac{35}{60}$	$\frac{39}{60}$

The only fraction greater than $\frac{2}{3}$ is $\frac{3}{4}$

Exercise B

1 Sort each set of fractions in order from smallest to biggest.

a $\frac{3}{4}$ $\frac{2}{3}$ $\frac{4}{5}$ **b** $\frac{2}{5}$ $\frac{1}{4}$ $\frac{7}{20}$ **c** $\frac{5}{6}$ $\frac{7}{8}$ $\frac{3}{4}$

d $\frac{2}{3}$ $\frac{7}{10}$ $\frac{3}{5}$ **e** $\frac{5}{8}$ $\frac{3}{4}$ $\frac{9}{16}$ **f** $\frac{2}{9}$ $\frac{1}{3}$ $\frac{2}{3}$

g $\frac{3}{4}$ $\frac{3}{5}$ $\frac{7}{10}$ **h** $\frac{1}{4}$ $\frac{2}{5}$ $\frac{3}{10}$ $\frac{9}{20}$

2 Write each pair of fractions as equivalent fractions with a common denominator.
State which is the bigger.

a $\frac{4}{5}$ or $\frac{5}{7}$ **b** $\frac{4}{9}$ or $\frac{2}{3}$ **c** $\frac{5}{8}$ or $\frac{5}{6}$ **d** $\frac{2}{5}$ or $\frac{4}{9}$

3 For each set of fractions, find the fraction that is nearest to $\frac{1}{2}$

a $\frac{1}{3}$ $\frac{3}{4}$ $\frac{2}{5}$ **b** $\frac{3}{4}$ $\frac{5}{8}$ $\frac{7}{10}$ **c** $\frac{3}{5}$ $\frac{4}{7}$ $\frac{3}{10}$ **d** $\frac{1}{6}$ $\frac{1}{5}$ $\frac{2}{3}$ $\frac{7}{15}$

4 Find the fractions that are greater than $\frac{1}{4}$

a $\frac{1}{3}$ $\frac{1}{2}$ $\frac{2}{5}$ **b** $\frac{3}{10}$ $\frac{1}{5}$ $\frac{2}{7}$ **c** $\frac{3}{7}$ $\frac{2}{9}$ $\frac{1}{6}$

5 Show that $\frac{11}{15}$ is greater than $\frac{5}{7}$

6 Show that $\frac{8}{21}$ is less than $\frac{9}{22}$

7 Find a fraction that is greater than $\frac{3}{4}$ and less than $\frac{7}{8}$

8 Find a fraction that is greater than $\frac{1}{5}$ and less than $\frac{1}{4}$

9 Ricardo says that $\frac{17}{20}$ is less than $\frac{9}{10}$, and that $\frac{20}{17}$ is greater than $\frac{10}{9}$
Show that this is true for both pairs of fractions.

10 Wei Yen says that $\frac{8}{40}$ is equivalent to $\frac{17}{85}$
Is she correct?
Show your working.

11 Which fraction is the odd one out?
$\frac{1}{2}$ $\frac{45}{90}$ $\frac{25}{50}$ $\frac{200}{400}$ $\frac{16}{80}$
Explain your answer.

10.6 Expressing one quantity as a fraction of another quantity

IN THIS SECTION YOU WILL

- Use fractions to compare quantities using the same or different units.
- Learn how to write one quantity as a fraction of another quantity.
- Learn how to simplify a fraction by using a calculator.
- Learn how to use the fraction button on a calculator.

On this test paper, the score was 7 out of 10

This is written as $\frac{7}{10}$

$\frac{7}{10}$ is the fraction of the total number of answers that are correct.

This is called writing a quantity as a fraction of another.
In this case 7 is written as a fraction of 10

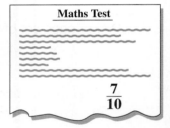

To write a quantity as a fraction of another:

- make sure that both quantities have the same units

- use the formula $\dfrac{\text{first quantity}}{\text{second quantity}}$

Remember to simplify any fractions as much as possible.

Example 1

a Write 17 as a fraction of 30   **b** Write 3 kg as a fraction of 10 kg.
c Write 70 cm as a fraction of 1 metre.

Solution 1

a 17 written as a fraction of 30 is $\frac{17}{30}$

b 3 kg written as a fraction of 10 kg is $\frac{3\,\text{kg}}{10\,\text{kg}}$

This simplifies by cancelling the common units to $\frac{3}{10}$

c 70 cm and 1 metre are not in the same units. Convert 1 m to 100 cm.
The fraction is $\frac{70\,\text{cm}}{100\,\text{cm}}$

This simplifies by cancelling to $\frac{7}{10}$

A calculator can be used to simplify large fractions. Make sure you know how to enter fractions and read fraction displays on your own calculator.

Exercise A

1 **a** Write 7 as a fraction of 10   **b** Write 3 as a fraction of 5
   c Write 4 as a fraction of 9   **d** Write 8 as a fraction of 11
   e Write 2 as a fraction of 7   **f** Write 20 as a fraction of 21

2 In each part, simplify your answer as fully as possible.
   a Write 8 as a fraction of 10   **b** Write 4 as a fraction of 20
   c Write 3 as a fraction of 6   **d** Write 9 as a fraction of 12
   e Write 8 as a fraction of 24   **f** Write 15 as a fraction of 25
   g Write 7 as a fraction of 21   **h** Write 25 as a fraction of 30

3 In each part, remember to simplify by cancelling the common units.
   a Write 3 cm as a fraction of 8 cm.
   b Write 4 litres as a fraction of 11 litres.
   c Write 6 grams as a fraction of 25 grams.
   d Write 9 cm^3 as a fraction of 17 cm^3.
   e Write 4 kg as a fraction of 13 kg.
   f Write 3 metres as a fraction of 10 metres.

4 In each part, simplify your answer as fully as possible.
   a Write 6 cm as a fraction of 10 cm.
   b Write 10 tonnes as a fraction of 15 tonnes.
   c Write 12 miles as a fraction of 36 miles.
   d Write £14 as a fraction of £28.
   e Write 8 km as a fraction of 12 km.
   f Write 25 kg as a fraction of 100 kg.
   g Write 21 cl as a fraction of 70 cl.
   h Write 12 cm^2 as a fraction of 30 cm^2.

5 In each part, remember to:
   ■ convert to common units
   ■ simplify your answer as fully as possible.
   a Write 40 cm as a fraction of 1 metre.
   b Write 8 inches as a fraction of 1 foot. (*Hint*: 12 inches = 1 foot)
   c Write 9 inches as a fraction of 3 feet.
   d Write 20 cl as a fraction of 1 litre.
   e Write 300 grams as a fraction of 1 kg.
   f Write 250 kg as a fraction of 1 tonne.
   g Write 75p as a fraction of £1.
   h Write 500 metres as a fraction of 1 kilometre.

6 1 mile = 1760 yards
   Use this fact to write 440 yards as a fraction of a mile.
   Simplify your answer as fully as possible.

7 2460 fish are caught in a net. 820 are too small and are thrown back into the sea. What fraction of the fish is thrown back in the sea? Simplify your answer as fully as possible.

8 936 people visit a theatre in London. 104 are from Yorkshire. What fraction of the total is from Yorkshire? Simplify your answer as fully as possible.

9 The total attendance at a football match is 21 600 people. 8640 support the away team. What fraction of the total attendance supports the away team? Simplify your answer as fully as possible.

10 Belinda spends £97.62 at the supermarket. £32.54 of this is on frozen food. What fraction of her total bill is spent on frozen food? Simplify your answer as fully as possible.

Exercise B

1 60 children go to a show. 40 are boys. What fraction of the children are girls?

2 A shape has 10 sides. Three of the sides are curved. The rest are straight. What fraction of the sides is straight?

3 A bag contains three red marbles, four blue marbles and five yellow marbles. What fraction of the marbles is **not** yellow?

4 A CD has 13 tracks. Four of the tracks were number one singles. What fraction of the tracks were **not** number one singles?

5 A shop has two offers. Which is the better value? Explain your answer.

> *BUY ONE GET ONE FREE*

> *BUY TWO GET THE THIRD FREE*

6 In a test a student scores 13 out of 15. In another test the same student scores 38 out of 45 In which test did the student do better? Explain your answer.

7 An 800 ml bottle contains 500 ml of water. Darren says this is more than half but less than two thirds full. Is he correct? Explain your answer.

8 A book contains 750 pages. 300 of the pages have pictures and no writing. 100 pages have pictures and writing. The rest have just writing. What fraction of the pages have pictures on them? Simplify your answer as fully as possible.

9 In a survey, 13 out of 20 girls have fair hair and 11 out of 25 boys have fair hair.
What fraction of people in the whole survey have fair hair?
Simplify your answer as fully as possible.

10 A shop has two offers.
Which is the better value?
Explain your answer.

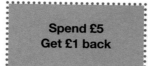

Spend £5
Get £1 back

Buy any three items
of the same value
Get the fourth free

Chapter summary

■ Remember these fractions, decimals and percentages.

Fraction	Decimal	Percentage
$\frac{1}{2}$	0.5	50%
$\frac{1}{4}$	0.25	25%
$\frac{3}{4}$	0.75	75%
$\frac{1}{10}$	0.1	10%
$\frac{1}{5}$	0.2	20%

Fraction	Decimal	Percentage
$\frac{1}{100}$	0.01	1%
$\frac{1}{3}$	0.333...	33.3...%
$\frac{2}{3}$	0.666...	66.6...%
$\frac{1}{8}$	0.125	12.5%

■ The denominator is the number of equal parts a quantity is divided into.
The numerator is the number of parts needed.

■ Percentage means number of parts per 100. % means per cent or 'out of 100'.

■ $10\% = \frac{10}{100} = \frac{1}{10}$ so finding 10% is the same as finding $\frac{1}{10}$ of a quantity.
5% is half of 10%. Use these facts to work out percentages.

■ To calculate 22% of £48
Either: calculate 1% = 48 ÷ 100 and then 22% = 48 ÷ 100 × 22 = £10.56
or: calculate $\frac{22}{100}$ × 48 = £10.56

■ Ascending order means from smallest to biggest.

■ Descending order means from biggest to smallest.

■ A place value table can be used to sort decimals into order of size.

■ To sort fractions into order of size, convert them to decimals.

■ To convert a percentage to a decimal, divide by 100
For example, 35% = 35 ÷ 100 = 0.35

■ To order a mixture of fractions, decimals and percentages, one method is to
convert all the values to decimals.

■ A common denominator of two fractions is a multiple of both denominators.

■ Equivalent fractions have the same value, for example $\frac{3}{4} = \frac{6}{8}$

■ To convert a fraction to an equivalent fraction, multiply both the numerator and

the denominator by the same number. For example, $\frac{3}{4} = \frac{3 \times 2}{4 \times 2} = \frac{6}{8}$

- To compare two fractions, write them as equivalent fractions with a common denominator.
- To write a quantity as a fraction of another:
  - make sure that both quantities have the same units
  - use the formula $\dfrac{\text{first quantity}}{\text{second quantity}}$

  Simplify the fraction as much as possible.

Chapter review

1 Write these fractions in order of size, with the smallest fraction first. $\frac{5}{6}$ $\frac{3}{4}$ $\frac{7}{9}$ $\frac{13}{18}$

2 Jack has 200 sacks of potatoes to sell.
$\frac{2}{5}$ of the sacks are red potatoes, the rest are white.
  a How many sacks are red potatoes? **b** Write $\frac{2}{5}$ as a decimal.
  c Write $\frac{2}{5}$ as a percentage.   **d** What fraction of the potatoes are white?

3 In a sale, a shop sells all its CDs at a discount of 30%.
What is the sale price of a CD that normally costs £12.50?

4 The money in Chris's building society account earned him £64 last year.
Chris had to pay 20% of this amount in tax. How much tax did he pay?

5 **a** Work out $\frac{1}{3}$ of 12
  b Jon uses the method shown to work out 11% of 800:   10% of 800 = 80
      Use Jon's method to work out 11% of 1300   + 1% of 800 =   8
      Show your working.   11% of 800 = 88
  c Work out 89% of 1300

6 Which of the following fractions are equal to $\frac{3}{4}$?
$\frac{12}{16}$ $\frac{16}{24}$ $\frac{18}{24}$ $\frac{28}{36}$ $\frac{45}{60}$

7 **a** What decimal is equivalent to $\frac{1}{4}$?   **b** Write 63% as a decimal.
  c What fraction is equivalent to 60%?

8 The diagram represents the petrol gauge in Mr Brown's car.
The shaded area indicates the amount of petrol in the tank.
The tank holds 50 litres when it is full.
  a What fraction of the tank is occupied by petrol?
  b Calculate the amount of petrol in the tank.

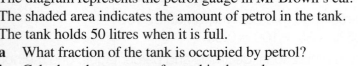

9 **a** This diagram is made from equilateral triangles.
      i What percentage of the diagram is shaded?
     ii What percentage of the diagram is not shaded?
  b Another diagram has 80% shaded.
      What fraction of the diagram is shaded? Simplify your answer.
  c Another diagram has $\frac{1}{4}$ shaded. Write $\frac{1}{4}$ as a decimal.

10 **a** Write these fractions in ascending order.

$\frac{2}{5}$ $\frac{1}{2}$ $\frac{3}{10}$

b **i** Work out 4.5% of 100 **ii** Which is greater, 4.5% or $\frac{1}{20}$?
Show your working.

11 **a** Which **two** of these fractions are equivalent to $\frac{2}{3}$?

$\frac{2}{6}$ $\frac{8}{12}$ $\frac{12}{18}$ $\frac{21}{30}$

b Write 40% as a decimal.

c Write $\frac{9}{10}$ as a decimal.

Two-dimensional shapes

11.1 Quadrilaterals

IN THIS SECTION YOU WILL

- Learn the names of some special quadrilaterals.
- Recognise quadrilaterals by their properties.
- Use coordinates to draw and complete quadrilaterals.
- Understand the word 'congruent'.

A *quadrilateral* is any shape with four straight sides.

Quadrilaterals with special properties have special names.

In the following diagrams and descriptions:

- equal lengths are marked with matching dashes
- equal angles are marked with matching arcs
- right angles are marked with squares
- parallel lines are marked with matching arrows
- *bisect* means 'cut in half'.

Rectangle

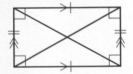

Opposite sides are equal in length.
Opposite sides are parallel.
All angles measure 90°.
Diagonals are equal in length.
Diagonals bisect each other.

Square

All sides are equal in length.
Opposite sides are parallel.
All angles measure 90°.
Diagonals are equal in length.
Diagonals cross at right angles.
Diagonals bisect each other.

Parallelogram

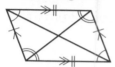

Opposite sides are equal in length.
Opposite sides are parallel.
Opposite angles are equal.
Diagonals bisect each other.

Rhombus

All sides are equal in length.
Opposite sides are parallel.
Opposite angles are equal.
Diagonals bisect each other.
Diagonals cross at right angles.

Kite

Two pairs of adjacent sides are equal.
One pair of opposite angles is equal.
Diagonals cross at right angles.

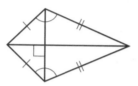

Trapezium

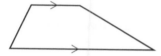

One pair of parallel sides.
If the non-parallel sides of a trapezium
are equal in length, then the shape is
called an *isosceles trapezium*.

An isosceles trapezium also has two
pairs of equal angles.
In an isosceles trapezium the diagonals
are equal in length.

Congruent shapes

When two shapes are exactly the same size
and shape they are said to be *congruent*.
These shapes are all congruent.

Example 1

The diagram shows some quadrilaterals.
a   Which shape is a parallelogram?
b   Which shape is a kite?
c   Which two shapes are congruent?

Solution 1

a   B is a parallelogram (opposite sides equal and parallel, opposite angles equal).
b   D is a kite (two pairs of adjacent sides equal, diagonals cross at right angles).
c   A and E are congruent (same shape and same size).

Exercise A

1 Copy and complete each of the statements below using the words from this box:

> rhombus   trapezium   rectangle   parallelogram

    a Shape F is a ....   **b** Shape G is a ....

2 Explain the differences between a rhombus and a parallelogram.

3 This question is about the shapes
in the diagram opposite.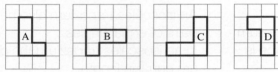

    a Write down the letter(s) of:

       i the shapes that are not quadrilaterals

      ii the kite

     iii the squares.

    b There are two pairs of congruent shapes in the diagram.
Write down the letters for each pair.

4 For each set of four shapes, write down the letter of the shape that is **not**
congruent to the other three.

    a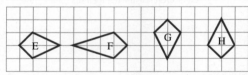

    b   **c**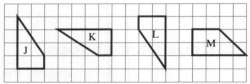

Example 2

ABCD is a square.
A is the point (6, 11), *B* is (13, 11), *C* is (13, 4).
Plot these points on a coordinate grid.
Find the coordinates of point *D*.

Solution 2

Plotting points *A*, *B* and *C* gives three
vertices of the square.
D must be plotted so that all four sides
are the same length and *AD* is at right
angles to *CD*. Its coordinates are (6, 4).

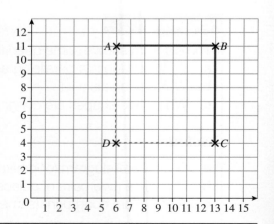

Exercise B

For questions **1** to **3**, copy the coordinate grid from Example 2 onto squared paper.

1 Draw the quadrilaterals with these coordinates.
Write down the special name for each shape.
  a (1, 2) (3, 2) (1, 4) (3, 4)
  c (6, 3) (8, 2) (8, 4) (12, 3)
  e (5, 11) (5, 14) (12, 11) (12, 14)
  b (4, 6) (6, 8) (8, 8) (10, 6)
  d (1, 7) (1, 11) (3, 13) (3, 9)

2 *ABCD* is a rectangle.
A is the point (2, 4), *B* is (2, 6), *C* is (4, 4).
Plot these points on a coordinate grid. Find the coordinates of point *D*.

3 *PQRS* is a parallelogram.
Q is the point (6, 7), *R* is (8, 4), and *S* is (4, 4).
Plot these points on a coordinate grid and find the coordinates of *P*.

4 The points (2, 3) and (4, 5) are two vertices of a square.
Write down the coordinates of two more points which would complete the square.

11.2 Reflection symmetry

CAN YOU REMEMBER

- What is meant by a 'mirror line'?
- The properties of different types of triangle: scalene, isosceles, equilateral?

IN THIS SECTION YOU WILL

- Draw lines of symmetry on triangles, quadrilaterals and other shapes.
- Complete diagrams using line symmetry.

These shapes have *line symmetry*.
When the shape is folded along the dotted line, one half of the shape fits exactly on top of the other half.

The dotted line is called the *line of symmetry*.
It divides the shape into two identical halves.

Line symmetry is sometimes called *reflection symmetry* as one half is a reflection of the other.

Some shapes have more than one line of symmetry.

Example 1

Draw the lines of symmetry on each shape.

Solution 1

A rectangle has two lines of symmetry.

A square has four lines of symmetry.

A parallelogram has no lines of symmetry.

Exercise A

1 Trace these shapes and draw in any lines of symmetry.

 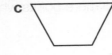

a   b   c   d   e   f

2 How many lines of symmetry has each of these letters?

M   **A**   **T**   **H**   **S**

3 How many lines of symmetry does each of these shapes have?

a   b   c   d

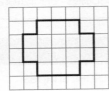   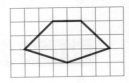

4 How many lines of symmetry does each triangle have?

scalene triangle   isosceles triangle   equilateral triangle

5 How many lines of symmetry does a kite have?

6 Copy this shape and draw in the line of symmetry.

To complete diagrams using a line of symmetry, a mirror or tracing paper may be used.

Example 2

Use the line of symmetry to complete the drawings.

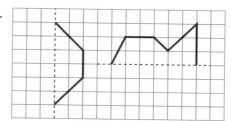

Solution 2

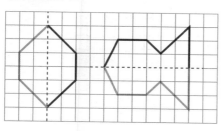

When a shape is reflected in a mirror line, both the object and the image are the same distance from the mirror line.

Example 3

Reflect the shaded shape in the mirror line shown.

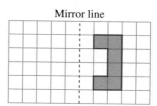

Solution 3

Exercise B

1 In each diagram below, the dotted line is the line of symmetry for that shape.
Copy each shape onto squared paper.
Use the line of symmetry to complete the other half of the shape.

a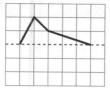
b
c
d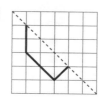

2 Copy each diagram onto squared paper.
Draw the reflection of the shape in the mirror line.

a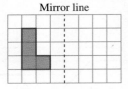

b

c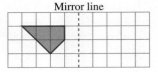

d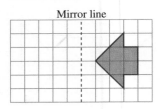

3 Copy each pattern onto squared paper.
On each pattern, shade in one more square so that the pattern has one line of symmetry.

a   **b**   **c**   **d**

4 On squared paper, draw a shape of your own that has exactly two lines of symmetry.

5 Copy this diagram onto squared paper.
Use both lines of symmetry (shown dotted)
to complete the shape.

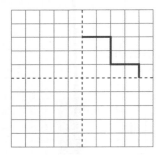

11.3 Rotation symmetry

CAN YOU REMEMBER

- The properties of different types of triangle?
- Properties of special quadrilaterals: rectangle, square, parallelogram, rhombus?
- How many degrees there are in a full turn?

IN THIS SECTION YOU WILL

- Understand and use the term 'rotational symmetry'.
- Find the order of rotational symmetry of triangles, quadrilaterals and other shapes.
- Complete diagrams using rotational symmetry.

A parallelogram has no line of symmetry.

If this parallelogram is rotated it fits into its outline in two positions:

1   in its original position

2   after a 180° turn.

It has rotational symmetry of *order* 2

   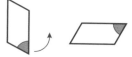

Example 1

What is the order of rotational symmetry of

a   a rectangle   **b**   a square   **c**   a trapezium?

Solution 1

a   A rectangle fits into its original outline:
1   in its original position
2   after a turn of 180°

So a rectangle has rotational symmetry of order 2

b   A square fits into its original outline:
1   in its original position
2   after a rotation of 90°
3   after a rotation of 180°
4   after a rotation of 270°

So a square has rotational symmetry of order 4

c   A trapezium only fits into its outline in the original position, it has no rotational symmetry.

Exercise A

1   State the order of rotational symmetry of each of the shapes shown.

a   **b**   **c**   **d**

2   What is the order of rotational symmetry of:
a   a kite   **b**   a rhombus   **c**   an equilateral triangle

3   Write down the order of rotational symmetry of each of these shapes.

   a   **b**   **c**   **d**

4   Which of these letters have rotational symmetry?

   N   O   P   X   Y   Z

Example 2

Describe the symmetry of this shape.

Solution 2

The shape has rotational symmetry of order 2.
2 lines of symmetry.

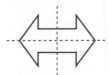

Exercise B

1   Describe the symmetry of each of the following shapes.
   If a shape has line symmetry copy the shape and draw in any lines of symmetry.

   a   **b**   **c**

   d   **e**   **f**

2   Copy these diagrams onto squared paper. Complete the diagrams as instructed.

   a   Colour in one more
   square so that the
   shape has rotational
   symmetry of order 4.

   b   Colour in two more
   squares so that the
   shape has rotational
   symmetry of order 2.

   c   Colour in two more
   triangles so that the
   shape has rotational
   symmetry of order 4.

   d   Colour in one more
   square and one
   triangle so that the
   shape has rotational
   symmetry of order 4.

11.4 Perimeters of simple shapes

CAN YOU REMEMBER

- How to add positive numbers and decimals?
- That a rectangle has two pairs of sides of equal length?
- That a square has four sides of equal length?

IN THIS SECTION YOU WILL

- Find perimeters of squares and rectangles.
- Work out the perimeters of shapes made from rectangles and squares.

The distance round the outside of a shape is called the *perimeter*.

The distance all the way round the rectangle is

4 cm + 3 cm + 4 cm + 3 cm = 14 cm.

So its perimeter is 14 cm.

The perimeter of a rectangle can be written as

length (l) + width (w) + length (l) + width (w)

So $P = l + w + l + w$ or $P = 2l + 2w$

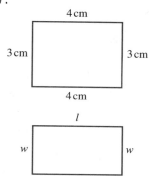

Example 1

A square has sides of 10 cm. Calculate the perimeter of the square.

Solution 1

A square has four equal-length sides.
Each side is 10 cm.

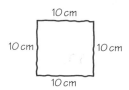

The perimeter of this square is

10 + 10 + 10 + 10 or 4 × 10 = 40 cm.

Example 2

In a rectangle $ABCD$, side AB = 5.2 cm and
side BC = 3.1 cm.
Find the perimeter of this rectangle.

A ⌐ 5.2 cm ⌐ B
| |
| 3.1 cm
D ⌐   ⌐ C

Not drawn accurately

Solution 2

Perimeter = 5.2 + 3.1 + 5.2 + 3.1   or $P = 2l + 2w$
                = 16.6 cm $= 2 \times 5.2 + 2 \times 3.1$
                                                                  $= 10.4 + 6.2 = 16.6$ cm

Exercise A

1 Work out the perimeter of each rectangle.

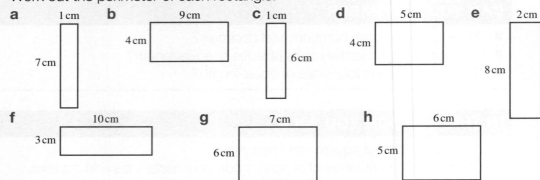

2 Work out the perimeter of the squares with the following side lengths:
  a 11 cm   **b** 8 cm   **c** 7 m   **d** 2.5 m   **e** 20 mm

3 **a** Which two rectangles have the same perimeter?
   b Which rectangle has the largest perimeter?
   c Which rectangle has the smallest perimeter?

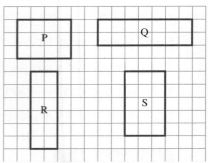

4 Write down the pairs of rectangles which have the same perimeter.

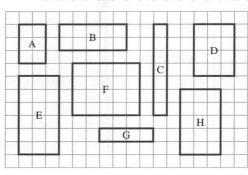

5 Calculate the perimeter of these rectangles.

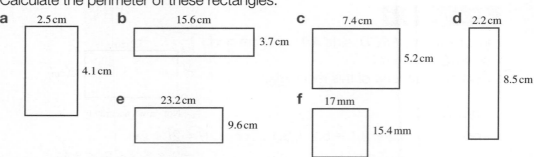

6 Work out the perimeter of the squares with the following side lengths:
  a 1.4 cm   **b** 8.7 cm   **c** 2.7 m   **d** 3.45 m   **e** 176.4 mm

Example 3

Work out the perimeter of this shape.

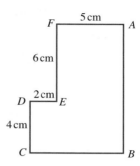

Solution 3

The lengths of *AB* and *BC* are not labelled.

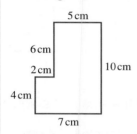

$AB = 6$ cm $+ 4$ cm $= 10$ cm

$BC = 2$ cm $+ 5$ cm $= 7$ cm

When all the lengths are known, the perimeter of the shape can be calculated.

The perimeter is $5 + 10 + 7 + 4 + 2 + 6 = 34$ cm

Exercise B

1 Work out the perimeter of each shape.

a 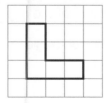 **b** 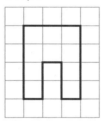 **c**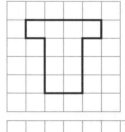

d 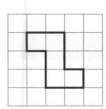 **e** 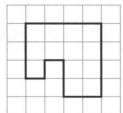 **f**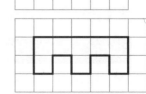

2 Calculate the perimeter of rectangles with:
 a length 9 cm and width 5 cm **b** length 4 cm and width 2 cm
 c length 15 cm and width 10 cm **d** length 8 cm and width 3.5 cm
 e length 35 cm and width 14 cm

3 The following diagrams are not drawn accurately. All the measurements are centimetres. Calculate the perimeter of each shape.

a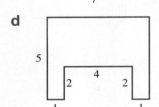

b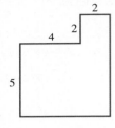

c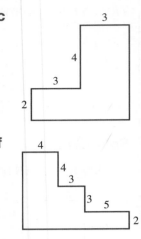

d

e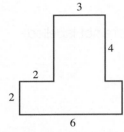

f

4 The perimeter of a square is 36 cm. What is the length of the side of the square?

5 The perimeter of a rectangle is 78 cm. The length of the rectangle is 24 cm. Calculate the width of the rectangle.

6 A farmer has a field which is 314 m long and 256 m wide.
What length of fencing does he need to completely surround the field?

7 Calculate the perimeter of rectangles with:
  a length 3.9 cm, width 4.5 cm   **b** length 12.7 cm, width 2.9 cm
  c length 15.25 cm, width 11.6 cm   **d** length 3.27 cm, width 1.56 cm
  e length 23.4 cm, width 18.6 cm

8 A rug is 1.9 m long and 0.8 m wide. Calculate the perimeter of the rug.

9 The length of a rectangle is 12.6 cm. The perimeter of the rectangle is 41.6 cm. Calculate the width of the rectangle.

11.5 Areas of simple shapes

CAN YOU REMEMBER

- How to multiply two whole numbers?
- How to multiply two decimals?

IN THIS SECTION YOU WILL

- Find areas of squares and rectangles by counting squares.
- Find areas of squares and rectangles by using a formula.

The *area* of a shape is the amount of space it covers.
Area is measured in square units, for example square
centimetres, written cm².

Very small areas can be measured in square millimetres, mm².
Large areas can be measured in square metres, m², or square kilometres, km².

On centimetre-squared paper, each square has area 1 cm².
Area can be found by counting the number of 1 cm² squares in the shape.

Example 1

These two shapes are drawn on
centimetre-squared paper.
Find the area of each shape.

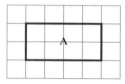

Solution 1

Rectangle A covers 8 squares. Area of rectangle A = 8 cm²

Shape B covers 8 squares. Area of shape B = 8 cm²

Exercise A

In this exercise take these diagrams to be drawn on centimetre-squared paper but they
are shown smaller here.

1 Find the areas of these rectangles by counting squares.

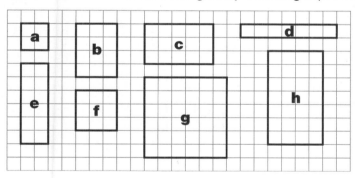

2 For the rectangles in the following
diagram write down:
  a the rectangle with the
     largest area
  b the rectangles that have the
     same area.

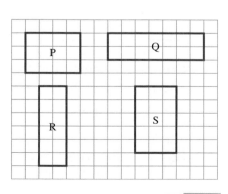

3 Write down the letters of these rectangles in order of size of area, smallest first.

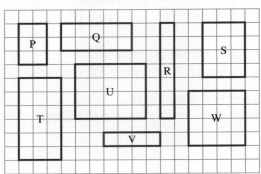

4 Find the area of each of these shapes by counting squares.

  a   **b**   **c**

  d   **e**   **f**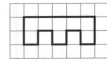

5 Match the pairs of shapes with the same area.

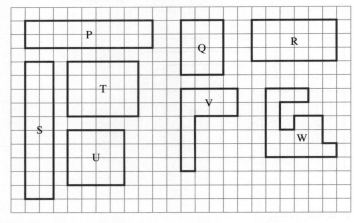

Counting squares to find areas can take a long time.
This rectangle has 4 rows of 5 squares.

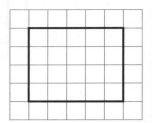

The total number of squares is $4 + 4 + 4 + 4 + 4 = 5 \times 4 = 20$

The length of the rectangle is 5 cm and the width is 4 cm.
So to find the area of a rectangle use the formula
  Area = length × width $A = l \times w$

Example 2

Find the area of this rectangle.

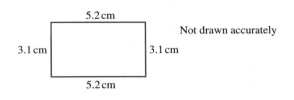

Not drawn accurately

Solution 2

Area = length × width
Area = 5.2 × 3.1 = 16.12 cm²

Example 3

Find the area of this shape.

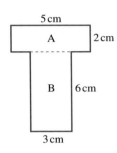

Solution 3

Divide the shape into two rectangles.
Work out the area of each rectangle separately:
Area rectangle A = 5 × 2 = 10 cm²
Area rectangle B = 6 × 3 = 18 cm²
Add the two areas together to give a total area of
10 + 18 = 28 cm²

Exercise B

1 Calculate the area of these rectangles.

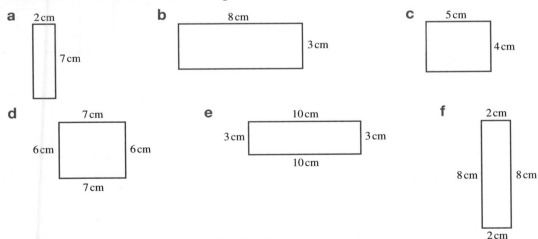

2 A rectangular room measures 4.5 m by 4 m.
What area of carpet is needed to cover the floor? Give your answer in m².

3 This rectangle has an area of 36 cm².
Find the length l of the rectangle.

4 Find the areas of these shapes. State the units of your answer.

a

3 cm
5 cm
4 cm
10 cm

b

3 cm
8 cm
2 cm
12 cm

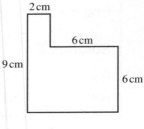

c

2 cm
6 cm
9 cm
6 cm

d

3 cm   3 cm
2 cm   2 cm
4 cm
10 cm
5 cm   5 cm

e

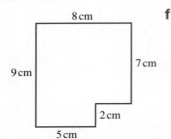

8 cm
7 cm
9 cm
2 cm
5 cm

f

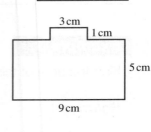

3 cm
1 cm
5 cm
9 cm

5 Which shape has the bigger area:
a square of side 5 cm, **or** a rectangle of length 7 cm and width 3 cm?
Show your working.

6 The diagrams in this question are not to scale.
Calculate the area of these shapes.

a

2.5 cm
4.1 cm

b

8.5 cm
2.2 cm

c

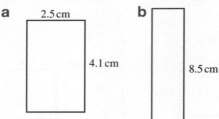

2 cm
2 cm
4 cm
5 cm

d

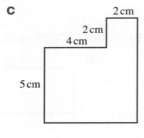

4 cm
4 cm
3 cm
3 cm
5 cm
2 cm

7 Find the area of the following rectangles:
   a   length 47 cm, width 8.5 cm   **b**   length 12.6 cm, width 9.2 cm
   c   length 17 cm, width 12 cm   **d**   length 22.5 cm, width 7.5 cm

8 A rug measures 1.6 m by 2.1 m.
What area of floor does it cover?

9 A square tile has an area of 81 cm^2.
How long are the sides of the tile?

10 Rectangles A and B have the same area.
Calculate the length, x, of rectangle B.

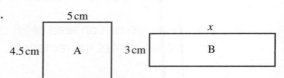

5 cm
4.5 cm   A
3 cm
x
B

Chapter summary

- A quadrilateral has four straight sides.
- Quadrilaterals with special properties have special names.
- Congruent shapes are the same shape and the same size.
- A shape has line symmetry if it can be folded so that one half of the shape fits exactly onto the other half.
- When a shape is reflected in a mirror line, both the object and the image are the same distance from the mirror line.
- A shape has rotational symmetry if it fits back into its original outline at least once during a full turn.
- The order of rotational symmetry is the number of positions where the shape fits its original outline in one full turn.
- The perimeter is the distance all the way around the outside of a shape.
- Perimeter of a rectangle = 2 × length + 2 × width
  $$= 2l + 2w$$
- The area of a shape is the space it covers.
- Area is measured in square units, e.g. mm^2, cm^2, m^2 or km^2.
- The area of a square or rectangle is given by the formula:
  area = length × width $A = l \times w$

Chapter review

1 Choose the correct name for each shape from this list.

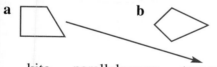

a   b   c   d

    kite   parallelogram   trapezium   rectangle   rhombus   square

2 **a** Copy the diagram.
Draw the reflection of shape A
in the mirror line.

   b The line PQ is part of shape B.
Shape B is congruent to shape A.
Complete shape B on the diagram,

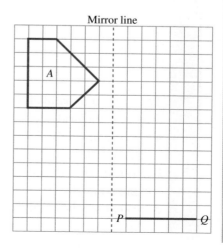

3   The diagram shows a sketch of a house.

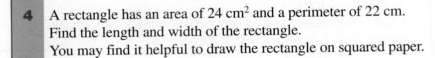

  a   What is the special name of the shape of the roof?
  b   The door is a rectangle.
        How many lines of symmetry does a rectangle have?
  c   The window is a square.
        What is the order of rotational symmetry of a square?
  d   Name a line that is parallel to *ED*.
  e   Name a line that is perpendicular to *ED*.
  f   From the list choose the correct description of the angle *AFE*.

  > acute   obtuse   reflex   right

4   A rectangle has an area of 24 cm^2 and a perimeter of 22 cm.
      Find the length and width of the rectangle.
      You may find it helpful to draw the rectangle on squared paper.

5   **a**   Copy the diagram.   **b**   Copy the diagram.
          Draw all the lines of   Shade three more squares so that the final
          symmetry on the figure.   figure has rotational symmetry of order 4

  c   Copy the diagram.
        Shade three more squares so that the
        final figure has line symmetry about the
        dotted line **and** rotational symmetry.

6   Calculate the area of this shape.
      You **must** show all your working.

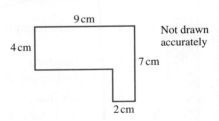

7   Two sides of a parallelogram are
      drawn on the grid opposite.
  a   Write down the coordinates of
        the point *A*.
  b   Write down the coordinates of
        the point *B*.
  c   What are the coordinates of the
        missing point *D* of the parallelogram?

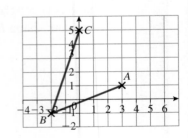

8 **a** A pattern has four lines of symmetry.
Part of the pattern is shown below.
Copy and complete the pattern.

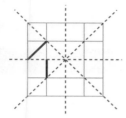

b A different pattern has rotational symmetry of order 4 and no line symmetry.
Part of the pattern is shown below.
Copy and complete the pattern.

9 The length of a rectangle is 9.6 cm.
The perimeter of the rectangle is 29.6 cm.
Calculate the width of the rectangle.

9.6 cm

width

Not drawn accurately

Using a formula

12.1 Using formulae written in words

CAN YOU REMEMBER

- How to substitute numbers into an expression?
- How to solve simple equations?
- The order of operations for calculations?

IN THIS SECTION YOU WILL

- Solve problems using a formula written in words.
- Learn how to write a formula in words.

A *formula* is a *rule* for working out one quantity from other quantities.
A formula can be written either in words or using letter symbols.
To work out an unknown quantity from a formula *substitute* known values into it.

Example 1

This formula is used to work out the cost of a school trip in pounds.

Cost of trip = 4 × number of students + 100

a   Mr Brown takes 20 students on the trip.
    What is the cost of Mr Brown's trip?

b   Mrs Smith's trip costs £220
    How many students does Mrs Smith take on the trip?

Solution 1

a   Cost of trip = 4 × number of students + 100
    The number of students is 20
    Cost of trip = 4 × 20 + 100
                 = 80 + 100 = 180   (multiply before adding)
    The cost of Mr Brown's trip is £180

b   Cost of trip = 4 × number of students + 100
    Cost of trip = £220
    220 = 4 × number of students + 100
    Use the balance method to solve this equation.

$$220 - 100 = 4 \times \text{number of students} + 100 - 100$$
$$120 = 4 \times \text{number of students}$$
$$120 \div 4 = 4 \times \text{number of students} \div 4$$
$$30 = \text{number of students}$$

So the number of students = 30

Subtract 100 from both sides

Divide both sides by 4

Example 2

Susan earns £7 per hour.

a   Write a word formula to work out Susan's pay for any number of hours she works.

b   On Monday Susan worked for 5 hours.
   Use the formula to work out how much Susan earned on Monday.

Solution 2

a   Pay (£) = number of hours worked × 7

b   Number of hours worked = 5 hours
   Pay (£) = 5 × 7 = 35
   So Susan earned £35 on Monday.

Exercise A

1   This formula can be used to work out the time in London from the time in New York.

Time in London = time in New York + 5 hours

   a   The time in New York is 9 am.
      What time is it in London?

   b   The time in London is 3 pm.
      What time is it in New York?

2   Denise uses this formula to work out the profit she makes when she buys and sells a car.

Profit = selling price − buying price

   a   Denise buys a car for £4000 and sells it for £6500. What is the profit?

   b   Denise buys a car for £3500. She sells the car and makes a profit of £800
      What is the selling price?

   c   Denise sells a car for £8000. She makes a profit of £1200
      What is the buying price?

3   This formula connects the quantities distance, speed and time.

Distance = speed × time

   a   Tom walks at a speed of 5 kilometres per hour for 2 hours.
      What distance does he walk?

   b   Sam cycles at a speed of 15 kilometres per hour.
      How long does it take him to cycle 45 kilometres?

   c   Matthew runs at a speed of 5 metres per second for 1 minute.
      What distance does he run?

4 This formula is used to work out the pay in pounds of workers in a factory.

> **Pay = hourly pay × hours worked + bonus**

Bill, James and Tajinder's hourly pay is £8 per hour.
a Bill works for 30 hours and earns a bonus of £100
What is his pay?
b James works for 35 hours. His pay is £300
What is his bonus?
c Tajinder's bonus is £50. His pay is £370
How many hours does he work?

5 a Copy and complete this word
formula for the area of a rectangle.
Area of rectangle = ... × ....
b This triangle is exactly half of the rectangle.
Write down a word formula for the area
of the triangle.

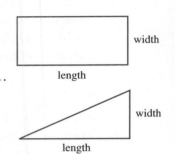

6 The cost (in pounds) of hiring a carpet cleaner is calculated from this formula.

> **Hire charge = 25 × hire period in days + 30**

a A carpet cleaner is hired for three days. What is the hire charge?
b Mr Patel pays a hire charge of £280. What is the hire period?

7 The cost of electricity in pounds can be worked out using this formula.

> **Cost = number of units used × 0.125**

a Work out the cost of 800 units.
b Work out the number of units used when the cost is £25.
c What is the cost of one unit of electricity?

8 The cost of hiring a minibus is £80 plus £0.62 for every mile travelled.
a Write down a word formula for the hire cost from the distance travelled.
b What is the cost of hiring the minibus for a journey of 265 miles?
c A school paid a hire cost of £255. How many miles did they travel?

9 The volume of a prism is given by the formula

> **Volume = area of base × height**

a The height of a prism is 12.5 cm and the area of its base is 16.2 cm^2.
Work out its volume.
b The volume of a prism is 122.5 cm^3 and the area of its base is 23.6 cm^2.
Work out its height.
c The volume of a prism is 1 cm^3 and its height is 0.2 cm.
Work out the area of its base.

10 In this pattern 10 matchsticks are used to make three squares in a row.

In this pattern 22 matchsticks are used to make seven squares in a row.

This formula connects the number of squares to the number of matchsticks.

> **Number of matchsticks = 3 × number of squares + 1**

   a How many matchsticks are needed to make 125 squares in a row?
   b How many squares in a row can be made with 169 matchsticks?

Example 3

The cost of hiring a van from Van Hire is worked out using this formula.

> **Hire charge in pounds = 50 × number of days + 80**

The cost of hiring a van from Hire-a-Van is worked out using this formula.

> **Hire charge in pounds = 0.55 × number of miles travelled + 100**

Mrs Jones wants to hire a van for 3 days. She estimates that she will travel 220 miles. Should Mrs Jones hire a van from Van Hire or Hire-a-Van?
Give a reason for your answer.

Solution 3

The cost of hiring a van from Van Hire for 3 days:
Hire charge = 50 × 3 + 80 = 150 + 80   (multiplication before addition)
So the hire charge from Van Hire is £230

The cost of hiring a van from Hire-a-Van for 220 miles:
Hire charge = 0.55 × 220 + 100 = 121 + 100   (multiplication before addition)
So the hire charge from Hire-a-Van is £221
It is cheaper to hire the van from Hire-a-Van.

Exercise B

1 This is how Print Easy works out photocopying charges in pence:

> **35 × number of colour prints + 10 × number of black-and-white prints**

Cheap Print work out their charges, in pence, like this:

> **50 × number of colour prints + 5 × number of black-and-white prints**

Sue needs 10 colour prints and 40 black-and-white prints.
Which company is the cheapest?
You **must** show your working.

2 The cost of hiring a cement mixer from Building Tools is worked out using this formula:

> **Hire charge in pounds = 50 × number of days + 30**

The cost of hiring a cement mixer from Tools of the Trade is worked out using this formula:

> **Hire charge in pounds = 40 × number of days + 70**

Which company is cheaper to hire from for:
a 2 days **b** 4 days **c** 6 days?

3 Three students are investigating the numbers of squares that can be made with different numbers of lines.

This table shows their results.

Each student writes down a rule to work out the number of squares from the number of lines.

Kim's rule

> **To find the number of squares, double the number of lines and then subtract 8**

Maninder's rule

> **To find the number of squares take 3 from the number of lines**

Allan's rule

> **To find the number of squares subtract 4 from the number of lines and then multiply by 2**

Diagram	Lines	Squares
	5	2
	6	4
	7	6

Show that one of the rules does **not** work for these diagrams and that the other two rules do work.

4 This formula works out the number of points for a football team.

> **Number of points = 3 × number of games won + number of games drawn**

Last season United won ten games and drew two and won the league.
City won eight games and drew six and came second in the league.
a How many more points did United get than City?
b Rovers drew two games and came third in the league with 29 points.
How many games did Rovers win?

5 Shireen works part-time in an office. John makes mobile phones in a factory.
Shireen's wages are worked out using this formula:

> **Amount earned in pounds = 6 × number of hours worked + 75**

John's wages are worked out using this formula:

> **Amount earned in pounds = 2.5 × number of phones made**

In one week Shireen works for 25 hours.
How many phones does John have to make to earn the same amount as Shireen?

6 A row of triangles and a row of
   squares is made using matchsticks.

   13 matchsticks can be used to make six triangles or four squares.
   This formula connects the number of triangles to the number of matchsticks:

   Number of matchsticks = 2 × number of triangles + 1

   This formula connects the number of squares to the number of matchsticks:

   Number of matchsticks = 3 × number of squares + 1

   a Matchsticks are used to make a row of three triangles.
      i How many matchsticks are used?
      The same number of matchsticks is used to make a row of squares.
      ii How many squares are in the row?
   b Matchsticks are used to make a row of nine triangles.
      How many squares can be made with the same number of matchsticks?
   c Find some more numbers of matchsticks that can be used to make both a row
      of complete triangles and a row of complete squares.

7 The diagram shows part of a spreadsheet.

   Column **B** = 2 × column **A** + 5

   Column **C** = column **B** squared

   Column **D** = 1000 − column **C**

   Work out the numbers in the gaps
   in the spreadsheet.

	A	B	C	D
1	1			
2		9		
3				775
4			625	

8 This rule can be used to estimate the time in hours that it takes to climb a mountain.

   Step 1: Divide the horizontal distance travelled in miles by 3
   Step 2: Divide the height climbed in feet by 1000
   Step 3: Add the answers from steps 1 and 2

   David is planning to climb a mountain.
   He uses a map to work out that he will travel 4 miles horizontally and climb 3700 feet.
   Use the rule to estimate the time he will take in hours.

9 This is how to check whether a parcel can be sent overseas by the Royal Mail.

   Step 1: Measure the length, height and width.
   **   Each of these must be less than 600 mm.**
   Step 2: Add together the length, height and width.
   **   This must be less than 900 mm.**

   a Check whether these parcels can be sent overseas by the Royal Mail:
      i Parcel 1: length = 343 mm, height = 289 mm and width = 267 mm
      ii Parcel 2: length = 605 mm, height = 140 mm and width = 145 mm
      iii Parcel 1: length = 425 mm, height = 278 mm and width = 198 mm

b A parcel has a length of 247 mm and a height of 476 mm.
Calculate the largest possible width that this parcel could be and still be sent overseas by the Royal Mail.

12.2 Using a formula written with letter symbols

CAN YOU REMEMBER

- How to use letter symbols to represent numbers?
- The meaning of 'square' and 'cube'?
- The order of operations for calculations?
- How to solve simple equations?

IN THIS SECTION YOU WILL

- Solve problems using a formula written with letter symbols.
- Learn how to write a formula using letter symbols.

Instead of using words, a *formula* often uses letter symbols to represent quantities.

Using words	Using letter symbols
Speed = distance ÷ time	$s = \dfrac{d}{t}$
Area of a triangle = base × height ÷ 2	$A = \dfrac{bh}{2}$
Volume of a cuboid = length × width × height	$V = lwh$

A formula that uses letter symbols always has an '=' symbol.

To use a formula written with letter symbols, substitute known values for the letters.

Sometimes substituting known values creates an *equation* to solve.

Example 1

A TV engineer charges a basic fee of £40, plus £18 per hour for repairs.
Write a formula for the charge, £C, the engineer makes for h hours' work.

Solution 1

The TV engineer charges £18 × h for h hours' work at £18 per hour.
Leaving out the multiplication sign, this *simplifies* to £18h.
Adding the basic fee, the total charge is £18h + £40
So the formula is $C = 18h + 40$

Example 2

The formula, $c = 3a + 2b$, connects the quantities a, b and c.

a Work out the value of c when $a = 4$ and $b = 3$

b Work out the value of b when $c = 14$ and $a = 2$

Solution 2

a Substitute $a = 4$ and $b = 3$ into the formula $c = 3a + 2b$ and insert $\times$ symbols.

$c = 3 \times 4 + 2 \times 3$ (Do **both** multiplications before the addition.)

$c = 12 + 6 = 18$

b Substitute $c = 14$ and $a = 2$ into the formula $c = 3a + 2b$ and insert $\times$ symbols.

$14 = 3 \times 2 + 2b$ (Do the multiplication first.)

$14 = 6 + 2b$

Use the balance method to solve the equation.

Subtract 6 from both sides $14 - 6 = 6 + 2b - 6$

$8 = 2b$

Divide both sides by 2 $8 \div 2 = 2b \div 2$

$b = 4$

Exercise A

1 Sort the following into two sets – formulae and expressions.

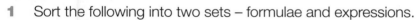

   a $2q + 5$ **b** $r = 3 + 5s$ **c** $\dfrac{t}{2} - 12$

   d $u = v^2 + w^2$ **e** $x^2 + y^3$

2 Calculate the values of A to J when $x = 2$, $y = 5$ and $z = 20$

   a $A = x + y + z$ **b** $B = z - x + y$ **c** $C = 3x$ **d** $D = xy$

   e $E = xyz$ **f** $F = 5y + 4$ **g** $G = \dfrac{z}{2}$ **h** $H = \dfrac{z}{y}$

   i $I = \dfrac{z}{4} + y$ **j** $J = \dfrac{xz}{y}$

3 Bag A contains a counters.

   a Bag B contains 5 more counters than bag A.
       Write down a formula for the number of counters, b, in bag B.

   b Bag C contains 2 fewer counters than bag A.
       Write down a formula for the number of counters, c, in bag C.

   c Bag D contains twice as many counters as bag A.
       Write down a formula for the number of counters, d, in bag D.

   d Write down a formula for the **total** number of counters, t, in bags A, B, C and D.

4 a A van costs £50 per day to hire.
Write down a formula for £H, the cost of hiring the van for d days.

b The width of a rectangle is x cm.
The length of the same rectangle is $2x$ cm.
Write down a formula for P, the perimeter of the rectangle
in centimetres.

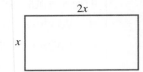

c Three friends win £x in a quiz on Tuesday and £y in a quiz
on Friday. They share the total prize money equally.
Write down a formula for £Q, the prize money that each of them receives.

5 The formula $l = mn + 10$ connects the quantities l, m and n.
  a Calculate l when $m = 2$ and $n = 3$ **b** Calculate l when $m = 4$ and $n = 5$

6 The formula $a = 5(b + c)$ connects the quantities a, b and c.
  a Calculate a when $b = 1$ and $c = 2$
  b Calculate a when $b = 4$ and $c = 6$

7 The formula $w = x(y + z)$ connects the quantities w, x, y and z.
  a Calculate w when $x = 5$, $y = 4$ and $z = 6$
  b Calculate w when $x = 4$, $y = 12$ and $z = 8$

8 The formula $p = (q + r)(s - t)$ connects the quantities p, q, r, s and t.
  a Calculate p when $q = 7$, $r = 3$, $s = 8$ and $t = 4$
  b Calculate p when $q = 2$, $r = 6$, $s = 30$ and $t = 5$

9 Calculate the value of each of the letter symbols A to H when $a = 2$, $b = 3$, $c = 4$
and $d = 12$

  a $A = \dfrac{d}{b}$ **b** $B = \dfrac{d - c}{a}$ **c** $C = d - \dfrac{c}{a}$ **d** $D = \dfrac{ad}{b}$

  e $E = \dfrac{c + d}{a}$ **f** $F = \dfrac{d}{b} - \dfrac{c}{a}$ **g** $G = \dfrac{a + c + d}{b}$ **h** $H = \dfrac{a + d}{b + c}$

10 a $s = r - t$
  Find r when $s = 7$ and $t = 8$

  b $y = 3x$
  Find x when $y = 12$

  c $a = 5b + c$
    i Find c when $a = 12$ and $b = 2$
    ii Find b when $a = 20$ and $c = 5$

  d $p = 3q + 2r$
    i Find r when $p = 19$ and $q = 3$
    ii Find q when $p = 26$ and $r = 4$

  e $l = \dfrac{m}{5} - n$
    i Find m when $l = 2$ and $n = 4$
    ii Find n when $l = 1$ and $m = 10$

  f $a = \dfrac{b}{c} + de$
    i Find b when $a = 17$, $c = 10$, $d = 2$
      and $e = 6$
    ii Find e when $a = 12$, $b = 12$, $c = 3$
      and $d = 2$

11 a $A = 5b - 32$
Find A when $b = 28$

b $C = 8(d + 12)$
Find C when $d = 16$

c $E = 2f + 3g$
Find E when $f = 16$ and $g = 4.5$

d $H = j(k + 9)$
Find H when $j = 12.5$ and $k = 22$

e $L = n + \dfrac{m}{5}$ Find L when $m = 8$ and $n = 7.5$

Example 3

A train contains x standard-class coaches and y first-class coaches. There are 84 seats in a standard-class coach and 62 seats in a first-class coach.

a **i** Write an expression for the number of standard-class seats on the train.
  ii Write an expression for the number of first-class seats on the train.
b Write a formula for N, the number of seats on the train.
c On a train, the number of seats, N, is 544
The number of standard-class coaches, x, is 5. Use the formula to work out y, the number of first-class coaches on the train.

Solution 3

a **i** x standard-class coaches have $x \times 84$ seats.
  Leaving out the multiplication sign, this *simplifies* to 84x.
  ii y first-class coaches have $y \times 62$ seats. This *simplifies* to 62y.
b There are 84x standard-class seats and 62y first-class seats.
So the total number of seats on the train is $N = 84x + 62y$
c Substitute $N = 544$ and $x = 5$ in the formula $N = 84x + 62y$ and insert $\times$ symbol.
$544 = 84 \times 5 + 62y$ (Do the multiplication first.)
$544 = 420 + 62y$
Use the balance method to solve the equation.

Subtract 420 from both sides $544 - 420 = 420 + 62y - 420$
$124 = 62y$

Divide both sides by 62 $124 \div 62 = 62y \div 62$
$y = 2$

So there are two first-class coaches on the train.

Example 4

The formula $P = 4(r - q)^2$ connects the quantities P, q and r:
Work out the value of P when $q = 3$ and $r = -2$

Solution 4

Substitute $q = 3$ and $r = -2$ into the formula $P = 4(r - q)^2$ and insert $\times$ symbols.
$P = 4 \times (-2 - 3)^2$ (Do the calculation inside the bracket first.)
$P = 4 \times (-5)^2$ (square before multiplication)
$P = 4 \times (-5) \times (-5)$ (negative $\times$ negative = positive)
$P = 4 \times 25 = 100$

Exercise B

1 Use $a = 2$, $b = -3$, $c = 4$ and $d = -5$ to calculate the values of A to N in the formulae below.

a $A = a - b$

b $B = 3a - b$

c $C = 3b + 6c$

d $D = ac + bd$

e $E = \dfrac{c}{a} - d$

f $F = \dfrac{c - d}{3}$

g $G = \dfrac{c - d - b}{a}$

h $H = d^2 + 5$

i $I = 5a + b^2$

j $J = b^2 + c^2$

k $K = 3b + c^3$

l $L = 5a^2 + d$

m $M = 3(a - b)$

n $N = (c - d)^2$

2 Use the formula $a = 5b - \dfrac{c}{4}$ to find the value of:

a a when $b = 8$ and $c = 28$

b b when $a = 12$ and $c = 32$

c c when $a = 10$ and $b = 1$

3 In a café tea costs 45 pence a cup and coffee costs 60 pence a cup.

a   i Write down an expression for the cost of x cups of tea.

ii Write down an expression for the cost of y cups of coffee.

b   Write down a formula for T, the total cost in pence, of x cups of tea and y cups of coffee.

c   A group of friends spends exactly £4.05 on teas and coffees.

i What is the largest possible number of tea drinkers?

ii What is the largest possible number of coffee drinkers?

4 These patterns are made from square white tiles surrounding square black tiles.

The formula $w = 2b + 6$ gives the rule for working out the number of white tiles, w, from the number of black tiles, b.

a   Sarah makes a similar pattern using 25 black tiles.
How many white tiles does she use?

b   Carlton makes a similar pattern using 196 white tiles.
How many black tiles does he use?

5 Pat and Sian are making this sequence of patterns using black and white tiles.

  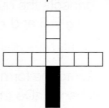

The formula for working out the number of white tiles, w, from the number of black tiles, b, is $w = 3b + 1$

a   Check that the formula works for the patterns shown above.

b Pat and Sian each make another pattern in the sequence.
Pat uses 10 black tiles and Sian uses 31 white tiles.
Explain why the patterns must be the same.

6 **a** $M = a + \dfrac{b}{c}$ $N = \dfrac{a + b}{c}$

Calculate $M + N$ when $a = 28.8$, $b = 35.2$ and $c = 0.8$

b $X = ab + c$ $Y = a(b + c)$ $Z = c(a - 1)$

  i Calculate $X - Y + Z$ when $a = 5$, $b = 4$ and $c = 3$

  ii Calculate $X - Y + Z$ when $a = 2.3$, $b = 1.9$ and $c = 5.4$

  iii Choose some different values for a, b and c and repeat **i** and **ii**.

7 **a** **i** $A = b^2 + 2b$
    Find A when $b = 16$

  ii $F = 3g^2$
    Find F when $g = 21$

  iii $H = 5j + k^3$
    Find H when $j = 14$ and $k = 6$

  iv $X = 3x - y^3$
    Find x when $X = 20$ and $y = 4$

  v $L = 2m - m^2$
    Find L when $m = 20$

b **i** $T = 2u$
    Find u when $T = 98$

  ii $A = bc + d$
    Work out b when $A = 256$, $c = 32$
    and $d = 16$

  iii $W = x + \dfrac{y}{z}$
    Work out y when $W = 60$, $x = 12$ and $z = 6$

8 The formula that converts temperature from degrees Fahrenheit (°F) to degrees
Celsius (°C) is $C = \dfrac{F - 32}{1.8}$

The formula that converts temperature from degrees Celsius (°C) to degrees
Fahrenheit (°F) is $F = 1.8C + 32$

a Convert 50 °F to °C.

b Convert 5 °C to °F.

c Convert −7 °F to °C.

d Convert 5 °F to °C.

e Show that the temperature −40 °F is the same as −40 °C.

9 The mean, m, of two numbers x and y is given by the formula $m = \dfrac{x + y}{2}$

a Calculate m when $x = 4.2$ and $y = 6.6$

b Calculate x when $m = 12$ and $y = 8$

c Write down a formula for the mean, m, of three numbers x, y and z.

10 $C = 2a + 3b$ $D = 5a - 2b$ $E = 2C + 3D$

    a Find C and D when $a = 4$ and $b = 2$

    b Find C and D when $a = 4.2$ and $b = 2.4$

    c Show that $E = 19a$

11 A fencing company uses the formula, $N = 85lh$, to estimate N, the number of nails it needs to make a wooden fence.

    l is the length and h is the height of the fence in metres.

    a The company makes a fence that is 15 metres long and 1.8 metres high. Estimate the number of nails it needs.

    b The company makes a 1.2 metre high fence around a bowling green. The bowling green is rectangular, 70 metres long and 45 metres wide. Estimate the number of nails needed to make the fence.

    c The fencing company estimates that 8160 nails are needed to build a fence 80 metres long. How high is the fence?

12 This formula can be used to work out the cooking time in minutes, T, of a chicken that weighs w kilograms.

    $T = 40w + 20$

    a Write an instruction for the cooking time of the chicken in words.

    b A chicken weighs 3.2 kg. Work out its cooking time.

    c A chicken has a cooking time of 2 hours. What does it weigh?

Chapter summary

- A *formula* is a rule for working out one quantity from other quantities.

- A formula can be written in words or using letter symbols.

- A formula that uses letter symbols is usually *simplified*. This means that the multiplication symbol is not used and a division line is used instead of the division symbol. For example: $m = k \times 5 \div 8$ simplifies to $m = \dfrac{5k}{8}$

- A formula must have an '=' symbol.
  An expression does not have an '=' symbol.

- To use a formula, substitute the known values into the formula and then work out the unknown values.

- Sometimes substituting known values forms an equation.
  Solve the equation to work out the unknown quantity.

Chapter review

1 Sally has n 10 pence coins and two 20 pence coins.
  a Write a formula for T, the total amount of money that Sally has in pence.
  b Find n when Sally has £2.10

2 The charges on a bus route are worked out using this formula.

> **40p per mile plus 25p**

  a Ameet travels six miles on the bus. How much is he charged?
  b Megan is charged £3.85. How far does she travel?

3 Mrs Johnson's recipe book states:

> **'To roast a leg of lamb: allow 25 minutes per pound and add 30 minutes.'**

How long does it take to cook a leg of lamb that weighs 4 pounds?
Give your answer in hours and minutes.

4 A car hire company makes the following charge:

> **£20 plus £15 per day**

  a How much will it cost to hire a car for four days?
  b Mark pays £170 to hire a car.
  For how many days does he hire the car?

5 Harry hires a minibus for a day.
The mileage cost is worked out using the formula

> **Mileage cost = number of miles travelled × rate per mile**

The rate per mile is £2. The number of miles travelled is 80
  a Work out the mileage cost.
  b The total cost of hiring the minibus is given by the formula

> **Total cost = mileage cost + fixed charge**

  The fixed charge is £30
  Work out the total cost.

6 You are given the formula $X = a^2 + ab$.
  a Calculate X when $a = 5$ and $b = -2$
  b Calculate b when $X = 10$ and $a = 2$

7 **a** Use the formula $a = 5b - \dfrac{c}{4}$ to find the value of a when $b = 12$ and $c = 24$
  b Given that $C = 3A + 2B$, work out:
    i C when $A = 4$ and $B = -3$
    ii the value of B when $C = 14$ and $A = 2$

8 Actual scores in a test, m, are changed to standard scores, s, using the formula

$$s = \frac{m}{2} + 30$$

   a The range of possible values of m is between 0 and 100
      What is the range of possible values of s?
   b Tim's actual score was 48. What is Tim's standard score?
   c Sally's standard score is 72. What was Sally's actual score?
   d David's standard score and actual score are the same.
      What score is this?

9 To change pounds (£) into euros

   Multiply the number of pounds (£) by 1.52

   a Change 380 euros into pounds.
   b Write a formula connecting euros, e, to pounds, p.

10 Jim's telephone bill is calculated each month according to the following rule:
    a fixed charge of £5, plus 4p for every call he makes.
    a In January, Jim paid for 250 calls. What was his total bill in January?
    b In February, Jim's telephone bill was for £13. How many calls did he make in
       February?
    c Using C pence for the total bill in any month and N for the number of calls, write
       down a formula for C in terms of N.

11 The surface area of a gift box in square centimetres can be found using this rule:

    Multiply the width in centimetres, w, by 19.4 and then add 552

    a Write a formula connecting the surface area, S, and w.
    b The surface area of a gift box is 730.48 cm^2.
       Work out the width of the gift box.

12 a A rental company works out its van hire charges, £V, using the formula

       $V = 24d + 0.12m$

       d is the number of days the van is hired.
       m is the distance travelled in miles.
         i Annie hires a van for two days. She travels 142 miles.
            How much is the hire charge?
         ii John hires a van for three days. The total hire charge is £105.60
            How many miles did he drive?
    b The rental company works out its car hire charges, £C, using the formula

       $C = 0.07\,(400d + m)$

       Use the formula to calculate the cost of hiring a car for six days and driving
       395 miles.

Averages

13.1 Mode

The *mode* for a set of data is the value which occurs the most times.

It can also be called the *modal value*. For data that is not numerical, the mode is called the *modal item*.

The mode or modal value is used as a measure of average.

Example 1

Find the mode for each list.

a 3   4   6   7   8   8   9   10

b burger   chips   fish   chips   pizza   burger   chips   salad

Solution 1

a Every number appears once except 8 which appears twice.
So mode = 8

b chips

If there are a lot of numbers in the data set, or the numbers are large, put them in order first.

If all the numbers or items appear the same number of times, there is no mode.

A data set can have two or more modes.

Example 2

Find, if possible, the mode or modes in these lists.
a 9 7 3 4 3 7 8 9 3 5 6 6 3 4 8
b 7 4 6 12 9 10 3 8
c 14 12 16 11 12 13 15 19 16

Solution 2

a Put the data values in order of size.

3 3 3 3 4 4 5 6 6 7 7 8 8 9 9

It is now easier to see that 3 occurs more than any other value. Mode = 3
b Every number in the set is different, so there is no mode.
c Putting the numbers in order:

11 12 12 13 14 15 16 16 19

All the numbers appear once each, except 12 and 16 which both appear twice.
So the modes are 12 and 16
We say that the data has two modes or is *bimodal.*

Exercise A

1 Write down the mode for each list.
There could be more than one mode, or no mode at all.
a 6 7 6 8 9 10
b 12 18 12 17 19 12 12
c 3 9 1 2 0 4 8 7 5
d 15 14 18 12 14 13 19 12 17 10 11 12 13 18 16 11 12
e 9 9 6 6 4 8 3 6 9
f $\frac{1}{2}$ $\frac{3}{4}$ $\frac{3}{4}$ $\frac{1}{4}$ $\frac{1}{2}$ $\frac{1}{2}$ $\frac{3}{4}$ $\frac{1}{2}$
g 0.5 0.2 0.3 0.1 0.4 0.8 0.7 0.9 0.6
h 31 28 31 30 31 30 31 31 30 31 30 31

2 Write down the modal item in each list.
a blue red red green brown red blue blue red
b windy rain sunny snow sunny sunny cloudy
c gold silver bronze bronze gold silver silver gold gold
d tea coffee milk water tea water tea coffee water water
e Sky BBC1 ITV1 C4 Five UK Gold MTV VH1
f win lose lose win draw draw win win lose win
g heads tails tails tails heads heads tails tails heads

3 A bag contains 20 counters.
Five are blue, four are red, four are green and the rest are yellow.
What is the modal colour?

4 **a** What is the modal coin in this set?

b Find **other** ways of making 99p with coins. For each way state the modal coin.

5 Work out the calculations. Find the modal answer for each part.
a $3 + 8$ $12 - 2$ 3×3 $14 - 3$ $7 + 3$ $5 + 11$ $20 - 11$ $3 + 3 + 3$ $13 - 8$
b 2×3 1×6 2×4 3×2 8×1 3×3 9×1 1×6
c 7×8 5×6 3×9 9×4 6×6 6×7 8×5 9×8 8×7

6 Work out the calculations. Find the modal answer for each part.
a 23×7 34×4 29×16 17×8 32×9 26×18 13×36 52×9
b 1×1 2×2 3×3 4×4 5×5 6×6 7×7 8×8 9×9 10×10
$1 \times 1 \times 1$ $2 \times 2 \times 2$ $3 \times 3 \times 3$ $4 \times 4 \times 4$ $5 \times 5 \times 5$ $6 \times 6 \times 6$
$7 \times 7 \times 7$ $8 \times 8 \times 8$ $9 \times 9 \times 9$ $10 \times 10 \times 10$

The mode can be found from a bar chart. The mode has the longest bar.

Example 3

30 children were asked
'What is your favourite drink?'
The bar chart shows the results.

Which is the modal drink?

Solution 3

The longest bar is for orange.
Orange is the modal drink.

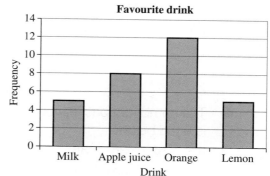

In a frequency table. The mode has the highest frequency.

Example 4

A market trader sells T-shirts.
The table shows how many of each size he sells one day.

What is the modal size of T-shirt?

Size	Number sold
Large	15
Medium	27
Small	23

Solution 4

The modal size of T-shirt is medium because the greatest number of these are sold.

Exercise B

1 30 children were asked
'What is your favourite colour?'
The bar chart shows the results.

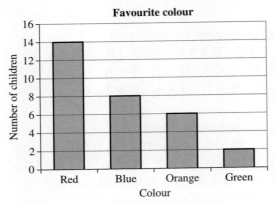

Which colour is the mode?

2 Students were asked how they
travelled to college.
The bar chart shows the results.

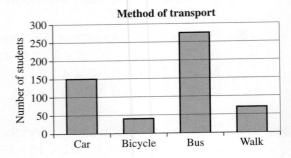

Which is the modal method
of transport?

3 The frequency table shows the number
of times Dexter heard certain
phrases one week.

Which is the modal phrase?

Phrase	Frequency
'You know what I mean'	14
'Over the moon'	3
'If you like'	18
'Get on with your work'	22

4 The number of packets of crisps sold at a school tuck shop each day for two weeks
is listed below.

45   52   36   38   41   51   48   47   33   25

a   Explain why these numbers have no mode.
b   Add one number to the list to make the set have a mode greater than 40.

5 The number of cars passing through a set of traffic lights each time the lights are
green is recorded. The numbers are:

12   15   24   21   18   16   19   22

a   Can you find the mode for this data? Explain your answer.
b   Add two extra values to the set of data to make it bimodal.

6 Write a list of 10 numbers which have a mode of 5

7 Write a list of 7 numbers which have modes of 3 and 4

8 Find the modal letter or letters used in this question.

13.2 Mean

IN THIS SECTION YOU WILL

- Learn how to calculate the mean.
- Understand what a mean represents.
- Learn how to compare the size of two means.

An average is a number which is typical of a set of data. For example, the average speed of cars on a motorway is 68 mph.
The **mean** is the average most commonly used.

There are two steps to finding the mean of a set of values:
Step 1: Add up all the data values to obtain the total.
Step 2: Divide the total by the number of data values.

The mean might not be a whole number.

Example 1

Calculate the mean of each set of data.

a 3   4   5   6   7   8   9   **b** 2   5   7   7   8   10

Solution 1

a *Step 1:* Add up all the data values:
$3 + 4 + 5 + 6 + 7 + 8 + 9 = 42$
Total = 42
Step 2: Divide the total by the number of data values.
There are 7 numbers in the list.
$\frac{42}{7} = 6$ mean = 6

b *Step 1:* $2 + 5 + 7 + 7 + 8 + 10 = 39$
Total = 39
Step 2: There are 6 numbers in the list.
$\frac{39}{6} = 6.5$ mean = 6.5

Example 2

The shoe sizes of eight people are listed below.

7   8   6   5   4.5   8.5   10   4

Calculate the mean shoe size.

> *Solution 2*
>
> *Step 1:* $7 + 8 + 6 + 5 + 4.5 + 8.5 + 10 + 4 = 53$
>
> *Step 2:* $\frac{53}{8} = 6.625$
>
> mean shoe size $= 6.625$

In Example 2, the mean is a value which cannot actually occur.

Often the mean is not a sensible value. For example, in Britain the mean number of children in a family is 2.4. The modal number of children in a family is 2
In this case the mode is a more sensible average to use, because the value 2 can occur in data of number of children, but 2.4 cannot.

Exercise A

1 Calculate the mean of each set of data.

a	8	5	7	3	7		**b**	2	5	7	9	12
c	3	6	7	8	11	13	**d**	2	3	4	5	6
e	7	4	8	3	9	5	**f**	6	4	7	5	8	6	9	11
g	9	9	9	9	9						

2 Debbie asks her friends how many times they went out last week.
Their replies are:

3   1   5   3   4   2   6   4   0   2

Find the mean number of times her friends went out last week.

3 Six children are asked how much pocket money they had last week.
Their replies are:

£3   £5   £11.75   £2.50   £4.75   £15

Calculate the mean amount of pocket money per child.

4 Oli asks his friends how many pets they each have.
Their answers are:

2   0   1   2   1   0   0   3   1   4

Calculate the mean number of pets for Oli's friends.

5 The list shows how many minutes each of 11 pensioners spent queuing at the post office one Monday morning.

22   15   35   27   10   14   17   23   31   23   26

Calculate the mean number of minutes queuing per pensioner.

6 A newsagent kept a record of the number of newspapers he sold each day.

    a Calculate the mean number of newspapers sold per day.

    b On how many days did the newsagent sell more newspapers than the mean?

Day	Number of newspapers sold
Monday	85
Tuesday	97
Wednesday	83
Thursday	77
Friday	65
Saturday	98

7 A cinema records the numbers in the audience for a new film over five days.

Day	Number in audience
Monday	96
Tuesday	96
Thursday	75
Friday	62
Saturday	96

    a Calculate the mean number in the audience per day.

    b How many seats does the cinema probably have? Explain your answer.

To compare two sets of data, it is often helpful to compare the means.

Example 3

The numbers of passengers boarding the Red bus at the bus station one day are:

12   15   12   10   16   18   9   5   14   19

a Calculate the mean number of passengers who boarded the Red bus.

The number of passengers who boarded the Yellow bus at the bus station on the same day had a mean of 16

b Which bus had more passengers boarding at the bus station on average? Explain your answer.

Solution 3

a Total for the Red bus = 130   Mean = $\frac{130}{10} = 13$

b The mean number of passengers boarding the Yellow bus was 16 which is greater than the mean for the Red bus. On average, more passengers boarded the Yellow bus at the bus station than the Red bus.

Example 4

The mean weight of a team of 15 rugby players is 95 kg.
a What is the total weight of the rugby players?
The total weight of a team of 11 football players is 968 kg.
b Who are heavier, on average, the rugby players or the football players?

Solution 4

a Each rugby player weighs an average of 95 kg.
So the total weight of the rugby players = 15 × 95 = 1425 kg.

b There are different numbers of people in each team, so compare the mean weight per player, not the total weights.
The mean weight of the football players = $\frac{968}{11}$ = 88 kg.
So, on average, the rugby players are heavier.

Exercise B

1 a Work out the mean for the following set of data.
      3   4   7   8   5   6   4   3
   b A second set of data has 10 values and a total of 120
      Work out the mean of this second set of data.
   c A third set of data has 9 values. The mean of this third set of data is 7
      Work out the total of this set of data.

2 The table shows the mean number of driving lessons needed to pass the driving test by pupils at two driving schools.
   Which driving school may be the better to learn to drive with?

Driving school	Mean number of lessons
ABC Motoring	18
LearnEZE	15

3 Greasy Joe's burger bar sold the following number of burgers and hot dogs last week.

   Compare the mean number of burgers sold with the mean number of hot dogs sold.

Day	Burgers sold	Hot dogs sold
Monday	12	8
Tuesday	9	9
Wednesday	14	11
Thursday	10	12
Friday	15	20

4 Alex lives in London. He recorded the temperature in degrees Celsius for 10 days in July. The results were:

18   23   20   21   26   27   24   28   25   25

a Calculate the mean temperature.

Alex's friend Hank lives in New York. Hank recorded the temperature for the same 10 days in July. His results were:

34   29   21   38   32   29   21   21   27   23

b Compare the mean temperature in New York and London.

5 The mean of 10 numbers is 252.
Nine of the numbers are:

187   302   343   176   257   243   276   199   350

Find the tenth number.

6 The college refectory and the college snack bar kept a record of the number of sandwiches they sold each day for one week.

Refectory	Number of sandwiches sold	Snack bar	Number of sandwiches sold
Monday	45	Monday	29
Tuesday	52	Tuesday	35
Wednesday	67	Wednesday	55
Thursday	43	Thursday	44
Friday	26	Friday	39

a Calculate the mean number of sandwiches sold per day for:
  i the refectory   **ii** the snack bar.

b Compare the two means.

7 The numbers of people on the roller-coaster at the Pleasure Beach on 12 successive rides are:

52   34   37   46   49   21   35   62   50   29   42   32

The total number of people riding the pirate ship in a half-hour period is 246.

The pirate ship ride lasts exactly 6 minutes, including loading and unloading the riders.

Compare the mean number of people per ride riding the roller-coaster and the pirate ship.

8 Gary recorded the length of ten of his daughter's phone calls.
The lengths, in minutes, were as follows:

5   8   3   4   45   7   3   5   4   1

a Calculate the mean length of time of these calls.
b Gary told his daughter that she spent too long on the phone and told her the mean value as the average. Comment on this.

9 Elsie played bingo 10 times one month. Her winnings were:

£0   £0   £0   £100   £0   £0   £0   £0   £0   £0

   a Find her mean winnings.

   b Why is the answer to part **a** misleading?

13.3 Median

CAN YOU REMEMBER

- How to list values in order of size?
- The meaning of 'odd' and 'even'?
- How to calculate the mean of two numbers?

IN THIS SECTION YOU WILL

- Learn the meaning of the term 'median'.
- Learn how to find the position of the median in a set of data which is arranged in order of size.
- Learn how to find the median for an odd number of values.
- Learn how to calculate the median for an even number of values.

The *median* is a measure of average for a set of data.

To find the median the data must be arranged in order of size. If the set of data has an odd number of values, the median is the middle value when the data is written in order.

To find the median of a small set of data:

Step 1: Put the numbers in order of size.

Step 2: Select the middle value in the ordered set of data.

Example 1

Find the median of this set of data.   4   6   7   3   4   8   9

Solution 1

Step 1:   Put the numbers in order of size.   3   4   4   6   7   8   9

Step 2:   Select the middle value in the ordered set of data.

Cross out one value from each end.   3̷   4̷   4̷   6   7̷   8̷   9̷

Repeat until only the middle value is left.

This is the median value.

The median is 6

To find the median of a large set of data:

Step 1: Put the numbers in order of size.   **Step 2:** Count the number of values (n).

Step 3: Add 1 to the number of values ($n + 1$).   **Step 4:** Divide by 2 $\left(\dfrac{(n + 1)}{2}\right)$

Step 5: Locate the $\dfrac{n + 1}{2}$ th number in the ordered list. The value in this position is the median.

Example 2

Find the median of this set of data.

3   6   8   12   9   4   10

Solution 2

Step 1:   Put the values in order of size. 3   4   6   8   9   10   12

Step 2:   Count the number of values. There are 7 values in this set of data ($n = 7$).

Step 3:   Add 1 to this number. $7 + 1 = 8$ ($n + 1 = 8$)

Step 4:   Divide by 2 $\dfrac{8}{2} = 4$ $\left(\dfrac{n + 1}{2} = 4\right)$

Step 5:   Locate the fourth number in the ordered list. 3   4   6   **8**   9   10   12

The median is 8

The data can be ordered from smallest to largest (ascending) or from largest to smallest (descending).

Exercise A

1   Write down the median of each set of data.

   a 2   3   4   5   6   7   8

   b 3   5   7   9   11

   c 13   12   11   10   9   8   7

   d 10   15   20   25   30

   e 3   6   9   11   16   24   28

   f 66   53   42   38   26   17   14

   g −5   −3   −1   0   3   6   8   −8   8

2   Find the median of each set of data.

   a 6   7   3   8   2   4   9

   b 3   5   4   6   6   5   4   2   6

   c 9   4   7   3   7   1   7   2   8

   d 44   23   33   17   21   48   29

   e 10   12   14   9   8   15   17   9   10

   f 23   22   24   23   26   27   27   23   21

   g −6   3   −5   2   −8   7   −9   10   −4

3 James counts the number of pieces of homework he is set over a period of five weeks. His results are:

3   6   2   7   8

Find the median number of pieces of homework he is set.

4 Sarah counts the number of joggers she sees each day in the park.

8   5   7   3   6   10   12

Work out the median number of joggers that Sarah sees.

5 In a charity event nine students each collect sponsor money. The amounts, in pounds, they collect are

25   37   32   18   10   16   30   35   40

Find the median amount of sponsor money.

6 The sizes of the 11 pairs of shoes in the window of a shoe shop are:

4   6   7   8   5   6   3   5   8   9   10

What is the median shoe size?

7 The number of questions written on each of seven examination papers was:

8   9   7   10   9   8   11

Work out the median number of questions.

8 The times, in seconds, for five boys to complete a 400 m race were:

68.3   65.2   62.0   74.9   67.8

Work out the median time.

9 The number of cars passing through a set of traffic lights when they are on green is listed below.

22   34   33   12   16   18   26

Find the median.

10 The numbers of telephone calls Jade makes each day for three weeks are:

5   3   6   0   2   4   1   1   5   3   4   6   2   2   3   4   5   3   0   3   2

Work out the median number of telephone calls Jade makes.

If the set of data has an even number of values, the median is the mean of the two middle values when the data is written in order.

To find the **positions** of the middle two values in a set of ordered data follow these steps.

Step 1: Put the values in order of size.

Step 2: Count the number of values (n).

Step 3: Add 1 to this number ($n + 1$).

Step 4: Divide by 2 $\left(\dfrac{n + 1}{2} \right)$

This will give you a number ending in $\frac{1}{2}$

For example in a set of data with 10 values $\dfrac{n+1}{2} = 5\frac{1}{2}$

This shows that the fifth and the sixth values
are the middle two values.

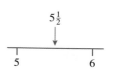

Step 5: Locate the two middle values and calculate their mean.

The median need not be a value from the original list.

Example 3

Calculate the median of this set of data.

4   6   7   3   4   8   9   8

Solution 3

Step 1:   Put the values in order of size. 3   4   4   6   7   8   8   9

Step 2:   Count the number of values ($n = 8$).

Step 3:   Add 1 to this number ($n + 1 = 9$)

Step 4:   Divide by 2 $\dfrac{(n+1)}{2} = \dfrac{8+1}{2} = \dfrac{9}{2} = 4\frac{1}{2}$

Step 5:   The fourth and fifth values are the middle two values.

3   4   4   **6**   **7**   8   8   9

Calculate the mean of the middle two values. $\dfrac{6+7}{2} = 6.5$

The median of this set of data is 6.5

Exercise B

1 Calculate the median for each set of data.

  a   3   5   6   8   8   9   10   10

  b   1   2   3   4

  c   9   8   7   5   5   3

  d   −6   −4   −3   −1   0   2   3   5   7   9

  e   23   19   16   14   12   11   8   5

  f   33   34   37   44   49   53   55   57   67   69   78   99

  g   −23   −20   −18   −16   −12   −10   −4   6   9   14

2 Calculate the median for each set of data.

  a   10   12   18   9

  b   22   27   31   25   28   33   25   23

  c   86   83   88   79   89   92

  d   3   15   7   12   13   18   0   13   16   14

  e   23   13   21   11   15   19   13   12   24   25   12   16

  f   4   6   8   1   3   9   10   12

  g   7   2   5   3   4   4   4   6

h	8	3	5	6	2	6	7	9	1	10	2	9
i	5	−4	9	7	−3	8	−12	10	−8	13		
j	−50	−45	−31	17	19	32	−12	18	24	32	0	−21

3 Enid asks some friends how many TVs they have at home. Her results are:

3   4   3   2   4   5   3   3   2   1

What is the median number of TVs?

4 Ian asks his friends to record how many text messages they each receive the next day. Their results are:

2   0   3   15   13   5   18   20

Calculate the median number of text messages.

5 For eight days, Joe counted the number of cars parked in a car park at 8 am. The results were:

48   65   53   39   55   72   34   67

Calculate the median.

6 Each day for two weeks the manager of a small museum records the number of people who enter the museum. Her results are:

22   25   16   34   38   41   18   10   16   34   39   44   38   20

Calculate the median.

7 Each day a snack bar records the number of flapjacks sold. The results are:

35   48   65   68   79   23   53   72

Calculate the median number of flapjacks sold.

8 The numbers of passengers boarding the earliest bus each day are:

15   18   22   14   12   16   19   24   30   26   18   16

Calculate the median.

9 a Write down five numbers that have a median of 8
  b Write down four numbers that have a median of 10
  c Write down nine numbers that have a median of 0
  d Write down 12 numbers that have a median of 100

10 a Write down four numbers that have a median of 9 and a mean of 10
  b Write down four numbers that have a median of 7.5
  c Write down six numbers that have a median of 2.5 and a mean of 4
  d Write down eight numbers that have a median of 5, a mode of 6 and a mean of 4

13.4 Range

IN THIS SECTION YOU WILL

- Learn the meaning of the term 'range'.
- Learn how to calculate the range of small sets of data.
- Learn how to calculate the range from a bar chart.
- Learn how to calculate the range from a pictogram.

The *range* of a set of data is the difference between the largest value and the smallest value in the set of data.

Range = largest value − smallest value

The range measures the spread of the data.

Example 1

Calculate the range of the following set of data.

| 12 | 16 | 18 | 22 | 11 | 30 | 29 | 24 | 14 |

Solution 1

Range = largest value − smallest value

= 30 − 11 = 19

The range is 19

Exercise A

1 Calculate the range of each set of data.

a 2   4   6   8   10   13   16

b 1   5   7   9   14

c 21   17   14   12   10   8   5

d 35   33   27   16   14   10

e 7   8   10   12   13   14   16

f −5   −4   −3   −2   −1   0   1   2   3   4

g −15   −12   −10   −7   −3   2   5   7   11

h 2   6   9   12   16   27   34   36   48

i 32   28   23   19   13   10   6   2

j 15   12   9   5   2   −1   −5   −7

2 Calculate the range of each set of data.

  a 4   6   3   7   10   12

  b 6   5   7   3   9   2   10   7

  c 23   25   13   17   28   34   16

  d 64   67   85   53   25   36   17

  e −5   −4   −13   −2   −10   0   1   12

  f 14   31   10   18   −5   2   0   −13

  g 45   63   77   23   18   0   9

  h 5   5   5   5   5   5   5

  i −20   −14   −23   −28   −15   −10

  j 0   −2   −4   −6   −10   −5

3 The temperature, in degrees Celsius, is recorded every three hours on one day. The results are:

  8   5   2   1   −1   −2   0   4

Calculate the range of these temperatures.

4 Eight students are sponsored for a charity event. The number of sponsors each student has is:

  4   5   16   2   13   10   9   18

Calculate the range of these numbers of sponsors.

5 The number of people living in each of ten houses is listed below.

  3   5   4   6   2   1   8   4   2   7

Write down the range of the number of people living in these houses.

6 The numbers of people queuing at a post office every Monday morning at 9 am, for a 9-week period, are shown below.

  20   25   31   19   22   33   17   27   22

Calculate the range of the numbers of people queuing.

7 The playing times, in seconds, of 10 tracks on a CD are:

  85   123   143   155   170   156   163   180   195   125

Calculate the range of these times.

8 A doctor records how many minutes he spends with each patient one morning. His results are:

  10   12   5   3   8   15   2   11   22   14

Calculate the range of these times.

9 The maximum daytime temperatures (in degrees Celsius) were recorded each day for two weeks in January. The results were:

  10   8   6   4   6   2   5   −1   −2   3   6   2   −4   1

Calculate the range of these temperatures.

10 Eight students were each timed, in minutes, to complete a test. Their results were:

25   28   33   37   31   27   23   19

Calculate the range of these times.

The range can be calculated from a bar chart or pictogram.

Example 2

The bar chart shows the annual attendances at a Christmas lecture over three years.
a Which year had the highest attendance?
b Calculate the range of the attendances.

Solution 2

a 2005 had the highest attendance.
b Range = largest value − smallest value

= 95 − 60 = 35

The range of attendances is 35

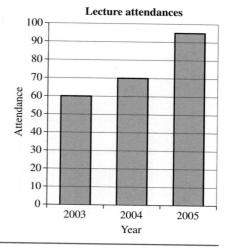

Example 3

The pictogram shows the number of dentists in each of five towns.
a Which town has the highest number of dentists?
b Calculate the range of the number of dentists.

Solution 3

a Town D has the highest number of dentists.
b Range = largest value − smallest value

= 15 − 4 = 11

The range of the number of dentists is 11

Town	Number of dentists
A	
B	
C	
D	
E	

Exercise B

1 The bar chart shows the total number of fish caught in each of three matches.
  a In which match were the most fish caught?
  b Calculate the range of the number of fish caught.

2 The bar chart shows the number of houses on three estates.
  a Which estate had the least number of houses?
  b How many houses were there altogether on the three estates?
  c Calculate the range of the number of houses on these estates.

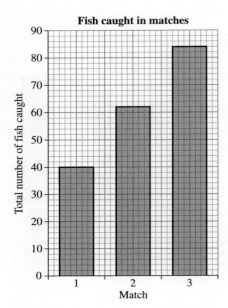

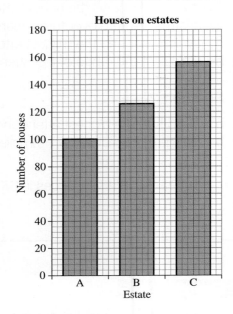

3 The bar chart shows the number of girls in each school year that were wearing trainers one day.
  a How many girls were wearing trainers in Year 9?
  b Which year group had the smallest number of girls wearing trainers?
  c Calculate the range of the numbers of girls wearing trainers.

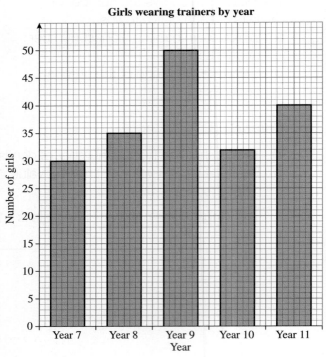

4 The bar chart shows the number of CDs owned by three girls.

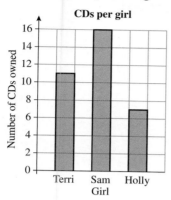

CDs per girl

a How many more CDs does Sam own than Terri?

b Calculate the range of the number of CDs owned by these girls.

5 The bar line graph shows the number of pens that each of four students had in their pencil cases.

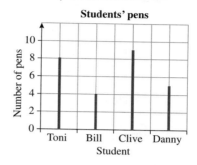

Students' pens

a Who had the most pens?

b How many more pens did Clive have than Danny?

c What is the range of the number of pens?

6 The horizontal bar chart shows the number of college leavers in each term of 2005.

a Which term had the greatest number of leavers?

b Oliver says that the range of the number of leavers is 11
  i Explain why Oliver is not correct.
  ii Calculate the range of the number of leavers.

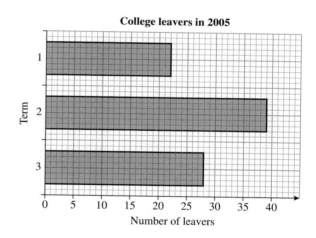

College leavers in 2005

7 The pictogram shows the number of DVDs owned by each of four friends.

Key ⊙ = 10 DVDs

Megan	⊙ ⊙
Ruth	⊙ ◖
Rachel	⊙ ⊙ ⊙ ◖
Dina	⊙

a How many DVDs does Megan own?

b Explain why the range of the number of DVDs owned is 25

8 The number of letters received each day over a week is shown in the pictogram.
   a On which day were the most letters received?
   b Calculate the range of the number of letters received.

Key ✉ = 2 letters

Monday	✉ ✉
Tuesday	✉ ✉ ◁
Wednesday	✉ ◁
Thursday	◁
Friday	✉ ✉ ✉ ✉
Saturday	✉

9 The number of drinks sold in a café each day one week is shown in the pictogram.
   a How many more drinks were sold on Thursday than on Wednesday?
   b Calculate the range of the number of drinks sold.

Key 🥤 = 4 drinks

Monday	🥤 🥤 🥤 🥤
Tuesday	🥤 🥤
Wednesday	🥤 🥤 🥤 🥤
Thursday	🥤 🥤 🥤 🥤 🥤 🥤
Friday	🥤 🥤 🥤 🥤 🥤

Chapter summary

- The mode of a data set is the value or item that occurs the most times.
- If there are a lot of numbers in the data set, or the numbers are large, put them in order first.
- Some data sets have no mode.
- Some data sets have two modes (bimodal data).
- The mode can be found from a bar chart. The longest bar represents the mode.
- In a frequency table the mode is the class that has the greatest frequency.
- An average is a number which is typical of a set of data.
- The **mean** is the average most commonly used.
- There are two steps to finding the mean of a set of values:
  - Step 1: Add up all the data values to obtain the total.
  - Step 2: Divide the total by the number of data values.
- The mean might not be a whole number.
- The mean may be a value that cannot actually occur, e.g. 2.4 children.
- To compare two sets of data, it is often helpful to compare the means.
- The median is a measure of average.
- To find the median the data must be put in order.
- If the set of data has an odd number of values then the median is the middle value when the data is written in order.
- If the data has an even number of values, then the median is the mean of the middle two values when the data is written in order.
- To find the median for a small set of data:
  - Step 1: Put the numbers in order of size.
  - Step 2: Select the middle value in the ordered set of data.
- To find the median of a larger set of data:
  - Step 1: Put the values in order.
  - Step 2: Count the number of values (n).
  - Step 3: Add 1 to this number ($n + 1$).
  - Step 4: Divide by 2 $\left(\dfrac{n + 1}{2}\right)$.
  - Step 5: Locate the $\dfrac{n + 1}{2}$th number in the ordered list.
- If n is a whole number, it gives the position of the middle value.
- If n ends in $\frac{1}{2}$, the whole numbers either side on the number line give the positions of the two middle values.
- Where there are two middle values, the median is the mean of these two values.
- The range is a measure of the spread of the data.
- Range = largest value − smallest value
- The range can be calculated from a set of data.
- The range can be found from a bar chart or a pictogram.

Chapter review

1 Eleven pupils took part in a sponsored swim.
The amount collected, in pounds, by each pupil, is as follows:

2   4   5   7   8   5   7   4   9   9   7

a Find the median of these amounts.

b What is the range of the amounts collected?

2 Megan records the number of goals scored by
her favourite football team in each of 40 matches.

a Write down the mode of the number of
goals scored.

b What is the range of the number of
goals scored?

Number of goals	Frequency
0	10
1	13
2	12
3	3
4	2

3 Diane asked her friends what they thought they spent the most money on.
Their replies were:

CDs   clothes   clothes   books   CDs   food
CDs   clothes   shoes   shoes   clothes

What was the modal response?

4 Sadie asks ten friends how many brothers and sisters they have. Her results are:

0   1   3   4   2   1   1   3   2   1

a Work out the median.   **b** Calculate the mean.

5 The number of ferries leaving a harbour each hour is shown below.

2   10   8   3   4   6   4   5   4   11   9

a Find the median of this data.   **b** Write down the mode of this data.

c Calculate the mean of this data.

6 This passage is from a reading book for children at primary school.

> *Harry went to his bedroom.*
> *He lay down on his bed and*
> *went to sleep.*

Number of letters in each word	Tally	Frequency
1		
2		
3		
4		
5		
6		
7		

a Complete this frequency table
by counting the number of
letters in each word in the
passage.

b Write down the mode of the
number of letters in a word in
the passage.

c What do you think would happen to the average word length if a similar passage
were chosen from a novel for adults?

7 The bar chart shows the number of people who used the Number 36 bus from Axton to Bixton on each day in a week.

a How many people used the bus on Thursday?

b On which day did the largest number of people travel?

c On Sunday, six Number 36 buses made the journey from Axton to Bixton. Calculate the mean number of passengers per bus on Sunday.

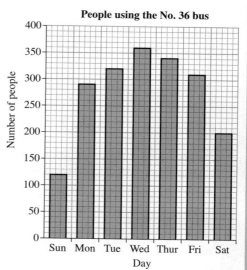

8 Dina asks each of her friends to record how many text messages they receive one day. Here are her results:

1   2   0   1   3   1   2   27   5   1   2

a Write down the mode.   b Find the median.

9 Hillary records the number of pets kept by each of the girls in her class. She recorded:

1   6   1   2   3   2   5   1   4   3   1

a Find the range.   b Calculate the mean.   c Find the median.

Hillary also asks ten of her teachers how many pets they have. The replies are:

0   1   1   0   2   1   2   0   0   3

d Compare the mean number of pets owned by Hillary's teachers with the mean number of pets owned by Hillary's classmates.

10 A company puts this advert in the local paper.

Kitchens Indirect
Fitter needed – average wage over £400 per week

The table shows the wages of seven people who work for the company.

a What is the mode of these wages?

b What is the median wage?

c Calculate the mean wage.

d Explain why this advert is misleading.

Job	Wage per week (£)
Apprentice	200
Cleaner	200
Electrician	375
Fitter	295
Manager	800
Sales adviser	575
Senior fitter	425

11 The sizes of pairs of shoes that a shop sells one morning are:

5   6   6   9   9   6   11   3   8   7   10

a What is the mode of the data?   b What is the median shoe size?

c Which of the mode or the median would be more useful when the shop is ordering more shoes? Explain your answer.

14

Solid shapes

14.1 Three-dimensional shapes

IN THIS SECTION YOU WILL

■ Learn the difference between a 2-D shape and a 3-D shape.
■ Learn the names of common 3-D shapes (solids).
■ Understand and use the terms 'face', 'edge' and 'vertex' for 3-D shapes.
■ Identify planes of symmetry of 3-D shapes.
■ Draw nets of 3-D shapes.

Triangles, rectangles and parallelograms are two-dimensional shapes. They have two dimensions – length and width.

Shapes that have a third dimension – height or thickness – are called *three-dimensional* (3-D) shapes or *solids*.

Here are some common three-dimensional shapes:

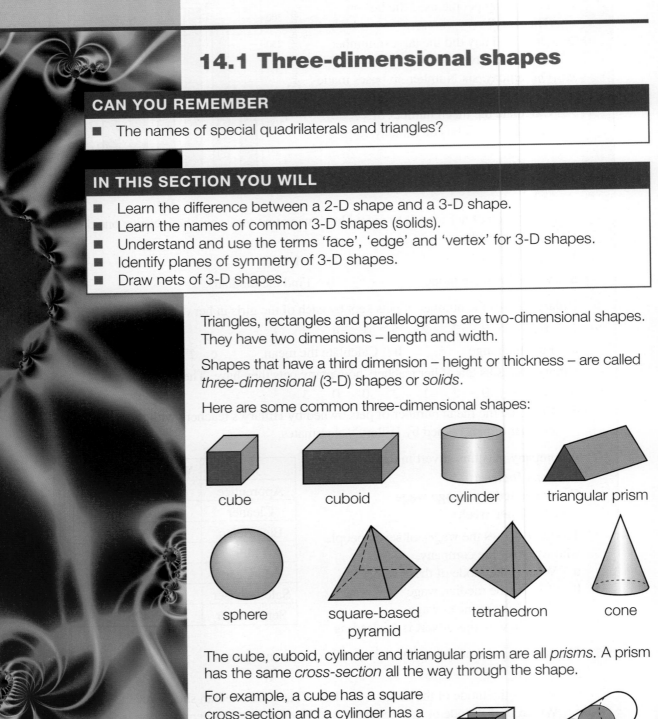

cube   cuboid   cylinder   triangular prism

sphere   square-based pyramid   tetrahedron   cone

The cube, cuboid, cylinder and triangular prism are all *prisms*. A prism has the same *cross-section* all the way through the shape.

For example, a cube has a square cross-section and a cylinder has a circular cross-section.

Three-dimensional shapes can have *plane symmetry*. A *plane of symmetry* divides the 3-D shape in two so that one half is the mirror image of the other half.

For example, a cuboid has three planes of symmetry.

 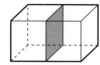 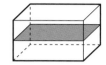

The surfaces of a three-dimensional shape are called *faces*.
The line where two faces meet is called an *edge*.
The point where edges meet is called a *vertex* (plural *vertices*).

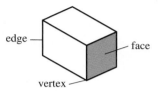

 A sphere has no edges or vertices and just one face.

Example 1

Write down the number of:
a faces   **b** edges   **c** vertices
for a cuboid.

Solution 1

a A cuboid has 6 faces (front, back, top, bottom and two ends).
b A cuboid has 12 edges.
c A cuboid has 8 vertices.

Exercise A

1 Here is a list of some mathematical shapes.

cylinder   square   rhombus   cone   parallelogram
triangular prism   sphere   rectangle

Write down from the list:
a the two-dimensional shapes   **b** the three-dimensional shapes

2 Write down the number of:
i faces   **ii** vertices   **iii** edges

for the following solids:
a cube
b triangular prism
c tetrahedron
d square-based pyramid

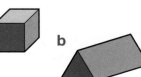

3 The diagram shows a triangular prism.
   Each end of the prism is an equilateral triangle.
   How many planes of symmetry does this prism have?

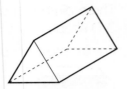

4 Here are some objects.

a  **b**   **c**  **d**

e   **f**   **g**

Copy the table below but add 6 more rows. Write in:
 i the name of the object and its mathematical name
 ii the number of faces, edges and vertices.
The first one has been done for you.

	Name of object	Name of solid	Number of faces	Number of edges	Number of vertices
a	box	cuboid	6	12	8
b					

A three-dimensional shape is made from a two-dimensional plan called a *net*.

This net is folded to form the cube.

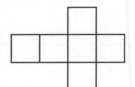

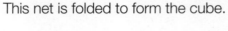

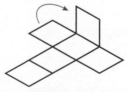 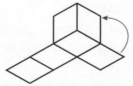 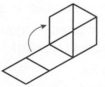

The diagrams below show how a triangular prism unfolds into its net.

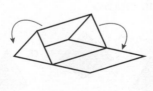 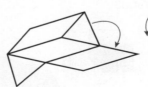 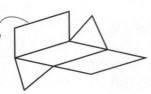 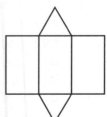

Example 2

Sketch the net of this cuboid. Label all the lengths.

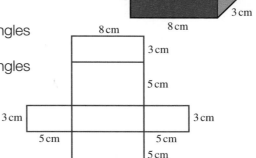

Solution 2

The cuboid has two faces which are rectangles measuring 8 cm by 5 cm (front and back).
The cuboid has two faces which are rectangles measuring 8 cm by 3 cm (top and base).
The two ends are rectangles measuring 5 cm by 3 cm.

Draw the net accurately on centimetre-squared paper.

Exercise B

1   Which one of these nets will **not** make a cube?

a   b   c   d

2   Sketch a net of each of these solids. Label all the lengths on your sketch.

a 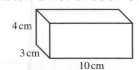   b 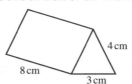   c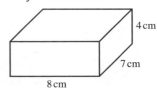

d 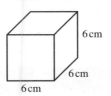   e 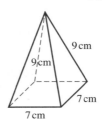   f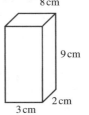

3   Name and sketch the solid which can be made from each of these nets.
Where dimensions are given write them on your sketch.

a    b 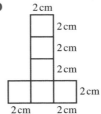   c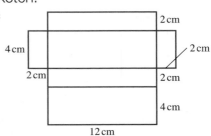

d

7 cm

6 cm

5 cm

6 cm   6 cm

6 cm

e

f

4 On centimetre squared paper make accurate drawings of the nets of these solid figures.

    a A cuboid 5 cm long, 3 cm wide and 2 cm high.

    b A cube with edges of 4 cm.

    c A cuboid 7 cm long, 2 cm wide and 4 cm high.

5 Each of these solid shapes is made from two solids.
Copy and complete the table below.

	Name of two solids used	Number of faces	Number of edges	Number of vertices
a				
b				

a

b

c

d

14.2 Volume of a cuboid

CAN YOU REMEMBER

- How to find the area of a rectangle by counting squares?
- The formula for finding the area of a rectangle?

IN THIS SECTION YOU WILL

- Find volumes of cuboids by counting cubes.
- Find volumes of cuboids using a formula.
- Calculate volumes of shapes made from cubes and cuboids.

Volume is the amount of space taken up by a three-dimensional shape.
This cube is 1 cm long, 1 cm wide and 1 cm high.
Its volume is 1 cubic centimetre, written 1 cm³.

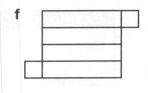

1 cm

1 cm³

1 cm

1 cm

Very small volumes can be measured in cubic millimetres, mm³.
Large volumes can be measured in cubic metres, m³, or cubic kilometres, km³.

Volume can be found by counting the number of cubic centimetres in a three-dimensional shape.

Example 1

These cuboids are made out of centimetre cubes.
What is the volume of each cuboid?

a
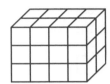

b

Solution 1

a   The shape is made of 8 cubes so the volume is 8 cm^3.

b   This shape is made from three layers of cubes.
    There are $4 \times 2 = 8$ cubes in each layer.
    So there are $3 \times 8 = 24$ cubes in the cuboid.
    Its volume is 24 cm^3.
    The volume of the cuboid above is found by multiplying

$$4 \quad \times \quad 2 \quad \times \quad 3$$
$$\text{length} \times \text{width} \times \text{height}$$

The volume of any cuboid can be calculated using the formula:

Volume = length × width × height

This can be written using letter symbols as $V = l \times w \times h$ or $V = lwh$

Since length × width is the area of the rectangular base of the cuboid, the formula
can also be written

Volume = area of base × height

Example 2

What is the volume of each cuboid?

a
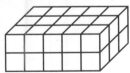

b
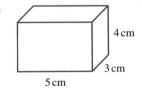

4 cm

3 cm

5 cm

Solution 2

a   For this cuboid, length = 5 cm, width = 3 cm, height = 2 cm
    Volume = length × width × height = $5 \times 3 \times 2 = 30$ cm^3

b   Volume = length × width × height
    Volume = $5 \times 3 \times 4 = 60$ cm^3

Exercise A

1 These cuboids are made out of centimetre cubes.
They are not drawn lifesize.
  i Count the number of cubes in one layer of each shape.
  ii Hence calculate the volume of each shape.

a    **b** 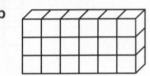   **c**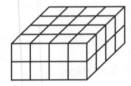

d   **e** 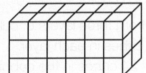   **f**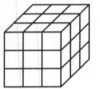

2 Repeat question **1** using the formula $V = lwh$ to work out the volume of each cuboid. Check that your answers match your answers to question **1**.

3 For each of the empty boxes below work out:
  i how many centimetre cubes are needed to cover the bottom of the box
  ii how many layers of cubes will fit in the box
  iii the volume of the box in cm^3.

a 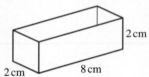   **b** 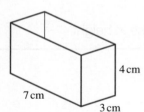   **c**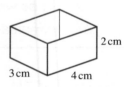

d 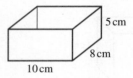   **e** 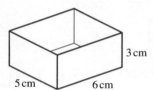   **f**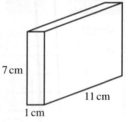

4 These solid shapes are made from 1-centimetre cubes.
Find the volume of each shape.

a   **b** 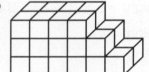   **c**   **d**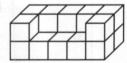

5 Calculate the volume of these cubes and cuboids.
State the units in your answers.

a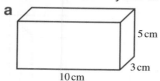
5 cm
10 cm
3 cm

b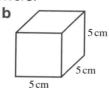
5 cm
5 cm
5 cm

c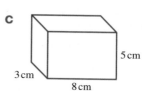
5 cm
3 cm
8 cm

d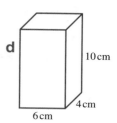
10 cm
4 cm
6 cm

6 Which has the largest volume:
a cube of side 6 cm or a cuboid measuring 8 cm by 6 cm by 2 cm?
Show your working.

7 The table below gives the measurements of five cuboids.
Copy and complete the table.

Cuboid	Length (cm)	Width (cm)	Height (cm)	Volume (cm³)
a	4.5	3.2	7	
b	13	9.7	8.4	
c	27	15	10	
d	7.4	3.9	5	
e	1.4	0.8	0.5	

8 A box of biscuits is in the shape of a cuboid.
The box is 9.4 cm long, 4.2 cm wide and 3.3 cm high.
Find the volume of the box.

9 A concrete beam is 8.6 m long, 0.6 m wide and
1.4 m high. Calculate how many cubic metres
of concrete were used to make this beam.

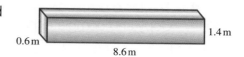
0.6 m
8.6 m
1.4 m

Example 3

A cuboid is 5 cm long and 4 cm wide. The volume of this cuboid is 60 cm³.
Calculate the height of the cuboid.

Solution 3

Sketch the cuboid and label the height h.

Volume = length × width × height

Substituting in the values given:

$$60 = 5 \times 4 \times h$$
$$60 = 20 \times h$$

Divide both sides by 20 $60 \div 20 = 20 \times h \div 20$

$$3 = h$$

Height = 3 cm

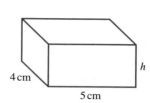
4 cm
5 cm
h

Exercise B

1 Calculate the height of these cuboids.

a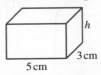

5 cm 3 cm h
Volume = 60 cm^3

b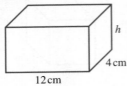

12 cm 4 cm h
Volume = 480 cm^3

c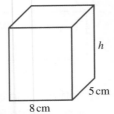

8 cm 5 cm h
Volume = 120 cm^3

d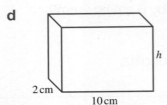

2 cm 10 cm h
Volume = 180 cm^3

e

h 15 cm 2 cm
Volume = 150 cm^3

f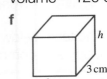

3 cm 3 cm h
Volume = 27 cm^3

2 Use the formula $V = lwh$ to find
 a l when $w = 3$ cm, $h = 5$ cm and $V = 90$ cm^3
 b w when $l = 15$ cm, $h = 10$ cm and $V = 300$ cm^3
 c l when $w = 5$ cm, $h = 9$ cm and $V = 180$ cm^3
 d w when $l = 12$ cm, $h = 12$ cm and $V = 144$ cm^3

3 A box of breakfast cereal is 25 cm high and 20 cm wide. Its volume is 2500 cm^3.
 Calculate the length of the box.

4 The table below gives the measurements of five cuboids.
 Copy and complete the table.

Cuboid	Length (cm)	Width (cm)	Height (cm)	Volume (cm^3)
a	12.2	4.5		384.3
b		9	22	2574
c	3.5		3.5	42.875
d	20	1.4		14
e		7.5	32	4200

5 A cuboid-shaped packet 4 cm wide, 4 cm long and 12 cm high holds
 eight biscuits. Calculate the volume of:
 a the packet **b** one biscuit

6 Twelve dictionaries are packed tightly into a box.
 The box is 28 cm long, 22 cm wide and 18 cm high.
 Calculate the volume of:
 a the box **b** one dictionary

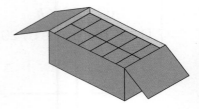

Chapter summary

- A three-dimensional shape has length, width and height.
- A plane of symmetry divides a 3-D shape into two so that one half is the mirror image of the other.
- The surfaces of a three-dimensional shape are called faces.
- The line where two faces meet is called an edge.
- The point where edges meet is called a vertex.
- A net is a two-dimensional drawing that makes a three-dimensional shape.
- The volume of a shape is the amount of space occupied by that shape.
- Volume is measured in cubic units, e.g. cm^3, m^3.
- The volume of a cuboid can be found using the formula:
  Volume = length × width × height = $l \times w \times h = lwh$
  or Volume = area of base × height

Chapter review

1 This shape is made of centimetre cubes.
What is the volume of the shape?

2 A rectangular box has length 5 cm, width 2 cm and height 4 cm.
The box is to be filled with centimetre cubes.

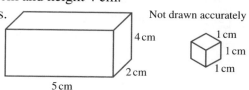

Not drawn accurately

a How many centimetre cubes are needed to fill the box?

b Write down the volume of the box.

3 The diagram shows a cuboid of length 7 cm, width 3 cm and height 2 cm.
Draw the net of the cuboid.

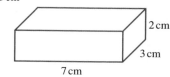

4 The diagram shows the net of a solid.

a What is the name of the solid?

b The net has rotational symmetry.
What order of rotational symmetry does it have?

c Copy the diagram and add two more squares so that it has line symmetry.

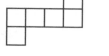

5 The diagram shows a cuboid.

a How many faces does a cuboid have?

b Draw an accurate net of the cuboid.

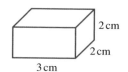

6 The diagram shows a triangular prism.

  a Write down the number of:

    i vertices   **ii** faces   **iii** edges

  b Make a labelled sketch of a net of
    this triangular prism.

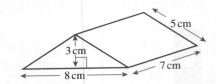

7 A hall is in the shape of a cuboid.
The hall is 25 m long, 14 m wide and 3.5 m high.
Calculate the volume of the hall.

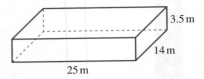

8 The diagram shows the net of a cube.
The side of the cube is 7 cm.

  a Calculate the area of the net, stating your units.

The net is folded to make the cube.

  b Calculate the volume of the cube.

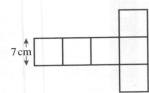

9 A cuboid is shown opposite.
The cuboid has volume 40 cm³.
The base is 4.9 cm long and 3.4 cm wide.
Calculate the height of the cuboid.
Give your answer correct to one decimal
place.

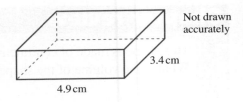

10 The diagram shows the net of a cuboid
on a 1 cm grid.
The net can be folded to make a cuboid.

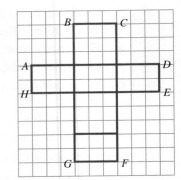

  a Calculate the surface area of the cuboid.

  b Calculate the volume of the cuboid.

  c When the net is folded, corner *A* is joined to two other corners.
    Write down the letters of the corners that join *A* when the net is folded.

Sequences

15.1 Continuing and completing sequences

CAN YOU REMEMBER

- The meaning of 'difference'?
- How to add, subtract, multiply and divide positive and negative integers?

IN THIS SECTION YOU WILL

- Use a term-to-term rule to continue a sequence.
- Describe in words a rule for continuing in a sequence.
- Use a term-to-term rule to find missing terms in a sequence.

A *sequence* is a list of numbers that follows a pattern. The numbers in a sequence are called *terms*.

For example, in the sequence 3, 7, 11, 15, …

1st term = 3
2nd term = 7   2nd term − 1st term = 7 − 3 = 4
3rd term = 11   3rd term − 2nd term = 11 − 7 = 4
4th term = 15   4th term − 3rd term = 15 − 11 = 4

The *difference* between consecutive terms is always 4

A *term-to-term rule* that describes the difference pattern in the sequence. It can be used to continue a sequence or to find missing terms in a sequence.

The sequence 3, 7, 11, 15, … has term-to-term rule $\boxed{\text{Add } 4}$

Term-to-term rules can use any number operations.

For example, in the sequence 2, 8, 32, 128, … the term-to-term rule is $\boxed{\text{Multiply by } 4}$

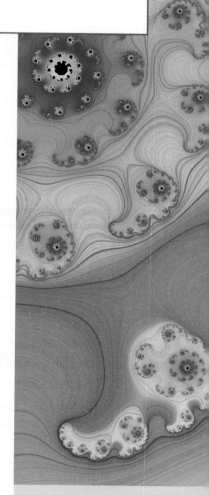

Example 1

a   Describe in words the rule for continuing the sequence 5, 11, 17, 23, ...
Use the rule to find the next two terms in the sequence.
Repeat part **a** for the following sequences.

b   31, 25, 19, 13, ...

c   3, 6, 12, 24, ...

d   1, 3, 4, 7, 11, ...

Solution 1

a   5, 11, 17, 23, ...

$11 - 5 = 6, 17 - 11 = 6, 23 - 17 = 6, ...$

The term-to-term rule is $\boxed{\text{Add 6}}$

$$5 \xrightarrow{+6} 11 \xrightarrow{+6} 17 \xrightarrow{+6} 23 \xrightarrow{+6} ... \xrightarrow{+6} ...$$

5th term $= 23 + 6 = \mathbf{29}$
6th term $= \mathbf{29} + 6 = \mathbf{35}$

The next two terms are 29 and 35

c   3, 6, 12, 24, ...

$$3 \xrightarrow{\times 2} 6 \xrightarrow{\times 2} 12 \xrightarrow{\times 2} 24 \xrightarrow{\times 2} ... \xrightarrow{\times 2} ...$$

The term-to-term rule is $\boxed{\text{Multiply by 2}}$

5th term $= 24 \times 2 = \mathbf{48}$
6th term $= \mathbf{48} \times 2 = \mathbf{96}$

The next two terms are 48 and 96

b   31, 25, 19, 13, ...

$$31 \xrightarrow{-6} 25 \xrightarrow{-6} 19 \xrightarrow{-6} 13 \xrightarrow{-6} ... \xrightarrow{-6} .$$

The term-to-term rule is $\boxed{\text{Subtract 6}}$

5th term $= 13 - 6 = \mathbf{7}$
6th term $= \mathbf{7} - 6 = \mathbf{1}$

The next two terms are 7 and 1

d   1, 3, 4, 7, 11, ...

The term-to-term rule is

$\boxed{\text{Add the previous two terms}}$

6th term $= 7 + 11 = 18$
7th term $= 11 + 18 = 29$

The next two terms are 18 and 29

Example 2

Find the missing terms in the sequence 3, 7, 11, ..., ..., 23, 27,

Solution 2

3, 7, 11, ..., ..., 23, 27,

$$3 \xrightarrow{+4} 7 \xrightarrow{+4} 11 \xrightarrow{+4} ... \xrightarrow{+4} ... \xrightarrow{+4} 23 \xrightarrow{+4} 27$$

The difference between consecutive terms is 4

The term-to-term rule is $\boxed{\text{Add 4}}$

4th term $= 11 + 4 = 15$ 5th term $= 15 + 4 = 19$

The inverse term-to-term rule can be used to find previous terms in a sequence.

Example 3

A sequence has term-to-term rule │Add 7│
The third term of the sequence is 4
a Find the fourth term of the sequence.
b Find the first term of the sequence.

Solution 3

a The sequence is

$$... \rightarrow ... \rightarrow 4 \rightarrow ...$$
$$+7 \quad +7 \quad +7$$

4th term = 3rd term + 7 = 4 + 7 = 11

b Look at the sequence in reverse, using the inverse term-to-term rule.

$$... \leftarrow ... \leftarrow 4 \leftarrow 11$$
$$-7 \quad -7 \quad -7$$

2nd term = 3rd term − 7 = 4 − 7 = −3
1st term = 2nd term − 7 = −3 − 7 = −10

Exercise A

1 Describe in words the rule for continuing each of these sequences.
   Then write down the next three terms.
   a 1, 3, 5, 7, ...
   b 1, 4, 7, 10, ...
   c 2, 4, 6, 8, ...
   d 7, 13, 19, 25, ...
   e 2, 5, 8, 11, ...
   f 7, 11, 15, 19, ...
   g 1, 6, 11, 16, ...
   h 30, 39, 48, 57, ...
   i 8, 15, 22, 29, ...
   j 7, 10, 13, 16, ...
   k 4, 10, 16, 22, ...
   l 17, 32, 47, 62, ...
   m 2, 6, 10, 14, ...
   n 10, 23, 36, 49, ...
   o 11, 23, 35, 47, ...

2 Describe in words the rule for continuing each of these sequences.
   Then write down the next three terms.
   a 35, 30, 25, 20, ...
   b 30, 26, 22, 18, ...
   c 60, 50, 40, 30, ...
   d 36, 30, 24, 18, ...
   e 27, 23, 19, 15, ...
   f 32, 29, 26, 23, ...
   g 14, 11, 8, 5, ...
   h 30, 21, 12, 3, ...
   i 16, 13, 10, 7, ...
   j 27, 7, −13, −33, ...

3 Give the term-to-term rule for each of these sequences.
   Then write down the next two terms.
   a 1, 2, 4, 8, ...
   b 5, 10, 20, 40, ...
   c 4, 20, 100, 500, ...
   d 1, 10, 100, 1000, ...
   e $\frac{1}{4}$, 1, 4, 16, ...
   f $\frac{1}{5}$, 1, 5, 25, ...
   g 0.3, 3, 30, 300, ...
   h 0.001, 0.01, 0.1, 1, ...

4 Give the term-to-term rule for each of these sequences.
Then write down the next two terms.

a 4000, 2000, 1000, 500, …   b 100 000, 10 000, 1000, 100, …

c 288, 144, 72, 36, …   d 12 500, 2500, 500, 100, …

e 36, 18, 9, 4.5, …   f 20 000, 2000, 200, 20, …

g 3000, 300, 30, 3, …   h 500, 50, 5, 0.5, …

5 Give the term-to-term rule for each of these sequences.
Then write down the next three terms.

a −1, 8, 17, 26, …   b 15, 12, 9, 6, …

c −9, −7, −5, −3, …   d 11, 3, −5, −13, …

e 2, 20, 200, 2000, …   f 6000, 600, 60, 6, …

g 0.1, 0.3, 0.5, 0.7, …   h 1, 3, 9, 27, …

i −1, 3, −9, 27, …   j 32, 16, 8, 4, …

k 3, −6, 12, −24, …   l 0.2, 0.4, 0.6, 0.8, …

6 Write down the next two terms in each of these sequences.

a 1, 2, 3, 5, 8, …   b 1, 3, 4, 7, 11, …

c −2, 1, −1, 0, −1, …   d 1, 2, 3, 6, 11, 20, …

e 1, 3, 5, 9, 17, 31, …   f 0, 1, 1, 2, 3, …

7 Copy each of these sequences. Fill in the missing terms.

a …, 6, 10, 14, 18, …,   b 3, 8, …, 18, 23, …,

c …, …, 11, 14, 17, 20,   d …, 1, 10, 100, 1000, …,

e 0.3, 0.7, …, 1.5, 1.9, …,   f …, …, 11, 18, 29, 47,

g 1, 20, …, 8000, 160 000, …,   h 3, …, 41, …, 79, 98,

i 300, …, 3, …, 0.03, 0.003,   j 33, 25, 17, …, …, −7,

8 The term-to-term rules and 1st terms of five different sequences are given below.
Find the 3rd term for each sequence.

a Term-to-term rule: $\boxed{\text{Add 1}}$ b Term-to-term rule: $\boxed{\text{Subtract 5}}$
1st term = 4   1st term = 8

c Term-to-term rule: $\boxed{\text{Multiply by 10}}$ d Term-to-term rule: $\boxed{\text{Divide by 2}}$
1st term = 0.05   1st term = 2

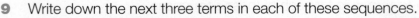

9 Write down the next three terms in each of these sequences.

a 1.2, 3.5, 5.8, 8.1, …   b −0.02, 1.96, 3.94, 5.92, …

c 7.64, 3.82, 1.91, 0.955, …   d 1, 0.5, 0.25, 0.125, …

e 2, −3, 4.5, −6.75, …   f −0.1, 0.01, −0.001, 0.0001, …

g 17.6, 14.2, 10.8, 7.4, …   h 1, 1.1, 1.21, 1.331, …

For the sequence 2, 4, 8, 14, 22, ... the differences between consecutive terms are:

$$2 \rightarrow 4 \rightarrow 8 \rightarrow 14 \rightarrow 22$$
$$\quad +2 \quad +4 \quad +6 \quad +8$$

The differences between the terms are consecutive even numbers.

The term-to-term rule is $\boxed{\text{Add consecutive even numbers}}$

To find the next term in the sequence add the next even number.

The next even number is 10

6th term = 5th term + 10 = 22 + 10 = 32

Example 4

a The first two terms of a sequence are 1, 5
  The term-to-term rule is $\boxed{\text{Add consecutive multiples of 4}}$
  Find the first five terms of the sequence.
b You are given the sequence 36, 35, ..., 30, 26, 21, ...
  i What is the term-to-term rule of this sequence?
  ii What is the missing term in this sequence?

Solution 4

a 2nd term − 1st term = 5 − 1 = 4
  So the difference pattern is 4, 8, 12, 16, ...

$$1 \rightarrow 5 \rightarrow \ldots \rightarrow \ldots \rightarrow \ldots$$
$$\quad +4 \quad +8 \quad +12 \quad +16$$

  3rd term = 5 + 8 = **13**   4th term = **13** + 12 = **25**   5th term = **25** + 16 = 41
b i 36, 35, ..., 30, 26, 21, ...

$$36 \rightarrow 35 \rightarrow \ldots \rightarrow 30 \rightarrow 26 \rightarrow 21$$
$$\quad -1 \quad \ldots \quad \ldots \quad -4 \quad -5$$

  The term-to-term rule is $\boxed{\text{Subtract consecutive whole numbers}}$
  ii 3rd term = 2nd term − 2 = 35 − 2 = 33
  The missing term is 33

Some sequences have two-stage term-to-term rules.

Example 5

The second term of a sequence is 13. Its term-to-term rule is $\boxed{\text{Multiply by 3 then add 1}}$
Find the first three terms of the sequence.

Solution 5

$$\ldots \quad \rightarrow \quad 13 \quad \rightarrow \quad \ldots$$
$$\quad \times 3 \rightarrow +1 \quad \times 3 \rightarrow +1$$

3rd term = 3 × 2nd term + 1 = 3 × 13 + 1 = 40

To find the 1st term look at the sequence in reverse and use the inverse term-to-term rule.

The number machine for the term-to-term rule is

The number machine for the inverse term-to-term rule is

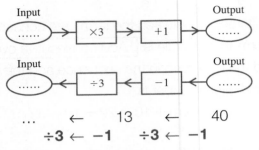

$$... \quad \leftarrow \quad 13 \quad \leftarrow \quad 40$$
$$\div 3 \leftarrow -1 \quad \div 3 \leftarrow -1$$

1st term = (2nd term − 1) ÷ 3 = (13 − 1) ÷ 3 = 12 ÷ 3 = 4
The first three terms of the sequence are: 4, 13, 40

Exercise B

1 Give the term-to-term rule for each of these sequences.
Then write down the next two terms.

   a 1, 2, 4, 7, 11, ...
   b 1, 2, 5, 10, 17, ...
   c 1, 3, 7, 13, 21, ...
   d 1, 4, 10, 19, 31, ...
   e 30, 29, 27, 24, 20, ...
   f 3, 6, 11, 18, 27, ...
   g 45, 43, 39, 33, 25, ...
   h 12, 11, 8, 3, −4, ...
   i 100, 80, 40, −20, −100, ...
   j −10, −8, −4, 2, 10, ...

2 **a** The third term of a sequence of numbers is 15
     The rule for continuing this sequence is $\boxed{\text{Multiply by 2 then add 1}}$
     Write down the first five terms of the sequence.
  b The second term of a sequence of numbers is −4
     The rule for continuing this sequence is $\boxed{\text{Divide by 4 then subtract 8}}$
    i Write down the third term of the sequence.
    ii Write down the first term of the sequence.

3 The first three terms of a sequence are 2, 6, 18
James says that the fourth term of the sequence is 38
Tom says that the fourth term is 54
Show that both James and Tom could be correct.

4 **a** **i** Copy and complete this statement.
      All the terms in the sequence 4, 8, 12, 16, ... are multiples of ...
    ii Explain why 122 is **not** a term in the sequence 4, 8, 12, 16, ...
  b Show that 151 is a term in the sequence 1, 6, 11, 16, 21, ...

5 Find the missing term(s) in each of these sequences.
   a 3, 5, ..., 15, 23, 33, 45, ...
   b ..., 7, 17, 32, 52, 77, ...
   c 4, 7, 13, ..., 34, 49, 67, ...
   d 22, 21, ..., 16, 12, 7, 1, ...
   e ..., 3, 2, ..., −3, −7, −12, ...

6 Lilin and Dipak are investigating sequences with the first two terms 1, 7, …
Lilin's sequence has term-to-term rule $\boxed{\text{Add 6}}$

Dipak's sequence has term-to-term rule $\boxed{\text{Add consecutive multiples of 6}}$
Write down the first five terms of Lilin's and Dipak's sequences.

7 Here are the first three lines of a number pattern:
  a Write down the fourth line of the pattern.
  b Write down the seventh line of the pattern.
  c Copy and complete the following line of the pattern:
    $10 \times \ldots - 5 = 99 \times 5$

$$10 \times 1 - 5 = 1 \times 5$$
$$10 \times 2 - 5 = 3 \times 5$$
$$10 \times 3 - 5 = 5 \times 5$$

8 This rule is used to produce different sequences of numbers:
$\boxed{\text{Multiply by 2 and then add 3}}$

  a The first term in one of the sequences is -1
    What is the second term in this sequence?
  b The second term in another of the sequences is 13
    What is the first term in this sequence?
  c Explain why 100 is not a term in any of the sequences.

9 Use the patterns to copy and complete each of these sequences of calculations.

  a $3 \times 5 = 15$
    $33 \times 5 = 165$
    $333 \times 5 = 1665$
    $3333 \times 5 = 16\,665$
    $33\,333 \times 5 = \ldots\ldots$

  b $1 \times 9 = 9$
    $21 \times 9 = 189$
    $321 \times 9 = 2889$
    $4321 \times 9 = 38\,889$
    $54\,321 \times 9 = \ldots\ldots\ldots$
    $87\,654\,321 \times 9 = \ldots\ldots\ldots$

  c $1 + 9 \times 0 = 1$
    $2 + 9 \times 1 = 11$
    $3 + 9 \times 12 = 111$
    $4 + 9 \times 123 = 1111$
    $5 + 9 \times 1234 = \ldots\ldots\ldots$
    $\ldots + 9 \times \ldots = 111\,111\,111$

  d $1 \times 81 = 81$
    $21 \times 81 = 1701$
    $321 \times 81 = 26\,001$
    $4321 \times 81 = 350\,001$
    $54321 \times 81 = \ldots\ldots\ldots$
    $\ldots\ldots \times 81 = 7\,100\,000\,001$

10 Two **different** sequences start with the same three terms shown in the table.

Term number	1	2	3
Term	7	9	11

The term-to-term rules for the sequences are:

  a $\boxed{\text{Add 2}}$ **b** $\boxed{\text{Add the previous two terms then subtract 5}}$

Write down the next three terms in each of the sequences.

11 Find the first five terms of each of these sequences.

    a 1st term = 1 Term-to-term rule │ Multiply by 2 then subtract 1 │

    b 1st term = 2 Term-to-term rule │ Multiply by 2 then subtract 2 │

    c 1st term = 2 Term-to-term rule │ Multiply by 3 then subtract 4 │

    d 1st term = 5 Term-to-term rule │ Multiply by 5 then subtract 20 │

    Find some more sequences where each term is the same.

12 A sequence has 2nd term 4.788

    Its term-to-term rule is │ Multiply by 0.12 and then add 4.35 │

    Write down the first three terms of this sequence.

15.2 Sequences from patterns of shapes

CAN YOU REMEMBER

- How to use term-to-term rules to continue and complete sequences?

IN THIS SECTION YOU WILL

- Draw the next pattern in a sequence of patterns.
- Find sequences of numbers from sequences of patterns.
- Use term-to-term rules to work out the number of dots or matchsticks in a larger pattern.
- Connect term-to-term rules to sequences of patterns.
- Use a formula to work out the number of dots or matchsticks in a pattern.

Sequences can be shown as sequences of patterns made, for example, from dots or matchsticks. The numbers of dots or matchsticks give the terms of the sequence.

Example 1

Here are the first three patterns in a sequence of dot patterns.

Pattern **1**   Pattern **2**   Pattern **3**

  a Draw pattern **4**.
  b What is the term-to-term rule for the sequence of the number of dots in each pattern?

c Complete the table to show the number of dots in each pattern.

Pattern number	1	2	3	4
Number of dots				

d Which pattern in the sequence has 100 dots?

Solution 1

a The next pattern is

• • • • •
• • • • •

Pattern **4**

b To make the next pattern in the sequence add **2** dots to the previous pattern.
The term-to-term rule is ⬚Add 2⬚

c The number of dots in pattern 4 is 10
There are six patterns between pattern 4 and pattern 10
So the number of dots added from pattern 4 to pattern 10 is 6 × 2 = 12
So the number of dots in pattern 10 is 10 + 12 = 22

Pattern number	1	2	3	4	10
Number of dots	4	6	8	10	22

d Pattern **1** has four dots.
100 − 4 = 96
To make the pattern with 100 dots, add 96 dots to pattern 1
From one pattern to the next two dots are added.
96 ÷ 2 = 48
48 patterns are added from pattern **1** to make the pattern with 100 dots.
1 + 48 = 49
Pattern **49** has 100 dots.

Exercise A

1 Here are the first three patterns in a sequence of dot patterns.

• • •   • • • •   • • • • •
Pattern **1**   Pattern **2**   Pattern **3**

a Draw pattern **4**
b Copy and complete the table to show the number of dots in each pattern.

Pattern number	1	2	3	4
Number of dots				

c What is the term-to-term rule for the sequence made up of the number of dots in each pattern?
d How many dots are there in pattern **10**?

2 The diagrams show patterns made from matchsticks.

Pattern **1**   Pattern **2**   Pattern **3**   Pattern **4**

  a How many **more** matchsticks are needed to make pattern **5**?
  b What is the term-to-term rule for the sequence made up of the number of matchsticks in each pattern?
  c How many **more** matchsticks are needed to make pattern **10** from pattern **5**?
  d Which pattern in the sequence has 51 matchsticks?

3 Black and white counters are used to make these patterns.

Pattern **1**   Pattern **2**   Pattern **3**

  a What is the total number of counters in pattern **4**?
  b Copy and complete the table to show the number of black counters and white counters in each pattern.

Pattern number	1	2	3	4	5
Number of black counters	1				
Number of white counters	3				

  c How many white counters are there in pattern **100**?

4 These patterns are made from dots.
  a How many **more** dots are needed to draw pattern **4**?

Pattern **1**   Pattern **2**   Pattern **3**

  b Draw pattern **4**
  c Peter is describing the pattern and how it grows.

  There are dots on the perimeter of a rectangle. The length has _____ more dot than the width.
  This is what happens from one pattern to the next.
  _____ more dot is added to each length. _____ more dot is added to each _____.
  This means that _____ more dots are needed to draw the next pattern.
  Copy and complete Peter's description.

d   How many dots will there be in pattern **5**?
e   How many dots will there be in pattern **10**?
f   Joe makes pattern **10**. Sally makes pattern **20**
    How many more dots are in Sally's pattern than in Joe's?

5   This sequence of hexagon patterns is made from matchsticks.

a   How many matchsticks are needed to make four hexagons?
b   Copy and complete the table to show the number of matchsticks in each pattern.

Number of hexagons	1	2	3	4	5
Number of matchsticks					

c   How many **more** matchsticks are needed to make the pattern with six
    hexagons from the pattern with five hexagons?
d   How many matchsticks are needed to make ten hexagons?
e   Jenny uses the pattern with ten hexagons to make the pattern with 20 hexagons.
    How many more matchsticks does she use?

6   These diagrams show patterns made from black and white square tiles.

 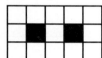 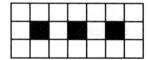

a   Draw the next pattern.
b   Copy and complete this table.

Number of black tiles	1	2	3	4	5
Number of white tiles	8				

c   How many more white tiles are needed to make the pattern with six black tiles
    from the pattern with five black tiles?
d   How many white tiles are needed to make the pattern with ten black tiles?
e   How many black tiles are in the pattern with 103 white tiles?

7   The diagram shows a sequence of
    dot patterns.

Pattern 1   Pattern 2   Pattern 3

a   What is the term-to-term rule for the sequence made from the number of dots in
    each pattern?
b   How many more dots are there in pattern 10 than in pattern 1?
c   Show that pattern 16 has 50 dots.

8 This pattern of diagrams is made from black square tiles.

Pattern 1   Pattern 2   Pattern 3

   a How many more tiles are needed to make pattern 4?

   b How many tiles are needed to make pattern 10?

   c What pattern number uses 77 tiles?

Example 2

These patterns illustrate the square numbers 1, 4, 9, 16

1^2 2^2 3^2 4^2

   a Use the patterns to complete this table up to 7^2

   b Complete this statement:

      'To work out 10^2 add the first

      .... '

Square number		Value
1^2	1	1
2^2	$1 + 3$	4

Solution 2

a

Square number		Value
1^2	1	1
2^2	$1 + 3$	4
3^2	$1 + 3 + 5$	9
4^2	$1 + 3 + 5 + 7$	16
5^2	$1 + 3 + 5 + 7 + 9$	25
6^2	$1 + 3 + 5 + 7 + 9 + 11$	36
7^2	$1 + 3 + 5 + 7 + 9 + 11 + 13$	49

b To work out 10^2 add the first 10 odd numbers.

The rule for how a pattern grows may be given as a formula.

Example 3

These patterns are made from matchsticks.

Pattern 1   Pattern 2   Pattern 3

The *formula* for finding the number of matchsticks, m, in pattern n, is $m = 3n + 4$

a Show that this formula works for pattern 4

b Use the formula to find the number of matchsticks for pattern 100

c Use the formula to find the number of the pattern that uses 154 sticks.

Solution 3

a The numbers of matchsticks in patterns 1, 2 and 3 are 7, 10 and 13, respectively.
The difference between consecutive terms in the sequence 7, 10, 13, … is 3
So there are $13 + 3 = 16$ matchsticks in pattern 4
For pattern 4, $n = 4$. Substitute $n = 4$ in the formula $m = 3n + 4$
$m = 3 \times 4 + 4 = 12 + 4 = 16$
So the formula works for pattern 4

b For pattern 100, $n = 100$
$m = 3 \times 100 + 4 = 300 + 4 = 304$

c Number of matchsticks, $m = 154$
so $3n + 4 = 154$
Subtract 4 from both sides: $3n = 150$
Divide both sides by 3: $n = 50$
Pattern 50 uses 154 matchsticks.

Exercise B

1 a These patterns illustrate the triangular numbers 1, 3, 6, 10

Pattern 1   Pattern 2   Pattern 3   Pattern 4

Copy this table and complete it up to pattern 5

Pattern number		Number of small squares
1	1	1
2	1 + 2	3
3	1 + 2 + 3	6

b The sequence of triangular patterns is used to make this sequence of rectangular patterns.

Pattern 1

Pattern 2

Pattern 3

Pattern 4

Copy this table and complete it up to pattern 5

Pattern number		Number of small squares
1	1 × 2	2
2	2 × 3	6
3	3 × 4	12

c Copy and complete this statement:

> To work out the number of squares in the triangular patterns ....
> the number of squares in the rectangular patterns by ....

d How many squares are there
   i in pattern 10 in the sequence of rectangular patterns?
   ii in pattern 10 in the sequence of triangular patterns?
   iii in pattern 20 in the sequence of triangular patterns?

2 These patterns of towers are made from building blocks.

Tower 1

Tower 2

Tower 3

a Draw the next tower in the sequence.
b Copy and complete the table up to tower 6.
c Amelie makes tower 6
   Ben makes tower 8
   How many more blocks does Ben use than Amelie?
d Show that tower 10 has 120 blocks.

Tower		Number of blocks
1	3	3
2	3 + 5	8
3	3 + 5 + 7	15

3 These patterns are made from matchsticks.

Pattern 1

Pattern 2

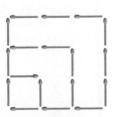

Pattern 3

a Draw pattern 4
b Copy and complete the table up to pattern 6
c Show that pattern 10 has 130 matchsticks.

Pattern		Number of matchsticks
1	4	4
2	4 + 6	10
3	4 + 6 + 8	18

4 This sequence of patterns is made from matchsticks.

Pattern 1

Pattern 2

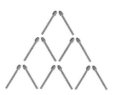

Pattern 3

a Draw the next pattern in the sequence.
b Copy and complete this table up to pattern 6.

Pattern		Number of matchsticks
1	1 × 2	2
2	2 × 3	6
3	3 × 4	12
4		

c How many matchsticks are there in pattern 10?
d Which pattern has 420 matchsticks?

5 This sequence of triangles is made from matchsticks.

Pattern 1

Pattern 2

Pattern 3

a Draw pattern 4
b Copy and complete the table up to pattern 6.
c Work out the number of matchsticks in pattern 10

Pattern	Number of matchsticks
1	3
2	7
3	12

6 These patterns are made from black and white tiles.

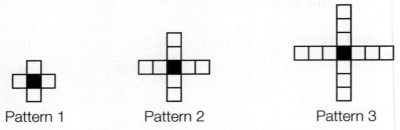

Pattern 1   Pattern 2   Pattern 3

This *formula* gives the total number of tiles, *s*, in pattern *n*: $s = 4n + 1$

  a Which part of the formula gives the number of white tiles?
Explain your answer.
  b What is the total number of tiles in pattern number 20?
  c What pattern number has a total of 173 tiles?

7 These patterns are made from red and blue dots.

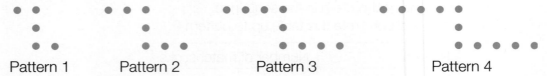

Pattern 1   Pattern 2   Pattern 3   Pattern 4

This *formula* gives the total number of red and blue dots, *d*, in pattern *n*: $d = 2n + 3$

  a Which part of the pattern is represented by $+ 3$ in the formula?
Explain your answer.
  b What is the total number of dots in pattern 50?
  c Which pattern number has a total number of 223 dots?
Show your working.

8 This sequence of patterns illustrates
the difference between consecutive
square numbers.

  a Draw the pattern for $5^2 - 4^2$

  b Copy and complete this table
up to $10^2 - 9^2$

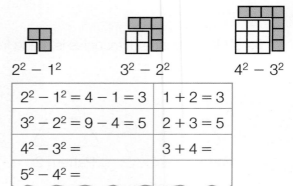

$2^2 - 1^2$ $3^2 - 2^2$ $4^2 - 3^2$

$2^2 - 1^2 = 4 - 1 = 3$	$1 + 2 = 3$
$3^2 - 2^2 = 9 - 4 = 5$	$2 + 3 = 5$
$4^2 - 3^2 =$	$3 + 4 =$
$5^2 - 4^2 =$	

  c **i** Work out $21^2 - 20^2$ **ii** Work out $1000^2 - 999^2$
iii $500^2 = 250\,000$
Work out 501^2

Chapter summary

- A sequence is a list of numbers that follow a pattern.
- The numbers in a sequence are called *terms*.
- The rule for getting from one term to the next in a sequence is called a *term-to-term* rule.
- Term-to-term rules are used to continue a sequence or find missing terms in a sequence. They can use any number operations.
- The inverse of the term-to-term rule is used to find previous terms in a sequence.
- In more complicated sequences the differences between terms are not the same each time. Examples of term-to-term rules for these sequences are

  | Add consecutive odd numbers | | Subtract consecutive multiples of 5 |

- Some sequences have term-to-term rules that involve more than one operation: for example | Multiply by 3 then add 1 |
- Sequences can be shown as sequences of patterns. The numbers of dots or matchsticks in the patterns give the terms of the sequence.
- The rule for how a pattern grows may be given as a formula connecting the pattern number n to the number of dots or matchsticks.

Chapter review

1 Matchsticks are used to make a sequence of patterns.
The first three patterns are shown.

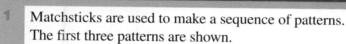

Pattern 1   Pattern 2   Pattern 3

a Draw pattern 4

b Complete the table showing the number of matchsticks in each pattern.

Pattern number	1	2	3	4	5
Number of matchsticks	8	11	14		

c What pattern do you notice in the numbers of matchsticks?

2 Look at the sequence   ..., 4, 10, 16, 22, ...
a What is the number that comes **after** 22 in the sequence?
b What is the rule for finding numbers in the sequence?
c What is the number that comes **before** 4 in the sequence?

3 A sequence of numbers begins 40, 37, 34, 31, ...
a What is the next number in the sequence?
b Describe in words the rule for continuing the sequence.

4 **a** Write down the next two numbers in the sequence 1, 8, 15, 22, …

b Write down the next number in the sequence 2, 6, 12, 20, …

c Write down the rule for continuing the sequence 5, 2, −1, −4, …

5 Fill in the two missing numbers in the sequence 33, 31, 27, 21, …, 3, …

6 **a** **i** Write down the next three terms in this sequence: 1, 3, 5, 7

  ii What type of numbers are the terms in the sequence?

b These patterns are made from squares.

  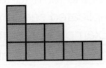

Pattern 1   Pattern 2   Pattern 3

  i Draw pattern 4   **ii** Copy and complete the table below.

Pattern number	1	2	3	4	5
Number of squares in each pattern					

  iii Explain how you worked out the number of squares in patterns 4 and 5

7 Patterns are made of matchsticks.

Pattern 1   Pattern 2   Pattern 3

Here is the rule for working out the number of matchsticks:

| Multiply the pattern number by 2 and add 3 |

a How many matchsticks will be in pattern 200?

b Which pattern will have 27 matchsticks?

8 **a** Here is a sequence of numbers.

33, 29, 25, 21, 17

  i Write down the next two numbers in the sequence.

  ii Write down the rule for continuing the sequence.

b Another sequence of numbers begins: 2, 3, 5, 9

The rule for continuing this sequence is: | Multiply by 2 and subtract 1 |

  i What is the next number in the sequence?

  ii The same rule is used for a sequence that starts with the number 11
What is the second number in this sequence?

  iii The same rule is also used for a sequence that starts with the number −3
What is the second number in this sequence?

9 The rule for continuing a sequence is:

| Multiply by 3 then subtract 3 |

a A sequence using this rule begins 2, 3, 6, 15, …
What is the next number in the sequence?

b Another sequence, using the same rule, starts with 4
What is the next number in this sequence?

c Another sequence, using the same rule, starts with -6
What is the next number in this sequence?

10 Dots are used to make a sequence of patterns.

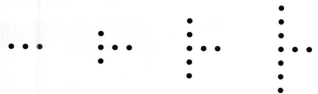

Pattern 1   Pattern 2   Pattern 3   Pattern 4

a How many dots will pattern 5 have?

b The rule to work out the number of dots, d, for pattern number, p, is
$d = 2p + 1$

  i Use the rule to work out the number of dots in pattern 10

  ii Use the rule to work out the pattern number that has 51 dots.

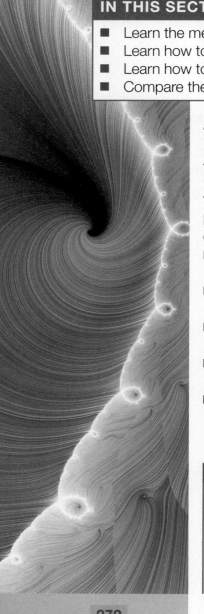

Probability

16.1 Chance

CAN YOU REMEMBER

■ The meaning of 'impossible', 'unlikely', 'certain', 'likely'?

IN THIS SECTION YOU WILL

■ Learn the meaning of the terms 'event' and 'outcome'.
■ Learn how to describe in words the chance of an event happening.
■ Learn how to explain why some events are more likely to happen than others.
■ Compare the chances of two, or more, events happening.

A bus can be early, on time or late. The three possible results 'early', 'on time' or 'late' are called the three *outcomes*.
An event is one particular outcome.
For the bus example, 'being on time' is an *event.*

The *chance* of an event happening is a measure of how likely it is to happen.
Chance can be described using words such as 'likely' or 'impossible'.

■ Events that can never happen are *impossible*, e.g. a person living to be 250 years old.
■ Events that will always happen are *certain*, e.g. it will rain somewhere in the world today.
■ Events that rarely happen are *unlikely* or *very unlikely*, e.g. it will snow in June in England.
■ Events that often happen are *likely* or *very likely*, e.g. daffodils will bloom in March.
■ Some events have an *even chance* of happening or they have a 50% chance of happening (sometimes we say 50-50 chance), e.g. throwing a fair coin and it lands on heads.

Example 1

Describe the chance of each event happening. Explain your reasons.
a The next person that passes the school gate will be right-handed.
b The next car that parks in the supermarket car park will be orange.
c There will be ice on the roads this winter.
d The 2012 Olympic Marathon will be run in under 2 minutes.
e A coin drops on the floor and lands showing heads.

Solution 1

a Likely – because there are many more right-handed people than left-handed people.
b Unlikely – there are very few orange cars compared to cars of other colours.
c Very likely – almost every winter the roads have ice on them at some time.
d Impossible – there is no chance that the Olympic Marathon could be run in under 2 minutes.
e Evens – because there is a 50-50 chance that the coin will land showing heads.

Exercise A

1 Match up a word from this list with each statement.

likely   evens   impossible   certain   unlikely

   a It will snow in London in July.
   b I will see two different relatives on Christmas Day.
   c Next month there will be seven Mondays.

2 Describe the chance of each event occurring.
Give reasons for your answers.
   a A baby born today will live into the next century.
   b Your children will go to the same school as you do.
   c You will be alive in the year 2150.

3 Write down an event which is:
   a impossible   **b** certain   **c** unlikely
   d evens   **e** likely.

4 A pack of coloured cards is shown in the diagram.
A card is picked without looking.
   a Describe the chance of the following events:
     i The card picked is red.
     ii The card picked is yellow.
     iii The card picked is blue.
   b Arrange the above events on a line starting with the least likely.

5 John works out that the telephone calls to his house are:
  ■ 70% for his mother   ■ 25% for his father
  ■ 4% for John   ■ 1% the wrong number.

| unlikely   certain   very unlikely   impossible   likely |

Use words from the box to describe the chance that when the telephone rings the call is:
   a for his mother   **b** for his father   **c** for John
   d a wrong number   **e** for the next-door neighbour.

The chances of two or more events can be compared.

Example 2

James throws a coin and Janice spins this triangular spinner. James says that the chance of him getting a head is greater than the chance of Janice's spinner landing on red. Explain why James is correct.

Solution 2

Throwing a coin can only result in a head or a tail. Each result is equally likely. James has an even (50-50) chance of getting a head.
Janice's spinner can land on red, white or blue.
The chance that Janice's spinner lands on red is unlikely.
So James has more chance of getting a head than Janice has of getting red.

Exercise B

1 Carol and Ann each have a bag of sweets.
Carol's bag has a lot more chews than toffees.
Ann's bag has the same number of chews as toffees.
They each pick a sweet from their own bag,
without looking.
Which girl is more likely to pick a chew?
Explain your answer.

2 Peter drives to work. He is frequently late for work.
Paul always takes the bus to work. He is rarely late for work.
Who has the most chance of being late for work?
Explain your answer.

3 Sally and Gemma each have a pack of cards. Sally has equal numbers of green, red and yellow cards in her pack. Gemma has twice as many green cards as red cards in her pack and no yellow cards.
They each pick a card from their own packs without looking.
  a Who is more likely to pick a green card? Explain your answer.
  b Who is more likely to pick a red card? Explain your answer.
  c Describe the chance that Gemma picks a yellow card from her pack.

4 Frank and David play the lottery each week.
Frank buys 4 tickets each week. David buys 1 ticket each week.
  a Who is more likely to win the lottery, Frank or David? Explain your answer.
  b Describe the chance of winning the jackpot on the lottery.
  c What could David do to increase his chances of winning?

5 Ted and Brian each own a greyhound.
Ted's greyhound ran 400 metres in under
14 seconds five times in its last six races.
Brian's greyhound ran 400 metres in under
14 seconds six times in its last twelve races.
Whose greyhound has the better chance of running
the next 400 metre race in under 14 seconds?
Explain your answer.

6 A class of 30 students has 8 more girls than boys.
The teacher chooses a student's name from the class register without looking.
Describe the chance that:
  a the student chosen is a girl   **b** the student chosen is a boy
  c the student chosen is from this class.

7 In a board game the dice score tells the
player how to move:

Dice score	Move
6	Forward three squares
2 or 4	Forward one square
Odd number	Stay where you are

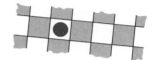

  a Describe the chance of getting
each move in the table.
  b What is the chance of moving
forward two squares only in this
game in one go?

8 A certain type of plant produces coloured flowers.
The colours of the flowers are red or yellow
in the ratio of 3 : 1
  a Which colour is more likely?
  b Describe the chance of a plant producing yellow flowers.
A gardener bought 200 seeds of these plants.
  c Is it certain that he will have some plants producing yellow flowers?

16.2 Probability scales and calculations

CAN YOU REMEMBER

- The meaning of the words 'event', 'outcome' and 'chance'?
- How to describe the chance of an event happening in words?

IN THIS SECTION YOU WILL

- Learn the meaning of 'probability'.
- Learn the meaning of 'equally likely', 'fair' and 'biased'.
- Learn how to calculate simple probabilities.
- Learn how to draw and use a probability scale.

Probability measures the chance of an event happening.

Probabilities can be shown on a *probability scale* from 0 to 1:

Probabilities can be written as fractions, decimals or percentages.
For example, a weather forecast says that there is a 70% chance of rain tomorrow.

Probability of rain = 70%.

70% can also be written as
$\frac{70}{100} = \frac{7}{10} = 0.7$

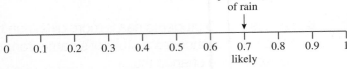

If an event has no chance of happening and is impossible, the probability is 0
If an event is bound to happen and is certain, the probability is 1

This spinner has five equal sections.
One of the sections is blue.
The spinner is *fair*. This means it has the same
chance of landing on each section.
There is a one in five chance of the spinner landing on blue.

The probability of landing on blue is $\frac{1}{5}$

To calculate probabilities use this formula:

Probability of an event happening = $\dfrac{\text{number of ways an event can happen}}{\text{total number of outcomes}}$

For the spinner above: Probability = $\frac{1}{5}$
- the number of ways the event 'landing on blue' can happen is 1
- the total number of outcomes is 5 (the five colours).

This formula can only be used if all outcomes are *equally likely*, that is if the situation is *fair*. If all outcomes are not equally likely, the situation is *biased*. For example, a dice that is weighted to be more likely to score 6 is biased.

Example 1

A fair dice is thrown.
a Calculate the probability that the dice lands showing:
    i the number 5   **ii** an even number.
b Show these probabilities on a probability scale.

Solution 1

a   **i** Each number on the dice is equally likely.   Probability of 5 = $\frac{1}{6}$
       Number of ways event can happen = 1
       Total number of outcomes = 6 (the numbers 1 to 6)

   ii Number of ways event can happen = 3 (the numbers 2, 4 or 6)
       Total number of outcomes = 6 (the numbers 1 to 6)
       Probability of even number = $\frac{3}{6} = \frac{1}{2}$

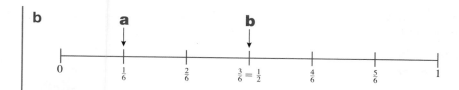

Example 2

Jenny's bag of sweets contains one bubble gum, four toffees and five chews.
She picks a sweet from her bag without looking.
Draw and label a probability scale to show the probability of her picking each type of sweet.

Solution 2

Probability of bubble gum (B): Number of ways event can happen = 1
Probability of B = $\frac{1}{10}$ Total number of outcomes = 10 (1 + 4 + 5)

In the same way:
Probability of toffee (T) = $\frac{4}{10}$ Probability of chew (C) = $\frac{5}{10}$

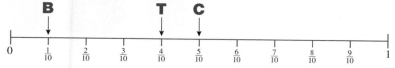

Exercise A

All coins and dice in this exercise are fair unless otherwise stated.

1 Copy this probability scale.

Label the probability scale using decimals.

2 Copy this probability scale.

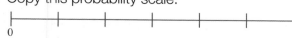

Label the probability scale using fractions.

3 Copy this probability scale.
Show the probability of each of the
following events on the scale.

    a A coin is thrown and it lands showing heads.
    b A six-sided dice is thrown and it lands showing the number 2
    c A dice is thrown and it lands showing tails.

4   Copy the probability scale.
Show the probability of each event
on the probability scale.

   a   A dice lands showing the number 6

   b   When this spinner is spun it lands on a number less than 5

   c   A coin lands showing tails.

5   There are ten beads in a bag.
Five beads are white, three beads are pink and the rest are yellow.
A bead is picked from the bag without looking.
Copy this probability scale.

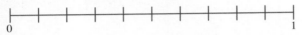

Label the probability of each event on the probability scale.

   a   The bead is white.   **b**   The bead is yellow   **c**   The bead is green.

6   A set of cards contains two red,
four green and six yellow cards.
A card is picked from the set without looking.
Copy this probability scale.

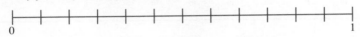

Label the probability of each of the following events on the scale.

   a   The card picked is red.   **b**   The card picked is yellow.

7   Here is a set of five picture cards.
The cards are shuffled and placed
face down.
One card is turned face up.

On a copy of the probability scale, label the probability that the card has:

   a   a circle on it   **b**   a triangle on it   **c**   a square on it.

8   A fair dice is thrown.
Mark the probabilities of each of the following events on a probability scale.

   a   The dice lands showing the number 3

   b   The dice lands showing an odd number.

   c   The dice lands showing the number 9

Example 3

The probabilities of the following events have been marked on the probability scale.
a The next baby born at the town hospital will be a girl.
b The next person to enter the cinema will be over 80 years old.
c The day after Saturday will be a Sunday.

Label each arrow with a letter to show which event it represents.

Solution 3

Estimate the probability of each event.
a Roughly half of all babies born are girls.
The probability of the event is approximately $\frac{1}{2}$
b It is unlikely that the next person to enter the cinema will be over 80 years old.
The probability of the event is close to zero.
c It is certain that the day after Saturday will be a Sunday.
The probability of the event is 1

Exercise B

1 The probabilities of the following events have been marked onto the probability scale below.
  a A fair three-sided spinner coloured red, blue and yellow will land on blue.
  b The next person to enter the school gate will be right-handed.
  c The day two days before Friday is Monday.

Copy the probability scale and the arrows.
Label each arrow with a letter to show which event it represents.

2 The probabilities of the following events have been marked onto the probability scale.
  a The next car that passes you will have only one person in it.
  b It will snow in Scotland next winter.
  c A red pen is picked from a bag of black pens.
  Copy the probability scale and the arrows.
  Label each arrow with a letter to show which event it represents.

3 Draw a probability scale.
Label it with the probability of the following events happening.
  a Picking a red pen from a box of red pens.
  b A fair six-sided dice showing a number greater than 3
  c Picking a black disc from a bag containing only white discs.

4 An ordinary six-sided fair dice is thrown.
  a Work out the probability that the dice lands showing:
    i a number greater than or equal to 1   **ii** a number less than 3
    iii the number 2, 3 or 4   **iv** the number 5
  b Draw a probability scale and label it to show these probabilities.

5 A bag of coloured discs contains two red, three blue, five white and ten yellow discs.
A disc is picked from the bag without looking.
  a Work out the probability of picking:
    i a red disc   **ii** a white disc   **iii** a yellow disc   **iv** a purple disc.
  b Draw a probability scale and label it to show these probabilities.

6 A DVD catalogue lists 500 DVDs. 150 are comedy films, 50 are children's films, the rest are adventure films. To choose a DVD, Neale closes his eyes and sticks a pin onto one page of the catalogue.
Work out the probability that the film he chooses is:
  a a comedy film   **b** an adventure film   **c** not a children's film.

7 Sandeep has a large box of books. Three quarters of the books are paperbacks, the rest are hardbacks. His sister Prita picks a book from the box without looking.
  a What is the probability that she picks a hardback book?
  b Show this probability on a probability scale.

8 Work out the probability of a fair ten-sided dice showing:
  a an 8   **b** less than 7   **c** at least 6   **d** a number below 15
  e Show each of the probabilities **a–d** on a probability scale.

16.3 Listing outcomes

CAN YOU REMEMBER

- The meaning of 'event' and 'outcome'?
- The meaning of 'fair' and 'equally likely'?

IN THIS SECTION YOU WILL

- Learn how to list all of the outcomes of a single event.
- Learn how to list all of the outcomes of two events.

Every event has at least one possible outcome. The event 'throwing an ordinary dice' has six possible outcomes 1, 2, 3, 4, 5 or 6

Sometimes an event can happen in more than one way.
For example, for an ordinary dice, the event 'odd number' happens if the dice shows 1, 3 or 5

Example 1

A spinner has five coloured sections. Two sections are red, two are blue and one is white. The spinner is spun once.
a List all the possible outcomes.
b The spinner is fair. Is each colour equally likely?

Solution 1

a There are three possible outcomes: red, blue or white.
b The spinner is fair so it is equally likely to land on any one of the five sections.
The colours do not appear an equal number of times on the spinner.
There are more red and blue sections than white sections.
So the spinner is not equally likely to land on each of the three colours.

Example 2

A six-sided dice has each of its sides labelled with one of the letters making up the word HUMBUG. The dice is thrown and lands showing a letter. List the possible outcomes.

Solution 2

There are six letters but two of them are the same, U.
There are five different outcomes: H, U, M, B, G.

Exercise A

1 List all of the possible outcomes for each event below.
   a Flipping a coin.
      List the possible outcomes for the side of the coin facing up.
   b Spinning a spinner with three sections coloured yellow, green and red.
      List the possible colours that the spinner lands on.
   c Picking one disc from a bag of black and white discs.
      List the possible colours of the disc picked.

281

2 A six-sided spinner has three red sections, two blue and one black.
    a List the possible outcomes when the spinner is spun.
    b The spinner is fair. Is each colour equally likely?
      Explain your answer.

3 A bag contains ten balls. The balls are numbered from 1 to 10
    A ball is chosen from the bag.
    List all of the possible outcomes.

4 A 'lucky bag' contains a toy whistle, a key ring, a pencil sharpener and a toy watch.
    Jimmy chooses one item from the bag without looking.
    List all of the possible outcomes for Jimmy's choice.

5 Each month Sarah pays for groceries, petrol, clothes and meals with her credit card.
    She keeps her credit card receipts in a drawer.
    Sarah picks a receipt from her drawer.
    List the possible items that could be on the receipt.

6 Amit has a pocket full of change.
    He chooses one coin from his pocket.
    List all of the possible outcomes for the coin that he chooses.

7 A six-sided fair spinner has one section numbered 1,
    two sections numbered 2 and three sections numbered 3
    The spinner is spun once.
    a List all the possible outcomes.
    b Explain why each outcome is not equally likely.

8 Matt has a four-socket adaptor for his computer.
    He can use any of the four sockets A, B, C and D
    as shown in the diagram.
    Matt connects his computer to one of the sockets.
    List all of the possibilities for the socket he uses.

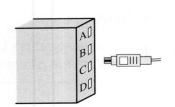

9 Mary has six cereal dishes in her cupboard.
    Half of the dishes are patterned and the rest are plain.
    She chooses a dish for her cereal one morning.
    List the outcomes for the type of dish she chooses.

10 The letters of the word MATHEMATICS are each written onto separate cards and
    placed inside a bag.
    Harry picks one letter from the bag.
    a List all of the possible outcomes for the letter Harry picks.
    b Which letters are more likely to be chosen?
    c Write down an outcome that is impossible.

11 A six-sided dice has each of its sides labelled with one of the letters making up the word LIKELY. The dice is thrown and lands showing a letter. List the possible outcomes.

Events can happen together, or one after the other. For example, in a game you can throw a dice and pick a card.
All the possible outcomes of two events can be written as a list.

Example 3

Katherine buys an ice-cream and a drink from a shop.
The ice-cream comes in three flavours, vanilla (V), strawberry (S) and chocolate (C).
The drinks are orange (O), lemon (L) and water (W).
List all the possible combinations of ice-cream and drinks that Katherine can choose.

Solution 3

Work systematically to make sure all possible outcomes are included.

VO	VL	VW
SO	SL	SW
CO	CL	CW

Possible outcomes for two events can also be shown in a table.

Example 4

A coin is thrown and an ordinary dice is rolled.
Copy and complete the table to show all of the possible outcomes.

Dice

		1	2	3	4	5	6
Coin	**heads**	H1	H2				
	tails						T6

Solution 4

The coin can show heads or tails.
The dice can show the number 1, 2, 3, 4, 5 or 6
The outcome H1 means that the coin shows heads and the dice shows 1
This is the completed table.

Dice

		1	2	3	4	5	6
Coin	**heads**	H1	H2	H3	H4	H5	H6
	tails	T1	T2	T3	T4	T5	T6

Exercise B

1 Jamie goes to his local shop to buy a bottle of pop and a packet of crisps.
The shop sells orange, lemonade or cola flavours of pop.
It sells plain, beef or chicken flavoured crisps.
List all of the possible combinations that Jamie can buy.

2 A café offers four choices of vegetable with the Sunday roast

    peas (P)   carrots (C)   broccoli (B)   leeks (L)

List all the possible outcomes for a customer who chooses **two** of these vegetables.

3 A three-sided spinner has sections labelled 1, 2 and 3 as shown.
The spinner is spun twice. The numbers that it lands on are
added to give a score.
Copy and complete the table to show all the possible scores.

First spin

		1	2	3
Second spin	**1**	2	2 + 1 = 3	
	2			
	3	4		

4 Four discs each have one letter on them, A, B, C or D.   (A) (B) (C) (D)
The discs are put in a bag. One disc is picked from the
bag without looking. The letter on the disc is recorded.
The disc is then replaced in the bag. A second disc is chosen from the bag.
This letter is also recorded. Write down all possible outcomes for the two letters.

5 An ordinary dice is thrown twice.
The numbers that the dice shows are **added** to give a score.
  a Copy and complete the table to show all the possible scores.

First throw

	+	1	2	3	4	5	6
	1	2	3				
	2						
Second throw	**3**						
	4						
	5						
	6						12

  b How many **different** scores are there?
  c Which score occurs more often than any other score?

6 A three-sided spinner has sections labelled 1, 2 and 3
The spinner is spun once and an ordinary dice is thrown once.

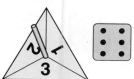

$3 \times 6 = 18$

The number that the spinner lands on is **multiplied** by the number that the dice shows to give the score.

a Copy and complete the table to show all possible scores.

Dice

×	1	2	3	4	5	6
1	1					
2						
3						18

Spinner (labels rows 1, 2, 3)

b How many **different** scores are there?
c What is the range of the scores?

7 A fair square spinner has sections labelled 2, 3, 4 and 5
The spinner is spun twice.
The numbers that it lands on are **added** together to give a score.
a Draw a table to show all of the possible scores.
b Which score is the most likely to occur?

16.4 Calculating probabilities

CAN YOU REMEMBER

- The meaning of 'probability' and 'fair'?
- How to calculate simple probabilities?
- How to simplify a fraction by cancelling?

IN THIS SECTION YOU WILL

- Learn the meaning of 'equally likely outcomes'.
- Understand the meaning of 'at random'.
- Learn how to calculate probabilities of events with equally likely outcomes.

Outcomes which have an equal chance of happening are *equally likely*.
Equally likely outcomes have equal probabilities.

When items are chosen *at random*, each item has an equal chance of being chosen.
So the outcomes are equally likely and have equal probabilities.

For example, for a fair coin showing heads or showing tails:

Probability of head $= \frac{1}{2}$; probability of tail $= \frac{1}{2}$

A fair ordinary dice shows 1, 2, 3, 4, 5 or 6

Probability of 1 = probability of 2 = ... = probability of 6 $= \frac{1}{6}$

Probability of an event happening $= \dfrac{\text{number of successful outcomes}}{\text{total number of outcomes}}$

Example 1

An ordinary fair dice is thrown.
Write down the probability that the dice lands on:
a   the number 3   b   a number greater than 4
c   an even number   d   the number 9

Solution 1

a   Probability of an event happening $= \dfrac{\text{number of successful outcomes}}{\text{total number of outcomes}}$

Probability that the dice lands on the number 3 $= \frac{1}{6}$

b   On a dice, the numbers greater than 4 are 5 and 6
So probability of 5 or 6 $= \frac{2}{6} = \frac{1}{3}$ (cancelling the fraction)

c   The probability that the dice shows an even number is the probability that it shows
2, 4 or 6
Probability of 2, 4 or 6 $= \frac{3}{6} = \frac{1}{2}$ (cancelling the fraction)

d   There is no number 9 on the dice so the probability is 0

Exercise A

1   A bag contains 12 discs.

The discs are numbered 1, 2, ..., 12
A disc is chosen from the bag at random.
What is the probability that the chosen disc is numbered 5?

2   An ordinary dice is thrown.
Write down the probability that the dice lands on the number:
a   6   b   1   c   7   d   3 or 4

3   This spinner has eight sections.
The spinner has the same probability of landing on each section.
   a   Is the spinner fair? Explain your answer.
   b   Write down the probability that the spinner lands on a
section labelled:
       i 1   **ii** 3

4   A bag contains three red, four blue and five yellow marbles.
A marble is picked from the bag at random.
Write down the probability that the marble picked is:
   a   red   **b**   blue   **c**   yellow   **d**   white.

5   Twenty-six discs are each labelled with a different letter of the alphabet.
The discs are placed in a bag. A disc is chosen from the bag without looking.
Write down the probability that the chosen disc is:
   a   the letter X
   b   a vowel (A, E, I, O, U)
   c   one of the first ten letters of the alphabet.

6   A raffle is held to raise money for charity. The tickets sold are numbered 001 to 250
What is the probability that the ticket that wins first prize is:
   a   ticket number 143   **b**   a ticket with number 200 or higher
   c   ticket number 265   **d**   an odd-numbered ticket?

In a table (or list) of outcomes for two equally likely events, each outcome in the table is
equally likely.

To find the probability of two events:

Step 1: Make a table (or list) of all the possible outcomes.

Step 2: Count the number of successful outcomes and the total number of outcomes in
the table (or list).

Step 3: Calculate the probability using the formula:

Probability of an event $= \dfrac{\text{number of successful outcomes}}{\text{total number of outcomes}}$

Example 2

This dice is thrown and the spinner is spun. The number on the dice and the number
on the spinner are added together to give the score.
   a   Make a table of all the possible outcomes for the score.
   b   Calculate the probability of a score of 10
   c   Calculate the probability of a score of 8

Solution 2

a

Dice

+	1	2	3	4	5	6
1	2	3	4	5	6	7
2	3	4	5	6	7	8
3	4	5	6	7	8	9
4	5	6	7	8	9	10

Spinner labels rows 1–4.

b   The total number of outcomes is 24
For a score of 10, the number of successful outcomes is 1
Probability of score $10 = \frac{1}{24}$
c   For a score of 8, the number of successful outcomes is 3
Probability of score $8 = \frac{3}{24} = \frac{1}{8}$

Example 3

A fair spinner is spun once. The probability that the spinner lands on each section is $\frac{1}{10}$
a   How many sections does the spinner have?
The probability that the spinner lands on a white section is $\frac{1}{2}$
b   How many white sections does the spinner have?

Solution 3

a   The spinner is fair so the probability that it lands on each section is equally likely.
Probability it lands on each section is $\frac{1}{10}$, so the total number of outcomes is 10
The spinner must have ten sections.
b   The probability that the spinner lands on a white section is $\frac{1}{2}$
So half of the sections of the spinner must be white.
$\frac{1}{2}$ of 10 = 5. The spinner has five white sections.

Exercise B

1   An ordinary dice is thrown twice.
The numbers that the dice shows
are **added** to give a score.
a   Copy and complete
the table to show
all the possible
scores.
b   Calculate the
probability of
getting a
score of:
   i 12   ii 4   iii 7

First throw

+	1	2	3	4	5	6
1						
2						
3						
4						
5						
6						

Second throw labels the rows.

2 A three-sided spinner has sections labelled 3, 4 and 5
The spinner is spun once and an ordinary dice is thrown once.
The number that the spinner lands on is **added** to the number that
the dice shows to give the score.

  a Copy and complete the table
    to show all the possible
    scores.
  b Calculate the probability
    that the score is:
     i 2
     ii 6
     iii an odd number.

		Dice					
+	**1**	**2**	**3**	**4**	**5**	**6**
3						
4						
5						

(Spinner)

3 A bag contains five discs numbered 1, 2, 3, 4 and 5
A disc is chosen from the bag at random. Its number is recorded and it is put back
into the bag. A second disc is chosen at random and its number recorded.
The numbers on the discs are **added** to give a score.
  a Make a table to show all the possible scores.
  b Write down the probability that the score is:
    i 7   **ii** 15   **iii** an even number.

4 A fair coin is flipped and a fair six-sided dice is thrown. When the coin shows heads
the number shown by the dice is the score. When the coin shows tails the number
shown by the dice is doubled to give the score.

  a Copy and complete
    the table to show
    all the possible
    scores.
  b Write down the
    probability that
    the score is:

		Dice					
	1	**2**	**3**	**4**	**5**	**6**
Heads			3			
Tails					10	

(Coin)

    i 5   **ii** 12   **iii** an even number.

5 A square spinner with sections numbered 2, 4, 6 and 8 is spun twice.
The numbers that the spinner lands on are **added** to give a score.

  a Draw a table to show all the possible scores.
  b Write down the probability that the score is:
    i 4   **ii** 10   **iii** odd.

6 The probability of a particular ball being thrown out of a children's ball pool is $\frac{1}{500}$
  a How many balls are there in the ball pool?
  b 150 of the balls are red, the rest are blue.
    What is the probability that the next ball to be thrown out of the ball pool is blue?

7 The probability that a fair spinner lands on any one of its sections is $\frac{1}{20}$
Half of the sections are red, one quarter are blue and the rest are orange.
  a How many sections does the spinner have?
  b Calculate the number of sections that are orange.

8 A fair coin is flipped three times.

   a One possible outcome is three heads (HHH).
      List all of the possible outcomes.

   b Write down the probability that the outcome:
      i is three tails (TTT)   **ii** has exactly one head.

16.5 Probability for mutually exclusive outcomes

CAN YOU REMEMBER

- How to write probabilities as fractions, decimals or percentages?
- The meaning of 'event' and 'outcome'?
- How to show all the outcomes of two events in a table?

IN THIS SECTION YOU WILL

- Understand the meaning of 'mutually exclusive outcomes'.
- Learn that the sum of the probabilities of all the mutually exclusive outcomes is 1
- Learn how to calculate probabilities for mutually exclusive outcomes.

Outcomes that cannot happen at the same time are called *mutually exclusive outcomes*.

The two outcomes 'the dice shows 5' and 'the dice shows 2' cannot both happen at the same time. They are mutually exclusive.

The two outcomes 'spinner lands on **blue**' and 'spinner lands on **red**' are mutually exclusive.

The two outcomes 'coin shows heads' and 'coin shows tails' are mutually exclusive.

Example 1

Here are some events from rolling an ordinary dice.

  a Rolling a 6   **b** Rolling an even number
  c Rolling a number less than 3   **d** Rolling a number greater than 0

Which two events are mutually exclusive? Explain your answer.

Solution 1

Events **a** and **c** are mutually exclusive because they cannot happen at the same time.
Any other pair of events can happen at the same time,
e.g. **a** and **b** both happen if a 6 is rolled.

a and **d** both happen if a 6 is rolled.   **b** and **c** both happen if a 2 is rolled.
b and **d** both happen if a 2, 4 or 6 is rolled.   **c** and **d** both happen if a 1 or 2 is rolled.

The probabilities of all the mutually exclusive outcomes of an event add up to 1
For example, a fair spinner has six equal sections.
One section is green (G), two are yellow (Y) and the rest are white (W).
The spinner is spun once.
Green, yellow and white are mutually exclusive outcomes.

The table shows the probabilities of each of these outcomes.

Outcome	G	Y	W
Probability	$\frac{1}{6}$	$\frac{2}{6}$	$\frac{3}{6}$

The sum of the probabilities is $\frac{1}{6} + \frac{2}{6} + \frac{3}{6} = \frac{6}{6} = 1$

In the same way:
Probability that an event happens + probability that the event does not happen = 1

So rearranging,
Probability that an event happens = 1 − probability that the event does not happen

'Event happens' and 'event does not happen' are mutually exclusive, because the event cannot 'happen' and 'not happen' at the same time.

Example 2

The probability that this fair spinner lands on a yellow section is 0.4
Calculate the probability that the spinner does **not** land on
a yellow section.

Solution 2

Probability that the spinner does not land on yellow
= 1 − the probability that it lands on yellow
= 1 − 0.4 = 0.6

Example 3

David takes an apple, an orange or a pear to work every day.
The table shows some of the probabilities for the fruit that
he takes to work. Calculate the probability that David takes
a pear to work next Monday.

Fruit	Probability
Apple	50%
Orange	30%
Pear	

Solution 3

Probability that David takes a pear to work on Monday
= 100% − the probability that he does not take a pear to work on Monday
= 100 − (50 + 30)
= 100 − 80 = 20%

Exercise A

1 The probability that a girl at St Joseph's school has blonde hair is 0.3. Work out the probability that a girl chosen at random from St Joseph's does **not** have blonde hair.

2 Joe and Steve play a game. There is only one winner. The probability that Joe wins is 0.6. Work out the probability that Joe does not win.

3 Peter is a darts champion. The probability that he hits the bull with his first throw is 0.7. Work out the probability that Peter misses the bull with his first throw.

4 The probability that Simon misses the bus to college is 0.5 Work out the probability that he does **not** miss the bus to college.

5 Work out the probability that a packet of Bixey cereals chosen at random does **not** contain a prize. Give your answer as a percentage.

6 The table shows some of the probabilities of patients arriving early, on time or late for a doctor's appointment. Work out the probability that a patient arrives late.

Patient arrives	Probability
Early	0.1
On time	0.6
Late	

7 When Penny goes to the cinema she always buys one item from the kiosk. The table shows some of the probabilities for the items she buys. Work out the probability that Penny buys crisps on her next visit to the cinema.

Item	Probability
Popcorn	0.2
Drink	0.4
Ice-cream	0.3
Crisps	

8 Katy has a bag of beads. One quarter of the beads are red. Katy picks a bead from the bag. Work out the probability that the bead she picks is:
   a red
   b **not** red.

9 The probability that Susan does **not** hand in her Mathematics homework on time is 0.52. Calculate the probability that Susan does hand her Mathematics homework in on time.

10 The table shows some of the probabilities for a biased spinner. Calculate the probability that the spinner lands on green.

Colour	Probability
Red	0.21
Blue	0.36
Green	
Yellow	0.32

Example 4

Two ordinary fair dice are thrown.
The numbers shown on the dice are added to
give a score.

a Draw a table to show all the possible scores.
b Calculate the probability that the score is 7
c Calculate the probability that the score is **not** 7

Solution 4

a

First dice

Second dice		1	2	3	4	5	6
	1	2	3	4	5	6	7
	2	3	4	5	6	7	8
	3	4	5	6	7	8	9
	4	5	6	7	8	9	10
	5	6	7	8	9	10	11
	6	7	8	9	10	11	12

b Probability that the score is $7 = \frac{6}{36} = \frac{1}{6}$

c **Method 1**

Probability that the score is **not** 7
$= 1 -$ probability that the score is 7
$= 1 - \frac{1}{6} = \frac{5}{6}$

Method 2

There are 30 outcomes that are not 7
Probability that the score is **not** $7 = \frac{30}{36} = \frac{5}{6}$

Exercise B

1 A five-sided spinner has sections numbered 1, 2, 3, 4 and 5. The spinner is spun
twice. The numbers that the spinner lands on are added to give a score.

a Copy and complete the table to show all possible scores.

First spin

Second spin	+	1	2	3	4	5
	1	2				
	2	3				
	3					
	4					
	5				9	10

b Calculate the probability that the score is:
   i 6   **ii** **not** 6

293

2 A fair six-sided dice and a coin are thrown.
If the coin shows heads, the score is double the number shown on the dice.
If the coin shows tails, the score is one less than the number shown on the dice.
  a Copy and complete the table to show the possible scores.

Dice

		1	2	3	4	5	6
Coin	**Heads**	2					12
	Tails	0					5

  b Calculate the probability that the score is:
    i 0   **ii** odd   **iii** even.

3 A bag contains seven discs numbered from 1 to 7
A disc is taken from the bag and then replaced in the bag.
A second disc is then taken from the bag.
The numbers on the two discs are added to give a score.
  a Make a table to show all of the possible scores.
  b What is the probability that the score is 14?
  c Calculate the probability that the score is 12 or more.
  d Use your answer to **c** to calculate the probability that the score is less than 12

4 In a raffle for a new car 200 tickets are sold. Andrew buys one ticket. James buys
five tickets. Write down the probability that the car is won by:
  a Andrew   **b** James   **c** neither Andrew nor James.

5 68% of the population own a mobile phone.
  a Write down the percentage of the population that do **not** own a mobile phone.
A survey found that 75% of under-12s do **not** have a mobile phone.
  b Write down the percentage of under-12s that have a mobile phone.
  c Explain why there is a difference between the population figures and the survey
figures.

6 The table shows some of the probabilities of the number of cars queuing for petrol
at a petrol station.

Number of cars	0	1	2	3	4 or more
Probability	0.23	0.28	0.14	0.11	

Calculate the probability that the number of cars queuing is:
  a 4 or more   **b** less than 2   **c** more than 1
  d What is the most likely number of cars queuing?

7 Mr and Mrs Smith and their daughter Jane live together.
Mr Smith has a 40% chance that a phone call to their house is for him.
Mrs Smith says she has a probability of 0.6 that a phone call is for her.
Jane claims that, on average, 1 in every 20 calls is for her.
a Explain why these probabilities cannot be correct.
In fact only Mrs Smith's probability of getting a phone call is incorrect.
b Calculate the correct probability that a phone call to their house is for Mrs Smith.

8 A fair 10-sided dice has faces numbered from 1 to 10
The probability that it lands showing an even number is 0.5
The probability that it lands showing 6, 7 or 8 is 0.3
Tanya says: 'the probability that the dice shows either an even number or 6, 7 or 8 is 0.5 + 0.3 = 0.8'
a Explain why Tanya is wrong. **b** Work out the correct probability.

Chapter summary

- The chance of an event happening is a measure of how likely it is to happen.
- The chance of an event happening can be described using these words.

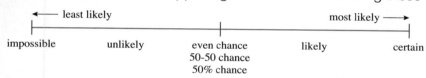

- *Probability* measures the chance of an event happening.
- Probabilities can be written as fractions, decimals or percentages.
- Probabilities can be shown on a probability scale:

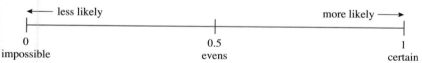

- Probability of an event $= \dfrac{\text{number of ways an event can happen}}{\text{total number of outcomes}}$

  This formula can only be used if all outcomes are equally likely, that is if the situation is *fair*.
- If all outcomes are not equally likely, the situation is *biased*.
- Equally likely outcomes have equal probabilities.
- When items are chosen at random, each item has an equal chance of being chosen. So the outcomes are equally likely and have equal probabilities.
- Probability of an event $= \dfrac{\text{number of successful outcomes}}{\text{total number of outcomes}}$
- In a table (or list) of outcomes for two equally likely events, each outcome in the table is equally likely.

- To find the probability of two events:
  Step 1: Make a table (or list) of all the possible outcomes.
  Step 2: Count the number of successful outcomes and the total number of outcomes in the table (or list).
  Step 3: Calculate the probability using the formula above.
- Mutually exclusive outcomes cannot happen at the same time.
- The probabilities of all the mutually exclusive outcomes of an event add to 1
  For example, for a coin, probability of heads + probability of tails = 1
- Probability that an event happens = 1 − probability that the event does **not** happen.

Chapter review

1 This fair five-sided spinner is spun once.
  a   **i**   Which colour is the spinner most likely to land on?
    ii   What is the probability that the spinner lands on white?
  b   Write down the probability of each of the following events:
    i   throwing a fair coin and getting a tail
    ii   throwing a 5 with a fair six-sided dice
    iii   picking a green pen from a box of green pens.

2 A fair six-sided dice is thrown once.
  The probabilities of the following events have been
  marked in the probability scale below.
  a   a number more than 0 is thrown
  b   an odd number is thrown   **c**   a 2 is thrown.

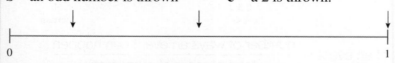

0   1

Copy the probability scale and label each arrow with the letter to show which event it represents.

3 There are 10 beads in a bag. Three beads are blue, four are red and three are green. One bead is taken out of the bag at random. The probabilities of three events have been marked on the probability scale below. The events are:
  a   the bead is red   **b**   the bead is yellow   **c**   the bead is not green.

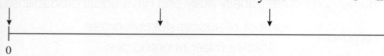

0   1

Copy the probability scale and label each arrow with the letter to show which event it represents.

4 In a game, a blue spinner and a yellow spinner are spun. Both spinners are fair and are numbered 0, 1, 2, 4.

The numbers on the two spinners are multiplied together to produce a score.

Blue spinner

		0	1	2	4
	0				
Yellow	**1**			2	
spinner	**2**	0			8
	4				

a Copy and complete the table to show all the possible scores.
b What is the probability of getting a score of 1?
c What is the probability of getting a score of more than 4?

5 Henry asked all his class how they had come to school on Tuesday and he recorded the results.
Henry chooses one pupil from his class at random. What is the probability that this pupil came to school by bus?

Method of travel	Frequency
Foot	12
Car	9
Bicycle	5
Bus	7

6 Dina picks up her post when she comes back from holiday.
The table shows the number of each type of letter there is.

Bank statement	Bill	Junk mail	Postcard	Other
1	2	10	1	7

Dina picks a letter at random from the post.
What is the probability that the letter she picks is:
a junk mail   **b** **not** a bill?

7 a Harry has a spinner which has six equal sections.
Three sections are green, two are yellow and one is blue.
Harry spins the spinner once.
On which colour is the spinner most likely to land?

b Harry has a second spinner.
Two sections are green, two are yellow and one is blue.
What is the probability that this spinner does **not** land on yellow?

c Harry says, 'There are three colours on each spinner.
I think that there is the same chance of getting blue on both spinners.' Explain why Harry is wrong.

8 Ten boys were asked what their favourite sport is.
The results are shown in the table.

Sport	Frequency
Cricket (C)	3
Football (F)	5
Rugby (R)	2

a One of the boys is chosen at random.
What is the probability that this boy likes
rugby (R) the best?

b Two of the boys are chosen at random.
Copy and complete the table to show their possible
choice of favourite sport.

First boy	Second boy
C	C
C	F

9 a Megan's pencil case contains four black, one red and three blue pens.
She picks a pen at random.
What is the probability that Megan picks a black pen?

b Rachel's pencil case contains 16 pens of which six are black.
What is the probability that the pen Rachel picks is **not** black?

c Who is more likely to pick a black pen? Explain your answer.

10 The sections of a biased six-sided spinner are numbered 1, 2, 3, 4, 5 and 6
The table shows the probabilities of landing on some of the numbers.

Number	1	2	3	4	5	6
Probability	0.18	0.03	0.39		0.16	0.07

a Calculate the missing probability in the table.

b Calculate the probability that the spinner lands on a number less than 4

Calculating with fractions and decimals

17.1 Addition and subtraction of fractions

To add fractions, use the following steps.

Step 1: Write the fractions with a common denominator.

Step 2: Add the numerators.

Step 3: Write the answer in its simplest form.

Example 1

Work out   **a** $\frac{1}{9} + \frac{4}{9}$ **b** $\frac{3}{10} + \frac{1}{10}$

Solution 1

a   **Step 1:** The fractions already have a common denominator of 9

   Step 2: Add the numerators: $\frac{1}{9} + \frac{4}{9} = \frac{1+4}{9} = \frac{5}{9}$

   Step 3: $\frac{5}{9}$ does not simplify. $\frac{1}{9} + \frac{4}{9} = \frac{5}{9}$

b   **Step 1:** The fractions already have a common denominator of 10

   Step 2: Add the numerators: $\frac{3}{10} + \frac{1}{10} = \frac{3+1}{10} = \frac{4}{10}$

   Step 3: Simplify by cancelling: $\frac{4}{10} = \frac{4 \div 2}{10 \div 2} = \frac{2}{5}$

   $\frac{3}{10} + \frac{1}{10} = \frac{2}{5}$

Example 2

Work out $\frac{1}{3} + \frac{5}{12}$

Solution 2

Step 1: Find a common denominator.
Multiples of 3: 3, 6, 9, **12**, 15, ...
Multiples of 12: **12**, 24, 36, ...
12 is the smallest number that is a multiple of both 3 and 12

$$\frac{1}{3} = \frac{1 \times 4}{3 \times 4} = \frac{4}{12}$$

Step 2: Add the numerators:

$$\frac{1}{3} + \frac{5}{12} = \frac{4}{12} + \frac{5}{12} = \frac{4+5}{12} = \frac{9}{12}$$

Step 3: Simplify by cancelling: $\frac{9}{12} = \frac{9 \div 3}{12 \div 3} = \frac{3}{4}$

$$\frac{1}{3} + \frac{5}{12} = \frac{3}{4}$$

To subtract fractions, use the following steps.
Step 1: Write the fractions with a common denominator.
Step 2: Subtract the numerators.
Step 3: Write the answer in its simplest form.

Example 3

Work out $\frac{2}{3} - \frac{2}{5}$

Solution 3

Step 1: Find a common denominator.
Multiples of 3: 3, 6, 9, 12, **15**, ...
Multiples of 5: 5, 10, **15**, 20, 25, ...
15 is the smallest number that is a multiple of both 3 and 5

$$\frac{2}{3} = \frac{2 \times 5}{3 \times 5} = \frac{10}{15} \qquad \frac{2}{5} = \frac{2 \times 3}{5 \times 3} = \frac{6}{15}$$

Step 2: Subtract the numerators: $\frac{2}{3} - \frac{2}{5} = \frac{10}{15} - \frac{6}{15} = \frac{10-6}{15} = \frac{4}{15}$

Step 3: $\frac{4}{15}$ does not simplify.

$$\frac{2}{3} - \frac{2}{5} = \frac{4}{15}$$

Example 4

Use a scientific calculator to work out $\frac{2}{5} - \frac{1}{7}$

Solution 4

Enter $\frac{2}{5}$ as a fraction on the calculator.

Enter 'subtract'.

Enter $\frac{1}{7}$ as a fraction.

$$\frac{2}{5} - \frac{1}{7} = \frac{9}{35}$$

It is important to know how to enter fractions and read the display on a calculator.

Exercise A

1 Work out:

   a $\frac{1}{7} + \frac{2}{7}$ **b** $\frac{2}{9} + \frac{5}{9}$ **c** $\frac{3}{5} + \frac{1}{5}$ **d** $\frac{3}{17} + \frac{6}{17}$ **e** $\frac{2}{13} + \frac{3}{13}$

   f $\frac{7}{9} - \frac{2}{9}$ **g** $\frac{6}{11} - \frac{4}{11}$ **h** $\frac{4}{7} - \frac{2}{7}$ **i** $\frac{4}{5} - \frac{3}{5}$ **j** $\frac{8}{19} - \frac{3}{19}$

2 Work out:

   a $\frac{1}{10} + \frac{1}{20}$ **b** $\frac{1}{5} + \frac{1}{10}$ **c** $\frac{1}{4} + \frac{1}{2}$ **d** $\frac{1}{4} + \frac{3}{8}$ **e** $\frac{1}{6} + \frac{2}{3}$

   f $\frac{5}{8} - \frac{1}{4}$ **g** $\frac{7}{10} - \frac{3}{5}$ **h** $\frac{5}{6} - \frac{2}{3}$ **i** $\frac{9}{16} - \frac{3}{8}$ **j** $\frac{11}{14} - \frac{1}{7}$

3 Work out:

   a $\frac{1}{3} + \frac{1}{4}$ **b** $\frac{1}{5} + \frac{1}{2}$ **c** $\frac{1}{6} + \frac{1}{4}$ **d** $\frac{1}{8} + \frac{1}{5}$ **e** $\frac{1}{2} + \frac{1}{3}$

   f $\frac{1}{4} - \frac{1}{5}$ **g** $\frac{3}{7} - \frac{1}{5}$ **h** $\frac{2}{3} - \frac{1}{4}$ **i** $\frac{5}{6} - \frac{2}{5}$ **j** $\frac{7}{9} - \frac{1}{3}$

4 Work out these fraction calculations.
Give your answers in their simplest form.

   a $\frac{1}{12} + \frac{1}{12}$ **b** $\frac{2}{9} + \frac{1}{9}$ **c** $\frac{3}{10} + \frac{1}{10}$ **d** $\frac{5}{18} + \frac{1}{18}$ **e** $\frac{2}{15} + \frac{7}{15}$

   f $\frac{8}{9} - \frac{2}{9}$ **g** $\frac{5}{12} - \frac{1}{12}$ **h** $\frac{3}{10} - \frac{1}{10}$ **i** $\frac{9}{16} - \frac{1}{16}$ **j** $\frac{11}{20} - \frac{3}{20}$

5 Work out these calculations.
Give your answers in their simplest form.

   a $\frac{1}{12} + \frac{1}{4}$ **b** $\frac{2}{5} + \frac{1}{10}$ **c** $\frac{1}{3} + \frac{1}{6}$ **d** $\frac{3}{10} + \frac{1}{5}$ **e** $\frac{5}{12} + \frac{1}{3}$

   f $\frac{3}{4} - \frac{1}{20}$ **g** $\frac{10}{21} - \frac{1}{7}$ **h** $\frac{2}{3} - \frac{1}{6}$ **i** $\frac{5}{6} - \frac{1}{2}$ **j** $\frac{7}{10} - \frac{1}{5}$

6 Work out these calculations.
Simplify your answers if possible.

   a $\frac{1}{8} + \frac{3}{8}$ **b** $\frac{3}{5} + \frac{3}{10}$ **c** $\frac{3}{4} + \frac{1}{12}$ **d** $\frac{2}{9} + \frac{4}{9}$ **e** $\frac{5}{18} + \frac{2}{3}$

   f $\frac{3}{4} - \frac{3}{16}$ **g** $\frac{6}{7} - \frac{1}{7}$ **h** $\frac{9}{20} - \frac{1}{4}$ **i** $\frac{11}{12} - \frac{1}{6}$ **j** $\frac{1}{2} - \frac{2}{17}$

7   Copy these rectangles.
Shade in the rectangles to complete the fraction sum.

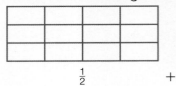 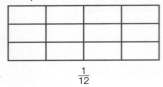 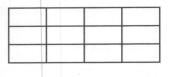

$\frac{1}{2}$ $+$ $\frac{1}{12}$ $=$ ....

8   Copy these rectangles.
Shade in the rectangles to complete the subtraction.
Give your answer in its simplest form.

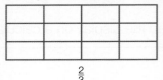 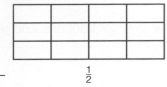 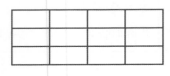

$\frac{2}{3}$ $-$ $\frac{1}{2}$ $=$ ....

9   Use a calculator to check your answers to questions **1** to **6**

There are two methods for adding mixed numbers, e.g. $4\frac{1}{5} + 2\frac{3}{4}$

Method 1
Step 1: Add the whole number parts.
Step 2: Add the fraction parts using the method in Exercise A.
Step 3: Combine the answers to **Step 1** and **Step 2**

Method 2
Step 1: Convert the mixed numbers to improper fractions.
Step 2: Add the improper fractions using the method in Exercise A.
Step 3: Convert the answer (an improper fraction) back to a mixed number.

Example 5

Work out $4\frac{1}{5} + 2\frac{3}{4}$

Solution 5

Method 1
Step 1: Add the whole number parts: $4\frac{1}{5} + 2\frac{3}{4} = 6 + \frac{1}{5} + \frac{3}{4}$

Step 2: Add the fraction parts: 20 is a multiple of both 4 and 5
Write the fractions with common denominator 20

$$\frac{1}{5} = \frac{1 \times 4}{5 \times 4} = \frac{4}{20} \qquad\qquad \frac{3}{4} = \frac{3 \times 5}{4 \times 5} = \frac{15}{20}$$

Step 3: Combine the answers:

$$6 + \frac{1}{5} + \frac{3}{4} = 6 + \frac{4}{20} + \frac{15}{20} = 6 + \frac{19}{20}$$
$$4\frac{1}{5} + 2\frac{3}{4} = 6\frac{19}{20}$$

Method 2

Step 1: Convert the mixed numbers into improper fractions:

Convert $4\frac{1}{5}$ $\frac{5}{5} = 1$ so $4\frac{1}{5} = \underbrace{\frac{5}{5} + \frac{5}{5} + \frac{5}{5} + \frac{5}{5}}_{4} + \frac{1}{5}$

$$= \frac{4 \times 5 + 1}{5} = \frac{21}{5}$$

Convert $2\frac{3}{4}$ $\frac{4}{4} = 1$ so $2\frac{3}{4} = \frac{4}{4} + \frac{4}{4} + \frac{3}{4} = \frac{11}{4}$

$$4\frac{1}{5} + 2\frac{3}{4} = \frac{21}{5} + \frac{11}{4}$$

Step 2: Work out $\frac{21}{5} + \frac{11}{4}$

20 is a multiple of both 5 and 4
Write the fractions with common denominator 20

$$\frac{21}{5} = \frac{21 \times 4}{5 \times 4} = \frac{84}{20} \qquad\qquad \frac{11}{4} = \frac{11 \times 5}{4 \times 5} = \frac{55}{20}$$

$$4\frac{1}{5} + 2\frac{3}{4} = \frac{21}{5} + \frac{11}{4} = \frac{84}{20} + \frac{55}{20} = \frac{84 + 55}{20} = \frac{139}{20}$$

Step 3: Convert this back to a mixed number: $139 \div 20 = 6$ remainder 19

so $4\frac{1}{5} + 2\frac{3}{4} = 6\frac{19}{20}$

There are two methods for subtracting mixed numbers, e.g. $5\frac{1}{2} - 3\frac{3}{4}$

Method 1
Step 1: Subtract the whole number parts.
Step 2: Subtract the fraction parts using the method in Exercise A.
Step 3: Combine the answers to **Step 1** and **Step 2**

Method 2
Step 1: Convert the mixed numbers to improper fractions.
Step 2: Subtract the fraction parts using the method in Exercise A.
Step 3: Convert the answer (an improper fraction) back to a mixed number.

Example 6

Work out $5\frac{1}{2} - 3\frac{3}{4}$

Solution 6

Method 1
Step 1: Subtract the whole number parts: $5\frac{1}{2} - 3\frac{3}{4} = 5 + \frac{1}{2} - 3 - \frac{3}{4} = 2 + \frac{1}{2} - \frac{3}{4}$

Step 2: Subtract the fraction parts: 4 is a multiple of both 2 and 4
Write the fractions with common denominator 4

$$\frac{1}{2} = \frac{1 \times 2}{2 \times 2} = \frac{2}{4}$$

$$\frac{1}{2} - \frac{3}{4} = \frac{2}{4} - \frac{3}{4}$$

Subtract the numerators: $= \frac{2-3}{4} = -\frac{1}{4}$

Step 3: Combine the answers.

$$5\frac{1}{2} - 3\frac{3}{4} = 2 - \frac{1}{4} = \frac{8}{4} - \frac{1}{4}$$ (writing 2 as a fraction with denominator 4)

$$= \frac{7}{4} = 1\frac{3}{4}$$

$$5\frac{1}{2} - 3\frac{3}{4} = 1\frac{3}{4}$$

Method 2
Step 1: Convert the mixed numbers into improper fractions.

For $5\frac{1}{2}$ $\frac{2}{2} = 1$ so $5\frac{1}{2} = \underbrace{\frac{2}{2} + \frac{2}{2} + \frac{2}{2} + \frac{2}{2} + \frac{2}{2}}_{5} + \frac{1}{2} = \frac{5 \times 2 + 1}{2} = \frac{11}{2}$

For $3\frac{3}{4}$ $\frac{4}{4} = 1$ so $3\frac{3}{4} = \underbrace{\frac{4}{4} + \frac{4}{4} + \frac{4}{4}}_{3} + \frac{3}{4} = \frac{15}{4}$

$$5\frac{1}{2} - 3\frac{3}{4} = \frac{11}{2} - \frac{15}{4}$$

Step 2: Work out $\frac{11}{2} - \frac{15}{4}$

4 is a multiple of 2 and 4
Write the fractions with common denominator 4

$$\frac{11}{2} = \frac{11 \times 2}{2 \times 2} = \frac{22}{4}$$

$$5\frac{1}{2} - 3\frac{3}{4} = \frac{11}{2} - \frac{15}{4} = \frac{22}{4} - \frac{15}{4} = \frac{22 - 15}{4} = \frac{7}{4}$$

Step 3: Convert $\frac{7}{4}$ to a mixed number. $7 \div 4 = 1$ remainder 3

So $5\frac{1}{2} - 3\frac{3}{4} = 1\frac{3}{4}$

Exercise B

1   Use the method you prefer to work out these mixed number calculations.
     Give the answers as mixed numbers.

a $1\frac{1}{2} + 2\frac{1}{4}$	**b** $2\frac{1}{3} + 4\frac{1}{2}$	**c** $1\frac{1}{4} + 3\frac{1}{5}$	**d** $7\frac{1}{2} + 3\frac{1}{6}$
e $3\frac{3}{4} - 1\frac{1}{2}$	**f** $4\frac{5}{6} - 2\frac{1}{3}$	**g** $8\frac{1}{3} - 5\frac{1}{6}$	**h** $2\frac{4}{5} - \frac{3}{10}$

2 Use any method to work out these calculations.
Give the answers as mixed numbers where necessary.

a $1\frac{1}{2} + 2\frac{3}{4}$ b $5\frac{2}{3} + 2\frac{1}{2}$ c $6\frac{3}{4} + 2\frac{4}{5}$ d $9\frac{1}{2} + 1\frac{5}{6}$

e $2\frac{1}{4} - 1\frac{1}{2}$ f $4\frac{1}{6} - 2\frac{2}{3}$ g $4\frac{1}{6} - 3\frac{5}{6}$ h $2\frac{1}{5} - 1\frac{7}{10}$

3 Use any method to work out these calculations.
Give the answers as mixed numbers where necessary.

a $1\frac{5}{12} + 5\frac{3}{4}$ b $7\frac{2}{3} + 2\frac{11}{15}$ c $4\frac{3}{4} + 2\frac{9}{20}$ d $6\frac{5}{6} + 2\frac{7}{8}$

e $4\frac{1}{20} - 3\frac{3}{5}$ f $7\frac{1}{9} - 2\frac{3}{7}$ g $3\frac{2}{3} - 2\frac{5}{11}$ h $2\frac{1}{4} - 1\frac{7}{24}$

4 A jug holds $1\frac{1}{4}$ pints of milk.

How many jugs are needed to hold at least 1 gallon?

1 gallon = 8 pints

5 A bottle holds $\frac{7}{10}$ of a litre of wine. A glass holds $\frac{1}{8}$ of a litre of wine.

Two glasses are poured from the bottle.

What fraction of a litre of wine is left in the bottle?

6 Jack says that $1\frac{1}{2} + 2\frac{1}{5} = 3\frac{2}{7}$

By working out the correct answer, show that he is incorrect.

7 a Use a calculator to work out

$1 + \frac{1}{2} + \frac{1}{4} + \frac{1}{8} + \frac{1}{16}$

b The pattern of adding fractions is continued.
Will the answer ever be greater than 2?
Explain your answer.

8 Use a calculator to check your answers to questions **1** to **3**

17.2 Multiplication and division of fractions

CAN YOU REMEMBER?

- The meaning of 'integer'?
- How to simplify a fraction by cancelling common factors?
- How to calculate a fraction of a quantity, e.g. $\frac{1}{4}$ of $8 = 8 \div 4$?

IN THIS SECTION YOU WILL:

- Learn how to multiply and divide a fraction by an integer.
- Learn how to multiply and divide a fraction by a unit fraction, e.g. $\frac{1}{5}$
- Learn how to multiply and divide a fraction by a general fraction, e.g. $\frac{3}{5}$

To multiply a fraction by an integer, either use diagrams or follow these steps.
Step 1: Write the integer as a fraction with a denominator of 1
Step 2: Write the multiplication as a single fraction.

Step 3: Simplify by cancelling any common factors.
Step 4: Multiply the numerators and multiply the denominators.
Step 5: If the answer is an improper fraction, write it as an integer or mixed number.

Example 1

Work out $\frac{1}{3} \times 7$

Solution 1

Method 1 – Diagrams

$$\frac{1}{3} \times 7 = \bigcirc \times 7$$

$$= \bigcirc + \bigcirc + \bigcirc + \bigcirc + \bigcirc + \bigcirc + \bigcirc$$

$$= \bigcirc + \bigcirc + \bigcirc = 2\frac{1}{3}$$

Method 2
Step 1: Write the integer as a fraction with a denominator of 1:

$$\frac{1}{3} \times 7 = \frac{1}{3} \times \frac{7}{1}$$

Step 2: Write the multiplication as a single fraction:

$$\frac{1}{3} \times \frac{7}{1} = \frac{1 \times 7}{3 \times 1}$$

Step 3: $\frac{1 \times 7}{3 \times 1}$ does not have any common factors (other than 1).

Step 4: Multiply the numerators and multiply the denominators:

$$\frac{1 \times 7}{3 \times 1} = \frac{7}{3}$$

Step 5: The answer is an improper fraction, so convert to a mixed number.
$7 \div 3 = 2$ remainder 1

$$\frac{7}{3} = 2\frac{1}{3}$$

To multiply a unit fraction by a unit fraction, use diagrams or follow these steps.
Step 1: Write the multiplication as a single fraction.
Step 2: Multiply the numerators and multiply the denominators.

Example 2

Work out $\frac{1}{5} \times \frac{1}{3}$

Solution 2

Method 1 – Diagrams

$\dfrac{1}{5}$ $\quad$ $\dfrac{1}{5} \times \dfrac{1}{3}$

Remember that multiplication by $\dfrac{1}{3}$ is the same as division by 3

$$\dfrac{1}{5} \times \dfrac{1}{3} = \dfrac{1}{15}$$

Method 2

Step 1: Write the multiplication as a single fraction:

$$\dfrac{1}{5} \times \dfrac{1}{3} = \dfrac{1 \times 1}{5 \times 3}$$

Step 2: Multiply the numerators and multiply the denominators:

$$\dfrac{1 \times 1}{5 \times 3} = \dfrac{1}{15}$$

To multiply a fraction by a fraction, use diagrams or follow these steps.

Step 1: Write the multiplication as a single fraction.

Step 2: Simplify by cancelling any common factors.

Step 3: Multiply the numerators and multiply the denominators.

Step 4: If the answer is an improper fraction, write it as an integer or mixed number.

Example 3

Work out $\dfrac{9}{20} \times \dfrac{4}{15}$

Solution 3

Step 1: Write the multiplication as a single fraction:

$$\dfrac{9}{20} \times \dfrac{4}{15} = \dfrac{9 \times 4}{20 \times 15}$$

Step 2: Simplify by cancelling common factors:
3 is the highest number that is a common factor of 9 and 15
Dividing the numerator and denominator by 3 gives

$$\dfrac{9 \times 4}{20 \times 15} = \dfrac{{}^{3}\cancel{9} \times 4}{20 \times \cancel{15}_{5}} = \dfrac{3 \times 4}{20 \times 5}$$

4 is the highest number that is a common factor of 4 and 20
Dividing the numerator and denominator by 4 gives

$$\dfrac{3 \times 4}{20 \times 5} = \dfrac{3 \times \cancel{4}^{1}}{{}_{5}\cancel{20} \times 5} = \dfrac{3 \times 1}{5 \times 5}$$

Step 3: Multiply the numerators and multiply the denominators:

$$\frac{3 \times 1}{5 \times 5} = \frac{3}{25}$$

Step 4: The answer is a proper fraction:

$$\frac{9}{20} \times \frac{4}{15} = \frac{3}{25}$$

Exercise A

1 Copy this 4 by 3 rectangle onto squared paper.
  a Shade $\frac{1}{4}$ of the rectangle.
  b Use diagrams to find:
    i $\frac{1}{4} \times 8$ **ii** $\frac{1}{4} \times \frac{1}{3}$ **iii** $\frac{1}{4} \times \frac{2}{3}$

    Give your answers in their simplest form.

2 Copy this 5 by 4 rectangle onto squared paper.
  a Shade $\frac{1}{5}$ of the rectangle.
  b Use diagrams to find:
    i $\frac{1}{5} \times 15$ **ii** $\frac{1}{5} \times \frac{1}{4}$ **iii** $\frac{1}{5} \times \frac{3}{4}$

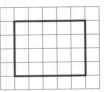

3 Work out, leaving each answer as an integer:
  a $\frac{1}{4} \times 8$ **b** $\frac{1}{5} \times 5$ **c** $\frac{1}{2} \times 10$ **d** $\frac{1}{3} \times 9$
  e $\frac{1}{6} \times 24$ **f** $\frac{1}{10} \times 50$ **g** $\frac{1}{8} \times 16$ **h** $\frac{1}{9} \times 27$

4 Work out, leaving each answer as a mixed number:
  a $\frac{1}{4} \times 9$ **b** $\frac{1}{5} \times 7$ **c** $\frac{1}{2} \times 5$ **d** $\frac{1}{3} \times 14$
  e $\frac{1}{6} \times 13$ **f** $\frac{1}{10} \times 23$ **g** $\frac{1}{8} \times 25$ **h** $\frac{1}{9} \times 20$

5 Work out, leaving each answer as a proper fraction:
  a $\frac{1}{4} \times \frac{1}{5}$ **b** $\frac{1}{5} \times \frac{1}{2}$ **c** $\frac{1}{2} \times \frac{1}{6}$ **d** $\frac{1}{3} \times \frac{1}{4}$
  e $\frac{1}{6} \times \frac{1}{10}$ **f** $\frac{1}{10} \times \frac{1}{9}$ **g** $\frac{1}{8} \times \frac{1}{2}$ **h** $\frac{1}{9} \times \frac{1}{3}$

6 Work out, leaving each answer as a proper fraction:
  a $\frac{2}{3} \times \frac{1}{5}$ **b** $\frac{3}{4} \times \frac{1}{2}$ **c** $\frac{5}{7} \times \frac{1}{6}$ **d** $\frac{3}{8} \times \frac{1}{4}$
  e $\frac{7}{10} \times \frac{1}{10}$ **f** $\frac{4}{9} \times \frac{1}{9}$ **g** $\frac{5}{8} \times \frac{1}{2}$ **h** $\frac{7}{9} \times \frac{1}{3}$

7 Work out, giving each answer as a proper fraction in its simplest form:
  a $\frac{2}{3} \times \frac{1}{4}$ **b** $\frac{3}{4} \times \frac{1}{6}$ **c** $\frac{5}{7} \times \frac{1}{10}$ **d** $\frac{3}{8} \times \frac{1}{9}$
  e $\frac{7}{10} \times \frac{1}{7}$ **f** $\frac{4}{9} \times \frac{1}{12}$ **g** $\frac{5}{8} \times \frac{1}{20}$ **h** $\frac{7}{9} \times \frac{1}{14}$

8 Work out, giving each answer as a proper fraction in its simplest form:
  a $\frac{2}{3} \times \frac{3}{4}$ **b** $\frac{3}{4} \times \frac{5}{6}$ **c** $\frac{5}{7} \times \frac{7}{10}$ **d** $\frac{3}{8} \times \frac{2}{9}$
  e $\frac{7}{10} \times \frac{5}{7}$ **f** $\frac{4}{9} \times \frac{3}{16}$ **g** $\frac{5}{8} \times \frac{4}{15}$ **h** $\frac{7}{9} \times \frac{3}{14}$

9 Use a calculator to check your answers to questions **1** to **8**

Division by an integer can be changed to multiplication by a fraction.
For example, dividing by 5 is the same as multiplying by $\frac{1}{5}$
To divide a fraction by an integer:

Step 1: Change division by an integer into multiplication by a fraction,
e.g. change $\div 2$ into $\times \frac{1}{2}$

Step 2: Work out the multiplication.

Example 4

Work out $\frac{1}{8} \div 2$

Solution 4

Change the division by 2 into multiplication by $\frac{1}{2}$

$$\frac{1}{8} \div 2 = \frac{1}{8} \times \frac{1}{2}$$

Method 1 – Diagrams

$\frac{1}{8}$ 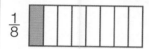 $\frac{1}{8} \times \frac{1}{2}$ 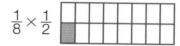 $\frac{1}{8} \div 2 = \frac{1}{16}$

Method 2
Step 1: Write the multiplication as a single fraction: $\frac{1}{8} \times \frac{1}{2} = \frac{1 \times 1}{8 \times 2}$

Step 2: $\frac{1 \times 1}{8 \times 2}$ does not have any common factors (other than 1).

Step 3: Multiply the numerators and multiply the denominators: $\frac{1 \times 1}{8 \times 2} = \frac{1}{16}$

Step 4: The answer is a proper fraction: $\frac{1}{8} \div 2 = \frac{1}{16}$

Dividing by 8 is the same as multiplying by $\frac{1}{8}$

In the same way, dividing by $\frac{1}{8}$ is the same as multiplying by 8

To divide an integer by a fraction:

Step 1: Change division by a fraction into multiplication by an integer,
e.g. change $\div \frac{1}{2}$ into $\times 2$

Step 2: Work out the multiplication.

Example 5

Work out $7 \div \frac{1}{8}$

Solution 5

$7 \div \frac{1}{8} = 7 \times 8 = 56$

Dividing by any fraction is the same as multiplying by the inverted fraction.

Example 6

Work out $\frac{5}{8} \div \frac{3}{4}$

Solution 6

$\frac{5}{8} \div \frac{3}{4} = \frac{5}{8} \times \frac{4}{3}$ (dividing by $\frac{3}{4}$ is the same as multiplying by $\frac{4}{3}$)

Step 1: Write the multiplication as a single fraction: $\frac{5}{8} \times \frac{4}{3} = \frac{5 \times 4}{8 \times 3}$

Step 2: Simplify by cancelling any common factors: $\frac{5 \times 4}{8 \times 3} = \frac{5 \times \overset{1}{\cancel{4}}}{_2\cancel{8} \times 3} = \frac{5 \times 1}{2 \times 3}$

Step 3: Multiply the numerators and multiply the denominators: $\frac{5 \times 1}{2 \times 3} = \frac{5}{6}$

Step 4: The answer is a proper fraction: $\frac{5}{8} \div \frac{3}{4} = \frac{5}{6}$

Exercise B

1 Work out, leaving each answer as a proper fraction:

   a $\frac{1}{4} \div 2$ **b** $\frac{1}{3} \div 5$ **c** $\frac{1}{2} \div 10$ **d** $\frac{1}{3} \div 2$

   e $\frac{1}{6} \div 10$ **f** $\frac{1}{10} \div 5$ **g** $\frac{1}{8} \div 3$ **h** $\frac{1}{9} \div 9$

2 Work out, leaving each answer as an integer:

   a $\frac{1}{4} \div \frac{1}{8}$ **b** $\frac{1}{3} \div \frac{1}{9}$ **c** $\frac{1}{2} \div \frac{1}{10}$ **d** $\frac{1}{3} \div \frac{1}{6}$

   e $\frac{1}{2} \div \frac{1}{6}$ **f** $\frac{1}{5} \div \frac{1}{20}$ **g** $\frac{1}{8} \div \frac{1}{40}$ **h** $\frac{1}{9} \div \frac{1}{18}$

3 Work out these division calculations.
Give each answer as a mixed number.

   a $\frac{1}{4} \div \frac{1}{5}$ **b** $\frac{1}{5} \div \frac{1}{6}$ **c** $\frac{1}{2} \div \frac{1}{3}$ **d** $\frac{1}{3} \div \frac{1}{5}$

   e $\frac{1}{6} \div \frac{1}{7}$ **f** $\frac{1}{2} \div \frac{1}{9}$ **g** $\frac{1}{8} \div \frac{1}{9}$ **h** $\frac{1}{9} \div \frac{1}{11}$

4 Work out these division calculations.
Give each answer as a proper fraction in its simplest form.

   a $\frac{2}{3} \div \frac{4}{3}$ **b** $\frac{3}{4} \div \frac{7}{8}$ **c** $\frac{5}{7} \div \frac{5}{6}$ **d** $\frac{3}{16} \div \frac{1}{4}$

   e $\frac{7}{10} \div \frac{9}{10}$ **f** $\frac{4}{9} \div \frac{2}{3}$ **g** $\frac{3}{8} \div \frac{1}{2}$ **h** $\frac{2}{9} \div \frac{1}{3}$

5 Work out, giving each answer as a mixed number:

   a $\frac{2}{3} \div \frac{4}{9}$ **b** $\frac{3}{4} \div \frac{1}{10}$ **c** $\frac{5}{7} \div \frac{1}{2}$ **d** $\frac{3}{5} \div \frac{1}{4}$

   e $\frac{3}{10} \div \frac{1}{8}$ **f** $\frac{4}{9} \div \frac{1}{6}$ **g** $\frac{3}{8} \div \frac{2}{7}$ **h** $\frac{2}{9} \div \frac{3}{20}$

6 Use a calculator to check your answers to questions **1** to **5**

17.3 Addition and subtraction of decimals

CAN YOU REMEMBER

- The place value headings?
- How to add and subtract whole numbers and simple decimals?
- How to solve an equation?

IN THIS SECTION YOU WILL

- Reinforce your knowledge of adding and subtracting decimals.
- Add and subtract harder decimals.
- Check your answers using a calculator.

To add or subtract decimals, write the numbers under the place value headings so that the decimal points are in the same column.
To add 325.21 and 1064.08

Thousands	Hundreds	Tens	Units	.	tenths	hundredths	thousandths
	3	2	5	.	2	1	
1	0	6	4	.	0	8	

This makes sure that digits with the same place value are added or subtracted.

Example 1

325.21 + 1064.29

Solution 1

Set out the decimals in columns as shown above.
Carry out the addition in the same way as for whole numbers.
Remember to insert the decimal point after the units digit in the answer.

$$
\begin{array}{r}
3\,2\,5\,.\,2^1 1 \\
+\,1\,0\,6\,4\,.\,2\,9 \\
\hline
1\,3\,8\,9\,.\,5\,0
\end{array}
$$

$$325.21 + 1064.29 = 1389.5$$

Example 2

a 946.27 + 528.61

b 518.32 − 270.19

Solution 2

a
$$
\begin{array}{r}
9\,4^1 6\,.\,2\,7 \\
+\;\;\,5\,2\,8\,.\,6\,1 \\
\hline
1\,4\,7\,4\,.\,8\,8
\end{array}
$$

$$946.27 + 528.61 = 1474.88$$

b
$$
\begin{array}{r}
{}^4\!5\,{}^1 1\,8\,.\,{}^2\!3\,{}^1 2 \\
-\;\;\,2\,7\,0\,.\,1\,9 \\
\hline
2\,4\,8\,.\,1\,3
\end{array}
$$

$$518.32 − 270.19 = 248.13$$

Exercise A

1 Work out:
   a 0.2 + 0.5   **b** 0.3 + 0.6   **c** 1.4 + 3.5
   d 5.1 + 3.8   **e** 6.2 + 3.7   **f** 3.5 + 0.4
   g 12.4 + 33.3   **h** 23.7 + 41.2

2 Work out:
   a 0.52 + 0.41   **b** 0.46 + 0.23   **c** 4.31 + 3.65
   d 9.16 + 0.43   **e** 17.02 + 41.97   **f** 45.22 + 13.26
   g 102.63 + 563.26   **h** 911.77 + 36.01

3 Work out:
   a 0.8 − 0.3   **b** 0.7 − 0.1   **c** 3.4 − 2.1
   d 6.5 − 1.2   **e** 7.7 − 3.5   **f** 8.6 − 2.4
   g 74.2 − 30.2   **h** 496.38 − 261.15

4 Work out:
   a 0.85 − 0.31   **b** 0.77 − 0.22   **c** 0.83 − 0.61
   d 5.66 − 2.13   **e** 8.27 − 2.14   **f** 8.68 − 7.55
   g 29.76 − 15.52   **h** 34.29 − 12.16

5 Work out:
   a 0.6 + 0.5   **b** 0.7 + 0.8   **c** 1.5 + 3.5
   d 5.3 + 4.8   **e** 6.6 + 3.5   **f** 8.7 + 1.4
   g 12.7 + 33.6   **h** 28.9 + 43.7

6 Work out:
   a 0.32 + 0.49   **b** 0.48 + 0.25   **c** 6.37 + 2.45
   d 9.76 + 0.48   **e** 17.62 + 43.99   **f** 45.67 + 13.56
   g 132.85 + 563.26   **h** 909.78 + 46.85

7 Work out:
   a 2.3 − 1.4   **b** 3.7 − 1.8   **c** 3.4 − 2.6
   d 7.5 − 1.9   **e** 7.6 − 3.8   **f** 2.6 − 1.7
   g 51.2 − 31.5   **h** 130.24 − 78.15

8 Work out:
   a 0.84 − 0.35   **b** 0.62 − 0.17   **c** 0.94 − 0.68
   d 5.36 − 3.29   **e** 8.47 − 2.84   **f** 7.63 − 5.82
   g 37.16 − 15.52   **h** 34.21 − 17.26

9 Use a calculator to check your answers to questions **1** to **8**

Example 3

Work out the missing values in each calculation.
a $0.7 + \ldots = 1.9$ b $\ldots - 4.71 = 9.32$

Solution 3

Call the missing value x.

a $0.7 + x = 1.9$
    Subtract 0.7 from both sides: $x = 1.9 - 0.7$
                                    $x = 1.2$

    The missing value is 1.2

b $x - 4.71 = 9.32$
    Add 4.71 to both sides: $x = 9.32 + 4.71$
                              $x = 14.03$
    The missing value is 14.03

Example 4

Work out $3.4 - 1.27$

Solution 4

Write 3.4 as 3.40 so that all numbers in the calculation have the same number of decimal digits after the decimal point.

$3.40 - 1.27$

$$
\begin{array}{r}
3 \, . \, {}^3\!4\,{}^1 0 \\
- 1 \, . \, 2 \; 7 \\
\hline
2 \, . \, 1 \; 3
\end{array}
$$

$3.4 - 1.27 = 2.13$

Exercise B

1   Find the missing values.
    a $0.3 + \ldots = 0.7$ b $1.7 + \ldots = 2.8$ c $5.1 + \ldots = 7.5$
    d $15.5 + \ldots = 18.9$ e $34.1 + \ldots = 77.6$ f $1.24 + \ldots = 6.88$
    g $61.21 + \ldots = 88.76$ h $19.7 + \ldots = 199.9$

2   Find the missing values.
    a $0.31 + \ldots = 0.46$ b $2.15 + \ldots = 4.84$ c $5.62 + \ldots = 8.91$
    d $25.6 + \ldots = 38.4$ e $\ldots + 37.5 = 56.2$ f $\ldots + 1.37 = 6.91$
    g $\ldots + 61.66 = 84.27$ h $\ldots + 29.43 = 200.16$

3 Find the missing values.

a ...... − 0.1 = 0.2   **b** ...... − 1.7 = 1.8   **c** ...... − 3.2 = 8.7

d ...... − 6.3 = 11.1   **e** ...... − 8 = 16.2   **f** ...... − 10.3 = 7.9

g ...... − 6.9 = 21.4   **h** ...... − 4.5 = 19.3

4 Find the missing values.

a 0.6 − ...... = 0.2   **b** 2.4 − ...... = 1.8   **c** 25.6 − ...... = 8.7

d 12.7 − ...... = 8.1   **e** 35.6 − ...... = 16.2   **f** 18.7 − ...... = 6.9

g 62.5 − ...... = 30.4   **h** 29.4 − ...... = 13.2

5 Work out:

a 1.3 − 0.26   **b** 1.8 − 0.87   **c** 8.1 − 5.15

d 18.7 − 10.01   **e** 29.4 − 24.63   **f** 154 − 20.71

6 Find the missing values.

a 0.15 + 0.27 + ... = 0.83   **b** 1.7 + ... + 0.92 = 2.75

c 15.5 + ... − 8.9 = 18.9   **d** 10.24 + 2.8 = 6.88 + ...

e 18.28 − 4.23 = ... − 88.76   **f** 90.6 − 12.7 − ...... = 40.6

7 Use a calculator to check your answers to questions **1** to **6**

17.4 Multiplication and division of decimals

CAN YOU REMEMBER

- The grid method and column method for multiplication?
- That division is the inverse of multiplication?
- How to multiply a fraction by an integer?
- Simple fraction and decimal equivalents?

IN THIS SECTION YOU WILL

- Learn how to multiply and divide using decimals.
- Check your answers using a calculator.
- Check your answers using approximate values.
- Use the answer to one calculation to work out the answer to a similar calculation.

Look at the multiplication 83 × 7 = 581
This can be worked out using different methods.

Grid method

×	7
80	560
3	21
	560 + 21 = 581

Column method

$$\begin{array}{r} 8\,3 \\ \times \quad 7 \\ \hline 5\,\overset{2}{8}\,1 \end{array}$$

Now look at $83 \times 0.7 = 58.1$

This can be worked out using the same methods.

Grid method

×	0.7
80	56
3	2.1
	56 + 2.1 = 58.1

$$80 \times 0.7 = 80 \times \frac{7}{10} = \frac{80 \times 7}{10} = 8 \times 7 = 56$$

$$3 \times 0.7 = 3 \times \frac{7}{10} = \frac{3 \times 7}{10} = \frac{21}{10} = 2.1$$

Column method

First, find the answer to the multiplication as if the numbers were integers.

$$\begin{array}{r} 83 \\ \times \quad 7 \\ \hline 581 \end{array} \rightarrow \begin{array}{r} 83 \\ \times \quad 0.7 \\ \hline 58.1 \end{array}$$

This number has moved *one* place to the right.

The answer is moved *one* place to the right.

It can also be worked out using the equivalent fraction method.

$$83 \times 0.7 = 83 \times \frac{7}{10} = \frac{83 \times 7}{10} = \frac{581}{10} = 58.1$$

One calculation can be used to work out the answer to another with the same digits.

For example, the calculation 83×7 can be used to help work out the calculation 83×0.7

$$83 \times \quad 7 = 581$$

$$83 \times 0.7 = \quad 58.1$$

Example 1

Use the grid method to work out 14.3×4

Solution 1

×	4
10	40
4	16
0.3	1.2
	40 + 16 + 1.2 = 57.6

$14.3 \times 4 = 57.6$

Example 2

Use the column method to work out 32×0.8

Solution 2

First work out 32×8

$$
\begin{array}{r}
3\,2 \\
\times \quad 8 \\
\hline
\scriptstyle 1 \\
2\,5\,6
\end{array}
\quad \rightarrow \quad
\begin{array}{r}
3\,2 \\
\times \quad 0.8 \\
\hline
\scriptstyle 1 \\
2\,5.6
\end{array}
$$

This number has moved *one* place to the right.

The answer is moved *one* place to the right.

Example 3

Use the column method to work out 5.3×6

Solution 3

First work out 53×6

$$
\begin{array}{r}
5\,3 \\
\times \quad 6 \\
\hline
\scriptstyle 1 \\
3\,1\,8
\end{array}
\quad \rightarrow \quad
\begin{array}{r}
5.3 \\
\times \quad 6 \\
\hline
\scriptstyle 1 \\
3\,1.8
\end{array}
$$

This number has moved *one* place to the right.

The answer is moved *one* place to the right.

Example 4

Use the column method to work out 7.1×1.5

Solution 4

First work out 71×15

$$
\begin{array}{r}
7\,1 \\
\times \quad 1\,5 \\
\hline
3\,5\,5 \\
7\,1\,0 \\
\hline
1\,0\,6\,5
\end{array}
\quad \rightarrow \quad
\begin{array}{r}
7.1 \\
\times \quad 1.5 \\
\hline
3\,5\,5 \\
7\,1\,0 \\
\hline
1\,0.6\,5
\end{array}
$$

This number has moved *one* place to the right.

This number has moved *one* place to the right.

The answer is moved $1 + 1 = 2$ places to the right.

Decimals can be written as equivalent fractions. For example $0.6 = 6$ tenths $= \frac{6}{10}$

$4.2 = 4$ whole ones $+ 2$ tenths

$= \frac{10}{10} + \frac{10}{10} + \frac{10}{10} + \frac{10}{10} + \frac{2}{10} = \frac{42}{10}$

To multiply two decimals using equivalent fractions
Step 1: Convert the two decimals to equivalent fractions.
Step 2: Multiply the two fractions.
Step 3: Convert back to a decimal.

Example 5

Use the equivalent fraction method to work out 9.7×0.3

Solution 5

$9.7 \times 0.3 = \dfrac{97}{10} \times \dfrac{3}{10} = \dfrac{97 \times 3}{10 \times 10} = \dfrac{291}{100} = 29.1$

Use estimation to check where to put the decimal point in a calculation.

Example 6

Use the fact that $32 \times 18 = 5760$ to work out the answer to 3.2×1.8

Solution 6

The digits in 32×18 are the same as the digits in 3.2×1.8
The answers will also have the same digits (5, 7, 6, 0)
3.2×1.8 is approximately the same as $3 \times 2 = 6$
So 3.2×1.8 is approximately equal to 6
The exact value is $3.2 \times 1.8 = 5.760 = 5.76$

Exercise A

1 Work out:
   a 1.5×3 b 2.1×4 c 3.5×7 d 2.5×5
   e 1.6×2 f 4.4×6 g 6.1×8 h 5.8×2

2 Work out:
   a 12×0.5 b 38×0.2 c 24×0.3 d 15×0.4
   e 28×0.6 f 42×0.9 g 35×0.7 h 27×0.8

3 Work out:
   a 0.3×2 b 0.6×2 c 0.4×3 d 0.7×6
   e 0.8×9 f 0.5×5 g 0.1×6 h 0.4×7

4 Work out:
   a 0.1×0.2 b 0.2×0.3 c 0.6×0.2 d 0.3×0.5
   e 0.7×0.2 f 0.8×0.8 g 0.5×0.5 h 0.8×0.9

5 Work out:
   a 1.5×2.1 b 1.2×3.2 c 5.1×1.3 d 6.3×2.5
   e 4.8×2.4 f 9.1×1.7 g 6.4×3.6 h 8.1×2.7

6 Work out:
   a 15.1×4.2 b 82.3×3.6 c 24.5×4.2 d 17.2×1.5
   e 18.1×3.9 f 54.6×1.4 g 62.7×1.7 h 74.3×3.7

7 Use the fact that $17 \times 18 = 306$ to write down the answers to:

   a 1.7×1.8 **b** 0.17×1.8 **c** 0.17×0.18

8 **a** Use any method to work out 32×165

     b Use your answer to part **a** to write down the answer to 3.2×16.5

9 **a** Use any method to work out 24×26

     b Use your answer to part **a** to write down the answer to 2.4×2.6

10 Use a calculator to check your answers to questions **1** to **6**.

To divide by a decimal follow these steps.

Step 1: Write the division as a fraction.

Step 2: Multiply the numerator and denominator by the same number (10 or 100) to give whole numbers.

Step 3: Divide the numerator by the denominator.

Example 7

Work out:

  a $24 \div 0.4$ **b** $3.6 \div 0.3$ **c** $4.2 \div 0.02$

Solution 7

a **Step 1:** Write the division as a fraction:

$$24 \div 0.4 = \frac{24}{0.4}$$

Step 2: Multiply the numerator and denominator by 10:

$$\frac{24}{0.4} = \frac{24 \times 10}{0.4 \times 10} = \frac{240}{4}$$

Step 3: Divide the numerator by the denominator:

$$\frac{240}{4} = 240 \div 4 = 60$$

b **Step 1:** Write the division as a fraction:

$$3.6 \div 0.3 = \frac{3.6}{0.3}$$

Step 2: Multiply the numerator and denominator by 10:

$$\frac{3.6}{0.3} = \frac{3.6 \times 10}{0.3 \times 10} = \frac{36}{3}$$

Step 3: Divide the numerator by the denominator:

$$\frac{36}{3} = 36 \div 3 = 12$$

c   **Step 1:** Write the division as a fraction:

$$4.2 \div 0.02 = \frac{4.2}{0.02}$$

Step 2: Multiply the numerator and denominator by 100:

$$\frac{4.2}{0.02} = \frac{4.2 \times 100}{0.02 \times 100} = \frac{420}{2}$$

Step 3: Divide the numerator by the denominator:

$$\frac{420}{2} = 420 \div 2 = 210$$

Estimation can be used to check that an answer to a calculation is the right size.

Example 8

a   Work out the exact value of 3.15×7.4
b   Check that your answer to part **a** is the right size, using estimation.

Solution 8

a   **Column method**

```
    3 1 5    →        3.1 5     The numbers move two places to the right.
×     7 4    →    ×   7.4       The numbers move one place to the right.
      2
  1 2 6 0    →      2 3.3 1 0   The numbers move 2 + 1 = 3 places to the right.
    1 3
  2 2 0 5 0
      1
  2 3 3 1 0
```

$3.15 \times 7.4 = 23.31$

Grid method

×	70	4	
300	21 000	1200	
10	700	40	
5	350	20	
	21 000 + 700 + 350 = 22 050	1200 + 40 + 20 = 1260	22 050 + 1260 = 23 310

$315 \times 74 = 23\,310$

Equivalent fraction method

$$3.15 \times 7.4 = \frac{315}{100} \times \frac{74}{10} = \frac{315 \times 74}{100 \times 10} = \frac{23\,310}{1000} = 23.310 = 23.31$$

b   Using estimates, 3.15×7.4 is approximately the same as $3 \times 7 = 21$
So the exact answer 23.31 is the right size.

Example 9

Chesney uses his calculator to work out 5.6×17.7
His answer is 991.2
Is he correct? Use estimation to explain your answer.

Solution 8

5.6×17.7 is approximately $6 \times 20 = 120$ so he is not correct.
The exact answer is 99.12

Example 10

You are given that $3.67 \times 21 = 77.07$
a   Write down the answer to 36.7×21 b   Write down the answer to 0.367×2.1

c   Write down the answer to $\dfrac{77.07}{2.1}$

Solution 10

a $36.7 = 3.67 \times 10$
$36.7 \times 21 = 3.67 \times 21 \times 10 = 77.07 \times 10 = 770.7$
Check by using estimation:
36.7×21 is approximately $40 \times 20 = 800$ which is close to 770.7

b $0.367 = 3.67 \div 10$
$2.1 = 21 \div 10$ $0.367 \times 2.1 = 3.67 \div 10 \times 21 \div 10$
$= 3.67 \times 21 \div 10 \div 10 = 77.07 \div 10 \div 10 = 0.7707$
Check by using estimation:
0.367×2.1 is approximately $0.4 \times 2 = 0.8$ which is close to 0.7707

c $\dfrac{77.07}{2.1} = \dfrac{77.07 \times 10}{2.1 \times 10} = \dfrac{77.07}{21} \times 10 = 3.67 \times 10 = 36.7$

Checking by using estimation:

$\dfrac{77.07}{2.1}$ is approximately $\dfrac{80}{2} = 40$ which is close to 36.7

Exercise B

1   Work out:
   a $24 \div 0.2$ b $32 \div 0.8$ c $36 \div 0.6$ d $10 \div 0.2$
   e $28 \div 0.7$ f $30 \div 0.3$ g $63 \div 0.9$ h $18 \div 0.3$

2   Work out:
   a $3.2 \div 0.2$ b $1.8 \div 0.6$ c $2.5 \div 0.5$ d $4.9 \div 0.7$
   e $5.3 \div 0.1$ f $4.2 \div 0.6$ g $2.7 \div 0.9$ h $7.2 \div 0.8$

3   Work out:
   a 1.54×3.2 b 2.16×4.8 c 6.31×2.7
   d 10.26×1.7 e 17.54×8.3 f 6.15×4.6

4 Check the values of your answers to question **3** by using estimation.

5 You are given that $84 \times 76 = 6384$
   a Write down the answers to:
      i 8.4×76 **ii** 84×0.76 **iii** 8.4×7600
   b Use estimations to check your answers to part **a**.

6 You are given that $9.1 \times 102 = 928.2$
   a Write down the answers to:
      i 91×102 **ii** 0.91×10.2 **iii** $928.2 \div 91$
   b Use estimations to check your answers to part **a**.

7 You are given that $3.12 \times 7.8 = 24.336$
   a Write down the answers to:
      i 312×7.8 **ii** 31.2×0.78 **iii** $243.36 \div 312$
   b Use estimations to check your answers to part **a**.

8 You are given that $18.6 \div 1.2 = 15.5$
   a Write down the answers to:
      i 15.5×12 **ii** $18.6 \div 12$ **iii** $1860 \div 1.2$
   b Use estimations to check your answers to part **a**.

9 You are given that $240 \div 1.5 = 160$
   a Write down the answers to:
      i 160×15 **ii** $240 \div 15$ **iii** $240 \div 1.6$
   b Use estimations to check your answers to part **a**.

 10 Check your answers to questions **1** to **3** using a calculator.

Chapter summary

- To add (or subtract) proper fractions, such as $\frac{2}{3}$ and $\frac{1}{5}$, follow these steps:
  Step 1: Write the fractions with a common denominator.
  Step 2: Add (subtract) the numerators.
  Step 3: Write the answer in its simplest form.
- This method can be extended to add (or subtract) mixed numbers by either
  Method 1
  Step 1: Add (subtract) the whole number parts.
  Step 2: Add (subtract) the fraction parts.
  Step 3: Combine the answers to **Step 1** and **Step 2**
  Method 2
  Step 1: Convert the mixed numbers to improper fractions.
  Step 2: Add (subtract) the improper fractions.
  Step 3: Convert the answer (an improper fraction) back to a mixed number.

- To multiply by a fraction, use diagrams or the following steps:
Step 1: Write the multiplication as a single fraction.
Step 2: Simplify by cancelling any common factors.
Step 3: Multiply the numerators and multiply the denominators.
Step 4: If the answer is an improper fraction, write it as a mixed number.
- To divide by a fraction, invert the fraction and multiply.
Then use diagrams or follow the steps for multiplying fractions.
- To add or subtract decimals: write the numbers under the place value headings so that the decimal points are in the same column.
Write the numbers with the same number of digits after the decimal point.
- There are several methods for multiplying decimals:
  - Grid method:

$\times$	2	0.7	
1	2	0.7	
0.8	1.6	0.56	
	$2 + 1.6 = 3.6$	$0.7 + 0.56 = 1.26$	$3.6 + 1.26 = 4.86$

$18 \times 27 = 486$

  - Column method: First find the answer to the multiplication as if the numbers were integers. Work out how many places to move the answer.

$$
\begin{array}{rcl}
15 & \to & 1.5 \quad \text{The number moves one place to the right.} \\
\times\ 32 & \to & \times\ 3.2 \quad \text{The number moves one place to the right.} \\
\hline
30 & \to & 4.80 \quad \text{The numbers move } 1 + 1 = 2 \text{ places to the right.} \\
450 & & \\
\hline
480 & &
\end{array}
$$

- Equivalent fraction method:
Step 1: Convert the two decimals to equivalent fractions.
Step 2: Multiply the two fractions.
Step 3: Convert back to a decimal.
- One calculation can be used to work out the answer to another with the same digits. For example, $21 \times 6 = 126$

$$2.1 \times 0.6 = 1.26$$

- You can use estimation to check where to put the decimal point.
For example, to work out 9.6×3.4, use any method to work out $96 \times 34 = 3264$
9.6×3.4 is approximately $10 \times 3 = 30$
$9.6 \times 3.4 = 32.64$
- To divide by a decimal:
Step 1: Write the division as a fraction.
Step 2: Multiply the numerator and denominator by the same number (10 or 100) to give whole numbers.
Step 3: Divide the numerator by the denominator.

Chapter review

1 a What fraction of this rectangle is shaded?

b Copy the grids and shade them to complete the fraction sum.

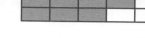

 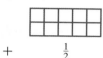

$$\frac{1}{5} \quad + \quad \frac{1}{2} \quad = \quad \ldots\ldots\ldots$$

2 Work out $\frac{3}{4} + \frac{2}{5}$ giving your answer as a fraction.

3 Work out:

a $\frac{5}{6} \times 24$ **b** 0.2×0.5 **c** $\frac{4}{5} \div 8$ **d** $\frac{3}{4} - \frac{3}{5}$

4 Calculate:

a $\frac{3}{8} - \frac{1}{4}$ **b** $\frac{3}{5} \times \frac{5}{6}$

5 Work out:

a 0.3×0.7 **b** $\frac{3}{4} \times \frac{2}{5}$

6 Owen, Ben and Tom use their calculators to work out the value of

$$\frac{29.35}{(5.86 \times 0.54)}$$

Owen gets 92.75, Ben gets 2.705 and Tom gets 9.275

Use approximations to show which one of them is correct.

You **must** show all your working.

7 Work out:

a 800×0.2 **b** $800 \div 0.2$

8 Find the value of $5\frac{2}{3} - 2\frac{4}{5}$

9 a Work out $4\frac{1}{2} - 3\frac{3}{4}$

b Find the value of $\dfrac{\left(\frac{1}{3} \times 15\right)}{\left(\frac{1}{8} \times 2^3\right)}$

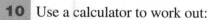

10 Use a calculator to work out:

a $1\frac{7}{8} + 4\frac{5}{9}$ **b** $2\frac{3}{13} - 1\frac{7}{9}$ **c** $\frac{9}{16} \times \frac{7}{11}$ **d** $\frac{4}{7} \div \frac{11}{17}$

Straight line graphs

18.1 Patterns of coordinates

CAN YOU REMEMBER

- How to plot and name a point on a grid?
- The meaning of 'sequence' and 'term-to-term rule'?

IN THIS SECTION YOU WILL

- Plot and name points in all four quadrants of a graph.
- Use the letter symbols x and y as names for coordinates.
- Begin to look at patterns of coordinates that lie on a straight line.

Coordinates are used to describe the position of any point on a grid from a starting point called the *origin*, O.

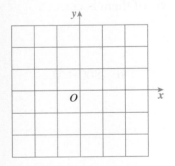

The **horizontal** line through the origin is called the *x-axis*.

The **vertical** line through the origin is called the *y-axis*.

The axes divide the grid into four sections called *quadrants*.

Each point on the grid has two coordinates, written (x, y).

- The **first** coordinate, x, means move **horizontally** a distance x along the x-axis, starting from the origin. If x is positive move **right**. If x is negative move **left**.
- The **second** coordinate, y, means move **vertically** a distance y, parallel to the y-axis. If y is positive move up. If y is negative move **down**.

Example 1

a   Plot and label the point A (0, 3) on the diagram.
b   Write down the coordinates of the point labelled B.

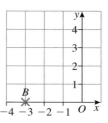

Solution 1

a   For the point A (0, 3), the x coordinate $= 0$
and the y coordinate $= 3$
Start at O, move right 0 (stay on the y-axis) and then move up 3
b   Start at O, move left 3 and then up 0. The coordinates of B are $(-3, 0)$.

Example 2

a   Plot the points A (3, 5) and B (−4, −2). Join them with a straight line.
b   Plot the points C (−3, 2) and D (5, −2). Join them with a straight line.
c   Write down the coordinates of the point where the two lines cross.

Solution 2

a, b

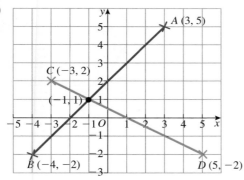

c   The two lines cross at $(-1, 1)$.

Exercise A

1   Write down the coordinates of
points A to L on this diagram.

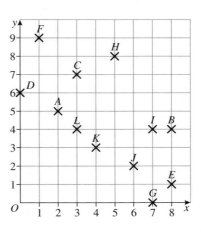

2 **a** Copy this grid.
Plot and label the points A to L.

A (7, 7)	B (2, 10)
C (10, 2)	D (3, 7)
E (6, 2)	F (0, 8)
G (4, 0)	H (1, 2)
I (8, 4)	J (0, 6)
K (1, 5)	L (5, 3)

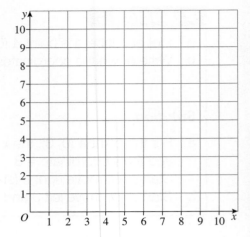

b Which points have coordinates that add up to 8?

c Which point has x and y coordinates that are equal?

3 Copy this diagram.

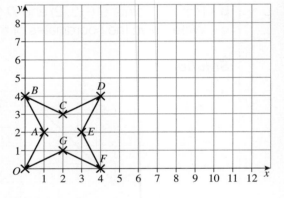

a Which vertex of the star has coordinates:

   i (1, 2)   **ii** (2, 1)

   iii (4, 0)   **iv** (0, 4)?

b Copy the axes from part **a** onto squared paper.
Draw the two stars with these vertices:

   i (1, 4) (2, 6) (1, 8) (3, 7) (5, 8) (4, 6) (5, 4) (3, 5)

   ii (6, 1) (7, 3) (6, 5) (8, 4) (10, 5) (9, 3) (10, 1) (8, 2)

4 For each part **a** to **d** of this question, draw a new grid with the x-axis and y-axis both from 0 to 6

   a **i** Draw a vertical line passing through the point (2, 0).

      ii Draw a horizontal line passing through the point (0, 5).

      iii Write down the coordinates of the point where the two lines cross.

   b **i** Draw a vertical line passing through the point (5, 0).

      ii Draw a horizontal line passing through the point (0, 2).

      iii Write down the coordinates of the point where the two lines cross.

   c **i** Draw a vertical line passing through the point (4, 3).

      ii Give the coordinates of the point where this line crosses the x-axis.

   d **i** Draw a horizontal line passing through the point (4, 3).

      ii Give the coordinates of the point where this line crosses the y-axis.

   e **i** Which axis do all horizontal lines on a graph pass through?

      ii Which axis do all vertical lines on a graph pass through?

5 a Write down the coordinates of the points *A* to *L*.

b Three of the points lie on a vertical line. Write down the coordinates of these points. What do you notice?

c Four of the points lie on a horizontal line. Write down the coordinates of these points. What do you notice?

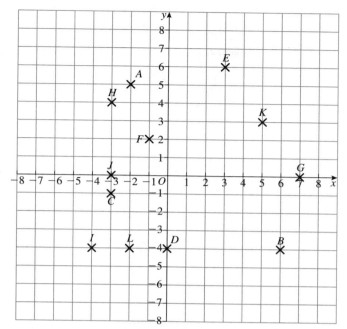

6 Copy the grid from question **5** (without the points *A* to *L*).

a Plot and label the points *A* to *L*.

A (2, 5)	*B* (6, −4)	*C* (−7, 4)	*D* (−3, −6)	*E* (8, 0)	*F* (4, 7)
G (−8, −5)	*H* (−6, 7)	*I* (0, −6)	*J* (−2, 1)	*K* (2, −8)	*L* (−5, −2)

b Five of the points lie on the same sloping straight line.

  i Write down the coordinates of these points.

  ii What do you notice about these coordinates?

7 Copy the grid from question **5**.
Plot each set of points and join them with straight lines.
Make sure you join the points in the order that they are given.

a (2, 3) (5, 3)   **b** (1, −2) (2, −1) (3, −2)

c (−5, 2) (−6, 3) (−5, 4)   **d** (2, −1) (2, −7)

e (−2, 3) (−6, 3)   **f** (1, −6) (2, −7) (3, −6)

g (4, 4) (5, 3) (4, 2)

h (1, 5) (2, 5) (0, 3) (2, 1) (1, 1) $(-\frac{1}{2}, 2\frac{1}{2})$ (−2, 1) (−3, 1) (−1, 3) (−3, 5) (−2, 5) $(-\frac{1}{2}, 3\frac{1}{2})$ (1, 5)

i (0, −1) (−1, −1) $(-2\frac{1}{2}, -3)$ (−4, −1) (−5, −1) (−3, −4) (−3, −6) (−2, −6) (−2, −4) (0, −1)

8 Draw a grid with both the *x*-axis and *y*-axis from −5 to 5
Make sure you join the points in the order that they are given.
Plot each of these points and join them with straight lines.

(0, 1) (1, 4) (3, 4) (3, 3) (4, 3) (4, 1) (1, 0) (4, −1) (4, −3) (3, −3) (3, −4) (1, −4) (0, −1)
(−1, −4) (−3, −4) (−3, −3) (−4, −3) (−4, −1) (−1, 0) (−4, 1) (−4, 3) (−3, 3)
(−3, 4) (−1, 4) (0, 1)

9 Messages are written in code, using the
coordinates of the letters on this grid.

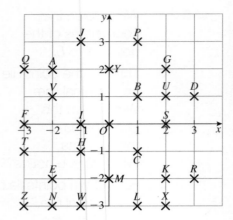

a Use the diagram to decode this message.
(2, 0) (−3, −1) (−2, 2) (3, −2) (−3, −1)
(−2, 2) (−3, −1)
(−3, −1) (−1, −1) (−2, −2)
(0, 0) (3, −2) (−1, 0) (2, 2) (−1, 0) (−2, −3)
(2, 2) (0, 0)
(3, −2) (−1, 0) (2, 2) (−1, −1) (−3, −1)
(0, 0) (3, −2)
(1, −3) (−2, −2) (−3, 0) (−3, −1)
(−3, −1) (−1, −1) (−2, −2) (−2, −3)
(2, 2) (0, 0)   (2, 1) (1, 3)
(0, 0) (3, −2)   (3, 1) (0, 0) (−1, −3) (−2, −3)

b Use the diagram to write the following in code.
   i x before y **ii** The y-axis is vertical

10 For each part **a** to **c** of this question, draw a new grid with both the x-axis and the
y-axis from −6 to 6

   a **i** Plot the points (−4, 4) and (5, −2).
      Join them with a straight line.
   ii Plot the points (3, 4) and (−5, 0).
      Join them with a straight line.
   iii Write down the coordinates of the point where the two lines cross.

   b **i** Plot the points (−4, −4) and (6, 2).
      Join them with a straight line.
   ii Plot the points (−2, 4) and (4, −6).
      Join them with a straight line.
   iii Write down the coordinates of the point where the two lines cross.

   c **i** Plot the points (−4, −5) and (1, 5).
      Join them with a straight line.
   ii Plot the points (−6, 1) and (6, −5).
      Join them with a straight line.
   iii Write down the coordinates of the point where the two lines cross.

Example 3

a Follow the patterns in the x and y coordinates to write two more coordinates in this
list of coordinates.
(−2, −3) (−1, −1) (0, 1) (1, 3) ...

b Plot the coordinates on a grid with the x-axis from −3 to 4 and the y-axis from
−4 to 8.

c What do you notice about the points you have plotted?

Solution 3

a The x coordinates are terms in the sequence $-2, -1, 0, 1, \ldots$
This sequence has term-to-term rule ⎢Add 1⎢
So the next two x coordinates are **2** and **3**
The y coordinates are terms in the sequence $-3, -1, 1, 3, \ldots$
This sequence has term-to-term rule ⎢Add 2⎢
So the next two y coordinates are **5** and **7**
So the next two coordinates are (**2**, **5**) and (**3**, **7**).

c The points lie on a straight line.

b The sequence of points is plotted below.

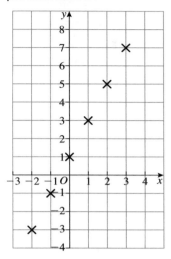

Exercise B

1

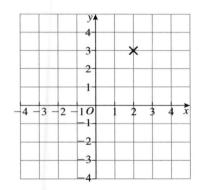

a James plots the point with coordinates (3, 2) on this grid.
Explain what James has done wrong.

b Billy says that the point with coordinates (25, 0) is on the y-axis.
Sarah says that it is on the x-axis.
Who is correct? Explain your answer.

c Penny says that the point with coordinates (3, 7) is 3 units from the origin.
Is this true? Explain your answer.

2 Draw a coordinate diagram with both the x-axis and the y-axis from 0 to 6

a **i** Plot five points with an x coordinate of 4 in one colour.

ii Plot five points with a y coordinate of 2 in a second colour.

iii Plot five points where the x coordinate equals the y coordinate in a third colour.

b Look at the sets of points you plotted in part **a**. What do you notice?

3 The points A to L are plotted on this grid.

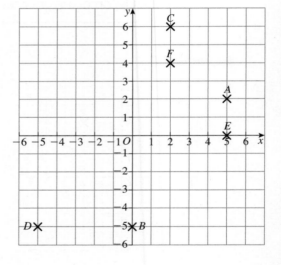

  a Which points have:
    i an x coordinate of 3
    ii a y coordinate of -4
    iii an x coordinate of -4
    iv a y coordinate of 5?
  b Write down the x coordinate of the points:
    i I **ii** K **iii** L.
  c Write down the y coordinate of the points:
    i C **ii** G **iii** L.
  d **i** Which point has the smallest x coordinate?
    ii Which point has the largest y coordinate?

4 **a** Match each point to one of the descriptions.
    i The y coordinate equals the x coordinate.
    ii The y coordinate equals 0
    iii The y coordinate is double the x coordinate.
    iv The sum of the x and y coordinates is 7
    v The x coordinate equals 0
  b One point does not have a description. Write a description for this point.

5 These diagrams show sets of points.
Each set lies on a straight line.
Write down the coordinates of the points in each set.
In each case write down what you notice about the coordinates.

  a

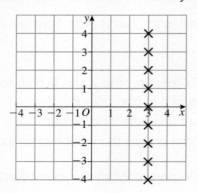

  b

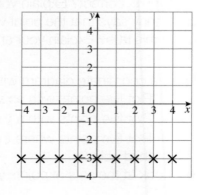

c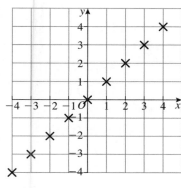

d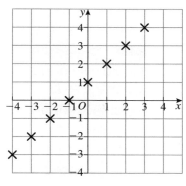

e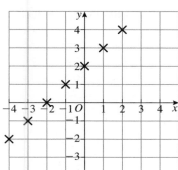

f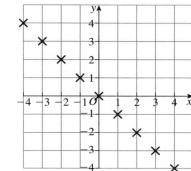

6 **a** A sequence of coordinates starts with the point (0, 1).
The term-to-term rules for continuing the sequence are:

x coordinate ⬚Add 1⬚ y coordinate ⬚Add 2⬚

   i Write down the first five coordinates in the sequence.
   ii Plot the coordinates on a coordinate diagram with the x-axis from 0 to 5 and
     the y-axis from 0 to 10
   iii What do you notice?

  b Another sequence of coordinates starts with the point (0, 8).
The term-to-term rules for continuing the sequence are:

x coordinate ⬚Add 1⬚ y coordinate ⬚Subtract 2⬚

   i Write down the first five coordinates in the sequence.
   ii Plot the coordinates on a coordinate diagram with the x-axis from 0 to 5 and
     the y-axis from 0 to 10
   iii What do you notice?

7 **a** In this set of coordinates the y coordinates are missing.
(0, …) (1, …) (2, …) (3, …) (4, …) (5, …)
The x and y coordinates are connected by this rule:

y coordinate = x coordinate + 2

   i Work out the missing y coordinates.
   ii Plot the coordinates on a coordinate diagram with both the x-axis and the
     y-axis from 0 to 8
   iii What do you notice about these points?

  b Repeat part **a** for:

  I Coordinates (2, …) (3, …) (4, …) (5, …) (6, …) (7, …) (8, …)

  Rule: **y coordinate = x coordinate − 2**

  Coordinate diagram: x-axis from 0 to 8; y-axis from 0 to 8

  II Coordinates (0, …) (1, …) (2, …) (3, …) (4, …) (5, …) (6, …)

  Rule: **y coordinate = 8 − x coordinate**

  Coordinate diagram: x-axis from 0 to 8; y-axis from 0 to 8

  III Coordinates (−2, …) (−1, …) (0, …) (1, …) (2, …)

  Rule: **y coordinate = 3 × x coordinate**

  Coordinate diagram: x-axis from −3 to 3; y-axis from −8 to 8

8 This is a map of Grid Town. In Grid Town, coordinates are used to describe positions. The grid lines represent roads and each grid square measures 1 kilometre by 1 kilometre. The x-axis runs from west to east and the y-axis runs from south to north.

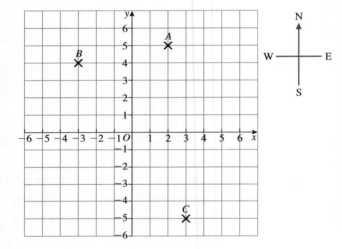

  a Tom is at A.
     He drives 4 km west and then 8 km south.
     What are the coordinates of Tom's new position?

  b Sam starts at B and drives to C. He starts by driving 6 km east.
     i How far does he then drive north or south?
     ii How far does Sam drive altogether to get from B to C?

  c Sue also starts at the origin. She drives for 10 km. Sue could be in 12 positions in Grid Town. Write down their coordinates.

9 The diagram shows how pieces of rectangular card measuring 2 by 3 are placed corner to corner on a coordinate diagram.

  a **i** Write a list of the coordinates of the corners of the rectangles marked on the diagram.
     ii Imagine the diagram is larger and that there are more rectangles.
        Add some more coordinates to your list.
  b Here are some other ways that the rectangles can be arranged corner to corner on the coordinate diagram.

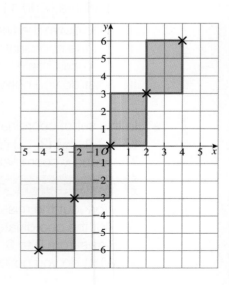

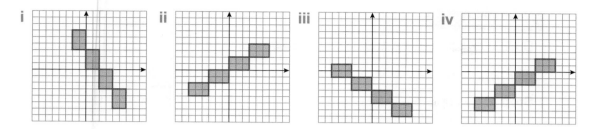

Repeat parts **a** and **b** for each of these arrangements.

c   Repeat for other arrangements and different-sized rectangles.

18.2 Drawing straight line graphs

CAN YOU REMEMBER

- How to substitute values into a rule?
- How to plot a point from its coordinates?

IN THIS SECTION YOU WILL

- Complete tables of coordinates and use them to plot points on straight line graphs.
- Start to recognise the sort of rules that give straight line graphs.
- Read values from a graph.

Each column in the table shows a pair of coordinates (x, y).

x	0	1	2	3	4
y	1	2	3	4	5

The whole table shows the set of coordinates (0, 1) (1, 2) (2, 3) (3, 4) (4, 5).

The rule connecting the x coordinate with the y coordinate is:

y coordinate = x coordinate + **1**

The rule can be written: $y = x + 1$

The coordinates that follow the rule
$y = x + 1$ can be plotted on a grid.

A line through points on a grid is called a *graph*.
The line on this grid is a straight line and is called
the graph of $y = x + 1$

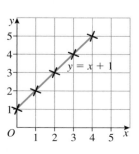

Example 1

Draw a graph of $y = x + 3$

Solution 1

Step 1: Complete a table of values by *substituting* values of x from the table in $y = x + 3$
When $x = 0$, $y = 0 + 3 = 3$
When $x = 1$, $y = 1 + 3 = 4$
When $x = 2$, $y = 2 + 3 = 5$

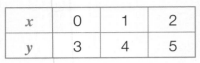

x	0	1	2
y	3	4	5

Step 2: Write a list of coordinates (x, y)
from the table: (0, 3) (1, 4) (2, 5)

Step 3: Plot the coordinates on a grid.

Step 4: Draw and label the line
through the coordinates.

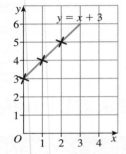

To draw a graph from a rule:

Step 1: Complete a table of values.

Step 2: Write a list of coordinates (x, y) from the table.

Step 3: Plot the coordinates on a grid.

Step 4: Draw and label the line through the coordinates.

Example 2

The table shows values of x and y.

x	0	1	2	3	4	5
y	2	3	4	5	6	7

a   What is the rule connecting the x coordinate with the y coordinate?

b   Write the values of x and y as a list of coordinates, (x, y).

c   Plot the coordinates on a grid. Draw and label the line through the points.

Solution 2

a   **y coordinate = x coordinate + 2**

This can be written as   **$y = x + 2$**

b   (0, 2) (1, 3) (2, 4) (3, 5) (4, 6) (5, 7)

c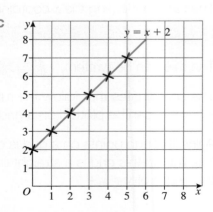

Horizontal and vertical lines on a grid

The line $y = 2$ is a **horizontal** line.
It passes through all points with a
y coordinate of 2
The line $y = -4$ is also horizontal.
It passes through all points with a
y coordinate of -4

All lines of the form $y = $ **a number**
are horizontal.

In a similar way, all lines of the form
$x = $ **a number** are **vertical**.

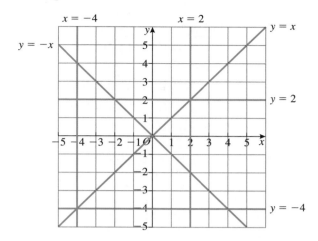

Diagonal lines through the origin

The line $y = x$ is a diagonal line passing through the origin.

It passes through all points in which the x coordinate and the y coordinate are equal
such as (1, 1) (−2, −2) ...

The line $y = -x$ is also a diagonal line passing through the origin.

It passes through all points in which the x coordinate and the y coordinate have the
same number but opposite signs such as (1, −1) (−2, 2) ...

Exercise A

1 The table shows values of x coordinates and y coordinates.

x	0	1	2	3	4	5
y	0	1	2	3	4	5

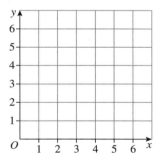

  a What is the rule connecting the x coordinate with
the y coordinate?
  b Write a list of coordinates from the table and then
plot them on a copy of the grid opposite.
  c Draw and label a line through the plotted points.

2 Repeat question **1** for these tables of values.
  a Use a grid with both the x-axis and the y-axis from 0 to 11

x	0	1	2	3	4	5
y	0	2	4	6	8	10

  b Use a grid with both the x-axis and the y-axis from 0 to 10

x	0	1	2	3	4	5
y	4	5	6	7	8	9

335

3 Draw and label a grid with both the x-axis and the y-axis from 0 to 10
   a Plot any three points with y coordinate 6. Draw a line through the points. Label the line $y = 6$
   b Plot any three points with x coordinate 8. Draw a line through the points. Label the line $x = 8$
   c **i** Draw and label the line $y = 2$ **ii** Draw and label the line $x = 2$
   d What is the name of the line that passes through the points (4, 0), (4, 5) and (4, 10)?

4 Label each of the lines on this grid.

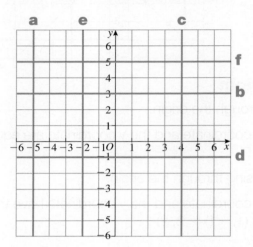

5 The table shows values of x coordinates and y coordinates. Some of the y coordinates are missing.

x	0	1	2	3	4
y	0	3			12

   a What is the rule connecting the x coordinate with the y coordinate?
   b Copy the table. Use the rule to complete it.
   c Write a list of coordinates from the table.
   d Plot the coordinates on a grid with both the x-axis and y-axis from 0 to 12 Draw and label the line through the points.

6 Draw a grid with the x-axis from −3 to 5 and the y-axis from −5 to 5
   a Copy and complete the tables for:
     i $y = x$

x	−2	−1	0	1	2	3	4
y		−1				3	

     ii $y = x - 1$

x	−2	−1	0	1	2	3	4
y		−2				2	

     iii $y = x - 2$

x	−2	−1	0	1	2	3	4
y			−2			1	

   b On the grid draw and label the graphs of:
     i $y = x$ **ii** $y = x - 1$ **iii** $y = x - 2$
   c What do you notice?

7 Draw a grid with the *x*-axis from −3 to 4 and the *y*-axis from −6 to 11
   a Copy and complete the tables for:

     i $y = x + 1$

x	−2	−1	0	1	2	3
y		0				4

     ii $y = 2x + 1$

x	−2	−1	0	1	2	3
y		−1				7

     iii $y = 3x + 1$

x	−2	−1	0	1	2	3
y		−2				10

   b On the grid draw the graphs of:
     i $y = x + 1$ **ii** $y = 2x + 1$ **iii** $y = 3x + 1$
   c What do you notice?

8 Draw a labelled grid with the *x*-axis from −1 to 6 and the *y*-axis from −1 to 10
   a Copy and complete the tables for:

     i $y = 5 - x$

x	0	1	2	3	4	5
y		4				0

     ii $y = 7 - x$

x	0	1	2	3	4	5
y		6				2

     iii $y = 9 - x$

x	0	1	2	3	4	5
y		8				4

   b On the grid draw the graphs of:
     i $y = 5 - x$ **ii** $y = 7 - x$ **iii** $y = 9 - x$
   c What do you notice?

9 Draw and label a grid with the *x*-axis from −4 to 3 and the *y*-axis from −6 to 11
   i Copy and complete this table for $y = 3x + 4$

x	−3	−2	−1	0	1	2
y		−2				10

   ii On the grid draw the graph of $y = 3x + 4$
   iii On the same grid draw the graph of $y = -x$
   iv Find the coordinates of the point where the graph of $y = 3x + 4$ crosses the graph of $y = -x$

Example 3

The diagram shows the graph of $y = 3x + 2$

a   Use the graph to find the value of y when $x = 1.5$

b   Use the graph to find the value of x when $y = -2.5$

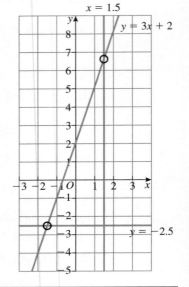

Solution 3

a   Draw the line $x = 1.5$ on the graph.
    The coordinates of the point where
    $x = 1.5$ meets $y = 3x + 2$ are (1.5, 6.5).
    So when $x = 1.5$, $y = 6.5$

b   Draw the line $y = -2.5$ on the graph.
    The coordinates of the point where
    $y = -2.5$ meets $y = 3x + 2$ are $(-1.5, -2.5)$.
    So when $y = -2.5$, $x = -1.5$

Example 4

a   Copy and complete this table
    for $x + y = 6$

b   Draw the graph of $x + y = 6$

x	-3	0	3	6	9
y		6			

Solution 4

a   Substitute the values of x in the table into $x + y = 6$. Find the values of y by
    inspection.

    When $x = -3$ $-3 + y = 6$ $y = 9$ When $x = 3$ $3 + y = 6$ $y = 3$

    When $x = 6$ $6 + y = 6$ $y = 0$ When $x = 9$ $9 + y = 6$ $y = -3$

    Complete the table.

x	-3	0	3	6	9
y	9	6	3	0	-3

b   From the table, coordinates
    on $x + y = 6$ are
    $(-3, 9)$ $(0, 6)$ $(3, 3)$ $(6, 0)$ $(9, -3)$

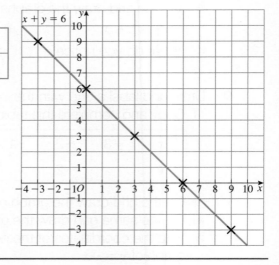

Exercise B

1 **a** Copy and complete the
table for $y = 3x - 1$

x	-2	-1	0	1	2	3
y						

    b   **i** Draw a grid with the x-axis from -3 to 4 and the y-axis from -8 to 9
       ii On the grid draw the graph of $y = 3x - 1$
    c Use the graph to find the value of y when $x = -0.5$
    d Use the graph to find the value of x when $y = 0.5$

2 The diagram shows the graph of $y = x - 3$

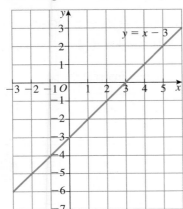

    a Use the graph to find the value of
       y when $x = 1.5$
    b Use the graph to find the value of
       x when $y = -2.5$

3 The diagram shows the graph of $y = 3 - 2x$
    a The point $(a, 5)$ lies on the graph
       of $y = 3 - 2x$
       What is the value of a?
    b The point $(-2.5, b)$ lies on the graph
       of $y = 3 - 2x$
       What is the value of b?

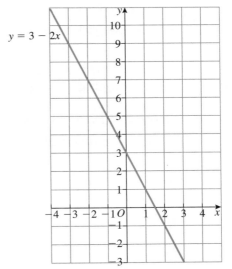

4 Draw a labelled grid with both the x-axis and y-axis from -6 to 11

    a   **i** Copy and complete the
       following table for $x + y = 10$

x	0	3	7	10
y				

       ii Copy and complete the
         following table for $x + y = 5$

x	0	2	3	5
y				

       iii Copy and complete the
         following table for $x + y = 0$

x	-5	0	5
y			

    b On the grid, draw the graphs of:

        i $x + y = 10$ **ii** $x + y = 5$ **iii** $x + y = 0$

    c On the same grid draw the graph of $x + y = 8$
       Explain your method.

    d Compare the lines on the grid with the line $y = -x$
       What do you notice?

5 Draw a grid with the x-axis from -1 to 7 and the y-axis from -6 to 8
    The coordinates $(0, -5)$, $(3, 1)$ and $(6, 7)$ lie on the graph of $y = 2x - 5$
    Draw the graph of $y = 2x - 5$
    Find the coordinates of the point where the graph of $y = 2x - 5$ meets:

    a the line $y = x$ **b** the line $x + y = 4$

6 Draw a labelled grid with both the x-axis and the y-axis from 0 to 14

    a Copy and complete the
       table for $x + y = 12$

x	0	4	8	12
y				

    b Copy and complete
       the table for $y = 2x$

x	0	2	4	6
y				

    c On the grid draw the graphs of:

        i $x + y = 12$ **ii** $y = 2x$

    d Write down the coordinates of the point where the graph of $x + y = 12$ crosses
       the graph of $y = 2x$

7 Draw a grid with the x-axis from -3 to 5 and the y-axis from -11 to 9

    a Copy and complete the table for $y = 3x - 4$

x	-2	-1	0	1	2	3	4
y							

    b On the grid draw the graph of $y = 3x - 4$

    c Write down the coordinates of the point where the graph of $y = 3x - 4$ meets
       the line $y = 3.5$

8 Draw a grid with the x-axis from -3 to 3 and the y-axis from -9 to 9

    a Copy and complete the
       table for $y = 4x$

x	-2	-1	0	1	2
y					

    b Copy and complete the
       table for $y = x + 3$

x	-2	-1	0	1	2
y					

    c On the grid draw the graphs of:

        i $y = 4x$ **ii** $y = x + 3$

    d Write down the coordinates of the point where the graph of $y = 4x$ crosses the
       graph of $y = x + 3$

9 Match the equations to the graph:

a $x = 5$

b $y = 5$

c $x + y = 5$

d $y = x + 5$

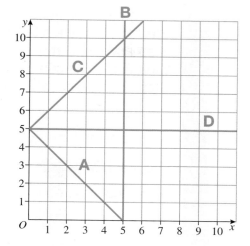

10 Draw a grid with the x-axis from -3 to 4 and the y-axis from -7 to 8

a Copy and complete the table for $y = 1 - 3x$

x	-2	-1	0	1	2
y	7				

b Copy and complete the table for $y = 2x - 4$

x	-1	0	1	2	3
y	-6				

c On the grid draw the graphs of:

   i $y = 1 - 3x$ ii $y = 2x - 4$

d Write down the coordinates of the point where the graph of $y = 1 - 3x$ crosses the graph of $y = 2x - 4$

Chapter summary

- *Coordinates* are used to describe the position of any point on a grid from a starting point called the *origin*, *O*.

- The horizontal line through the origin is called the *x-axis*.
  The vertical line through the origin is called the *y-axis*.
  The axes divide the grid into four sections called *quadrants*.

- Each point on the grid has two coordinates, written (x, y).

- The **first** coordinate, x, means move horizontally a distance x along the x-axis, starting from the origin. If x is positive move **right**. If x is negative move **left**.

- The **second** coordinate, y, means move vertically a distance y, parallel to the y-axis. If y is positive move **up**. If y is negative move **down**.

- To draw a graph from a rule:
  Step 1: Complete a table of values.
  Step 2: Write a list of coordinates (x, y) from the table.
  Step 3: Plot the coordinates on a grid.
  Step 4: Draw and label the line through the coordinates.

- All lines of the form $y = $ **a number** are **horizontal**.

  All lines of the form $x = $ **a number** are **vertical**.

- The graph of $y = x$ is a **diagonal** line through the origin. It passes through all points that have equal x coordinates and y coordinates such as (5, 5) (−2, −2) …

- The graph of $y = -x$ is the other **diagonal** line through the origin. It passes through all points that have x coordinates and y coordinates with the same number but opposite signs such as (−5, 5) (2, −2) …

Chapter review

1 Copy this grid.
  a The coordinates of P are (2, 1).
    What are the coordinates of Q?
  b Mark on the diagram the point R with coordinates (1, 4).

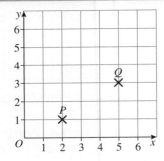

2 Copy the grid.
  $ABCD$ is a parallelogram.
  a Write down the coordinates of the point C.
  b Complete the parallelogram and write down the coordinates of D.

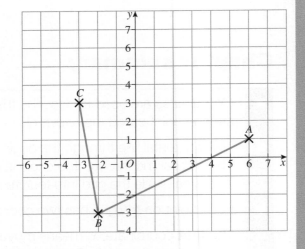

3 **a** Copy the grid from question **1**. Plot the points with coordinates (2, 1), (4, 1) and (4, 4).
  b Draw the line $y = 3$ on the grid.

4 **a** Copy and complete the table for $y = 3x - 1$

x	-1	0	1	2	3
y					

b Draw a grid with the x-axis from -2 to 4 and y-axis from -4 to 9. Draw the graph of $y = 3x - 1$

c Find the value of x when $y = 3.5$

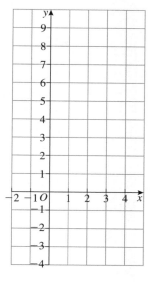

5 **a** Copy and complete this table for $y = 3x + 3$

x	0	1	2	3	4
y					

b Copy and complete this table for $y = 13 - x$

x	0	1	2	3	4
y					

c Copy the grid and draw the graphs of $y = 3x + 3$ and $y = 13 - x$

d Write down the coordinates of the point where the two graphs cross.

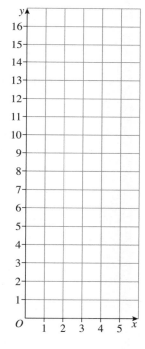

6 **a** Copy and complete the table of values for the graph $x + y = 5$

x	0	1	2	3	4	5
y	5				1	

b Copy the grid and draw the graph of $x + y = 5$

c P is a point on the line $x + y = 5$
Amy says, 'The x coordinate of P is two greater than the y coordinate of P.'
Write down the coordinates of P.

7 **a** Copy and complete the table of values for $y = 2x - 3$

x	-1	0	1	2	3
y	-5		-1		3

b Draw a grid with the x-axis from -2 to 4 and the y-axis from -6 to 4. Draw the graph of $y = 2x - 3$ for values of x from -1 to $+3$

c Find the coordinates of the point where the graph of $y = 2x - 3$ crosses the line $y = -2$

8 **a** Complete the following table for $y = x + 2$

x	0	1	2	3	4
y	2			5	

b Use the table to copy and complete this list of coordinates.
(0, 2) (1, …) (2, …) (3, 5) (4, …)

c Draw a grid with the x-axis and y-axis from 0 to 10. Plot the coordinates on the grid.

d The graph passes through the point $(a, 6.5)$. What is the value of a?

e Which two of the following points are on the line $y = x - 1$?
(2.5, 1.5) (10, 8) (7, 5.5) (8, 7)

9 **a** Draw a table of values of x and y for $x + y = 8$, for values of x from 0 to $+8$

b Draw a table of values of x and y for $y = 3x$ for values of x from 0 to $+3$

c Show that the graphs of $x + y = 8$ and $y = 3x$ cross at the point (2, 6).
Use a grid with x and y from 0 to 10 if you wish.

10 **a** Complete a table of values of x and y for $y = 2x$ for values of x from 0 to $+4$

b Show that the graph of $y = 2x$ and the line $x = -1$ cross at the point $(-1, -2)$.
Use a grid with x and y from -5 to 5 if you wish.

Transformations

19.1 Reflections

IN THIS SECTION YOU WILL

- Transform shapes by reflection in a mirror line.
- Transform shapes by reflection in the x-axis, y-axis and lines parallel to the axes.
- Transform shapes by reflection in the lines $y = x$ and $y = -x$.
- Describe reflections.

A *transformation* is the movement of a shape from one position to another.
A *reflection* is the *mirror image* of a shape or *object* in a given line.

This diagram shows a reflection of a shape in a mirror line.
The white triangle is the original shape or object.
The coloured triangle is the reflection or *image*.

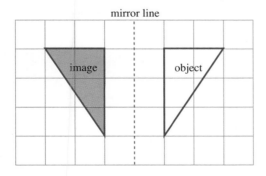

mirror line

image   object

- The image is the same distance from the mirror line as the object.
- The image is the same shape and size as the object.
- The object and the image are *congruent*.

These are true for all reflections.

Example 1

Draw the reflection of each shape in the line *AB*.

Solution 1

a
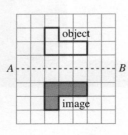

b
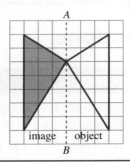

A point on the mirror line is reflected onto itself.

Example 2

This diagram shows an object and its image after reflection in a mirror line.
Draw in the mirror line.

Solution 2

The object and the image must both be the same
distance from the mirror line. Choose two matching
points, one on the object and one on the image.
Count the number of squares between the points.
Halve the distance between them.
This gives the position of the mirror line.
Check with another pair of matching points.

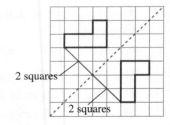

Example 3

Draw the image of this shape after reflection in the x-axis.

Solution 3

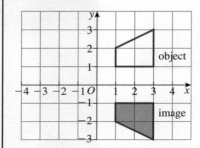

Exercise A

1 For each shape: **i** Copy the shape and the mirror line onto squared paper.

ii Draw the image of the shape after reflection in the mirror line.

a 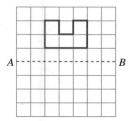 **b** 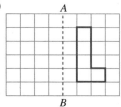 **c** 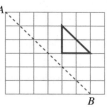 **d**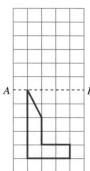

e 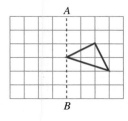 **f** 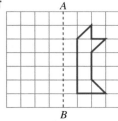 **g**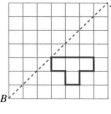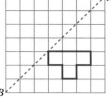

2 Each diagram shows an object and its image after reflection in a mirror line.
Copy each diagram onto squared paper. Draw in the mirror line.

a  **b** 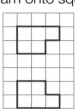 **c**   **d** 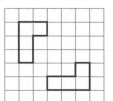 **e**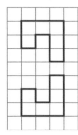

f   **g**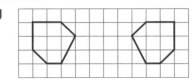

3 For each diagram: **i** Copy the axes and the shape onto squared paper.

ii Draw the image of the shape after reflection in the *x*-axis.

a 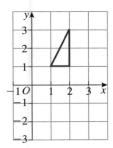 **b** 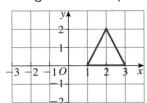 **c**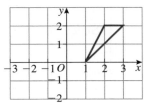

4 Copy the diagrams in question **3**.
Draw the image of each shape after reflection in the *y*-axis.

Any line on a graph may be used as a mirror line.
These lines are often used:
■ vertical lines, e.g. $x = 4$
■ horizontal lines, e.g. $y = -2$
■ the diagonal lines $y = x$ and $y = -x$

A description of a reflection must include:
■ the word 'reflection'
■ the name of the mirror line,
   e.g. $y = 2$, the x-axis.

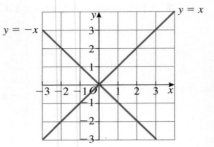

Example 4

Draw the image of shape A after reflection in the line
a $x = 2$ **b** $y = 1$

Solution 4

a

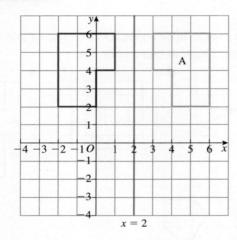

b

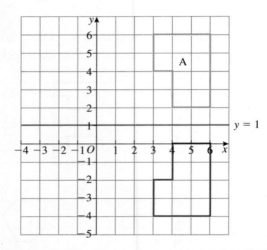

Example 5

Draw the image of the shape after reflection in the line $y = x$

Solution 5

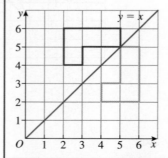

Example 6

Describe the single transformation
that moves triangle A to triangle B.

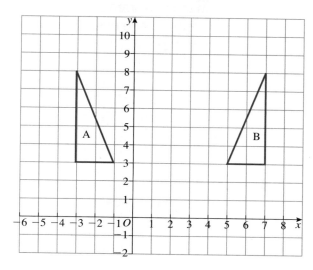

Solution 6

Triangle B is a reflection of triangle A.
The mirror line is halfway between
matching points on A and B.
The mirror line is $x = 2$
Triangle B is a reflection of triangle A in the line $x = 2$

Exercise B

1 Copy this diagram.

    a Draw the reflection of the
shape in the line $x = 1$
Label this shape A.

    b Draw the reflection of this
shape in the line $y = -1$
Label this shape B.

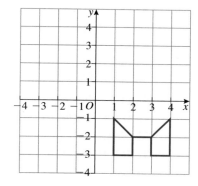

2 Copy the following diagrams onto squared paper.
For each diagram draw the image of shape A after reflection in the line $y = -x$

    a

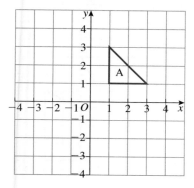

    b

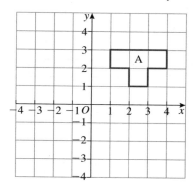

3 For each of the following diagrams:
  i Copy the diagram onto squared paper.
  ii Draw the image of shape A after reflection in the line $x = -1$

  a 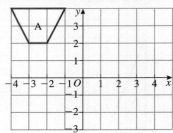   **b**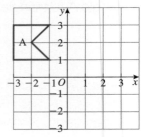

4 Copy each of these diagrams.
  Draw the image of each shape after reflection in the line $y = x$

  a 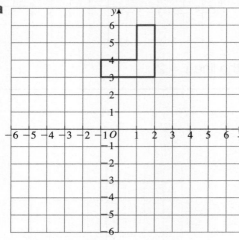   **b**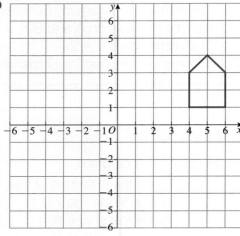

5 Look at these diagrams.
  a Describe the single transformation which
    moves shape A to shape B.
  b Describe the single transformation which
    moves shape A to shape C.

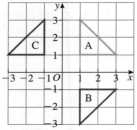

6 Describe fully the single transformation which
  moves object A to image B in each of these diagrams.

  a 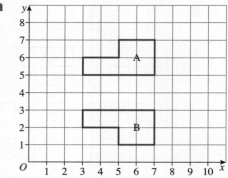   **b**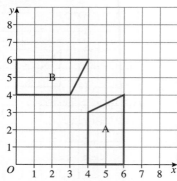

19.2 Enlargements

CAN YOU REMEMBER

- How to find the perimeter of a shape made from rectangles?
- The meaning of 'object' and 'image' in transformations?

IN THIS SECTION YOU WILL

- Enlarge shapes using positive scale factors.
- Identify the scale factor of an enlargement.
- Work out the lengths of sides of enlarged shapes.
- Understand the effect of enlargement on perimeter and area of a shape.

An *enlargement* is a transformation that increases or decreases the size of a shape.

When a shape is enlarged:

- its angles remain unchanged
- its lengths are changed in proportion. This means that all the lengths are multiplied by the same amount (for example, doubled, trebled, multiplied by 4).

For the rectangles shown, each length on the object has been multiplied by 2. The *scale factor* of the enlargement is 2

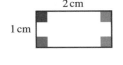

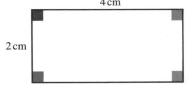

When one shape is an enlargement of another they are *similar*.

This means that they are the same shape, with the same angles, but a different size.

Example 1

The grid shows a rectangle, A.

a Enlarge shape A by scale factor 2
   Label this image B.

b Enlarge shape A by scale factor 3
   Label this image C.

c Calculate the perimeter of shapes B and C.
   Compare your answers to the perimeter of shape A.
   What do you notice?

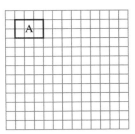

Solution 1

Scale factor 2 means that the length of each side is multiplied by 2. A is a rectangle with width 2 and length 3. The image B will be a rectangle with width $2 \times 2 = 4$ and length $3 \times 2 = 6$

a, b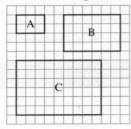

c Perimeter of A = 3 + 2 + 3 + 2 = 10 units
Perimeter of B = 6 + 4 + 6 + 4 = 20 units
Perimeter of C = 9 + 6 + 9 + 6 = 30 units
The perimeter of B is two times the perimeter of A.
The perimeter of C is three times the perimeter of A.
The perimeter is multiplied by the scale factor of the enlargement.

Example 2

In the diagram shape A has been enlarged to make shape B.
What is the scale factor of the enlargement?

Solution 2

The length of the top of shape A is 2 units.

The length of the top of shape B is 6 units.

$6 = 2 \times 3$

Each side of shape B is 3 times as long as the corresponding side of shape A.

The scale factor is 3

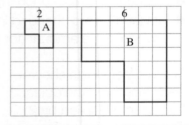

Exercise A

1 Copy each diagram onto squared paper. Draw the enlargement of each shape by a scale factor of 2

a 　　**b** 　　**c** 　　**d**

e 　　**f** 　　**g** 　　**h**

2 Copy each diagram onto squared paper. Draw the enlargement of each shape by a scale factor of 3

a 　　**b** 　　**c**

d　　**e**　　**f**

3 In the following diagrams shape B is the image of shape A after enlargement.
Work out the scale factor of each enlargement.

a

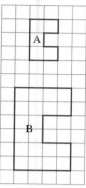

b

c

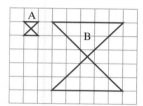

d

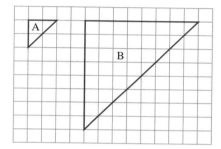

e

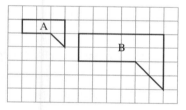

f

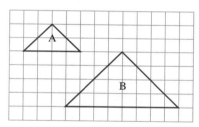

g

h

i

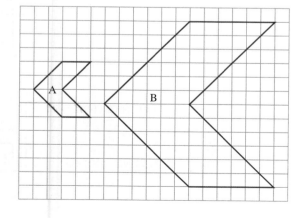

j

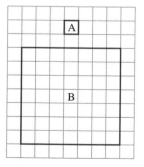

4 For each of the following sets of shapes write down the letters of the two shapes which are enlargements of each other.

a

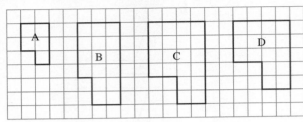

b

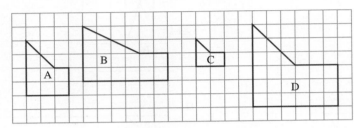

c

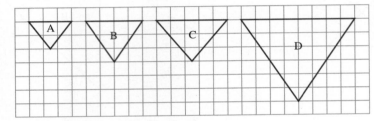

5 a i On a square grid draw a rectangle of length 4 cm and width 3 cm.
  ii Calculate the perimeter of the rectangle.
 b i Draw an enlargement of the rectangle by scale factor 3
  ii Calculate the perimeter of the enlarged rectangle.
 c What do you notice about the perimeters of the two shapes and the scale factor?

6 a Calculate the perimeter of the shape shown on the grid.
 b Enlarge the shape by scale factor 2
 c Calculate the perimeter of the enlarged shape.
 d What do you notice about the perimeters of the
   two shapes and the scale factor?

7 a Calculate the perimeter of the shape shown on the grid.
 b Enlarge the shape by scale factor 4
 c Calculate the perimeter of the enlarged shape.
 d What do you notice about the perimeters of the two shapes
   and the scale factor?

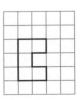

In an enlargement, the length of each side of a shape is multiplied by the scale factor. So the perimeter of the image is also multiplied by the scale factor.

An object can be enlarged about a *centre of enlargement*.
An enlargement about a centre fixes the position of the image.

Example 3

Enlarge this triangle by scale factor 2 with centre of enlargement (0, 0).

Solution 3

For an enlargement scale factor 2:
- the length of each side of the triangle is multiplied by 2
- the distance from the centre of enlargement (0, 0) to each point on the object is multiplied by 2

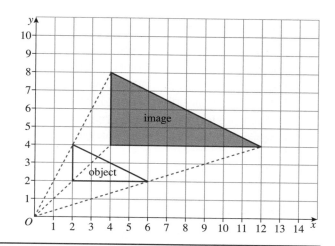

When the scale factor is a value between 0 and 1 the image of the shape will be *smaller* than the object.

Example 4

Enlarge this triangle by scale factor $\frac{1}{3}$ with centre of enlargement (1, 1).

Solution 4

For an enlargement scale factor $\frac{1}{3}$:
- the length of each side of the triangle is multiplied by $\frac{1}{3}$
- the distance from the centre of enlargement to each point on the object is multiplied by $\frac{1}{3}$

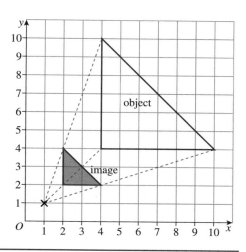

A description of an enlargement about a centre must include:
- the word 'enlargement'
- the scale factor of the enlargement
- the centre of enlargement.

Example 5

Describe the single transformation that transforms the unshaded object to the image.

Solution 5

The lengths of the sides of the image are four times the lengths of the object.
The scale factor of the enlargement is 4
The centre of enlargement is at the point of intersection of lines drawn through corresponding points on the object and image.
The centre of enlargement is (1, 0).
The transformation is an enlargement, scale factor 4, centre of enlargement (1, 0).

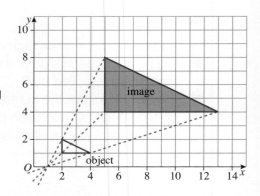

Exercise B

For questions **1** to **5** copy the diagrams, then answer the question.

1 Enlarge each shape by scale factor 2 with centre of enlargement (0, 0).

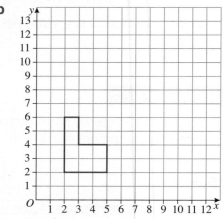

2 Enlarge the triangle by scale factor 3 with centre of enlargement (0, 0).

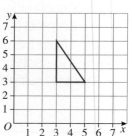

3 Enlarge each of the following diagrams using the given scale factor and centre of enlargement.

    a Scale factor 3, centre of enlargement (4, 1)

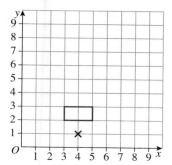

    b Scale factor 2, centre of enlargement (−3, −2)

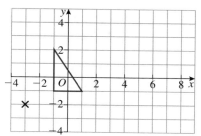

    c Scale factor 3, centre of enlargement (1, 2)

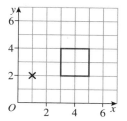

4 Enlarge this shape by scale factor $\frac{1}{2}$ with centre of enlargement (1, 2).

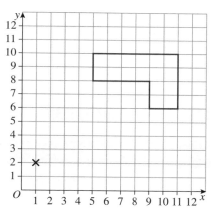

5 **a**   **i** Enlarge this shape by a scale factor of 3

      ii How many times bigger is the area of the enlarged shape than the area of the small shape?

> Hint: Count the squares.

    b   **i** Enlarge this shape by scale factor 2

      ii How many times bigger is the area of the enlarged shape than the area of the small shape?

6 For each diagram describe fully the single transformation that transforms the shape A to the shape B.

a

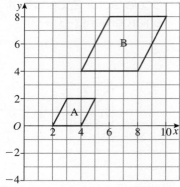

b

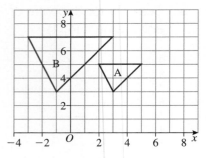

c

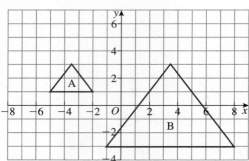

d

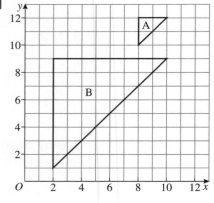

19.3 Rotations

CAN YOU REMEMBER

- That a quarter turn is a rotation of 90°, a half turn is a rotation of 180°, a full turn is 360°?
- The meaning of 'clockwise' and 'anticlockwise'?
- That congruent shapes are exactly the same shape and size?

IN THIS SECTION YOU WILL

- Transform a shape by rotating it about the centre of rotation.
- Learn how to find a centre of rotation.
- Describe transformations which involve rotations.

A *rotation* turns a shape about a fixed point, called the *centre of rotation*.
The angle of rotation can be given as a fraction of a turn or in degrees.

When an object is rotated the image is the same shape and size as the object.
The object and the image are *congruent*.

Example 1

Write down the single transformation that is equivalent to a rotation of 120° clockwise followed by a rotation of 50° anticlockwise.

Solution 1

It is equivalent to a rotation of 70° clockwise.

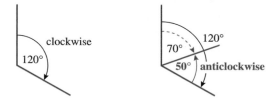

Tracing paper is useful when rotating shapes.

Example 2

Rotate triangle A through a quarter turn clockwise about the origin.

Solution 2

Trace the shape and the axes onto tracing paper. Use a pencil point to hold the tracing paper on the centre of rotation (0, 0).
Rotate the tracing paper through a quarter turn clockwise to show the position of the image.
Draw the image on the grid.

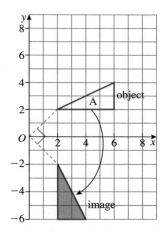

Example 3

Rotate shape B through 180° about (0, 0).

Solution 3

The direction is not given because 180° clockwise is the same as 180° anticlockwise.
The centre of rotation is (0, 0).

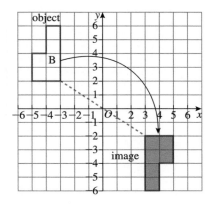

Exercise A

1   Copy and complete the following sentences:
   a   A rotation of 40° clockwise is equivalent to a rotation of .... anticlockwise.
   b   A rotation of 135° clockwise is equivalent to a rotation of .... anticlockwise.
   c   A rotation of 200° clockwise is equivalent to a rotation of .... anticlockwise.
   d   A rotation of 100° anticlockwise is equivalent to a rotation of .... clockwise.
   e   A rotation of 50° anticlockwise is equivalent to a rotation of .... clockwise.
   f   A rotation of 280° anticlockwise is equivalent to a rotation of .... clockwise.

2   Here is a list of angles:
   45°   50°   60°   90°   120°   135°   270°   300°
   From the list, write down an angle which is equivalent to:
   a   a quarter turn   **b** $\frac{1}{6}$ of a turn
   c $\frac{1}{3}$ of a turn   **d** $\frac{1}{8}$ of a turn.

3   Copy and complete the following sentences:
   a   A rotation of 90° clockwise followed by 63° anticlockwise is equivalent to a
       single rotation of ....
   b   A rotation of 300° clockwise followed by 40° anticlockwise is equivalent to a
       single rotation of ....
   c   A rotation of 58° clockwise followed by 32° clockwise is equivalent to a single
       rotation of ....
   d   A rotation of 132° clockwise followed by 150° anticlockwise is equivalent to a
       single rotation of ....

4   Copy the diagram onto squared paper.
   Rotate shape P a quarter turn
   anticlockwise about (0, 0).

5   Copy the diagram onto
   squared paper. Rotate shape
   Q a half turn about the origin.

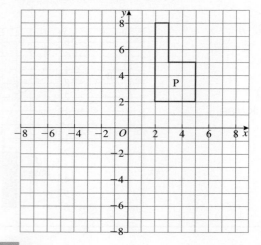

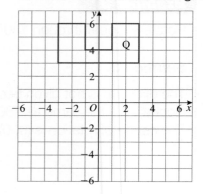

6 Which of the following shapes are rotations of the shaded shape?

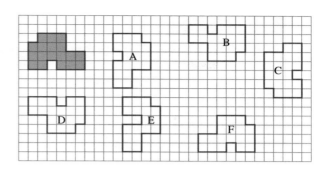

7 Rotate the shaded shape:
  a 90° clockwise about (0, 0). Label the image A.
  b 180° about (0, 0). Label the image B.
  c 90° anticlockwise about (0, 0). Label the image C.

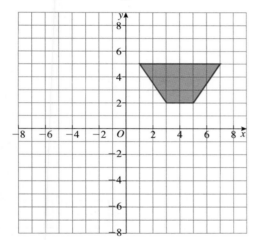

8 Rotate the shaded shape:
  a a quarter turn anticlockwise about the origin. Label the image A.
  b a half turn about the origin. Label the image B.
  c a quarter turn clockwise about the origin. Label the image C.

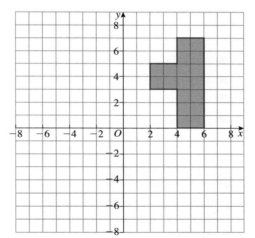

9 Rotate the shaded shape:
  a 90° clockwise about (0, 0). Label the image A.
  b 180° about (0, 0). Label the image B.
  c 90° anticlockwise about (0, 0). Label the image C.

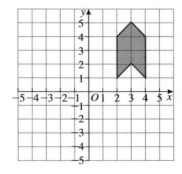

10 Rotate each of these shapes as described.

  a

  45° anticlockwise about O.

  b

  $\frac{1}{6}$ of a turn clockwise about O.

  c

  $\frac{1}{3}$ of a turn clockwise about O.

Example 4

Rotate the shaded shape 90° anticlockwise about (−1, 1).

Solution 4

Trace the shape and the axes onto tracing paper. Use a pencil point to hold the tracing paper on the centre of rotation (−1, 1).
Rotate the tracing paper through 90° anticlockwise to show the position of the image. Draw the image on the grid.

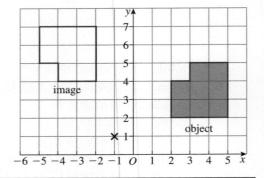

A description of a rotation must include:
- the word 'rotation'.
- the angle through which it turns
- the direction of the turn
- the centre of rotation.

Example 5

The diagram shows two identical shapes A and B. Describe fully the single transformation which takes shape A to shape B.

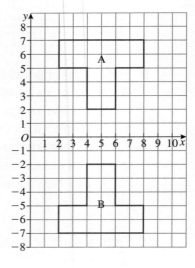

Solution 5

The transformation is a rotation.
Trace shape A and rotate it through different turns to find the size of turn which gives shape B.
The rotation is through 180°, so the direction of rotation is not needed.
To find the centre of rotation, rotate the tracing using different pivot positions. When the tracing is held at (5, 0), shape A fits exactly onto shape B.

The transformation is a rotation of 180° about (5, 0).

When a shape is rotated about one of its vertices, that vertex does not move.

Example 6

Describe the single transformation which takes the shaded shape to shape A.

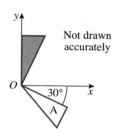

Not drawn accurately

Solution 6

The vertex of the triangle at O has not moved, so O is the centre of rotation.

The vertical line has been rotated $90° + 30°$ clockwise.

The single transformation is a rotation $120°$ clockwise about O.

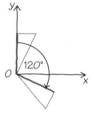

Exercise B

For questions **1** to **4**, copy the diagrams and then answer the question.

1

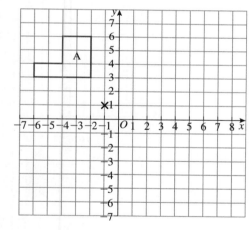

a Rotate shape A through $90°$ clockwise about $(-1, 1)$. Label the image B.

b Rotate shape A through $180°$ about $(-1, 1)$. Label the image C.

2 Rotate shape A $180°$ about $(6, 2)$. Label the image B.

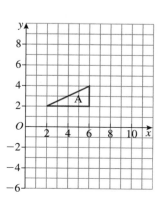

3   The diagram shows two identical
shapes, A and B.
Describe fully the single transformation which
takes shape A to shape B.

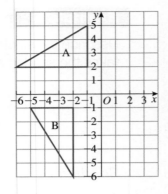

4   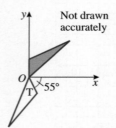   Rotate this shape 180° about (6, 5).

5   The diagram shows two identical
shapes, A and B.

Describe fully the single transformation
which takes shape A to shape B.

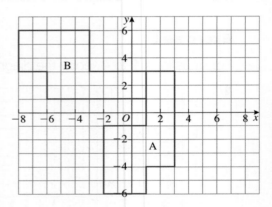

6   Copy the diagram.
  a   Rotate the shaded shape 180° about (3, 0).
        Label this shape A.
  b   Rotate shape A 90° clockwise about (0, 0).
        Label this shape B.
  c   Describe fully the single transformation which
        will take shape B back to the shaded shape.

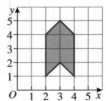

7   Describe the single transformation
which will take the shaded triangle
to triangle T.

8   Describe fully the single transformation
which will take shape A to shape B.

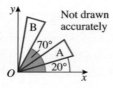

Use this diagram to answer questions **9** and **10**.

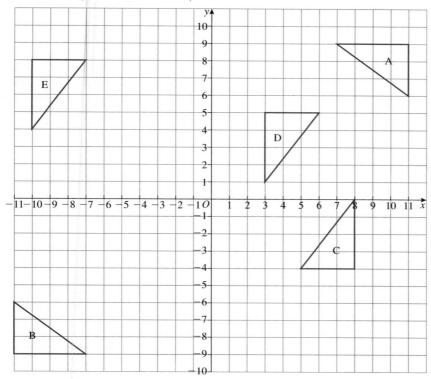

9 a Triangle C is rotated 90° anticlockwise about (−4, 3).
   Which triangle is the image of C under this transformation?
   b Triangle C is rotated 180° about (5.5, 0.5).
   Which triangle is the image of C under this transformation?

10 Describe fully the single transformation which will take:
   a A → B   **b** A → C   **c** A → D   **d** A → E

19.4 Translations

CAN YOU REMEMBER

■ That congruent shapes are exactly the same shape and size?
■ The meaning of 'object' and 'image'?

IN THIS SECTION YOU WILL

■ Learn the meaning of the term 'translation'.
■ Translate shapes by a given distance in the x-direction and the y-direction.
■ Learn how to use column vectors to translate shapes.
■ Describe translations in words and using column vectors.

A *translation* is the movement of a shape in the x-direction (horizontally) and the y-direction (vertically).

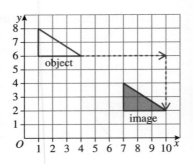

Every point in the shape moves in the same direction and through the same distance.

The object and its image are congruent.

Example 1

Draw the image of *ABCD* after a translation of five squares to the right and one square up.

Solution 1

From vertex *A* of the object, move five squares to the right and one square up and plot vertex *A′* for the image. Repeating this for the other vertices gives the position of the image.

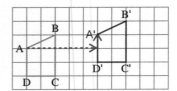

Example 2

Describe the transformation that takes shape A to shape B.

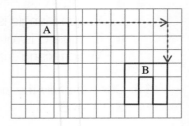

Solution 2

Choose a vertex on shape A. Count the squares across and down to the matching vertex on shape B. The shape has moved seven squares to the right and three squares down. This is a translation of 7 units to the right and 3 units down.

Exercise A

1   On a copy of the diagram, translate the shaded shape
    a   4 units to the right and 4 units up.
        Label this image A.
    b   3 units to the right and 4 units down.
        Label this image B.
    c   6 units to the left and 3 units down.
        Label this image C.
    d   4 units to the left and 5 units up.
        Label this image D.

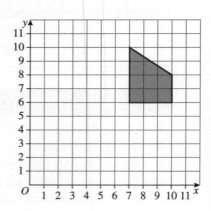

2 On a copy of the diagram, translate triangle A

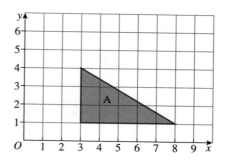

    a 2 units to the right and 5 units up. Label this triangle B.

    b 3 units to the right and 8 units down. Label this triangle C.

    c 10 units to the left and 6 units down. Label this triangle D.

    d 13 units to the left and 4 units up. Label this triangle E.

3

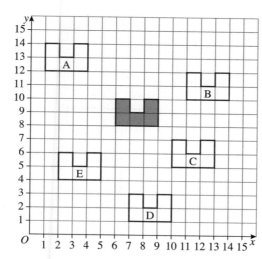

Describe the transformation that takes the shaded shape to:

    a shape A   **b** shape B   **c** shape C

    d shape D   **e** shape E.

4 On squared paper draw and label x- and y-axes from -10 to $+10$

    a Draw the rectangle with coordinates A (3, 1) B (3, 3) C (7, 3) D (7, 1).

    b Draw the image of $ABCD$ after a translation of 2 units to the right and 5 units up. Label this image P.

    c Draw the image of $ABCD$ after a translation of 3 units to the right and 8 units down. Label this image Q.

    d Draw the image of $ABCD$ after a translation of 9 units to the left and 6 units down. Label this image R.

    e Draw the image of $ABCD$ after a translation of 13 units to the left and 4 units up. Label this image S.

    f Describe the transformation of shape P to shape Q.

    g Describe the transformation of shape S to shape R.

5 Describe the transformation that takes the shaded shape to:

    a shape B   **b** shape C   **c** shape D   **d** shape E   **e** shape F.

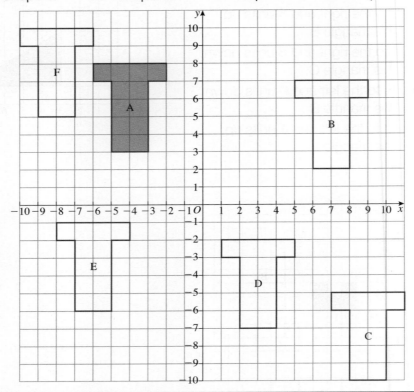

A translation can be described using a *vector*.

The vector $\begin{pmatrix} 2 \\ -3 \end{pmatrix}$ moves a point 2 units to the right and 3 units down.

The vector $\begin{pmatrix} -1 \\ 4 \end{pmatrix}$ moves a point 1 unit to the left and 4 units up.

The top number always describes movement in the *x*-direction. A **positive** value means movement to the **right**. A **negative** value means movement to the **left**.

The bottom number always describes movement in the *y*-direction. A **positive** value means movement **up**. A **negative** value means movement **down**.

Example 3

Write the following translations as vectors:

    a 3 units to the right and 2 units up   **b** 8 units to the left and 5 units up

    c 4 units to the left and 0 units up   **d** 2 units to the left and 6 units down.

Solution 3

a $\begin{pmatrix} 3 \\ 2 \end{pmatrix}$ **b** $\begin{pmatrix} -8 \\ 5 \end{pmatrix}$ **c** $\begin{pmatrix} -4 \\ 0 \end{pmatrix}$ **d** $\begin{pmatrix} -2 \\ -6 \end{pmatrix}$

Example 4

a Transform the shaded shape by a translation of $\begin{pmatrix} 0 \\ 7 \end{pmatrix}$
Label the image A.

b Transform the shaded shape by a translation of $\begin{pmatrix} -3 \\ 4 \end{pmatrix}$
Label the image B.

c Describe the transformation from shape A to shape B.

Solution 5

a Vector $\begin{pmatrix} 0 \\ 7 \end{pmatrix}$ moves the shaded shape

0 units to the right and 7 units up.

b Vector $\begin{pmatrix} -3 \\ 4 \end{pmatrix}$ moves the shaded shape

3 units to the left and 4 units up.

c Shape A to shape B is a translation of $\begin{pmatrix} -3 \\ -3 \end{pmatrix}$

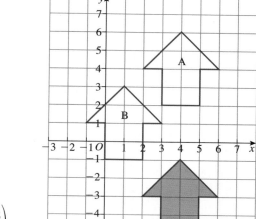

Exercise B

1 Write the following translations as vectors:
  a 4 units to the right and 9 units up
  b 6 units to the right and 5 units up
  c 10 units to the left and 3 units up
  d 7 units to the left and 1 unit down
  e 8 units to the right and 9 units down
  f 3 units to the left and 3 units up.

2 Describe in words the translations given by the following vectors.

  a $\begin{pmatrix} 2 \\ -9 \end{pmatrix}$ **b** $\begin{pmatrix} -4 \\ 4 \end{pmatrix}$ **c** $\begin{pmatrix} 10 \\ 3 \end{pmatrix}$ **d** $\begin{pmatrix} 2 \\ 0 \end{pmatrix}$ **e** $\begin{pmatrix} -1 \\ -1 \end{pmatrix}$ **f** $\begin{pmatrix} 5 \\ -4 \end{pmatrix}$

3 Use vectors to describe these translations.
  a A to B
  b A to D
  c A to F
  d A to H
  e G to E
  f G to C
  g G to B
  h D to H
  i H to C
  j F to B
  k H to F
  l H to A

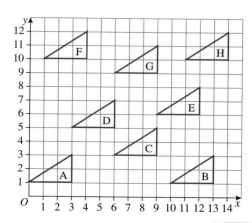

4   Copy the diagram onto squared paper.

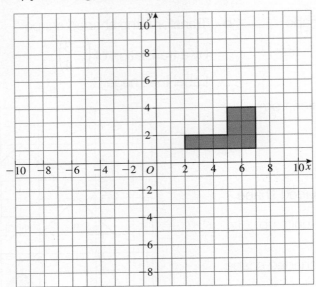

Translate the shaded shape using the following translation vectors.

a $\begin{pmatrix} 3 \\ 6 \end{pmatrix}$ Label the image A.

b $\begin{pmatrix} -9 \\ 2 \end{pmatrix}$ Label the image B.

c $\begin{pmatrix} -11 \\ -8 \end{pmatrix}$ Label the image C.

d $\begin{pmatrix} 3 \\ -6 \end{pmatrix}$ Label the image D.

5   Write down the vector for the translation which moves:
   a A (1, 1) to P (4, 7)   **b** A (1, 1) to Q (5, −2)
   c A (1, 1) to R (−3, 6)   **d** A (1, 1) to S (−2, −4)

6   The diagram shows a quadrilateral $ABCD$.
   Write down the coordinates of D after the shape
   has been translated by the vector:

   a $\begin{pmatrix} 2 \\ 5 \end{pmatrix}$ **b** $\begin{pmatrix} 1 \\ -3 \end{pmatrix}$ **c** $\begin{pmatrix} -4 \\ 2 \end{pmatrix}$ **d** $\begin{pmatrix} -3 \\ -2 \end{pmatrix}$ **e** $\begin{pmatrix} 1 \\ 0 \end{pmatrix}$

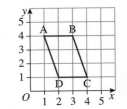

7   Look at the diagram opposite.
   a   **i** Write down the vector for the translation
            that takes triangle A to triangle B.
        ii Write down the vector for the translation
            that takes triangle B to triangle A.
        iii What do you notice about these
            two vectors?
   b   Triangle A is translated by vector

   $\begin{pmatrix} 3 \\ -4 \end{pmatrix}$ to give triangle C.

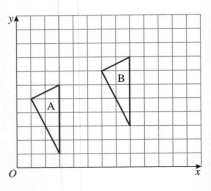

   Write down the vector for the translation that takes triangle C to triangle A.

Chapter summary

- When a shape is reflected:
  - the object and the image are the same distance from the mirror line
  - the object and the image are congruent

- A point on the mirror line is reflected onto itself.

- A description of a reflection must include:
  - the word 'reflection'
  - the name of the mirror line, e.g. $y = 2$, the x-axis.

- An enlargement is a transformation that increases or decreases the size of a shape.

- When a shape is enlarged:
  - its angles remain unchanged
  - its lengths are changed in proportion. This means that all the lengths are multiplied by the same amount.

- When one shape is an enlargement of another they are similar. This means that they are the same shape, with the same angles, but a different size.

- The scale factor of the enlargement is the number all lengths on the object are multiplied by to give the image.

- The perimeter of the image is also increased by the scale factor.

- For an enlargement with scale factor 2:
  - the length of each side of the object is multiplied by 2
  - the distance from the centre of enlargement to each point on the object is multiplied by 2

- A description of an enlargement about a centre must include:
  - the word 'enlargement'
  - the scale factor of the enlargement
  - the centre of enlargement.

- A rotation turns a shape about a fixed point, called the centre of rotation.

- The angle of rotation can be given as a fraction of a turn or in degrees.

- Rotations can be in a clockwise or anticlockwise direction.

- Tracing paper is useful when rotating shapes.

- A description of a rotation must include:
  - the word 'rotation'
  - the angle through which it turns
  - the direction of the turn
  - the centre of rotation.

- To find the centre of rotation, pivot a tracing of the object around different points until it fits exactly onto the image.

- When a shape is rotated about one of its vertices, that vertex does not move.

- A translation can be described using a vector:
  - the top number always describes movement in the *x*-direction. A positive value means movement to the right. A negative value means movement to the left.
  - the bottom number always describes movement in the *y*-direction. A positive value means movement up. A negative value means movement down.

  For example, $\begin{pmatrix} 2 \\ -3 \end{pmatrix}$ moves a point 2 units to the right and 3 units down.

- When an object is translated the object and the image are congruent.

Chapter review

1 Copy the shape and mirror line.
Draw a reflection of the shape in
the mirror line.

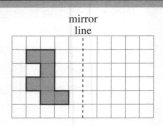

2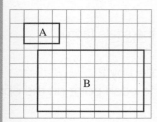

These rectangles are drawn on a centimetre-squared grid.
Rectangle A is enlarged to give rectangle B.
  a What is the scale factor of the enlargement?
  b Draw all the lines of symmetry on rectangle A.
  c Rectangle A is enlarged by scale factor 6 to give rectangle C.
  Write down the length and width of rectangle C.

3 a The diagram shows two shapes, P and Q.
  Describe fully the single transformation
  which takes shape P onto shape Q.
  b Copy the grid and triangle R below.
  The vertices of triangle R are (2, 1),
  (2, 3) and (5, 1).

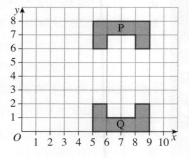

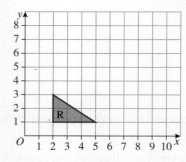

Enlarge triangle R by scale factor 2 with (0, 0) as the centre of enlargement.

4 **a** Copy the grid and shape.
Enlarge the shaded shape by scale factor 3

b How many times bigger is the area of the
enlarged shape than the area of the
small shape?

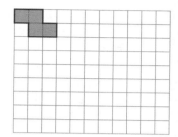

5

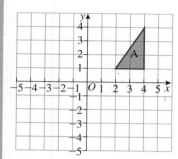

Copy the grid and triangle A.

a Reflect the triangle in the y-axis.
Label the triangle B.

b Rotate triangle A 90° clockwise about
the origin O.
Label the triangle C.

6 Copy the grid and triangle A.
Draw the new position of triangle
A after a rotation of 90° clockwise
about the origin.

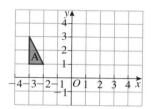

7 Copy the grid and shape A.

a On the graph, draw the finishing position when:

　i shape A is reflected in the line y = 1

　ii shape A is rotated through 180° about
　　the origin.

b Describe fully the transformation which will map
shape A onto shape B.

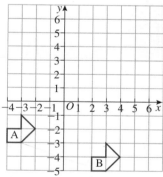

8 The grid shows several transformations
of the shaded triangle.

a Write down the letter of the triangle after
the shaded triangle is:

　i reflected in the line y = 1

　ii translated three squares to the right
　　and six squares down

　iii rotated 180° about the point (0, 2).

b Describe **fully** the transformation which takes:

　i triangle H onto triangle D　　**ii** triangle E onto triangle G.

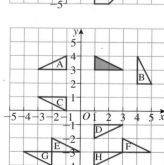

9 **a** Describe fully the **single** transformation
which takes triangle A onto triangle B.

b Triangle A is rotated onto triangle C.
  i Write down the angle of rotation.
  ii Write down the coordinates of the
  centre of rotation.

c Copy the grid and triangle D.

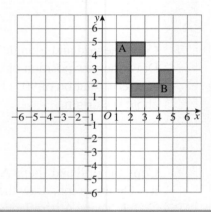

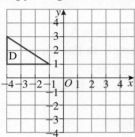

Triangle D is translated by the vector $\begin{pmatrix} 3 \\ -5 \end{pmatrix}$

Draw the new position of triangle D.

10 **a** Describe fully the single transformation
which maps shape A to shape B.

b Copy the grid and shape A.
  i Draw shape A after it has been rotated
  through $180°$ about the origin O.
  Label the shape C.
  ii Translate shape A by the vector $\begin{pmatrix} 2 \\ -6 \end{pmatrix}$

  Label the new shape D.

Real-life graphs

20.1 Conversion graphs and other real-life graphs

CAN YOU REMEMBER

- How to plot and name a point on a grid?
- How to read scales?
- How to convert from one unit to another?

IN THIS SECTION YOU WILL

- Draw and use conversion graphs to convert between units and quantities.
- Draw and use graphs to show how one quantity changes with another.

In each of the above problems one unit or quantity needs to be changed or *converted* into another.

One way of doing this is to use a *conversion graph*.

A conversion graph converts one unit or quantity to another.

Example 1

This graph can be used to convert British pounds (£) into euros (€).

Use the graph to convert:

a   £50 to euros
b   €100 to pounds
c   £180 to euros.

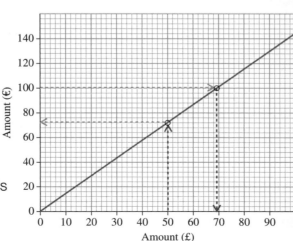

Solution 1

a The conversion graph passes through the point (50, 72), so £50 = €72
b The conversion graph passes through the point (69, 100), so €100 = £69
c The conversion graph cannot be used to convert £180 to euros directly.
The graph passes through (100, 144) and (80, 115).
So £100 = €144 and £80 = €115
£100 + £80 = €144 + €115
£180 = €259
Other combinations could be used.
For example, £180 = 3 × £60 = 3 × €86 = €258
or £180 = 2 × £90 = 2 × €130 = €260
The different answers result from slight inaccuracies in reading from the graph.

To draw a conversion graph:
Step 1: Use a pair of equivalent quantities to make a table of values.
Step 2: Write a list of coordinates from the table.
Step 3: Plot the coordinates on a grid.
Step 4: Draw the line through the coordinates.

Example 2

a Use the fact that **1 gallon = 4.55 litres**
to complete this table.
b Use the values in the table to draw a graph
that converts gallons to litres.
c A motorist fills his tank with 23 litres of petrol.
Use the conversion graph to show that 23 litres
is the same as 5 gallons.

Gallons	0	10	20
Litres			

Solution 2

a **1 gallon = 4.55 litres**

So   **0** gallons =   **0** × 4.55 = 0 litres
10 gallons = **10** × 4.55 = 45.5 litres
20 gallons = **20** × 4.55 = 91 litres

Gallons	0	10	20
Litres	0	45.5	91

b The graph goes through (0, 0), (10, 45.5) and (20, 91).
c From 23 on the litres axis draw a horizontal line
to the graph.
The line cuts the graph at 5 gallons.
The conversion graph goes through the point (5, 23).
23 litres is equivalent to 5 gallons.

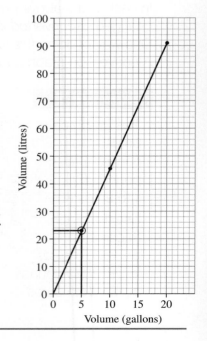

Exercise A

1 The graph shows the weight of different lengths of electric wire.

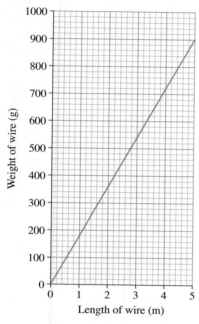

a Use the graph to work out the weight of 4 metres of wire.

b What length of wire weighs 300 grams?

c Work out the weight of 10 metres of wire.

2 This graph can be used to convert metres to feet.

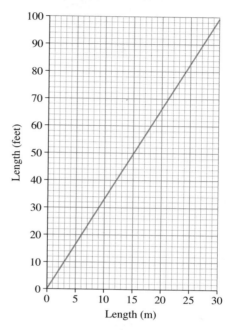

a Use the graph to convert these measurements to metres.
   i 40 feet   **ii** 70 feet
   iii 84 feet

b Use the graph to convert these measurements to feet.
   i 20 metres   **ii** 15 metres
   iii 8 metres

c Work out the number of feet in 40 metres.

3 This graph can be used to convert lengths measured in inches to millimetres.

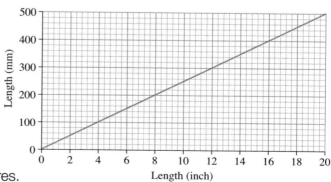

a Use the graph to convert
   i 10 inches to millimetres
   ii 400 millimetres to inches.

b Work out the difference in length between 15 inches and 350 millimetres.
Give your answer in millimetres.

c Work out the difference in length between 250 millimetres and 12 inches.
Give your answer in inches.

4 This graph can be used to convert euros (€) to US dollars ($).

    a Use the graph to convert
       i €40 to US dollars
      ii €75 to US dollars.

    b Use the graph to convert
       i $60 to euros
      ii $25 to euros.

    c Tim buys a radio for €70 and sells it for $100
       Work out the profit Tim makes in euros.

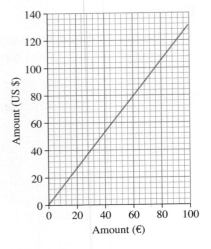

5 Areas of land are measured in either acres or hectares.

This graph can be used to convert acres to hectares.

    a Use the graph to convert these areas to acres.
       i 60 hectares   **ii** 50 hectares
     iii 36 hectares

    b Use the graph to convert these areas to hectares.
       i 100 acres   **ii** 175 acres
     iii 70 acres

    c **i** Work out the number of acres in 180 hectares.
      ii Work out the number of hectares in 400 acres.

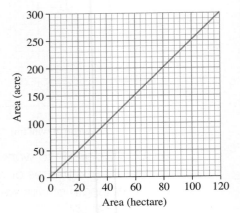

6 **a** Copy the table below.

Use the fact   **10 kilograms = 22 pounds**   to complete the table.

kg	0	5	20
lb	0		

    b Copy the grid opposite.
       Draw a graph to convert kilograms to pounds.

    c Use the graph to convert
       i 17 kilograms to pounds
      ii 10 pounds to kilograms.

    d Which is greater, 8 kilograms or 20 pounds?
       Show your working.

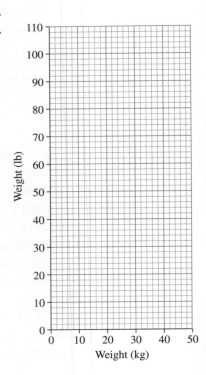

7 A bank in France sells euros (€) at the rate of
€15 for £10.

    a Copy and complete this table.

British pounds (£)	0	20	100
Euros (€)	0		

    b Copy the grid opposite.
       Draw a graph to convert euros to pounds.

    c **i** How many euros does Sam buy
         for £80?

      ii How many euros does Mr Jones
         buy for £250?

     iii Mrs Smith buys €360
         How many British pounds is this?

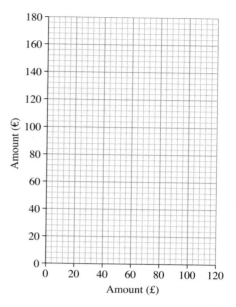

8 **a** Copy the table.

Metres (m)	0	50	100
Feet (ft)	0		

    Use the fact that **1 metre = 3.3 feet** to complete the table.

    b Copy the grid. Draw a graph to convert metres to feet.

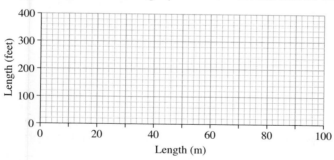

    c Halim throws the discus 14 metres.
       Use the conversion graph to work out this distance in feet.
       Give the answer to the nearest foot.

    d Tom throws the javelin 99 feet. What is this in metres?

    e Use the graph to work out the number of feet in 750 metres.
       Show your working.

9 A bank sells US dollars ($) at the rate of $1.89 = £1

    a Complete a copy of this table.

British pounds (£)	0	100	250
US dollars ($)	0		

b Copy the grid.
Draw a graph to convert pounds to US dollars.
c Use the graph to work out how many
US dollars Hayley gets for £80
d Use the graph to work out how much Bill pays
for $80
e Terry buys £1000 worth of US dollars.
He spends $1500
How many US dollars does Terry have left?
Show your working.

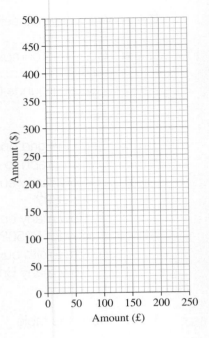

10 The graph can be used to convert speed in miles per hour to kilometres per hour.

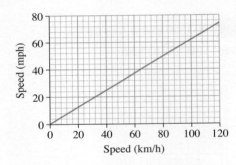

A car is travelling at 100 km/h on a road.
Show that the car is travelling faster than the speed limit of 60 mph.

Graphs can also be used to show how one quantity changes with another.

Example 3

200 g of chocolate costs £1.80
a Draw a graph to show the cost of chocolate for different weights up to 200 g.
b Betty spends £1 on chocolate.
Use your graph to work out the weight of chocolate that she buys.
c Tom buys 80 g of chocolate.
Use your graph to work out how much Tom spends on chocolate.

Solution 3

a 0 g of chocolate costs £0
So the graph passes
through (0, 0).
200 g of chocolate
costs £1.80
So the graph passes
through (200, 1.8).

b The graph passes
through (111, 1).
Betty buys 111 g
of chocolate.

c The graph passes
through (80, 0.72).
Tom spends 72p
on chocolate.

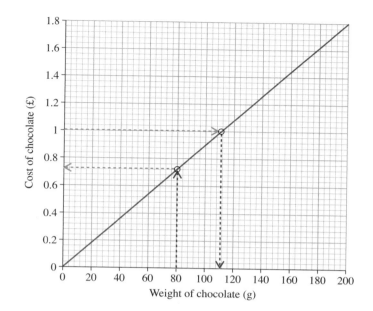

Exercise B

1 a Copy the table.

Volume of oil, litres	0	10	20
Weight of oil, kg			15

Use the fact

20 litres of oil weighs 15 kg

to complete the table.

b Copy the grid.
Draw a graph to show the relationship between
weight and volume of oil.

c i What is the weight of 12 litres of oil?
   ii What is the volume of 12 kg of oil?

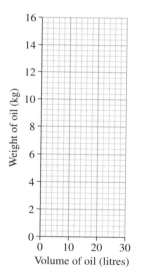

2 An electricity bill is calculated from

fixed charge + charge for the number of units of electricity used

The graph overleaf shows the bill for
different numbers of units used.

a Use the graph to find the bill for 60 units of electricity.

b Sue's electricity bill was £30
How many units of electricity did she use?

c How much is the fixedcharge?

d   Work out the charge for one unit of electricity in pence.

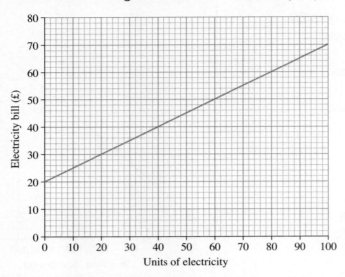

3   A gold bar has volume 100 cm³ and weight 1930 g.

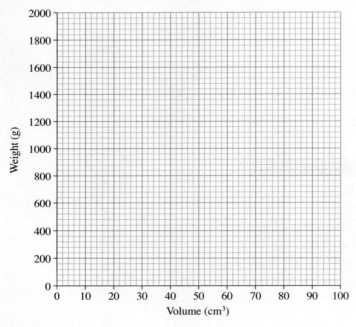

a   Copy the grid.
Draw a graph to show the relationship between the weight and volume of gold.

b   The gold bar is melted down and the gold is used to make medals.
Each medal weighs 500 g.
Use the graph to work out the volume of one medal.

4   The table shows the temperatures at the freezing point and boiling point of water in degrees Celsius (°C) and degrees Fahrenheit (°F).

Freezing point	Boiling point
32°F	212°F
0°C	100°C

a   Copy the grid. Extend the horizontal axis to
    220 °F. Extend the vertical axis to 100 °C.
    Use this information to draw a graph that
    converts °F to °C.

b   The average temperature in Newcastle in
    June is 20 °C.
    The average temperature in Moscow in
    January is 14 °F.
    Work out the difference between these
    temperatures.
    Give your answer both in °C and in °F.

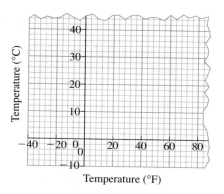

5   The charges made by two removal companies are:

EASYMOVE
Fixed charge £120
Plus £20 per hour

QUICKMOVE
FIXED CHARGE £50
PLUS £45 PER HOUR

a   Make one copy of the grid.
    Draw graphs to show the
    removal costs for **both**
    companies on the grid.

b   Use the graphs to decide which
    company it is cheaper to hire
    for 5 hours.
    How much cheaper is it?

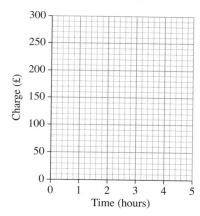

6   The graph shows the average heights of
        boys and girls between the ages 48 months
        and 60 months.

a   Matt and Sara are both 54 months old.
    Estimate the difference between their
    heights.

b   Bill and Mary are both 106 cm in height.
    Estimate the difference between their
    ages in months.

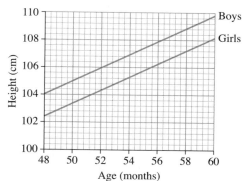

7   For every 100 gram weight that is hung on a spring,
        the spring stretches 2.3 cm.
        With no weight added, the spring has a length of 40 cm.
        Draw a graph to show how the length of the spring
        changes as the weight on it increases from zero to 1 kilogram.

20.2 Distance–time graphs

CAN YOU REMEMBER

- How to plot points on grids and read values from different scales?
- Metric and imperial units for distance?
- How to calculate times using the 24-hour clock?

IN THIS SECTION YOU WILL

- Use distance–time graphs to solve problems involving simple journeys.
- Draw distance–time graphs for journeys.

A *distance–time* graph illustrates a journey.

Example 1

The distance–time graph shows a car
journey between two towns,
Dunton and Markham.

a   At what time does the car start its
    journey?

b   Work out the total distance that the
    car travels between Dunton and
    Markham.

c   How many times does the car stop
    on the journey? Explain your answer.

d   Work out the total time that the car
    stops on the journey.

e   How far does the car travel after its last stop?

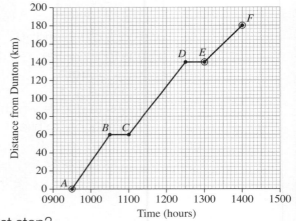

Solution 1

a   The start of the journey is at point A (0930, 0).
    The journey starts at 0930.

b   The end of the journey is at point F (1400, 180).
    The total distance the car travels is 180 km.

c   For the horizontal lines BC and DE the distance from home is not changing.
    The car has stopped. The car stops twice.

d   Line BC: the car stops for $\frac{1}{2}$ hour between 1030 and 1100
    Line DE: the car stops for $\frac{1}{2}$ hour between 1230 and 1300
    Total time the car stops is $\frac{1}{2} + \frac{1}{2} = 1$ hour.

e   Line EF illustrates the journey after the car's last stop.
    At point E (1300, 140) the car has travelled 140 km.
    The total distance the car travels is 180 km.
    So on the last part of the journey the car travels $180 - 140 = 40$ km.

Example 2

Pete walks 700 m from his house to a local shop.
He leaves home at 1030 and walks to the shop.
He takes 10 minutes to reach the shop and a further 20 minutes to do his shopping.
He then walks home at a steady speed, arriving at 1120
Draw a distance–time graph to illustrate Pete's journey.

Solution 2

Pete's journey starts at the point (1030, 0).
Pete gets to the shop at the point (1040, 700).
Pete leaves the shop at the point (1100, 700).
Pete arrives home at the point (1120, 0).
To draw the distance–time graph, plot these points and join them with straight lines.

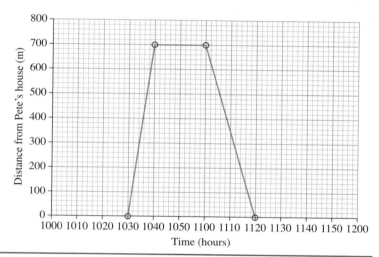

On a distance–time graph:
- the vertical axis shows distance from the starting point, the horizontal axis shows time
- a horizontal line shows that no distance is travelled and the person is stationary
- an **upward** sloping line shows that the distance from the starting point is **increasing**
- a **downward** sloping line shows that the distance from the starting point is **decreasing**.

Exercise A

1 The graph shows the distance travelled by Rosie during a bike race.
  a What is the total distance Rosie cycles?
  b How many seconds does she take to complete her journey?
  c How many seconds does she take to cycle 600 metres?
  d How many metres has she cycled after 250 seconds?

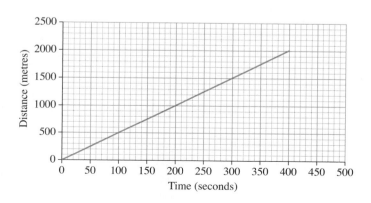

2 The graph shows the distance travelled by Jack on a bike ride.

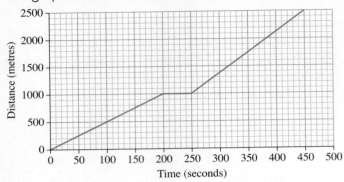

a What is the total distance Jack cycles?
b How many seconds does he take to complete his ride?
c i How many times does he stop on his ride?
 Give a reason for your answer.
 ii For how long does he stop?

3 Sue walks to the supermarket, does some shopping
and then walks home again.
The distance–time graph shows her journey.

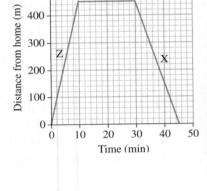

a Match each of these statements with the
 lines **X**, **Y** and **Z** on the graph.
 Sue is shopping.
 Sue walks home.
 Sue walks to the shop.
b How many minutes did it take for Sue to
 walk to the supermarket?
c How far did Sue walk altogether?
d How many minutes did Sue spend shopping?
e How many minutes did it take for Sue to walk home?
f Sue walks to the supermarket again the next day.
 On her way home she stops to talk to a friend.
 How does this change the last part of the distance–time graph?

4 This distance–time graph shows
David's car journey to his uncle's
house.

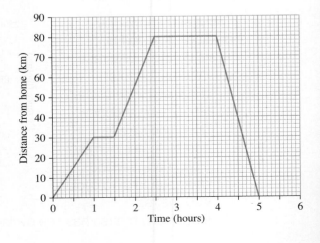

a Describe what is happening
 during each part of the graph.
b How long does David spend
 driving in total?
c How long does David spend at
 his uncle's house?
d Does David stop on his way to see
 his uncle or on his way home?
 Explain your answer fully.

5   This distance–time graph shows Adil's journey home from work.

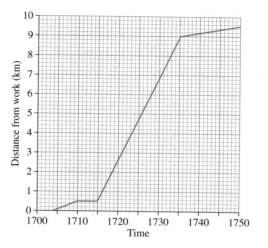

   a   At what time does Adil leave work?
   b   How far does he walk to the bus stop?
   c   How long does he wait for a bus?
   d   How far does Adil travel on the bus?
   e   What time does Adil arrive home?
   f   How long does it take Adil to travel from work to home?
   g   How far is it from Adil's work to his home?

6   On Monday Jane goes to school on the bus.
On Tuesday Jane's Mum gives her a lift to school.
The two journeys are shown on the distance–time graphs below.

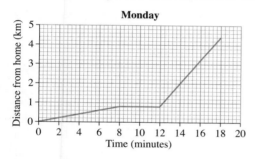
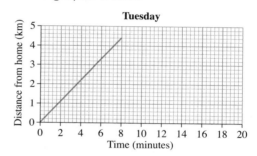

   a   How far is it from Jane's house to the school?
   b   How long did Jane take to walk to the bus stop on Monday?
   c   How long did Jane wait at the bus stop on Monday?
   d   How far is the bus stop from Jane's home?
   e   How long did the car journey take on Tuesday?
   f   How much quicker was the journey on Tuesday than the journey on Monday?

7   Ben walks the first 20 km of a 50 km walking race in 2 hours.
The next 20 km he walks in 1 hour 30 minutes.
The race starts at 1000 and Ben completes the race at 1430
On a copy of the grid, draw a distance–time graph for Ben's race.

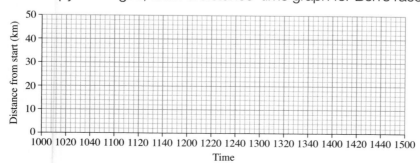

8   Jenny leaves her house at 1230 and walks to a local shop.
The shop is 750 metres from her house.
Jenny takes 10 minutes to walk to the shop.
She spends 30 minutes in the shop.
She then walks home, arriving at 1330
On a copy of the grid, draw a distance–time graph to show Jenny's journey.

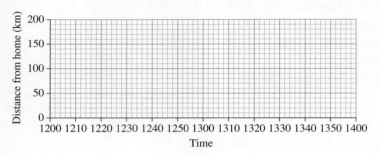

9   James cycles around a lake at a steady speed.
He starts at a picnic area at 1000 and gets back to the picnic area at 1230
The total distance that James cycles is 30 km.
Halfway around the lake James rests for 30 minutes.
Copy the grid and draw a distance–time graph to show James's journey.

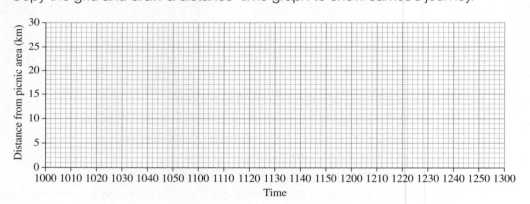

Distance–time graphs can be used to compare and calculate speeds.
By looking at the distance travelled in 1 hour you can calculate the speed.

Example 3

The graphs show how a lorry, a car and a moped complete a 100 km journey.

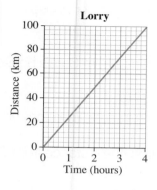

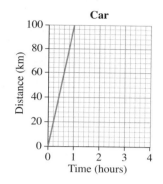

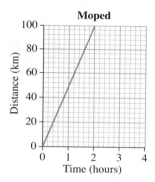

a   Which vehicle travels the fastest?   b   Which vehicle travels the slowest?
c   Work out the speed of the third vehicle.

Solution 3

The lorry takes 4 hours to travel 100 km.
The car takes 1 hour to travel 100 km.
The moped takes 2 hours to travel 100 km.

a   The car travels 100 km in the shortest time. So the car travels the fastest.
b   The lorry travels 100 km in the longest time. So the lorry travels the slowest.
c   The third vehicle is the moped. The moped travels 50 km in 1 hour.
Speed of the moped = 50 km/h.

The shorter the time to cover the distance, the faster the speed.

Example 4

At 0910 Sara and Ben both leave their houses
and start to walk towards each other.
When they meet they stop and talk for 5 minutes
and together walk to Ben's house.
This distance–time graph shows their journeys.

a   Which coloured line on the graph shows:
    i   Sara walking on her own
    ii Ben walking on his own
    iii Ben and Sara together?
    Give a reason for each answer.
b   Who walks the faster in the first 10 minutes
    of their journey?

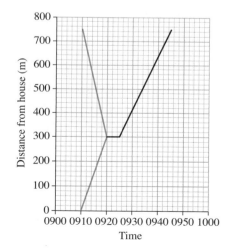

Solution 4

a   i They both end up at Ben's house. So on the graph, the vertical axis shows the distance from Sara's house.

As Sara walks on her own to meet Ben, her distance from her house is increasing, so her graph slopes upwards.

Sara's graph is the **red** line.

ii When Ben walks on his own to meet Sara, his distance from Sara's house is decreasing, so his graph slopes downwards.

Ben's graph is the **blue** line.

iii When Ben and Sara meet they are stationary for 5 minutes. Then they walk to Ben's house.

So their graph is horizontal and then slopes upwards (the distance from Sara's house is increasing).

The **black** line shows Ben and Sara together.

b   In the first 10 minutes Sara walks 300 metres and Ben walks 450 metres.
So Ben walks the faster.

Exercise B

1   The diagram illustrates Jim, Tom and Amit's 400 m race.

   a   Who runs the race the fastest?

   b   In which order do Jim, Tom and Amit finish the race?

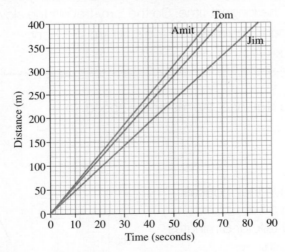

2   Work out the speed in kilometres per hour for each of the journeys on this distance–time graph.

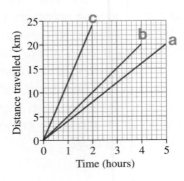

3 The graphs show five different bicycle journeys.

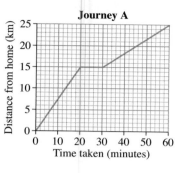

Journey A

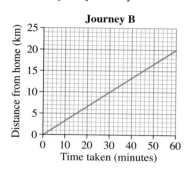

Journey B

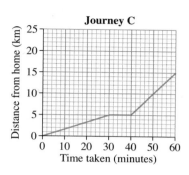

Journey C

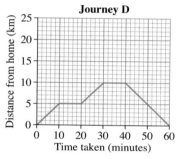

Journey D

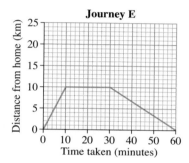

Journey E

a In which of the journeys
  i are there no stops
  ii is there one stop
  iii are there two stops
  iv does the cyclist return home?
  Explain your answers.
b Match each description to a graph.
  i Peter's journey started uphill. He rested before continuing his journey downhill.
  ii Tony cycled downhill to a friend's house. After his visit he cycled home.

4 a On Monday Rosie went to school by bus.

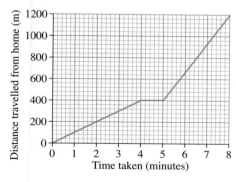

This distance–time graph shows her journey.
Describe Rosie's journey on Monday in as much detail as you can.

b On Tuesday Rosie missed the bus.
This distance–time graph shows her journey to school on Tuesday.

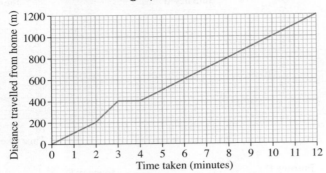

Describe Rosie's journey on Tuesday in as much detail as you can.

5 On Monday Katie got a lift to school in her Mum's car.
On Tuesday she walked to school.
On Wednesday she went to school on her bike.
This graph shows all her journeys.

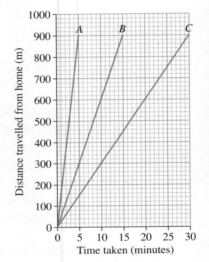

a Which line represents which day?

b Work out Katie's speed on:
 i Monday
 ii Tuesday
 iii Wednesday.

c Copy and complete the following statement.
The .... the graph the ....
the speed.

6 This graph shows John's lap on a running track.

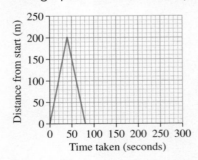

a How long is the running track?

b John completes another two laps.
Draw possible distance–time graphs if he:
 i runs all three laps at the same speed
 ii speeds up lap by lap
 iii slows down lap by lap.

7 A bus travels from Birmingham to Carlisle, a distance of 320 km, at an average speed of 64 km per hour.
This distance–time graph shows the journey.

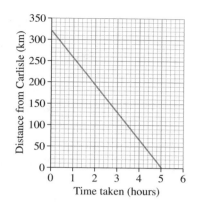

  a A car leaves Carlisle at the same time as the bus leaves Birmingham.
    The car travels on the same route and takes 4 hours to get to Birmingham.
    i Work out the average speed of the car.
    ii Copy the graph.
      On the same grid draw the distance–time graph for the car.
  b Clearly mark on the graph the point at which the bus and the car pass each other.
  c At what distance from Carlisle does the bus pass the car?

8 Mr Jones walks along a path by the river from Hexham to Corbridge, a distance of 8 km.
He leaves Hexham at 1520 and arrives at 1740
Mr Smith walks along the same path from Corbridge to Hexham.
He leaves Corbridge at 1500 and arrives at Hexham at 1720

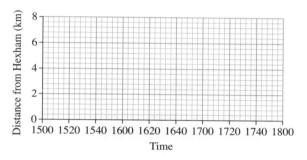

  a On a copy of the diagram above draw a distance–time graph to show both Mr Jones' and Mr Smith's walks.
  b Use your graph to work out the time that Mr Jones and Mr Smith pass each other on the path.

9 Liam leaves his house at 1100
He cycles to his friend's house 30 km away and arrives at 1230
He stays at his friend's house for 2 hours 30 minutes and then cycles home.
His return journey takes 2 hours.
  a At what time does Liam leave his friend's house to return home?
  b At what time does Liam arrive back at his own house?
  c Copy and complete the graph of Liam's journey.

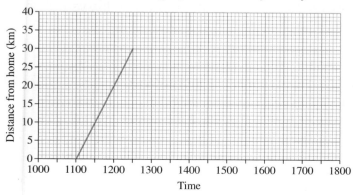

10 This graph shows the journeys of two motorists.
The first motorist travels from London to Preston.
The second travels from Preston to London.

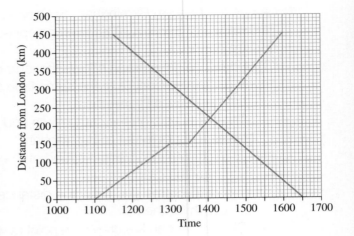

a Does the first motorist stop during his journey.
Explain how you know.

b Use the graph to work out:

i the time the first motorist arrives at Preston

ii the average speed of the second motorist

iii when and where the two motorists pass each other.

20.3 More real-life graphs

CAN YOU REMEMBER

■ How to draw and interpret conversion graphs and distance–time graphs?

IN THIS SECTION YOU WILL

■ Draw straight line graphs to represent real-life situations.
■ Read information from straight line and curved graphs and explain what it means.

Graphs are used in science and other real-life situations to show how one quantity changes with another.

On a graph:

■ a line sloping **upwards** shows that the quantity on the vertical axis is **increasing**
■ a **horizontal** line shows that the quantity on the vertical axis **stays the same**
■ a line sloping **downwards** shows that the quantity on the vertical axis is **decreasing**.

The graph shows the depth of water in a sink.
AB slopes **upwards**. The depth of water is **increasing**, so water is running into the sink.
BC is **horizontal**. The depth of water remains the same. There is no water running into or out of the sink.
CD slopes **downwards**. The depth of water is **decreasing**, so water is running out of the sink.

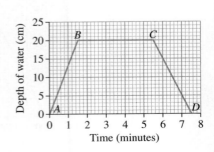

Example 1

A candle is 20 cm tall.
As the candle burns its height decreases by 4 cm each hour.
a   Complete this table to show how the height of the candle changes as it burns.

Time burning (hours)	0	1	2	3	4	5
Height of candle (cm)	20					

b   Draw a graph to show this information.
c   What feature of the graph shows that the height of the candle is decreasing?
d   Use the graph to find how long the candle has been burning when its height is 6 cm.
e   Use the graph to find the height of the candle after it has been burning for 1 hour 15 minutes.

Solution 1

a   After 1 hour, height = 20 − 4 = 16 cm
   After 2 hours, height = 16 − 4 = 12 cm
   After 3 hours, height = 12 − 4 = 8 cm
   After 4 hours, height = 8 − 4 = 4 cm
   After 5 hours, height = 4 − 4 = 0 cm

Time burning (hours)	0	1	2	3	4	5
Height of candle (cm)	20	16	12	8	4	0

b   These points lie on the graph: (0, 20) (1, 16) (2, 12) (3, 8) (4, 4) (5, 0).
c   The graph slopes downwards.
d   Look at the graph. The candle has been burning for $3\frac{1}{2}$ hours when its height is 6 cm.
e   Look at the graph. After 1 hour 15 minutes the candle is 15 cm tall.

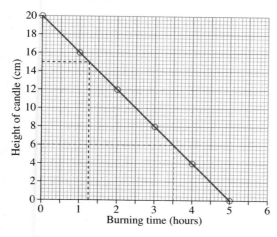

Exercise A

1 a This graph shows how the depth of water in a bath changes with time. Copy the graph.
Label the different sections of the graph *A*, *B* and *C* as follows.
A Depth of water increasing
B Depth of water decreasing
C Depth of water stays the same

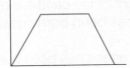

b This graph shows how the amount of oil in a tank changes with time. Copy the graph.
Label the different sections of the graph *D*, *E* and *F* as follows.
D Volume of oil increasing
E Volume of oil decreasing
F Volume of oil stays the same

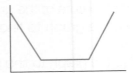

2 A big wheel at the fair makes one complete turn every 8 seconds.

a Copy and complete this table.

Number of turns	0	1	2	3	4
Time taken (seconds)					

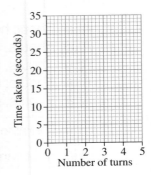

b On a copy of the grid, draw a graph to show the information given in the table.

c How many turns does the big wheel make in 20 seconds?

3 Ashley is dissolving the greatest amount of salt she can in beakers of water at different temperatures.
This table shows her results.

Temperature of water (°C)	10	20	30	40	50	60	70
Weight of salt dissolved (g)	16	21	26	31	36	41	46

a On a copy of the grid, draw a graph to show this information.

b Use the graph to find
  i the water temperature for 32 g of salt to dissolve in a beaker of water
  ii the greatest amount of salt that dissolves in a beaker of water at 22 °C.

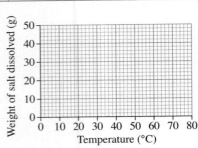

4 Aaron fills a 5 litre can with fuel.
The fuel leaks from a small crack in the bottom of the can.
  a Copy and complete this table.

Time since can was filled (hours)	0	1	2	3	4	5
Volume of fuel in can (litres)	5.0	4.1	3.2			0.5

  b **i** Copy the grid and extend
    both axes to 6. Draw a
    graph to show the information
    in the table.
    ii What feature of the graph shows
    that the volume of the fuel in
    the can is decreasing?
  c Use the graph to work out the
    total time it takes for all the
    fuel to leak from the can.

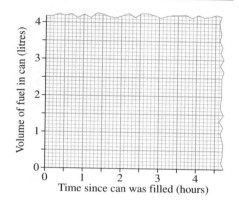

5 This graph shows the monthly repayments to
repay loans between £1000 and £5000 over
12 months.
  a What feature of the graph shows that as
    the loan increases the repayments increase?
  b Terry can afford to pay £280 per month.
    Use the graph to find out how much
    he can borrow.
  c Use the graph to find the monthly
    repayment on a loan of £2500
  d Sally borrows £4000
    How much more does Sally repay than she borrows?

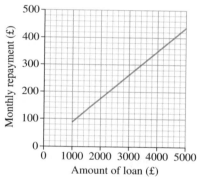

6 Sita collects information
from an experiment with
weights on a spring.
  a Copy the grid.
    Draw a graph to show
    this information.
    Extend the line of the
    graph to the vertical axis.
  b Use the graph to find the length of the spring with no
    weight on it.
  c What weight stretches the spring to 94 cm?

Weight (g)	Length of spring (cm)
10	88
20	103
30	118

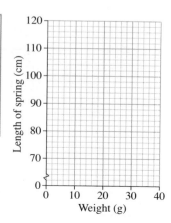

7 Adam spends £1.20 on Wine Gums and Sherbet Suckers.

    a Copy and complete this table to show some of the different ways that Adam can spend his money.

Wine Gums purchased (grams)	0	100	200	300	400
Sherbet Suckers purchased (grams)	600		300		0

    b Copy the grid and extend the vertical axis to 650. Draw a graph to show the information given in the table.

    c Adam buys the **same** weight of Wine Gums and Sherbet Suckers. Use the graph to work out how much of each he buys.

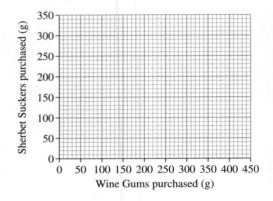

8 Every rectangle in set A has width 5 cm.
Every rectangle in set B has width 10 cm.
This diagram shows the connection between the perimeter and length of these rectangles for lengths up to 20 cm.

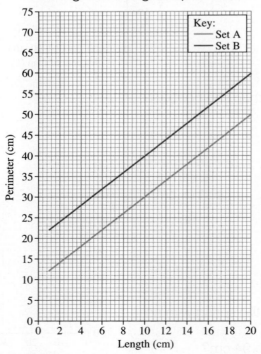

a Explain why the lines for set A and set B do **not** pass through the points (0, 10) and (0, 20).

b **i** A rectangle in set A has a perimeter of 30 cm.
Use the diagram to work out its length.

    ii A rectangle in set B has a perimeter of 30 cm.
Use the diagram to work out its length.

c A rectangle in set A has a length of 6 cm.
A rectangle in set B also has a length of 6 cm.
Use the diagram to work out the **difference** in their perimeters.

d A rectangle in set A has a perimeter of 40 cm.
A rectangle in set B also has a perimeter of 40 cm.
Work out the **difference** in their areas.

Graphs that show real-life situations can be curved. On a curved graph:

■ a slope **upwards** shows an **increasing** quantity

■ a slope **downwards** shows a **decreasing** quantity.

The steeper the slope, the faster the increase or decrease.

This graph shows how a boy's pulse rate changes when he starts running.

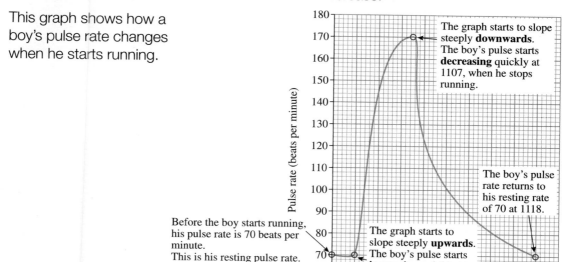

The graph starts to slope steeply **downwards**. The boy's pulse starts **decreasing** quickly at 1107, when he stops running.

The boy's pulse rate returns to his resting rate of 70 at 1118.

Before the boy starts running, his pulse rate is 70 beats per minute. This is his resting pulse rate.

The graph starts to slope steeply **upwards**. The boy's pulse starts **increasing** quickly at 1102, when he starts running.

This graph shows how the percentage of male and female smokers changes with age.

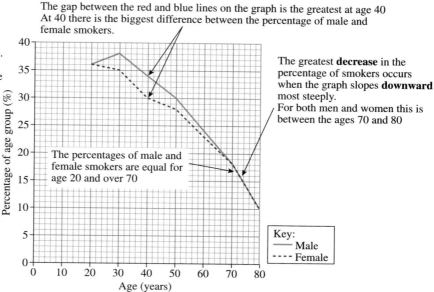

The gap between the red and blue lines on the graph is the greatest at age 40. At 40 there is the biggest difference between the percentage of male and female smokers.

Look at the male graph to the left of the point (50, 30). This shows that more than 30% of males below the age of 50 smoke.
Look at the female graph to the left of the point (40, 30). This shows that more than 30% of females below the age of 40 smoke.

The greatest **decrease** in the percentage of smokers occurs when the graph slopes **downward** most steeply.
For both men and women this is between the ages 70 and 80

The percentages of male and female smokers are equal for age 20 and over 70

Key:
—— Male
----- Female

Exercise B

1 This graph shows the growth in the number of cigarettes smoked worldwide from 1900 to 2000

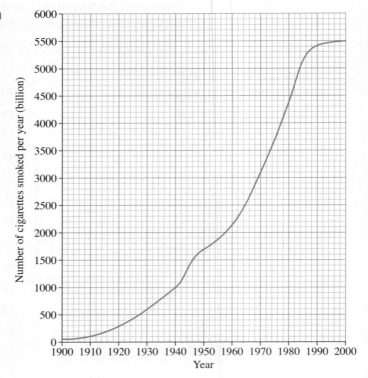

Use the graph to find
a the number of cigarettes smoked worldwide in 2000
b the year when the number of cigarettes smoked worldwide exceeded 1000 billion per year
c the 10-year period in which cigarette smoking increased the most
d the increase in the number of cigarettes smoked between 1900 and 2000

2 Dawn pours two cups of tea – one for herself and one for Lyn.
She leaves them in the kitchen.
This graph shows how the tea cools with time.
a What is the temperature of the tea immediately after it has been poured?
b i Lyn does not like to drink tea at a temperature above 70 °C.
How long does she have to wait before she can drink her tea?
ii Dawn waits about 7 minutes before starting to drink her tea.
How hot is her tea then?
c Give an estimate of the temperature in the kitchen.
Explain your answer.

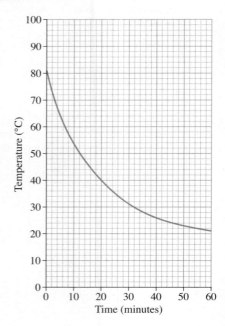

3

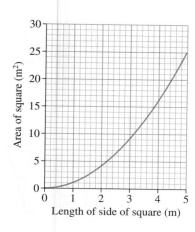

This graph shows the areas of squares up to size 5 metres by 5 metres.

a Use the graph to find the area of a square of side length 3.5 metres.

b Use the graph to find the length of the side of a square of area 20 m².

c Three square carpet tiles are placed in a line as shown in the diagram. The total area of the three squares is 26 m².
Use the graph to help work out the length x.

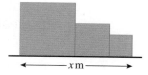

4 Andy throws a ball to Peter who catches it.
The graph shows the path of the ball as it moves from Andy to Peter.

a How far apart are Andy and Peter?

b How high is the ball above the ground when Peter catches the ball?

c At what height from the ground does the ball leave Andy's hand?

d What is the greatest height above the ground that the ball reaches?

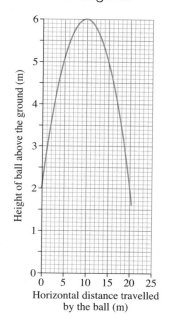

5 The graph below shows the wind speed on the North-East coast over a 12-hour period.

a What is the wind speed at 0900?

b Estimate the wind speed at 1230

c At what time is the wind speed greatest?

d **i** Between what times does the wind speed increase?

ii Between what times does the wind speed decrease?

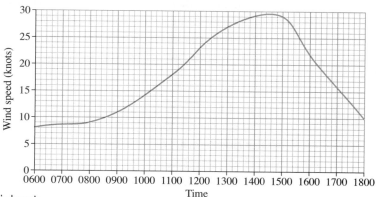

e What happens the quickest
— the increase or decrease in wind speed? Explain your answer.

6 This graph shows the average weight of
boys and girls aged from 5 to 10

    a What is the difference in weight between a boy
and a girl aged 7?

    b What is the difference in age between a boy
and girl of weight 19 kg?

    c At what age is the average weight of girls
first greater than the average weight of boys?

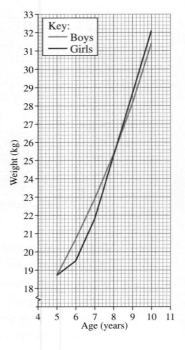

7 The graph shows how numbers of deaths from lung
disease changed between 1920 and 1960

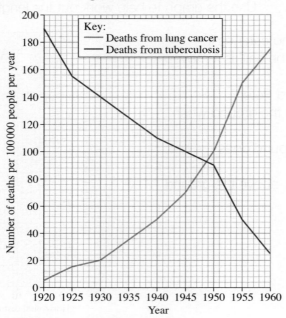

    a Use the graph to find

        i the number of deaths from lung cancer in 1940

        ii the number of deaths from tuberculosis in 1955

        iii the total number of deaths from both diseases in 1920

        iv the total number of deaths from both diseases in 1960

    b In which year did the number of deaths from lung cancer first become greater
than the number of deaths from tuberculosis?

    c In which 5-year period did the number of deaths from lung cancer increase the
most?

8 The shape of the Sydney Harbour Bridge
in Australia is called a **parabolic arch**.
A **smaller** bridge with a parabolic arch is
the Tyne Bridge in Britain.
The parabolic arch used in the Sydney Harbour
Bridge and that used on the Tyne Bridge are
shown on the graph.

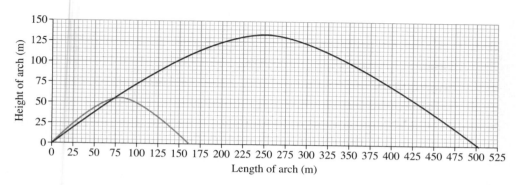

a   How much higher is the arch of the Sydney Harbour Bridge than the arch of the Tyne Bridge?

b   The span of the arch of the Tyne Bridge is 162 metres.
    How much longer is the span of the arch of the Sydney Harbour Bridge?

c   Another bridge that uses a parabolic arch is the Hells Gate Bridge in the USA.
    The arch of this bridge is 67 m high and its span is 310 m.
    Copy the graph showing the arches of Sydney Harbour Bridge and the Tyne Bridge.
    On the same diagram, sketch the arch of the Hells Gate Bridge.

Chapter summary

- A *conversion graph* converts one unit or quantity to another.
- To draw a conversion graph:
  Step 1: Use a pair of equivalent quantities to make a table of values.
  Step 2: Write a list of coordinates from the table.
  Step 3: Plot the coordinates on a grid.
  Step 4: Draw the line through the coordinates.
- Graphs can also be used to show how one quantity changes with another.
- A *distance–time* graph illustrates a journey. On a distance–time graph:
  - the vertical axis shows distance from the starting point, the horizontal axis shows time
  - a horizontal line shows that no distance is travelled and the person or object is stationary
  - an **upward** sloping line shows that the distance from the starting point is **increasing**
  - a **downward** sloping line shows that the distance from the starting point is **decreasing**.
- Distance–time graphs can be used to compare and calculate speeds.
- The shorter the time to cover the distance, the faster the speed.

- On a graph
  - a line (or curve) sloping **upwards** shows that the quantity on the vertical axis is **increasing**
  - a **horizontal** line shows that the quantity on the vertical axis **stays the same**
  - a line sloping **downwards** shows that the quantity on the vertical axis is **decreasing**.
- The steeper the slope, the faster the increase or decrease.

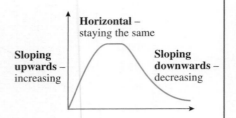

Horizontal – staying the same

Sloping upwards – increasing

Sloping downwards – decreasing

Chapter review

1 The graph shows a coach journey from *A* to *D*, stopping at *B* and *C*.

   a At what time does the coach leave *B*?

   b How far is it from *A* to *C*?

   c During which part of the journey does the coach travel the fastest? Explain your answer.

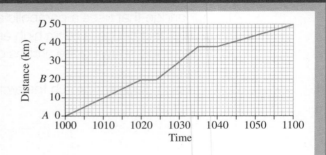

2 Sue knows that 8 kilometres is 5 miles.

   a Copy the grid.
       Use this information to produce a conversion graph.

   b Use your graph to convert 4.6 miles into kilometres.

   c Sue travels 40 km. How many miles is this?

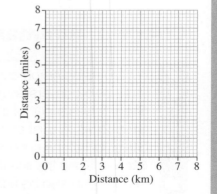

3 The graph shows the percentage of Internet connections that are broadband between 2001 and 2004

   a Use the graph to estimate the percentage of broadband Internet connections in June 2003

   b Use the graph to estimate in which month and year the percentage of broadband Internet connections was 30%.

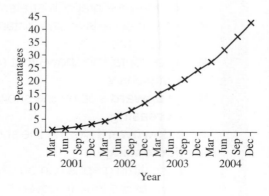

4 £1 = 220 Japanese yen (¥)

a Use this information to produce a conversion graph on a copy of this grid.

b Use the graph to convert
   i £2.50 to Japanese yen
   ii ¥1320 to British pounds.

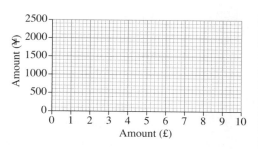

c James buys a CD in the UK for £8.50

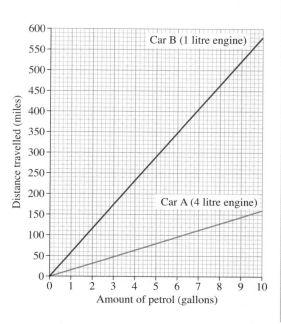

Makoto buys the same CD in Japan for ¥1760
Who pays the most and by how much?
Give your answer both in British pounds and in Japanese yen.

5 Ben cycles from Smalltown to Bigtown and then cycles back to Smalltown.
The distance–time graph shows Ben's journey.

a What is the distance between Smalltown and Bigtown?

b How long did Ben stay in Bigtown?

c How far was Ben from Bigtown at 1230?

d What was Ben's speed when he cycled from Bigtown back to Smalltown?

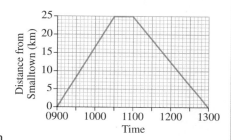

6 The graph shows the distances travelled by two cars, A and B, as they consume up to 10 gallons of petrol.

a What is the difference in the amount of petrol cars A and B consume after they each travel 100 miles?

b How much further than car B does car A travel after both cars consume 5 gallons of petrol?

7 Vehicles that travel faster need more distance
to stop when they brake.
The graph shows the stopping distances
for different speeds.

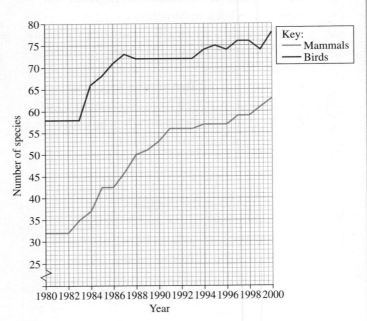

a At a speed of 70 mph the stopping
distance is 315 feet.
Mark this point on a copy of the graph.

b Use the graph to find the stopping
distance for a speed of 30 mph.

c Use the graph to estimate
  i the stopping distance for a speed of 45 mph
  ii the speed for a stopping distance of 200 feet.

d A car travels at a speed of 43 mph.
A van travels at a speed of 28 mph.
What is the difference between the stopping distances of the car and van?

8 The graph shows the
number of species of
endangered mammals
and birds in the USA
between 1980 and 2000

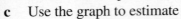

a Use the graph to work out
  i the number of endangered mammals in the USA in 1986
  ii the year in which there were 68 endangered bird species in the USA
  iii the difference between the number of endangered mammal species and
    endangered bird species in 1995

b What was the longest length of time that the number of endangered birds stayed
the same?
Explain how the graph tells you this.

c What **increased** most between 1980 and 2000 — the number of endangered
mammal species or the number of endangered bird species?
Explain how the graph tells you this.

Charts, graphs and diagrams

21.1 Pie charts

CAN YOU REMEMBER

- How many degrees are in a full circle?
- How to multiply by a fraction?
- How to use a protractor?

IN THIS SECTION YOU WILL

- Understand how a pie chart represents data.
- Learn how to calculate the angles for the sectors of a pie chart.
- Learn how to draw a pie chart.
- Learn how to interpret information from a pie chart.

A pie chart is a circular diagram split into sectors.
The angle of each sector of the pie chart is in proportion to the amount of information it represents.
There are 360° in a full circle.
The angles of the sectors in a pie chart add up to 360°.
The pie chart below shows how sales in a large store are divided between departments.

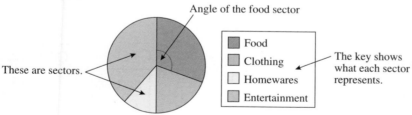

Entertainment is the largest sector. More money is spent on entertainment than the other items in the store.

Example 1

Draw a pie chart to represent this data.

Fish	Perch	Roach	Eel	Pike	**Total**
Number caught	12	16	5	3	**36**

Solution 1

Step 1: Calculate the angle for one fish.

360° in a circle represent 36 fish.

So 360° ÷ 36 represent one fish.

10° represent one fish.

Step 2: Calculate the angle for each sector.

There are 12 perch. Angle for perch = 12 × 10° = 120°

There are 16 roach. Angle for roach = 16 × 10° = 160°

Angle for eel = 5 × 10° = 50°

Angle for pike = 3 × 10° = 30°

Step 3: Check that the sum of all of the angles equals 360°

120° + 160° + 50° + 30° = 360°

Step 4: Draw a circle. Draw a straight line (a radius) from the centre of the circle to the circumference. Use a protractor to measure accurately and then draw the angle for each sector. Complete the pie chart by labelling each sector or using a key (but not both).

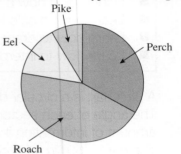

Pie chart to show the types of fish caught

Use the method in Example 1 when the total number is a multiple or factor of 360.

Example 2

 The table shows a family's gas bills. They receive one bill every three months. Draw a pie chart to represent the data.

	Cost of gas (£)
Jan–Mar	95
Apr–Jun	55
Jul–Sep	45
Oct–Dec	105

Solution 2

Step 1: Calculate the fraction of the whole that each sector represents.

Add up the values in the table to find the total amount.

95 + 55 + 45 + 105 = 300

The value for Jan–Mar is £95

So the Jan–Mar sector is $\frac{95}{300}$ of the whole circle (360°).

In the same way, Apr–Jun is $\frac{55}{300}$, Jul–Sep is $\frac{45}{300}$, Oct–Dec is $\frac{105}{300}$

Step 2: Calculate the angles for each sector.

The angle of the sector for Jan–Mar is $\frac{95}{300} \times 360° = 114°$ (using a calculator)
In the same way:

Apr–Jun	Jul–Sep	Oct–Dec
$\frac{55}{300} \times 360 = 66°$	$\frac{45}{300} \times 360 = 54°$	$\frac{105}{300} \times 360 = 126°$

Step 3: Check that the sum of all of the angles equals 360°

$114° + 66° + 54° + 126° = 360°$

Step 4:

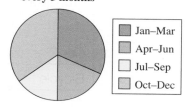

Pie chart to show the cost of gas
every 3 months

Jan–Mar
Apr–Jun
Jul–Sep
Oct–Dec

Use the method in Example 2 when the total number is not a multiple or factor of 360

Exercise A

1 a Copy the table below.

Transport	Frequency	Angle
Car	45	
Bus	35	
Train	10	40°
Total	**90**	**360°**

There are 90 'items'. Work out the angle for one item.
Work out the angle for each type of transport. Write the angles in the table.

b Draw a pie chart to represent the data.

2 For each part
　i Copy and complete the table   **ii** Draw a pie chart to represent the data.

a

Drink	Frequency	Angle
Cola	25	
Orange	20	
Lemon	10	
Other	5	
Total	**60**	**360°**

b

House	Frequency	Angle
Detached	60	
Semi-detached	80	
Terraced	40	
Total	**180**	

4 The following goods were sold by a clothes shop in one week.
  a Copy and complete the table opposite.
  b Draw a pie chart to represent the data.

Goods	Value (£)	Angle
T-shirts	100	
Shorts	64	
Jackets	306	
Suits	250	
Total	**720**	

5 **a** Copy the table opposite.
    Work out the fraction of the whole that each type of transport represents.
    Work out the angle for each type of transport.
    Write the angles in the table.
  b Draw a pie chart to represent this data.

Transport	Frequency	Angle
Bus	200	
Car	370	
Bicycle	85	
Taxi	25	
Total	**680**	

6 A travel company arranges visits to the town, seaside or countryside.
The number of these visits, over a year, is shown in the table.
Draw a pie chart to show this information.

Visit	Number
Town	25
Seaside	45
Countryside	30

7 The costs of a family holiday are shown in the table.
Draw a pie chart to represent this information.

Item	Costs (£)
Flights	600
Accommodation	350
Food	490
Spending money	720

On a pie chart, the largest sector represents the modal group.

Example 3

30 students were asked to choose their favourite leisure activity.

The pie chart shows the results.

  a What is the modal leisure activity?
  b Calculate the number of students who chose cinema.
  c **i** Measure and write down the angle of the gym sector.
    ii How many students chose gym?

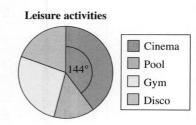

Leisure activities

144°

Cinema
Pool
Gym
Disco

Solution 3

a Cinema is the modal activity, as it has the largest sector in the pie chart.

b **Step 1:** Find the angle.

Step 2: Work out what fraction of the whole the sector represents.

Step 3: Calculate the fraction of the total amount.
12 students chose cinema.

Cinema sector angle $= 144°$

Cinema is $\frac{144}{360} = \frac{2}{5}$ of the whole.

$\frac{2}{5}$ of 30 students $= \frac{2}{5} \times 30 = 12$ students

c **i** **Step 1:** Gym sector angle $= 96°$

ii **Step 2:** Gym is $\frac{96}{360}$ of the whole.

Step 3: $\frac{96}{360} \times 30 = 8$

Eight students chose gym.

Exercise B

1 The table opposite shows how 90 students travel to school one day. Copy and complete the pie chart.

Transport	Frequency
Walk	20
Cycle	5
Bus	25
Car	40

2 There are 60 admissions to a hospital one day. The table shows the number of each type of admission.

Draw a pie chart to represent the data in the table.

Type of admission	Frequency
Medical (M)	18
Surgical (S)	12
Children (C)	6
Geriatric (G)	24

3

The pie chart shows the value of the sales of goods by a shop in September.

a Measure the size of the angle for coats.

b What fraction of the total sales were coats?

The goods in the table were sold by the shop in the month of October.

The total value of all the sales was £180.

c Draw a pie chart to represent these sales.

Goods	Value (£)
Hats	70
Scarves	50
Gloves	40
Umbrellas	20

4 The table shows the number of each type of house on an estate.

    a What fraction of the houses were terraced houses?

    b Draw a pie chart to represent this data.

Type of house	Number
Terraced (T)	180
Semi-detached (S)	141
Detached (D)	123
Bungalow (B)	96

5 The pie chart shows the annual costs of running a small family car.

    a What fraction of the annual cost is petrol?

    b The annual cost of maintenance is £350
       Work out the total annual cost of running this car.

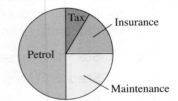

6 The IT staff at a college recorded how the computers were being used at lunchtime. The table shows the results.

Draw a pie chart to represent this data.

Used for	Number of computers
E-mail	30
Games	22
Work	25
Internet	23

7 The table shows the average weekly water use for a family of four.

Draw a pie chart to represent these figures.

Use of water	Amount of water (litres)
Washing machine	240
Bathing	500
Flushing toilet	820
Other	350

8 There are three types of day-visits which people take in the UK.

The table shows the percentages for each type of day-visit last summer.

A pie chart is to be drawn to represent the data.

    a Calculate the angle for countryside.

    b Draw a pie chart to represent this information.

Destination	Percentage
Countryside	40
Seaside	25
Town	35

9 The road distances travelled by different types of vehicle in Great Britain in 2005 are shown in the table.

Draw a pie chart to represent this data.

The government expects the road distances to increase by 10% each year. Shaun says, 'This means that in 2007 the distance travelled will be more than 800 billion kilometres.' Is he correct? Explain your answer.

Type of vehicle	Distance (billion km)
Car	420
Lorry	100
Bus	130
Motorcycle	50

10 The 900 customers who shopped in a department store one day paid for their purchases using either cash, cheque or credit card.
One quarter used cash and 120 used cheques.
  a How many people used credit cards?
  b Draw a pie chart to show this information.

11 The pie chart shows the usual method of travel to school for students at a particular school.

  a List the methods of transport in order of popularity, most popular first.
  b 480 students walk to this school. How many students use each of the other methods of transport?

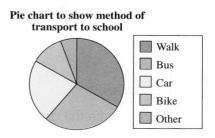

Pie chart to show method of transport to school

☐ Walk
☐ Bus
☐ Car
☐ Bike
☐ Other

21.2 Stem and leaf diagrams

CAN YOU REMEMBER

- The meaning of the word 'frequency'?
- How to find the median, the mode and the range?

IN THIS SECTION YOU WILL

- Learn how to draw an ordered stem and leaf diagram to represent data.
- Learn how to interpret data in a stem and leaf diagram.
- Find the median, the mode and the range from a stem and leaf diagram.
- Understand the advantages of using a stem and leaf diagram.

The *ordered stem and leaf* diagram below shows the number of passengers on each of 17 bus journeys.

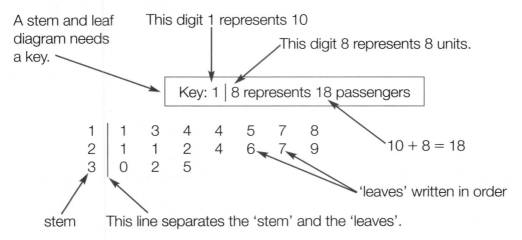

A stem and leaf diagram needs a key.

This digit 1 represents 10

This digit 8 represents 8 units.

Key: 1 | 8 represents 18 passengers

```
1 | 1  3  4  4  5  7  8
2 | 1  1  2  4  6  7  9
3 | 0  2  5
```

10 + 8 = 18

'leaves' written in order

stem

This line separates the 'stem' and the 'leaves'.

The mode, median and range can be found directly from a stem and leaf diagram.

Example 1

a Draw an ordered stem and leaf diagram to represent the following data.

12   14   32   9   15   23   31   19   14   6   25   20   16   28   7

b Work out the

i mode   **ii** median   **iii** range.

Solution 1

a Rewrite the data in order of size:

6	7	9	12	14
14	15	16	19	20
23	25	28	31	32

Key: 2 | 3 represents 23

Values less than 10 have 'stem' 0

```
0 | 6  7  9
1 | 2  4  4  5  6  9
2 | 0  3  5  8
3 | 1  2
```

b   **i** The **mode** is the value that occurs most times.

Mode = **14**

ii The **median** is the middle value in an ordered list.
In the stem and leaf diagram the values are in order.
There are 15 values.

$$\text{Median} = \frac{(15 + 1)}{2}\text{th value} = \textbf{eighth value} = \textbf{16}$$

iii   Range = **largest value** − **smallest value** = **32** − **6** = 26

Exercise A

1   Copy and complete the stem and leaf diagram for the following data.
Remember to complete the key.

12   15   16   11   18   20   22   25   29   14   22   23   28   31   33   35

Key: ..... | .... represents ....

```
1 | ...............................................................
2 | ...............................................................
3 | ...............................................................
```

2   The number of students in each of 20 classes is listed below.

14 17 22 23 24 22 15 16 10 31 15 21 25 20 13 18 25 12 18 21

Draw a stem and leaf diagram with a key to represent this data.

3 The number of customers queuing at a town's main post office each day at 12 noon is recorded for twenty days. The results are:

21 13 15 23 31 14 10 6 12 14 18 18 31 30 24 20 18 11 8 3

   a Draw a stem and leaf diagram to represent this data. Include a key.
   b Write down the mode.
   c Work out the range of the number of customers queuing.

4 Pupils in a class were asked to count how many CDs they owned.
The results are:

25	35	44	15	24	34	18	20	31	12	32	45	50
64	19	13	23	52	55	16	42	44	46	53	24	

   a Draw an ordered stem and leaf diagram with a key to represent this data.
   b Work out the range of the number of CDs owned.
   c Find the median.

5 The stem and leaf diagram represents the number of cars parked in a car park each day at 10 am for 15 days.
   a Work out the range.
   b Write down the mode.
   c Calculate the median.

Key: 4 | 5 represents 45 cars

```
4 | 2  3  5  7  8  9
5 | 0  1  2  6  6  8  9
6 | 2  3
```

6 The number of customers using a barber is recorded each week and is listed below:

123 131 129 111 102 105 117 119 120 128 135

   a Copy and complete the ordered stem and leaf diagram.
   b Work out the range.
   c Find the median.

Key: 10 | 5 represents 105 customers

```
10 | 2   5
11 |
12 |
13 |
```

A stem and leaf diagram shows the shape of a distribution, similar to a bar chart.

```
1 | 2  3  5
2 | 4  5  8  9
3 | 1  2  4  6  6  9
```

The raw data can be read from a stem and leaf diagram.
In a bar chart, the raw data is 'lost'.

Example 2

The stem and leaf diagram shows the number of driving lessons people had before they passed their driving test.
a   How many people were asked?
b   Write down the range of the number of driving lessons.
c   Calculate the median number of driving lessons.
d   Saleem passes his test. When his number of driving lessons is added to the stem and leaf diagram the median increases by 1 and the range increases by 1
Work out the number of driving lessons Saleem had.

| Key: 2 | 3 represents 23 lessons |

```
1 | 0  3  5  5  8
2 | 0  3  5  9
3 | 1  6
4 | 4
5 | 0  1
```

Solution 2

a   Count the number of leaves: 14 people were asked.

b   Range = largest value − smallest value = 51 − 10 = 41 lessons

c   Median = $\dfrac{(14 + 1)}{2}$ th value = 7.5th value

The 7.5th value is the average of the seventh value and the eighth value.

So median = $\dfrac{23 + 25}{2} = \dfrac{48}{2} = 24$ lessons

d   The range increases by 1 so the value is either 1 less than the smallest value (10 − 1 = 9) or 1 more than the largest value (51 + 1 = 52).
The median increases by 1 so the new number of driving lessons must be above the old median.
Saleem had 52 driving lessons.

Exercise B

1   A company records the number of days that employees are off sick.
The stem and leaf diagram shows the results.

| Key: 0 | 3 represents 3 days absent |

```
0 | 0  0  2  3  5  7  8
1 | 0  1  2  3  5
2 | 1  3
3 | 1
```

a   How many employees had no days off sick?
b   What was the greatest number of days off sick?
c   How many employees were off sick for more than 10 days?
d   Work out the median number of days off sick.
e   Explain an advantage of a stem and leaf diagram over a bar chart.

2 Dayton Rugby Club recorded the number of matches its supporters attended last season.
The stem and leaf diagram shows the number of matches from last season.

Key: 1 | 2 represents 12 games

```
0 | 8 9
1 | 0 0 2 3 3 5 6 9
2 | 0 1 1 2 2 2 3
```

  a Work out the range.   **b** Write down the mode.   **c** Find the median.

Annie's data was missed off the diagram. When it is added to the stem and leaf diagram the range did not change but the median was reduced.

  d How many matches could Annie have attended? Explain your reasons.

3 The ordered stem and leaf diagram represents the number of e-mails that each of 12 students received last week.
It contains three errors.
Describe each error.

```
1 | 0 5 3 5 8
2 | 0 3 9
3 | 1 6
4 | 4
```

4 A manager of a grocery shop recorded how much, to the nearest pound, each of 15 customers had spent.
The range was £19
The median was £11
Three customers spent over £20
The smallest amount spent was £2
Draw a stem and leaf diagram to represent this information. Invent the entries to complete the diagram.

5 The stem and leaf diagram shows the number of patients a doctor saw each day for 20 days.

Key: 1 | 0 represents 10 patients

```
0 | 6 7 8 9 9 9
1 | 0 1 3 3 5 7 8 8
2 | 0 1 2 2 3 5
```

  a Work out the range of the number of patients seen.

  b Write down the mode of the number of patients seen.

  c Calculate the median number of patients seen.

  d On the 21st day the doctor saw 28 patients. Write down the new range and the new median when this number of patients is added to the diagram.

6 A group of students measured their pulse rate after exercising. The results were:

  65   72   69   82   85   94   76   104

  67   120   118   95   128   122   86   63

  a Draw a stem and leaf diagram to represent this data. Include a key.

  b Work out the range.

  c Calculate the median.

  d Any student with a pulse rate above 90 was not allowed to do further exercise. What are the range and the median of the pulse rates of the students who could carry on exercising?

21.3 Scatter graphs

IN THIS SECTION YOU WILL

- Understand the meaning of the terms 'positive correlation', 'negative correlation' and 'no correlation'.
- Learn how to use and interpret a scatter diagram.
- Learn how to draw and use a line of best fit on a scatter graph.
- Learn when **not** to use a line of best fit.

Scatter graphs are used to investigate relationships between two sets of data.
A scatter graph may show a link or *correlation* between two variables.

For example, this scatter graph shows the hours of sunshine each day and the amount of rainfall (in mm) each day for 12 days.
The graph shows that as the amount of rainfall increases, the hours of sunshine decrease.
This suggests that the two variables 'hours of sunshine' and 'rainfall' are linked.

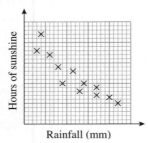

Correlation can be shown by a *line of best fit*. This is a straight line which is as close to the points as possible, drawn by eye. The line should have roughly the same number of points above it as below it.
If the line of best fit on a scatter graph has a positive gradient then the correlation is positive. If it has a negative gradient then the correlation is negative.

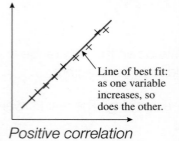

Positive correlation

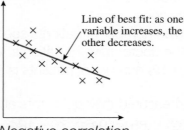

Negative correlation

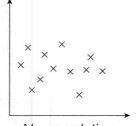

No correlation
The points are not close to a straight line.
There is no linear relationship between the two variables.

A line of best fit can be used to predict the value for one variable given a value of the other variable.

Example 1

The table shows the heights and weights of ten men.

Height (cm)	155	157	164	169	172	177	181	185	190	195
Weight (kg)	71	70	76	80	79	85	82	94	96	94

a Plot the points on a scatter graph.
b Draw a line of best fit on the scatter graph.
c Describe the relationship between height and weight.
d Use the line of best fit to estimate the weight of a man who is 182 cm tall.

Solution 1

a, b

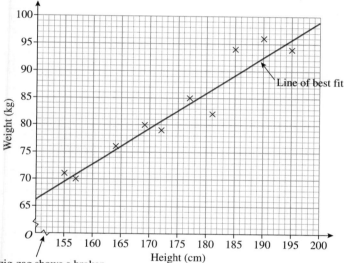

This zig-zag shows a broken scale. It jumps from zero to 155

c As the heights increase, so do the weights.
There is positive correlation between height and weight.
d Reading from a height of 182 cm gives a weight of 87.5 kg.

Exercise A

1 a Plot these points as a scatter graph.

Length and weight of pike

Length, inches	10	12	13	14	15	16	18	21	32
Weight, lb	3	10	18	14	22	25	28	32	36

b Draw a line of best fit.
c Comment on the relationship between length
and weight of pike.

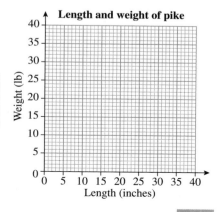

419

2   The shoe sizes and waist sizes of eight teenagers are recorded in the table.

Shoe size	3	3.5	4	5	6	6.5	8	9
Waist size (inches)	22	23	25	26	28	30	32	34

a   Plot the data as a scatter graph.

b   Comment on the relationship shown by your graph.

c   Draw a line of best fit.

d   Use your line of best fit to estimate the waist size of a teenager with shoe size 5.5

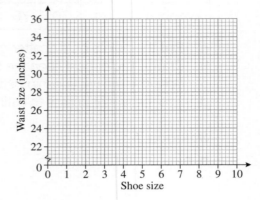

3   **a**   Draw a line of best fit.

b   Describe the type of correlation in the scatter graph.

c   Use your line of best fit to estimate the value of the vehicle when it was $2\frac{1}{2}$ years old.

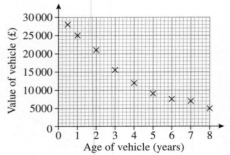

4   **a**   Draw a line of best fit.

b   Describe the type of correlation shown.

c   Use your line of best fit to estimate the score in Science test paper 1 for a student who scored 23 in Science test paper 2

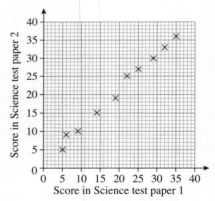

5

a   What type of correlation is shown in the scatter graph on the left?

b   Is there a relationship between the percentage marks in the French and the percentage marks in the Mathematics examinations? Explain your answer.

6 Eight pupils were asked how much time each of them spent on their computer and each of them spent watching TV on one day.
Their results are shown in the table.

Time spent on the computer (min)	10	20	30	35	40	45	50	60
Time spent watching TV (min)	120	100	80	60	50	30	40	20

a Plot the data as a scatter diagram.
b Draw a line of best fit.
c Describe the relationship between the time spent on the computer and the time spent watching TV.
d Another pupil spent 25 minutes on his computer that day.
Estimate the time he spent watching TV.

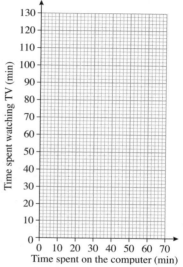

7 In a science experiment eight students were asked to time how fast they could catch a moving object.
The table shows their times before and after practising the experiment.

Time without practice (s)	2.5	3	3.5	4	4	5	5	6
Time with practice (s)	2	3	3	3.5	4	4	5.5	7

a Plot this data as a scatter graph.

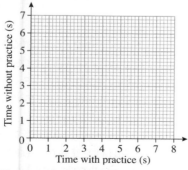

b Draw a line of best fit.
c Describe the relationship between the times without practice and times with practice.
d Use your line of best fit to estimate the time with practice of a pupil who took 5.5 seconds to catch the object without practice.

The closer the points are to a straight line, the stronger the correlation.

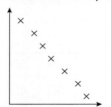

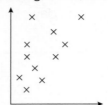

Strong correlation
(points close to being
in a straight line)

Weak correlation
(points follow a general
pattern)

No correlation
(points well scattered)

A line of best fit should only be used to estimate values within the range of a set of data. This is called *interpolation*. The line of best fit must not be extended beyond the actual data to make predictions, because there is no evidence that any pattern in the data will continue. Extending the line outside the data values is called *extrapolation*.

Example 2

The scatter diagram shows the amount of time spent on revision and the score obtained in a Mathematics examination for eight students.

a Draw a line of best fit on the scatter graph.

b What type of correlation is shown in the scatter graph?

c Use your line of best fit to estimate the exam score of a student who revised for 8 hours.

d Comment on the reliability of your estimate in part **c**.

e Explain why it is not sensible to use the line of best fit to estimate the exam score of a student who revised for 10 hours.

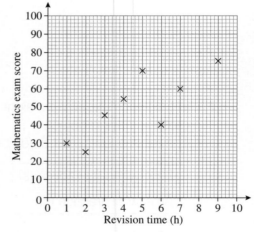

Solution 2

a

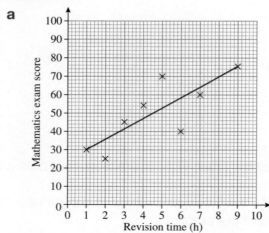

b Weak positive correlation, as the points are not very close to the line.

c Reading from 8 hours on the horizontal axis, the estimated exam score is 70

d The estimate is within the range of the data but the correlation is quite weak. So it may not be a very reliable estimate.

e This value is outside the given range of data. The pattern in the relationship may not continue.

Exercise B

1 Twelve people followed a special diet.
The scatter diagram shows the number of
weeks on the diet and the amount of
weight in kilograms lost by each person.

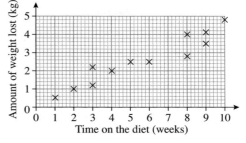

a Draw a line of best fit on a copy of the
diagram.
b What type of correlation is shown?
c Use your line of best fit to estimate how
much weight a person would be expected
to lose after seven weeks on the diet.
d Is your estimate in part **c** interpolation or extrapolation? Explain your answer.

2 At a job interview six candidates were tested for their numeracy and IT skills.
The table shows their scores.

Numeracy score	3	5	6	8	9	10
IT score	1	4	6	9	6	9

a Plot a scatter graph of this data.
b Draw on your scatter graph a line of best fit.
c What strength and type of correlation is shown in the scatter graph?
d Use your line of best fit to estimate the numeracy score of a candidate who had
an IT score of 7
e Comment on the reliability of your estimate.

3 a Match each scatter graph below with one of the following labels.

Perfect negative correlation	Weak negative correlation	Strong positive correlation
Strong negative correlation	No (zero) correlation	Perfect positive correlation

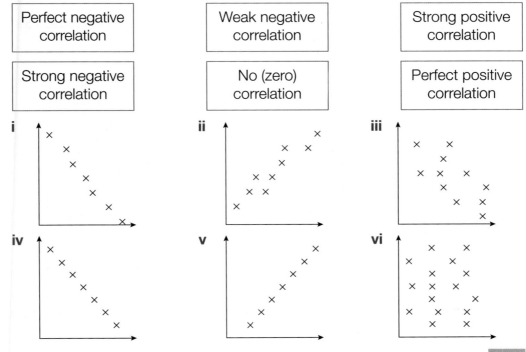

  b What type of correlation would you expect with these pairs of variables?

      i The heights and weights of a group of 11-year-old girls.

      ii The heights of fathers and their eldest son.

      iii The amount of time practising and the number of errors in a spelling test.

  c Write down a pair of variables which would show strong negative correlation.

4 Eight new cars with different engine sizes were tested for their fuel consumption during motorway driving.
The table shows the results.

Engine size (cm^3)	950	1000	1200	1400	1500	1800	2000	2200
Fuel consumption (mpg)	62	57	55	48	45	42	40	36

  a Draw a scatter graph for this data.
(Hint: Use 'broken' scales. Start the horizontal axis at 900 cm^3 and let 1 cm = 100 cm^3. Start the vertical axis at 30 and let 2 cm = 10 mpg.)

  b Draw a line of best fit on the scatter graph.

  c Describe the strength and type of correlation shown.

  d Use the line of best fit to estimate:

      i the consumption for a car with engine size 1300 cm^3

      ii the engine size of a car that has a consumption rate of 50 mpg.

  e Explain why the line of best fit should not be used to estimate the fuel consumption for cars with an engine size greater than 2200 cm^3.

5 In a survey on weekly spending habits six families recorded the amount they spent in one week on groceries.
The results are shown in the table.

Family size	2	3	4	4	6	6
Amount spent (£)	50	65	80	94	120	135

  a Plot the data as a scatter graph.

  b Describe the relationship shown by the scatter graph.

  c Draw a line of best fit on the scatter graph.

  d Use your line of best fit to estimate the weekly spend on groceries by:

      i a family of size 5

      ii a single person (a family of size 1).

  e Which of your estimates in part **d** is the least reliable?
Give a reason for your answer.

  f Explain why you should not use your line of best fit to estimate the weekly spend by a family of nine people.

21.4 Time series

CAN YOU REMEMBER

- How to plot points on a graph?
- How to work out the mean, mode, median and range of data?

IN THIS SECTION YOU WILL

- Understand the meaning of 'time series'.
- Learn to draw and interpret line graphs for time series.
- Learn when to use time series graphs to make estimates and predictions.

A graph with a time scale along the horizontal axis is called a *time series*.
A time series graph has data whose values change over time.
The time period could be minutes, hours, weeks, months or years.
The points in a time series graph are joined by straight lines.

To interpret a time series, look carefully at the scale.
These two graphs show the same data.

Graph A makes it look as if
sales are increasing rapidly.

Graph B shows the same increase, but
gives a more accurate picture.

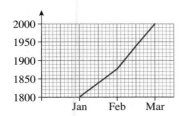

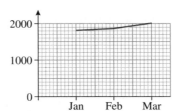

Example 1

George records the number of ripe tomatoes he picks during an eight-week period over the summer.
The results are shown in the table.

Week	1	2	3	4	5	6	7	8
Number of tomatoes	4	9	21	28	24	17	6	2

a Draw a time series graph showing the number of tomatoes picked over the eight-week period.

b Describe the pattern in the data shown by the graph.

Solution 1

a

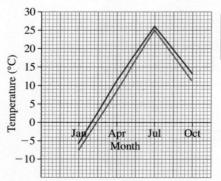

b Only a few tomatoes are picked at the beginning and end of the period. Most are picked in the middle weeks. Probably most of the tomatoes ripened around the same time, during these middle weeks.

Two sets of data can be compared by drawing their time series on the same axes.

Example 2

The table shows the average maximum daytime temperatures for two cities in Canada.

City	Average maximum daytime temperatures (°C)			
	January	April	July	October
Montreal	−6	11	26	13
Quebec	−8	8	25	11

a Draw time series graphs for the two cities on the same axes.
b Which city is generally warmer throughout the year?
c What is the range of temperature for Quebec?

Solution 2

a Plot the point −6 at January, 11 at April and so on.
Repeat for Quebec using a different colour.
Use a key to explain which colour represents which city.

b The temperature for Montreal is always higher than the temperature for Quebec.
So Montreal is warmer than Quebec.
c Quebec: lowest temperature = −8°C   highest temperature = 25°C
Range = 25 − −8 = 33°C

Exercise A

1 The heating bills, in pounds, over two years for a terraced house are shown in the table.

Quarter to	Jul 04	Oct 04	Jan 05	Apr 05	Jul 05	Oct 05	Jan 06	Apr 06
Heating costs (£)	25	38	55	75	32	43	68	70

   a Draw a time series graph.
   b Which bill was the highest?

2 The weekly attendances at a cinema are shown in the following table.

Week	1	2	3	4	5	6	7	8	9	10
Attendance	250	245	160	220	260	275	300	265	195	220

   a Draw a time series graph.
   b Which week had the highest attendance?
   c Work out the range of these attendances.

3 The number of patients missing appointments at a doctor's surgery each day over a two-week period is shown in the table.

Day	Week 1					Week 2				
	Mon	Tues	Wed	Thurs	Fri	Mon	Tues	Wed	Thurs	Fri
Number of patients	5	8	12	2	1	6	9	10	3	2

   a Draw a time series graph of this data.
   b Describe any pattern shown by the time series graph.
   c Calculate the mean number of patients per day missing appointments.

4 The average number of passengers catching the first Doncaster to London King's Cross train is recorded for each quarter. The table shows the results for 3 years.

Year	2003				2004				2005			
Quarter	1	2	3	4	1	2	3	4	1	2	3	4
Average number of passengers	56	68	82	75	61	74	90	88	72	80	104	99

   a Draw a time series graph for this data.
   b What is the range of the data for 2005?
   c Describe two patterns in the data.

5 The time series graph shows the share price, in pence, of a retail company.

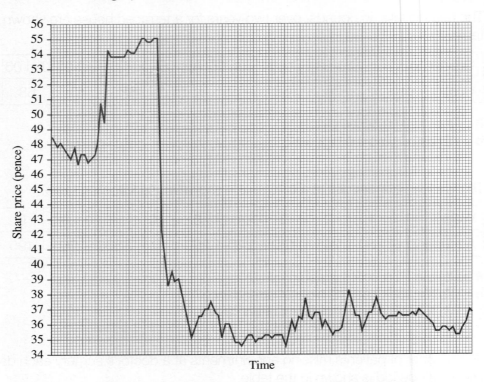

a What was the maximum price of this share over this period?

b After a takeover bid that failed the price of the share dropped dramatically. By how much did the share price fall before it rose again?

c Calculate the range of this share price.

d In what way is the graph misleading?

6 Geoff and Betty are both traffic wardens.
The table shows the number of parking tickets they issued over a six-day period.

Day	1	2	3	4	5	6
Geoff	23	16	19	25	21	20
Betty	8	32	11	13	28	10

a Draw two time series graphs on the same axes.

b Compare the numbers of tickets given by Geoff and Betty.

Time series graphs can be used to estimate missing data values.
Estimates within the range of data given (interpolation) are fairly reliable.
Estimates outside the range of data given (extrapolation) may not be reliable, as the pattern may not continue in the same way.

Example 3

A new-born baby is weighed at birth and every week for the first eight weeks of its life. The table shows the results in kilograms for baby Niles with two results missing.

Week	0	1	2	3	4	5	6	7	8
Weight (kg)	5.2	4.9	5.1	5.4	5.7	6.0			6.6

a Draw a time series graph for this data.
b Estimate baby Niles's weight after seven weeks.
c Predict Niles's weight after nine weeks.
d Which of the answers to parts **c** and **d** is more reliable? Explain your answer.

Solution 3

a

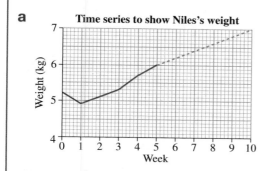

Time series to show Niles's weight

b About 6.4 kg.

c Draw an extension to the line.
Estimate for 9 weeks is 6.8–6.9 kg.

d The estimate for seven weeks is more reliable because it is within the given data (interpolation).
The estimate for nine weeks is less reliable, as it is outside the given data (extrapolation). It is not certain that the previous pattern in the data will continue beyond week eight.

Exercise B

1 Each week a baby rabbit is weighed. The graph shows its weekly weight up to week five.
In week six the rabbit weighed 107 g and in week ten its weight was 125 g.

    a Copy and complete the graph. Join the points with straight lines.

    b Use the graph to estimate the rabbit's weight in:

        i week seven

        ii week 11

    c Explain why it would not be sensible to use the graph to estimate the weight of the rabbit in week 20

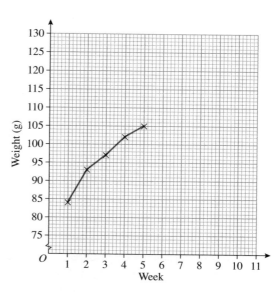

2   The graph shows the cost of insuring
a car over an eight-year period.

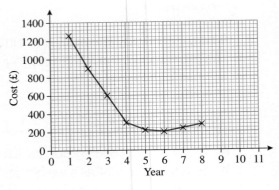

   a   For how many years did the cost fall?
   b   Give a reason why the cost may
have risen again after year 6
   c   In year 9 the cost doubled from
that in year 8
In years 10 and 11 the cost
then fell slightly each time.
Sketch how the graph may
look for years 9–11

3   Josh records the amount of money that he spends each month on his credit card.
His results for 11 months of 2005 are shown in the time series graph.

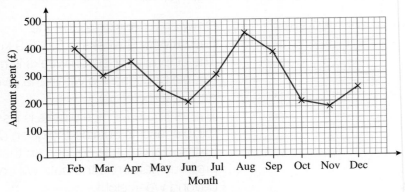

   a   Calculate the range of the amounts spent.
   b   Calculate the mean amount spent.
   c   Use your mean value in part **b** to estimate how much Josh spends in
January 2006
   d   Plot the mean value from part **b** as an estimate for the amount spent in
January 2006
   e   Why might your estimate in part **d** be unreliable?

4   Each day Jayne records the time it takes her to complete the
Rubik's cube puzzle.
The times are shown in the table.

Day	1	2	3	4	5	6	7	8	9	10
Time (s)	360	340	320	285	240	120	135	100	95	100

   a   Draw a time series graph for this data.
   b   Describe a pattern in the data.
   c   Is Jayne likely to ever complete the puzzle in under 60 seconds?
Explain your answer.
   d   Explain why it is not sensible to calculate the average of these times and use it
to estimate the time to complete the puzzle for day 11

5 Use the information and graphs below to answer the following questions.

  a Calculate the greatest difference between the maximum and minimum monthly temperatures in Cologne.

  b Calculate the range of the maximum daily temperatures in Cologne in the period 11–25 August 2005.

  c **i** Draw two time series graphs on the same axes to show the average maximum temperatures in °C for Torrejon and Madrid.

   ii Compare the average maximum temperatures in Torrejon and Madrid.

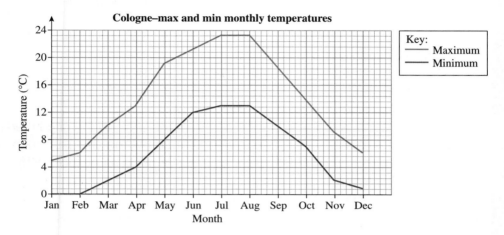

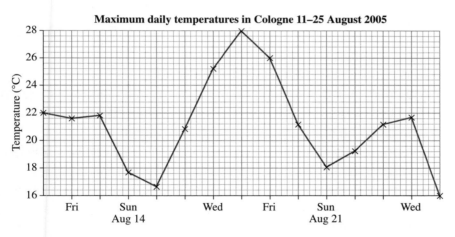

temperature (°C)	Jan	Feb	Mar	Apr	May	Jun	Jul	Aug	Sep	Oct	Nov	Dec
Torrejon	9.7	11.9	15.0	17.2	23.0	27.0	31.8	31.2	26.7	19.3	12.8	9.5
temperature (°C)	Jan	Feb	Mar	Apr	May	Jun	Jul	Aug	Sep	Oct	Nov	Dec
Madrid	5.3	6.7	9.7	12.0	16.1	20.8	24.6	23.9	20.5	14.7	9.3	6.0

Chapter summary

- The angle of each sector of a pie chart is in proportion to the amount of information it represents.
- There are 360° in a full circle.
- The angles of the sectors in a pie chart add up to 360°.
- To draw a pie chart:
  Step 1: When the total number is a multiple or factor of 360, calculate the angle for one item. OR
  When the total number is not a multiple or factor of 360, calculate the fraction of the whole that each sector represents.
  Step 2: Calculate the angle for each sector.
  Step 3: Check that the sum of all of the angles equals 360°.
  Step 4: Draw a circle.
  Draw a straight line (a radius) from the centre of the circle to the circumference.
  Use a protractor to measure accurately and then draw the angle for each sector.
  Complete the pie chart by labelling each sector or using a key (not both).
- To interpret a pie chart:
  Step 1: Measure the angle for a sector.
  Step 2: Work out what fraction of the whole the sector represents.
  Step 3: Calculate the fraction of the total amount.
- On a pie chart, the largest sector represents the modal group.
- In a stem and leaf diagram:
  - the data is written in order
  - a key is needed; for example 1 | 7 represents 17
- The mode, median and range can be found from a stem and leaf diagram.
- A stem and leaf diagram shows the shape of a distribution.
- The raw data can be read from a stem and leaf diagram.
- Scatter graphs are used to investigate relationships between two sets of data.
- A scatter graph may show a link or *correlation* between two variables.
- Correlation can be shown by a line of best fit. This is a straight line which is as close to the points as possible, drawn by eye. The line should have roughly the same number of points above it as below it.

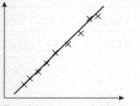

Positive correlation

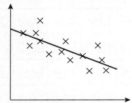

Negative correlation

No correlation
The points are not close
to a straight line.
There is no linear relationship
between the two variables.

- The closer the points are to a straight line, the stronger the correlation.

Strong correlation
(points close to a
straight line)

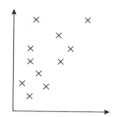

Weak correlation
(points follow a general
pattern)

- A line of best fit should only be used to estimate values within the range of a set of data. This is called *interpolation*.
- The line of best fit must not be extended beyond the actual data to make predictions, because there is no evidence that any pattern in the data will continue. Extending the line outside the data values is called *extrapolation*.
- A time series graph shows data whose values change over time.
- To interpret a time series, look carefully at the scale.
- Time series graphs can be used to estimate or predict missing data values. Estimates within the range of data given (interpolation) are fairly reliable. Estimates outside the range of data given (extrapolation) may not be reliable, as the pattern may not continue in the same way.

Chapter review

1 The graph shows the number of passengers going through airports in the UK between 1953 and 2004

   a Use the graph to estimate the number of passengers going through UK airports in 1980

   b Use the graph to estimate in which year the number of passengers was 120 million.

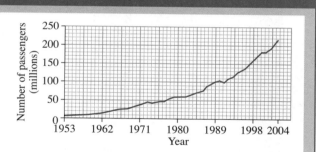

2 **a** Write down the type of correlation shown in each of the scatter graphs below.

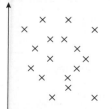

Scatter graph i

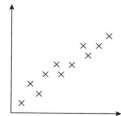

Scatter graph ii

b The marks for a group of pupils who sat two tests are shown in the scatter graph opposite.

  i Draw a line of best fit on a copy of the graph.

  ii Use your line of best fit to estimate the French test mark for a pupil who scored 50 marks in the Physics test.

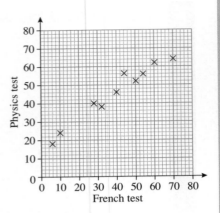

3 Abigail listed the favourite summer sports of the pupils in her class.

Sport	Tennis	Cricket	Swimming	Athletics	Golf
Number of pupils	7	6	11	4	2

Abigail wants to illustrate this information with a pie chart.

a How many degrees on the pie chart will represent one student?

b How many degrees on the pie chart will represent the students whose favourite summer sport is swimming?

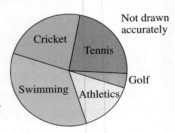

4 The stem and leaf diagram shows the number of miles travelled by a doctor on call each day for 21 days.

```
1 | 1  6  8  8
2 | 0  0  2  2  3  5  9
3 | 2  4  5  6
4 | 4  5  6
5 | 0  7
6 | 6
```

Key: 1 | 6 represents 16 miles travelled

a Find the range of this data.

b What is the median value?

c On how many days did the doctor travel between 30 and 60 miles?

5 The table shows the type of weather James recorded in his diary over 30 days.

a Display the data in a fully labelled pie chart.

b What was the modal type of weather?

Type of weather	Number of days
sunny	10
rain	9
cloudy but dry	8
snow	1
fog	2

6 The pie chart shows the proportions of destination countries for people going on holiday.

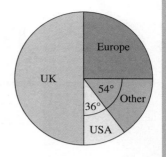

   a What proportion of people went on holiday in the UK?

   b 200 people went on holiday in Europe. How many people went on holiday altogether?

   c Work out the number of people who went on holiday in the USA.

7 The time that eight teenagers spent on their mobile phones and spent watching TV one day is recorded in the table.

Time on mobile phone (minutes)	20	30	30	50	60	60	70	70
Time spent watching TV (minutes)	60	50	40	45	35	25	15	20

   a Plot this data as a scatter graph.

   b Draw a line of best fit on your scatter graph.

   c Describe the relationship shown in the scatter graph.

8 Cambford College carried out a survey of the number of students in each year 13 class during the last teaching period of a day.

The results were: 9 12 15 19 10 6 12 18 20 12 19 8 14 9 22 21

Copy and complete the stem and leaf diagram to show these results.

```
0 |
1 |
2 |
```

Key: .... | ...... represents .... students

9 The table shows the type of transport used by 80 commuters. Draw and label a pie chart to represent this information.

Type of transport	Number of commuters
Car	35
Bus	25
Bike	18
Walk	2

10 A number of people were asked how many car journeys they had taken in a week. The results are shown in the stem and leaf diagram.

```
0 | 7
1 | 1   5   5   6   9
2 | 0   1   2   4   4   5   9
3 | 2   5   8
4 | 2
```

Key: 1 | 5 represents 15 car journeys

   a How many people were asked?

   b What was the median number of car journeys?

   c Work out the range of the number of car journeys.

Mental and written methods

22.1 More about squares, square roots, cubes and cube roots

To *square* a number, multiply it by itself.
For example, $6^2 = 6 \times 6 = 36$

The *square numbers* up to 15^2 are:

$1^2 = 1$	$2^2 = 4$	$3^2 = 9$	$4^2 = 16$	$5^2 = 25$
$6^2 = 36$	$7^2 = 49$	$8^2 = 64$	$9^2 = 81$	$10^2 = 100$
$11^2 = 121$	$12^2 = 144$	$13^2 = 169$	$14^2 = 191$	$15^2 = 225$

The inverse of squaring a number is finding its square root.

For example, $\sqrt{144} = 12$ because $12 \times 12 = 144$

Also, $-12 \times -12 = 144$. So the square root of 144 is also -12

This is written as $\sqrt{144} = 12$ or -12 or $\sqrt{144} = \pm 12$

Any positive number has both a positive and a negative square root.

To cube a number, multiply it by itself 3 times.

$1^3 = 1 \times 1 \times 1 = 1$ $\qquad$ $2^3 = 2 \times 2 \times 2 = 8$

$3^3 = 3 \times 3 \times 3 = 27$ $\qquad$ $4^3 = 4 \times 4 \times 4 = 64$

$5^3 = 5 \times 5 \times 5 = 125$ $\qquad$ $10^3 = 10 \times 10 \times 10 = 1000$

The inverse of cubing a number is finding its cube root, written $\sqrt[3]{}$.

For example, $\sqrt[3]{125} = 5$ because $5 \times 5 \times 5 = 125$

Learn:
- the square numbers up to 225 and their corresponding square roots
- the cubes of 1, 2, 3, 4, 5 and 10 and the corresponding cube root.

They are often used in calculations.

Example 1

Work out the value of $13^2 + 2^3$

Solution 1

From the tables above $13^2 = 169$, $2^3 = 2 \times 2 \times 2 = 8$

$13^2 + 2^3 = 169 + 8 = 177$

Square and cube numbers can be used to work out other squares and cubes.

Example 2

Use the square numbers up to 225 to work out:

a 20^2 **b** 400^2 **c** 40^3 **d** 0.4^3

Solution 2

a $20^2 = (2 \times 10)^2 = 2^2 \times 10^2 = 4 \times 100 = 400$

b $400^2 = (4 \times 100)^2 = 4^2 \times 100^2 = 16 \times 10\,000 = 160\,000$

c $40^3 = (4 \times 10)^3 = 4^3 \times 10^3 = 64 \times 1000 = 64\,000$

d $0.4^3 = \left(\dfrac{4}{10}\right)^3 = \dfrac{4^3}{10^3} = \dfrac{64}{1000} = 0.064$

Square roots can be found using the square root button on a calculator. Make sure you know how to work out square roots using your own calculator.

Exercise A

1 Write down the values of each of the following:
     a 1^2 **b** 9^2 **c** 12^2 **d** 15^2 **e** 7^2 **f** 13^2 **g** 11^2 **h** 14^2

2 Work out the values of each of the following:
     a $4^2 + 12^2$ **b** $5^2 + 14^2$ **c** $12^2 + 7^2$ **d** $13^2 + 2^2$
     e $15^2 - 12^2$ **f** $11^2 - 10^2$ **g** $14^2 - 11^2$ **h** $15^2 - 13^2$

3 Work out the values of each of the following:
     a 30^2 **b** 50^2 **c** 110^2 **d** 200^2
     e 800^2 **f** 1200^2 **g** 7000^2 **h** $14\,000^2$

4 Work out the values of each of the following:
     a 20^3 **b** 50^3 **c** 300^3 **d** 4000^3

5 Use the square numbers up to 225 to work out:
    a 0.1^2 **b** 0.5^2 **c** 0.8^2 **d** 0.9^2 **e** 1.5^2 **f** 1.3^2 **g** 1.1^2 **h** 1.4^2

6 Use the cube numbers up to 125 to work out:
    a 0.2^3 **b** 0.3^3 **c** 0.5^3

7 Write down the positive and negative values of each of the following:
    a $\sqrt{36}$ **b** $\sqrt{81}$ **c** $\sqrt{121}$ **d** $\sqrt{225}$
    e $\sqrt{100}$ **f** $\sqrt{144}$ **g** $\sqrt{196}$ **h** $\sqrt{169}$

8 Write down the values of each of the following:
    a $\sqrt[3]{8}$ **b** $\sqrt[3]{27}$ **c** $\sqrt[3]{125}$

9 Copy and complete the following sentences using consecutive integers:
    a   The positive square root of 20 is between .... and ....
    b   The positive square root of 75 is between .... and ....
    c   The positive square root of 125 is between .... and ....
    d   The positive square root of 150 is between .... and ....
    e   The negative square root of 20 is between .... and ....
    f   The negative square root of 75 is between .... and ....
    g   The negative square root of 125 is between .... and ....
    h   The negative square root of 150 is between .... and ....

10 Work out the values of each of the following using **positive** square roots:
    a $12^2 + \sqrt{225}$ **b** $\sqrt{144} - 3^3$ **c** $\sqrt{121} + \sqrt{144}$ **d** $5^3 + \sqrt{196}$
    e $\sqrt{225} - \sqrt{81}$ **f** $10^3 - \sqrt{169}$ **g** $\sqrt{169} + 4^3$ **h** $\sqrt{225} + \sqrt{225}$

11 Use a calculator to show that $\sqrt{56}$ is greater than 7.4 and less than 7.5

12 $196 = 4 \times 49$
    Use a calculator to show that $\sqrt{196} = \sqrt{4} \times \sqrt{49}$

A square number has an integer (whole number) square root.

Example 3

Explain how you know that
a   10   and   **b**   40   are not square numbers.

Solution 3

a   10 is between the square numbers 9 and 16
    So the positive square root of 10 is between $\sqrt{9} = 3$ and $\sqrt{16} = 4$
    $\sqrt{10}$ is not a whole number, so 10 is not a square number.

b   The positive square root of 40 is between 6 and 7 so 40 is not a square number.

Exercise B

1 Write down the square numbers from the list:

16   30   49   81   90   121   140   196

2 Explain how you know that 200 is **not** a square number.

3 Harriet says that the units digit of a square number is always one of the following:

0   1   4   5   9

Give an example to show that she is **not** correct.

4 $\sqrt{2916} = 54$

Write down the values of:

a $\sqrt{291\,600}$ **b** $\sqrt{29.16}$ **c** 0.54^2

5 Andrew says that all even square numbers are also multiples of 4. Give an example where this is true.

6 Here is a pattern using squares and cubes:

$1^2 = 1^3$
$(1 + 2)^2 = 1^3 + 2^3$
$(1 + 2 + 3)^2 = 1^3 + 2^3 + 3^3$

a   Write down the sixth line of the pattern.

b   Use a calculator to check that the pattern works for the sixth line.

7 a   Copy and complete the table for square numbers up to 225

Number	1		2		3		4		5		...	
Square number	1		4		9		16		25		...	
Difference		3		5		7		9				

b   What do you notice about the differences?

8 Use a calculator to find two integers between which $\sqrt{850}$ lies.

9 Use a calculator to find the greatest square number that is less than 1000

10 Use a calculator to find the smallest square number that is greater than 1000

11 Use a calculator to find two integers between which $\sqrt[3]{200}$ lies.

22.2 One significant figure and bounds

Quantities are *rounded* to make data or measurements more manageable.
A rounded number is an approximation of the accurate value of the number.

It is often sensible to round the answer to a calculation.
For example, using a calculator the answer to an area calculation is 4.121 134 1 m².
It is sensible to round this answer to 4 m².

The most *significant* digit in a number is the digit with the largest place value.

For example, in the number 7008 the most significant digit is 7, the thousands digit.
This is called the first significant figure.

Number	First significant figure	Second significant figure	Third significant figure	Fourth significant figure
7008	7 thousands	0 hundreds	0 tens	8 units
0.004 95	4 thousandths	9 ten thousandths	5 hundred thousandths	

Notice that all the digits after the first non-zero digit are significant, even the zeros.

Example 1

Round each number to one significant figure:
a 923.456   **b** 0.004 95

Solution 1

a The most significant figure is the 9. It has value 900
So for this number, rounding to one significant figure means rounding to the nearest hundred.
The number is between 900 and 1000. The digit 2 in the tens column shows that it is closer to 900
Answer = 900

b The most significant figure is the 4. It has value 0.004
So for this number, rounding to one significant figure means rounding to the nearest thousandth (0.001).
The number is between 0.004 and 0.005. The digit 9 in the ten thousandths column shows that it is closer to 0.005
Answer = 0.005

To round to one significant figure, round to the place value of the most significant digit in the number. A number rounded to one significant figure has only one non-zero digit.

Example 2

Darren spends £5 correct to the nearest pound.
What are the minimum and maximum amounts that Darren could have spent?

Solution 2

4.5 is the smallest number that rounds to 5
£4.50 is the lower bound. The minimum amount is £4.50
5.5 is the smallest number that rounds to 6, which means that £5.50 rounds up to £6
So £5.49 is the largest amount that rounds down to £5
£5.49 is the upper bound. The maximum amount is £5.49

Example 3

A bag contains 120 sweets correct to two significant figures.
What are the least and greatest possible numbers of sweets in the bag?

Solution 3

The least number of sweets is 115, because 115 is the smallest number that rounds to 120
The greatest number of sweets is 124, because 124 is the largest number that rounds to 120

Exercise A

1 Round the following numbers to one significant figure:

a 21	**b** 18	**c** 47	**d** 34
e 97	**f** 129	**g** 432	**h** 899
i 201	**j** 1200	**k** 3070	**l** 2008

2 Round the following decimals to one significant figure:

a	0.14	**b**	0.25	**c**	0.73	**d**	0.87
e	0.042	**f**	0.058	**g**	0.039	**h**	0.077
i	0.0708	**j**	0.0045	**k**	0.003 05	**l**	0.004 745

3 Round the following decimals to one significant figure:

a	8.7	**b**	1.55	**c**	21.8	**d**	1.71
e	8.34	**f**	3.76	**g**	9.14	**h**	12.6
i	142.1	**j**	203.5	**k**	591.4	**l**	301.2

4 The following amounts of money are given to the nearest pound.
Write down the maximum and minimum possible amounts of money for each amount.

a	£3	**b**	£10	**c**	£15	**d**	£30	**e**	£100	**f**	£2000

5 Three students guess the amount of money they each have in their pockets.
These are their answers:

£5   £2   £3.20

They are all correct to the nearest 10 pence.
What is the least amount that they could have altogether?

In a 100 metre sprint, two runners both
have a time of 10.3 seconds.

These times are rounded to three significant figures.

The exact times are between 10.25 seconds and
10.35 seconds.

10.25 seconds and 10.35 seconds are called
the *bounds* or *limits*.

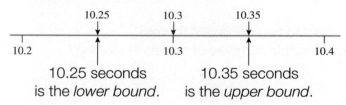

10.25 seconds   10.35 seconds
is the *lower bound*.   is the *upper bound*.

Example 5

A bag of sand weighs 20 kg:

a to the nearest   **b** to the nearest   **c** to the nearest half
kilogram   5 kilograms   a kilogram

In each case write down the upper and lower bounds of the amount of sand in the bag.

Solution 5

a Lower bound = 19.5 kg   **b** Lower bound = 17.5 kg   **c** Lower bound = 19.75 kg
Upper bound = 20.5 kg   Upper bound = 22.5 kg   Upper bound = 20.25 kg

Exercise B

1 The following quantities are given to the nearest whole number.
Write down the lower and upper bounds for each quantity.

a 5 grams   **b** 10 metres   **c** 25 kg   **d** 50 litres
e 124 miles   **f** 4 pints   **g** 100°   **h** 32 cm

2 The following measures are each given to one significant figure.
Write down the lower and upper bounds for each number.

a 20 grams   **b** 40 km   **c** 100 metres   **d** 6 pints
e 200 feet   **f** 0.2 litres   **g** 0.05 mm

3 The distance from Manchester to Birmingham is 90 miles to the nearest 5 miles.
Tom drives from Manchester to Birmingham and back again.
What is the shortest distance his journey could be?

4 Repeat question **1** parts **a–d** where the quantities are given to the nearest
   a five units   **b** half a unit

5 Repeat question **2** parts **a–c** where the quantities are given to the nearest 10 units.

22.3 Estimation

CAN YOU REMEMBER

- How to round numbers to one significant figure?
- How to divide by a decimal?

IN THIS SECTION YOU WILL

- Round to one significant figure in order to estimate answers to calculations.
- Understand that answers can be checked using estimation.
- Check answers by approximating values to one significant figure.

The answer to a calculation can be estimated using approximations.
Round each value in the calculation to one significant figure.

In the calculation $\dfrac{19.8 \times 50.2}{99}$

19.8 rounds to 20   50.2 rounds to 50   99 rounds to 100

So an estimate of the answer to the calculation is $\dfrac{20 \times 50}{100} = \dfrac{1000}{100} = 10$

Using a calculator, the exact answer to $\dfrac{19.8 \times 50.2}{99} = 10.04$

So the estimate is close to the exact answer.

Example 1

Use approximations to estimate the value of:

a 4.9×30.4

b $59.7 \div 10.3$

Solution 1

a 4.9×30.4
Rounding each value to one significant figure gives:
$5 \times 30 = 150$
4.9×30.4 is approximately equal to 150

b $59.7 \div 10.3$
Rounding each value to one significant figure gives:
$60 \div 10 = 6$
$59.7 \div 10.3$ is approximately equal to 6

Example 2

Estimate the cost of 9.8 metres of pipe at 39 pence per metre.

Solution 2

The calculation for the cost is 9.8×39 pence.
Rounding each value to one significant figure gives: 10×40 pence $= 400$ pence $= £4$
9.8 m of the pipe costs approximately £4

Exercise A

1 Use approximations to estimate the value of each of the following:

a $8.9 + 6.2$	**b** $1.2 + 8.4$	**c** $9.3 + 3.6$
d $2.7 + 8.1$	**e** $4.6 + 9.1$	**f** $8.2 + 10.4$
g $20.1 + 29.7$	**h** $6.1 - 4.2$	**i** $7.9 - 1.1$
j $9.8 - 3.1$	**k** $6.7 - 2.3$	**l** $19.9 - 5.01$
m $10.2 - 9.99$	**n** $39.6 - 20.3$	

2 Use approximations to estimate the value of each of the following:

a 6.1×8.7	**b** 1.03×7.98	**c** 9.99×2.17
d 14.9×1.98	**e** 7.1×3.2	**f** 5.8×8.8
g 3.89×6.04	**h** 10.2×7.14	**i** 3.14×21.98
j 4.68×5.21		

3 Use approximations to estimate the value of each of the following:

a $3.85 \div 2.01$	**b** $9.9 \div 1.89$	**c** $18.2 \div 3.7$
d $11.2 \div 1.78$	**e** $29.3 \div 3.05$	**f** $39.8 \div 5.2$
g $59.6 \div 5.59$	**h** $83.4 \div 19.7$	**i** $49.5 \div 10.1$
j $99 \div 20.2$		

4 Use approximations to estimate the value of each of the following:

a $\dfrac{2.8 \times 8.7}{3.1}$

b $\dfrac{4.2 \times 4.9}{9.9}$

c $\dfrac{6.03 \times 5.98}{6.2}$

d $\dfrac{3.9 \times 5.9}{1.9}$

e $\dfrac{7.2 \times 4.1}{2.02}$

f $\dfrac{10.16 \times 8.02}{19.7}$

g $\dfrac{8.3 \times 3.9}{7.9}$

h $\dfrac{29.2 \times 2.11}{5.79}$

5 Use approximations to estimate the value of each of the following:

a $\dfrac{203.1 \times 1.9}{3.8 + 6.1}$

b $\dfrac{104.3 \times 5.9}{1.8 + 4.3}$

c $\dfrac{975 \times 3.1}{0.9 + 1.9}$

d $\dfrac{52.2 \times 4.1}{8.6 + 0.9}$

e $\dfrac{38.3 + 62.5}{5.9 - 1.07}$

f $\dfrac{28.9 - 5.43}{7.12 - 1.95}$

6 Estimate the cost of:
   a 5 ice creams at 99 p
   b 20 biros at 49 p
   c 4.2 metres of cloth at 99 p per metre
   d 19 pens at £1.99 each
   e 8.7 kg of fruit at 31 p per kg
   f 31 litres of diesel at 97 p per litre
   g 18 drinks at £1.07 each
   h 11 books at £18.99 each.

7 Use the formula
   $$\text{Distance} = \text{speed} \times \text{time}$$
   to estimate the distance for each of the following journeys:
   a 20.3 mph for 9.7 hours
   b 42.1 km/h for 1.2 hours
   c 68 mph for 3 hours 10 minutes
   d 96 km/h for 4 hours 50 minutes.

8 Use the formula
   $$\text{Average speed} = \dfrac{\text{distance}}{\text{time}}$$
   to estimate the average speed for each of the following journeys:
   a 98 miles in 1 hour 56 minutes
   b 103 km in 2 hours 5 minutes
   c 3200 miles in 10.5 hours
   d 10 000 metres in 30 minutes 22 seconds. Give your answer in metres per hour.

9 Use a calculator to work out the exact answers to question **4**.
   If they are very different to your estimates, check your working.

Example 3

Sian calculates the answer to 3.5×0.61 to be 0.2135
a   Estimate an answer to her calculation using approximations.
b   Is her answer correct? Explain how you know.

Solution 3

a   Rounding each value to one significant figure gives:
    $4 \times 0.6 = 2.4$
    The correct answer is approximately 2.4
b   Sian is not correct. The decimal point is not in the correct place.
    The correct answer is 2.135

Example 4

Use approximations to estimate the value of: $\dfrac{310 \times 29}{0.49}$

Solution 4

$\dfrac{310 \times 29}{0.49}$ Rounding each value to one significant figure gives $\dfrac{300 \times 30}{0.5}$

Multiplying the numerator and denominator by 10 gives:

$\dfrac{300 \times 30}{0.5} = \dfrac{300 \times 30 \times 10}{0.5 \times 10} = \dfrac{90\,000}{5} = 18\,000$

$\dfrac{310 \times 29}{0.49}$ is approximately equal to 18 000

Exercise B

1 Use approximations to estimate the value of each of the following:

a $\dfrac{1.1}{0.51}$ b $\dfrac{6.03}{0.302}$ c $\dfrac{7.96}{0.17}$ d $\dfrac{4.89}{0.09}$

e $\dfrac{10.2}{0.49}$ f $\dfrac{9.05}{0.28}$ g $\dfrac{5.78}{0.59}$ h $\dfrac{7.11}{0.51}$

2 Use approximations to estimate the value of each of the following:

a $\dfrac{29}{0.51}$ b $\dfrac{41}{0.215}$ c $\dfrac{99}{0.19}$ d $\dfrac{39}{0.099}$

e $\dfrac{10.2}{0.51}$ f $\dfrac{29.7}{0.279}$ g $\dfrac{60.1}{0.58}$ h $\dfrac{49.6}{0.52}$

3 Use approximations to estimate the value of each of the following:

a $\dfrac{605 \times 4.99}{0.212}$

b $\dfrac{18.9 \times 22.3}{0.401}$

c $\dfrac{3.14 \times 7.9}{0.578}$

d $\dfrac{87.9 - 30.2}{0.62}$

e $\dfrac{6.9 \times 201}{0.71}$

f $\dfrac{5.04 \times 198.3}{0.507}$

4 Use approximations to estimate the value of each of the following:

a $\sqrt{5.1 \times 19.6}$

b $\sqrt{39.7 \times 41.2}$

c $\sqrt{\dfrac{1001}{9.7}}$

d $\sqrt{\dfrac{200.3}{49.5}}$

e $\sqrt{\dfrac{91\,200}{(10.1)^2}}$

f $\sqrt{\dfrac{413}{9.9^2}}$

g $\sqrt{\dfrac{3980}{5.01 \times 1.98}}$

h $\sqrt{\dfrac{1997}{2.05 \times 10.2}}$

5 Use approximations to estimate the value of each of the following:

a $3.9^2 + 6.2^2$

b $9.9^3 - 5.02^3$

c $6.01^2 + 7.95^2 - 2.88^2$

d $10.2^3 - 8.1^2$

e $\sqrt{3.99^2 + 3.01^2}$

f $\sqrt{4.96^2 + 12.02^2}$

g $\sqrt{10.21^2 - 6.04^2}$

h $\sqrt{4.1^3}$

6 Which is greater:

$7 \div 0.69,$ $\quad 4 \div 0.79$ $\quad$ or $\quad$ $5 \div 0.11?$

Use estimation to work out your answer.

7 Which is smaller:

$8 \div 0.81,$ $\quad 8 \div 0.41$ $\quad$ or $\quad$ $8 \div 0.21?$

a Use estimation to work out your answer.

b What do you notice about the divisor and the answer?

8

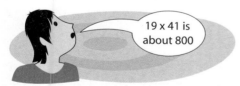

19 x 41 is about 800

Trevor is correct.
Explain how he worked it out.

9 Akuji says that $84 \times 9.1 = 7644$
Use estimation to show that he is
not correct.

10 Jill says that $19.1 \times 0.043 = 0.8213$
Use estimation to decide whether she
could be correct.

11 a Round each number to one significant figure to estimate the value of $\dfrac{3.98}{0.13}$

b Work out the difference between the estimated value of $\dfrac{3.98}{0.13}$ and the
exact value.

12 Use a calculator to work out the exact answers to questions **4** and **5**.
If they are very different to the estimated answers, check your working.

22.4 Reciprocals

CAN YOU REMEMBER

- How to multiply and divide by whole numbers, decimals and fractions?
- How to write an improper fraction as a mixed number?
- That to find the product of two numbers is to multiply them?
- How to input fractions on a calculator?

IN THIS SECTION YOU WILL

- Learn the meaning of the term 'reciprocal'.
- Work out the reciprocal of numbers in different forms: integers, fractions and decimals.
- Use reciprocals to carry out divisions.

The *reciprocal* of any number is 1 divided by the number. For example:

The reciprocal of 5 is $1 \div 5 = \dfrac{1}{5} = 0.2$

The reciprocal of $\dfrac{2}{3}$ is $1 \div \dfrac{2}{3} = 1 \times \dfrac{3}{2} = \dfrac{3}{2} = 1.5$

The reciprocal of a fraction is the fraction inverted.

Example 1

a   Work out the reciprocals of: **i** 7   **ii** −5
   Give your answers as fractions.

b   Work out the reciprocal of $\dfrac{1}{9}$

c   Work out the reciprocals of: **i** 0.3   **ii** $\dfrac{3}{4}$
   Give your answers as mixed numbers.

Solution 1

a   **i** Reciprocal of $7 = 1 \div 7 = \dfrac{1}{7}$ **ii** Reciprocal of $-5 = 1 \div -5 = \dfrac{1}{-5} = -\dfrac{1}{5}$

b   Reciprocal of $\dfrac{1}{9} = 1 \div \dfrac{1}{9} = 1 \times \dfrac{9}{1} = 9$

c   **i** Reciprocal of $0.3 = 1 \div 0.3 = \dfrac{1}{0.3} = \dfrac{1 \times 10}{0.3 \times 10} = \dfrac{10}{3} = 3\dfrac{1}{3}$

   ii Reciprocal of $\dfrac{3}{4} = \dfrac{4}{3} = 1\dfrac{1}{3}$

The product of any number and its reciprocal is equal to 1, e.g.

$5 \times \dfrac{1}{5} = 1$ or $\dfrac{2}{3} \times \dfrac{3}{2} = \dfrac{2 \times 3}{3 \times 2} = \dfrac{6}{6} = 1$

The reciprocal of a number can be worked out using a calculator.

Example 2

For each part, work out whether the numbers are reciprocals of each other.

a 8 and $\frac{1}{8}$ b -4 and $\frac{1}{4}$ c 0.25 and 4 d 0.6 and $1\frac{2}{3}$

Solution 2

If two numbers are reciprocals of each other their product is equal to 1

a $8 \times \frac{1}{8} = 1$

  8 and $\frac{1}{8}$ are reciprocals of each other.

b $-4 \times \frac{1}{4} = -1$

  -4 and $\frac{1}{4}$ are **not** reciprocals of each other.

c $0.25 \times 4 = 1$

  0.25 and 4 are reciprocals of each other.

d $0.6 \times 1\frac{2}{3} = \frac{6}{10} \times \frac{5}{3} = \frac{30}{30} = 1$

  0.6 and $1\frac{2}{3}$ are reciprocals of each other.

Exercise A

1 Write down the reciprocal of the following numbers.
Leave your answer as a fraction.

a 8 b 12 c 6 d 50
e 100 f 11 g -10 h -3
i -8 j -5 k -25 l -7

2 Write down the reciprocal of the following fractions.
Leave your answer as a whole number.

a $\frac{1}{8}$ b $\frac{1}{5}$ c $\frac{1}{7}$ d $\frac{1}{10}$ e $\frac{1}{11}$ f $\frac{1}{3}$

3 Write down the reciprocal of the following fractions.
Leave your answer as an improper fraction.

a $\frac{3}{8}$ b $\frac{2}{5}$ c $\frac{5}{7}$ d $\frac{3}{10}$ e $\frac{8}{11}$ f $\frac{2}{7}$

4 Work out the reciprocal of the following fractions.
Give your answer as a mixed number.

a $\frac{4}{7}$ b $\frac{2}{9}$ c $\frac{4}{11}$ d $\frac{7}{10}$ e $\frac{2}{15}$ f $\frac{3}{20}$

5 Work out the reciprocal of the following integers.
Leave your answer as a decimal.

a 4 b 10 c 2 d 5 e 100 f 20

6 Work out the reciprocal of the following integers.
Give your answer as a decimal to two decimal places.

a 3 b 9 c 11 d 13 e 7 f 19

7 Use a calculator to work out the reciprocal of the following mixed numbers.
Leave your answer as a fraction or as a decimal to two decimal places. The first one
has been done for you.

   a $1\frac{1}{2} = 1 \div 1\frac{1}{2} = 1 \div \frac{3}{2} = \frac{2}{3}$ **b** $3\frac{1}{4}$

   c $5\frac{1}{2}$ **d** $2\frac{1}{3}$ **e** $1\frac{1}{5}$ **f** $4\frac{1}{2}$

8 Use a calculator to work out the reciprocal of the following decimals.
Where necessary, give your answer as a decimal to two decimal places.

   a 0.2   **b** 0.5   **c** 0.8   **d** 0.75

   e 0.6   **f** 0.4   **g** 1.2   **h** 1.5

   i 2.5   **j** 3.2   **k** 4.5   **l** 2.7

9 For each part, work out whether the numbers are reciprocals of each other.

   a 7 and $\frac{1}{7}$ **b** 0.75 and 1.3   **c** 0.4 and 2.5

   d $2\frac{1}{3}$ and $\frac{3}{7}$ **e** 0.6 and $1\frac{2}{3}$ **f** $\frac{3}{4}$ and $1\frac{1}{3}$

10 Match the pairs of reciprocals.

One way of dividing by a number is to multiply by its reciprocal.

For example, $3 \div 5 = 3 \times \frac{1}{5} = \frac{3}{5}$ $\frac{2}{3} \div \frac{3}{4} = \frac{2}{3} \times \frac{4}{3} = \frac{8}{9}$

Exercise B

1 Use reciprocals to work out these divisions.

   a $7 \div 10$ **b** $6 \div \frac{1}{2}$ **c** $7 \div \frac{2}{3}$ **d** $\frac{1}{2} \div \frac{3}{5}$ **e** $\frac{3}{5} \div 7$ **f** $\frac{1}{4} \div \frac{3}{10}$

2 Here is a number machine.

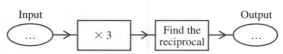

   a What is the output when the
input is 2?

   b What is the output when the input is -4?

   c What is the input when the output is 3?

3 Here is a number machine.

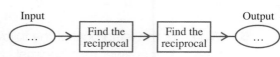

   a What is the output when the
input is 5?

   b What is the output when the input is 6?

   c What is the input when the output is $\frac{1}{2}$?

4 Which is the greater, the reciprocal of 5 or the reciprocal of 3?
Explain your answer.

5 x and y are both positive.
x is less than y.
Which is the greater, the reciprocal of x or the reciprocal of y?
Explain your answer.

6 I think of a number.
The reciprocal of the number is
equal to the number.
What number am I thinking of?

I think of a number. The reciprocal of the number is equal to the number. What number am I thinking of?

7 Pietro says, 'Zero has no reciprocal.'
He is correct.
Explain why he is correct.

8 Here is a number machine.
   a What is the output when the input is $1\frac{1}{4}$?
   b What is the output when the input is -7.5?
   c What is the input when the output is 10?

Input → Find the reciprocal → ÷ 0.5 → Output

9 Here is a number machine.
   a What is the output when the input is $\frac{1}{4}$?
   b What is the output when the input is 6?
   c What is the input when the output is 1?

Input → Find the reciprocal → Add 5 → Find the reciprocal → Output

10 Add together the reciprocal of 8 and the reciprocal of 10. Give your answer as a decimal.

11 I choose any number.
I square my number and then find the reciprocal of the answer.
If I find the reciprocal of my number first and then square it, the answer is the same.
Give an example to show that this works.

12 I choose any number.
I cube my number and then find the reciprocal of the answer.
If I find the reciprocal of my number first and then cube it, the answer is the same.
Give an example to show that this works.

Chapter summary

The square numbers from 1 (1^2) to 225 (15^2) are

$1^2 = 1$	$2^2 = 4$	$3^2 = 9$	$4^2 = 16$	$5^2 = 25$
$6^2 = 36$	$7^2 = 49$	$8^2 = 64$	$9^2 = 81$	$10^2 = 100$
$11^2 = 121$	$12^2 = 144$	$13^2 = 169$	$14^2 = 191$	$15^2 = 225$

- Any positive number has both a positive and a negative square root, e.g. $\sqrt{225} = \pm 15$

- The square numbers up to $15^2 = 225$ can be used to work out other squares.

- A square number has an integer (whole number) square root.

- Some cube numbers are
  $1^3 = 1 \quad 2^3 = 8 \quad 3^3 = 27 \quad 4^3 = 64 \quad 5^3 = 125 \quad 10^3 = 1000$

- The most significant digit in a number is the digit with the largest place value.

- To round to one significant figure, round to the place value of the most significant digit in the number.

- To round to two significant figures, round to the place value of the second significant digit in the number, and so on.

- The lower bound for a rounded value is the lowest possible value it could have.

- The upper bound for a rounded value is the highest possible value it could have. For example 7 g to the nearest gram: lower bound = 6.5 g, upper bound = 7.5 g.

- The answer to a calculation can be estimated using approximations. Round each value in the calculation to one significant figure.

- The *reciprocal* of any number is 1 divided by the number, e.g. the reciprocal of 5 is $1 \div 5 = \frac{1}{5}$

- The reciprocal of a fraction is the fraction inverted, e.g. the reciprocal of $\frac{2}{3}$ is $\frac{3}{2}$

- The product of any number and its reciprocal is equal to 1

- One way of dividing by a number is to multiply by its reciprocal, e.g. $7 \div 5 = 7 \times \frac{1}{5} \quad \frac{1}{2} \div \frac{3}{4} = \frac{1}{2} \times \frac{4}{3}$

Chapter review

1   Pat wants to calculate $53.76 \div 6.17$, but she doesn't have a calculator.
   a   Write each of the numbers in the calculation to the nearest whole number.
   b   Use these numbers to find an estimate of the answer to the calculation.

2   Estimate the value of $\dfrac{(3.8 \times 41.2)}{(6.15 + 1.87)}$

3   A tea-bag weighs 3 grams, correct to the nearest gram.
   a   What is the maximum possible weight of a tea-bag?
   b   What is the minimum possible weight of a tea-bag?

4   a   Write down the reciprocal of 3
   b   Write the reciprocal of $\frac{3}{8}$ as a mixed number.
   c   Which is greater, the reciprocal of 4 or the reciprocal of 5? Explain your answer.

5 Dina spends £12 on a DVD.
The amount is correct to the nearest pound.
Write down:
  a the minimum price that Dina could have paid
  b the maximum price that Dina could have paid.

6 **a** The number of students in a school is 1278
    What is the number of students to the nearest hundred?
  b Another school has 1100 students, correct to the nearest hundred.
    i What is the least possible number of students in the school?
    ii What is the greatest possible number of students in the school?

7 **a** Work out $\frac{1}{2} \div \frac{1}{8}$
  b Find the value of:
    i $\sqrt{196}$ **ii** $\sqrt{(2^2 \times 5^2)}$

8 Jason makes a true statement.
  a Write down the minimum age that Jason could be.
  b Write down the maximum age that Jason could be.

I am 16 years old.

9 Use your calculator to find the value of $\frac{(3.76 \times 0.82)}{(6.23 - 5.04)}$

Give your answer correct to three significant figures.

10 Calculate $\frac{(35.1 \times 27.9)}{24.8^2}$
  a Write down your full calculator display.
  b Write your answer to three significant figures.

11 Find the value of $\sqrt{(27.97^2 - 14.1^2)}$
  a Write down your full calculator display.
  b Write your answer to three significant figures.

Bearings and scales

23.1 Directions and bearings

IN THIS SECTION YOU WILL

- Learn how to describe directions as three-figure bearings.
- Draw and measure the bearing of one point from another.

Directions can be described using the points of the compass.

The angle between north and east is 90°.

North-east is exactly halfway between north and east. So the angle between north and north-east is 45°.

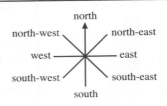

Directions can be described using *three-figure bearings*.

A three-figure bearing gives the direction as an angle measured from the north line in a clockwise direction.

For example:

The angle 72° only has two figures. To make a three-figure bearing, write zero before it, 072°.

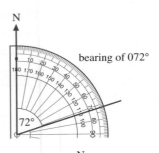

bearing of 072°

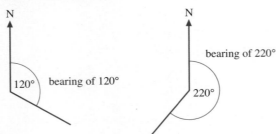

bearing of 120°

bearing of 220°

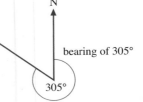

bearing of 305°

Example 1

Complete the sentence
The three-figure bearing for south-east is ......

Solution 1

The angle between north and south-east is 135°
in a clockwise direction.
The three-figure bearing for south-east is 135°.

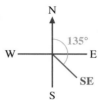

Example 2

Use a protractor to draw an accurate diagram to represent a bearing of 125°.

Solution 2

Step 1: Draw a vertical line to represent north.

N

Step 2: Measure an angle of 125° clockwise from the north line, and draw the line.

Step 3: Label the bearing.

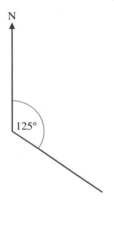

Exercise A

1   Copy and complete these sentences.
   a   The three-figure bearing for south is ......
   b   The three-figure bearing for north-west is ......
   c   The three-figure bearing for east is ......
   d   The three-figure bearing for south-west is ......

2   Copy and complete these sentences.
   a   A bearing of 270° represents the compass direction ....
   b   A bearing of 045° represents the compass direction ....
   c   A bearing of 225° represents the compass direction ....

3 Copy and complete the statements.
The first one has been done for you.
a   A bearing of 190° is between *south* and *south-west*.
b   A bearing of 060° is between .... and ....
c   A bearing of 110° is between .... and ....
d   A bearing of 340° is between .... and ....
e   A bearing of 250° is between .... and ....

4 Measure each of the following bearings.
Give your answers as three-figure bearings.

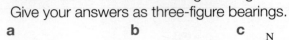

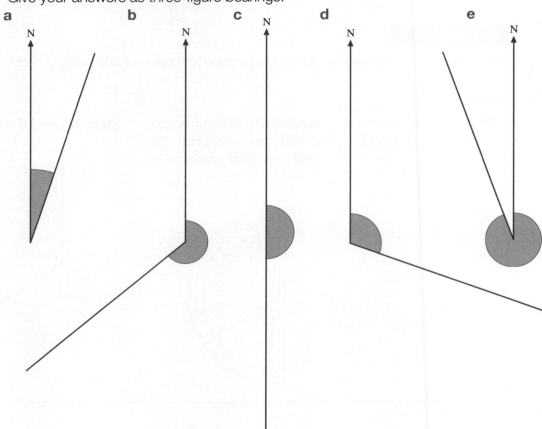

5 Use a protractor to draw accurate diagrams to represent these bearings.
a   035°   b   056°   c   081°   d   090°
e   098°   f   120°   g   142°   h   180°
i   195°   j   207°   k   235°   l   260°
m   270°   n   295°   o   326°   p   345°

6 a   Ben walks south. Then he turns around to face in the opposite direction.
Which direction is he now facing?
b   Megan walks south-east and turns around. Which direction is she now facing?
c   Owen walks north-east and turns around. Which direction is he now facing?

Example 3

The map shows the positions of a cottage, a church and a post office in a village.
a What is the bearing of the post office from the cottage?
b What is the bearing of the church from the cottage?

Solution3

a The angle between the north line at the cottage and the line to the post office measures 75°.
The three-figure bearing is 075°.
b The angle between the north line at the cottage and the line to the church measures 140°.
The three-figure bearing is 140°.

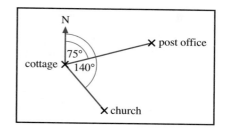

Example 4

Longbeck is on a bearing of 125° from Moorside.
Sketch the positions of Longbeck and Moorside.
Work out the bearing of Moorside from Longbeck.

Solution 4

Draw a north line at Longbeck.

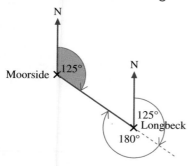

To face the direction of Moorside from Longbeck, the angle measured clockwise from north = 125° + 180° = 305°.
The bearing of Moorside from Longbeck is 305°.

Exercise B

1 The map shows the position of two ships, P and Q, and a lighthouse, L.
  a Measure the bearing of ship P from the lighthouse L.
  b Measure the bearing of ship Q from the lighthouse L.
  c Measure the bearing of ship P from ship Q.
  d What is the bearing of ship Q from ship P?

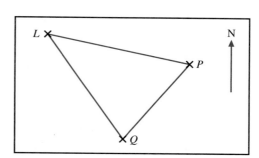

2 Cotfield is on a bearing of 128° from Newby.
What is the bearing of Newby from Cotfield? Use a sketch to help you.

3 Askham is on a bearing of 237° from Milburn.
What is the bearing of Milburn from Askham? Use a sketch to help you.

4 This is a map of an island.
P is a port.
A, *B* and *C* are villages.
H is a hotel.
  a Which village is on a bearing of 170° from the port *P*?
  b Which village is on a bearing of 045° from the hotel *H*?
  c Measure and write down the bearing of the hotel *H* from the port *P*.

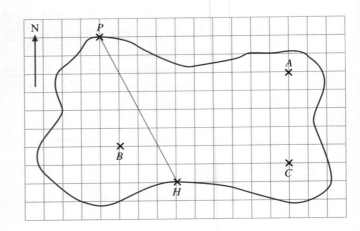

5 This map shows the positions of three towns, *R*, *S* and *T*, and an airport, *A*.
  a **i** Which town is due east of the airport?
      ii Write down the bearing of this town from the airport.
  Trace the diagram.
  b Measure and write down the bearing of town *R* from the airport.
  c Measure and write down the bearing of town *T* from town *R*.

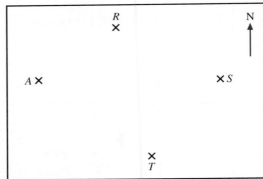

6 The diagram shows two points, *A* and *B*. Trace the diagram.
  a Measure the bearing of *B* from *A*.
  b Point *C* is east of *A*.
      Draw the line east of *A* on which *C* must lie.
  c Point *C* is north-east of *B*.
      Draw the line north-east of *B* on which *C* must lie.
  d Mark the position of *C* on your diagram.
  e Point *D* is on a bearing of 240° from *A* and 285° from *B*.
      Mark the position of *D* on your diagram.

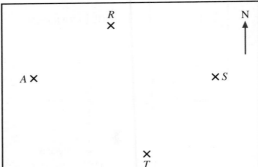

23.2 Maps and scale drawings

CAN YOU REMEMBER

- 100 centimetres = 1 metre, 1000 metres = 1 kilometre?
- How to construct a triangle using ruler and compasses?
- That three-figure bearings are measured clockwise from the north line?

IN THIS SECTION YOU WILL

- Make scale drawings.
- Use a given scale to calculate real distances.
- Use a scale to find distances between points on a map.
- Make scale drawings to show bearings.

Maps and plans are *scale drawings* of real-life situations. Each length on a scale drawing is in proportion to the real length.

There are two ways to describe a scale:

Using units
- Scale 1 cm to 2 km or scale: 1 cm represents 2 km
  A length of 1 cm on the scale drawing represents an actual length of 2 km.
- Scale 2 cm : 3 km
  A length of 2 cm on the scale drawing represents an actual length of 3 km.

Using ratio
- Scale 1 : 50 000
  A length of 1 unit on the map represents an actual length of 50 000 units.
- Scale 3 : 10 000
  A length of 3 units on the map represents an actual length of 10 000 units.

Example 1

The scale of a map is 1 cm represents 5 km.

a A road is 4.5 cm long on the map.
   Calculate the actual length of the road.

b The distance between two towns is 35 km.
   What is the distance between the two towns on the map?

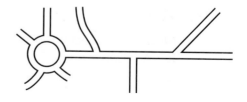

Solution 1

a 1 cm represents 5 km. So 4.5 cm represents 4.5 × 5 km = 22.5 km.
   The road is 22.5 km long.

b Actual distance = 35 km
   5 km is represented by 1 cm.   35 ÷ 5 = 7
   35 km = 7 × 5 km is represented by 7 × 1 cm.
   On the map the distance between the two towns is 7 cm.

Example 2

A rectangular garden measures 20 m by 12 m.
Use a scale of 1 cm : 4 m to make an accurate scale drawing of the garden.

Solution 2

1 cm represents 4 m.
Divide the number of metres by 4
to find the length on the drawing.
$20 \div 4 = 5$
20 m is represented by 5 cm on the scale drawing.
$12 \div 4 = 3$
12 m is represented by 3 cm on the scale drawing.

Scale 1 cm : 4 m

Example 3

On a map, the distance between two villages is 3.4 cm.
The scale of the map is 1 : 50 000
What is the actual distance, in kilometres, between these two villages?

Solution 3

1 cm represents 50 000 cm.
3.4 cm represents $3.4 \times 50\,000$ cm $= 170\,000$ cm.
Divide by 100 to convert centimetres to metres.
$170\,000$ cm $= 170\,000 \div 100 = 1700$ m
Divide by 1000 to convert metres to kilometres.
1700 m $= 1700 \div 1000 = 1.7$ km
The actual distance between the two villages is 1.7 km.

Exercise A

1   Models are made using a scale of 1 cm to represent 3 m.
   a   A model boat is 6 cm long. What is the length of the real boat?
   b   A model bus has length 2 cm. What is the length of the real bus?
   c   A model train is 40 cm long. What is the length of the real train?

2   Here is a sketch of a garden.
   Use a scale of 1 cm : 2 m to
   make an accurate scale
   drawing of this garden.

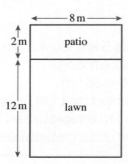

3 Here is a sketch of a triangle.
Use a scale of 1 cm : 100 mm to make
an accurate scale drawing of this triangle.

4 This is a plan of a field.
The scale is 1 cm represents 20 m.
The dotted line shows a path from one
corner of the field to the opposite corner.
  a Measure and write down the length
  of the dotted line.
  b Calculate the actual length of this path.

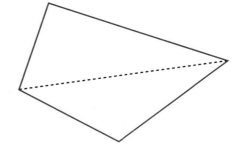

5 A map has a scale of 1 : 50 000
Two towns are 3 cm apart on the map. Find the actual distance, in kilometres,
between the two towns.

6 A plan of the floor of a house is drawn to a scale of 1 : 150
  a Calculate the actual dimensions of the floors of the following rooms.
  Give your answers in metres.
    i Lounge: measures 3 cm by 2.5 cm on the plan.
    ii Kitchen: measures 2.1 cm by 1.8 cm on the plan.
  b The hall floor measures 1.95 m by 1.2 m.
  Calculate the dimensions of the hall on the plan.

7 A map of a park has a scale of 1 cm : 50 m.
  a The boating lake and the playground are 220 m apart.
  How far apart are they on the map?
  b The café and the playground are 2.3 cm apart on the map.
  What is the actual distance from the café to the playground?

8 The diagram shows a map of a
cross-country course.
The runners start at *A* and pass
markers *B* and *C* to finish at *A*.
The scale of the map is 1 : 25 000
Calculate the total distance around
the course.
Give your answer in kilometres.

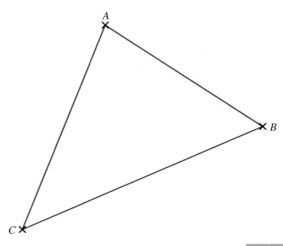

Example 4

The map of an island is shown. P and Q are the positions of two hotels on the island.
a   Work out the bearing of Q from P.
b   Calculate the actual distance from P to Q.
Give your answer in kilometres.

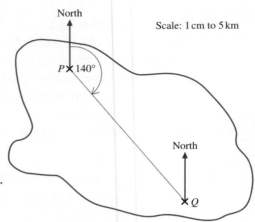

Scale: 1 cm to 5 km

Solution 4

a   Draw a line from P to Q. Measure the
bearing clockwise from the north line at P.
The bearing of Q from P is 140°.
b   The line PQ is 5 cm long.
The scale of the map is 1 cm to 5 km.
So 5×1 cm represents 5×5 km $= 25$ km.
The actual distance from P to Q is 25 km.

Example 5

Here is a sketch of a triangle with sides of 30 m, 40 m and 50 m.
Using ruler and compasses only, make an accurate scale
drawing of the triangle. Use a scale of 1 cm to represent 5 m.

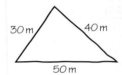

Solution 5

Calculate the length of each side on the drawing.
Divide the number of metres by 5 to find the length in cm.
$30 \div 5 = 6$ 30 m is represented by 6 cm on the drawing.
$40 \div 5 = 8$ 40 m is represented by 8 cm on the drawing.
$50 \div 5 = 10$ 50 m is represented by 10 cm on the drawing.
Construct the triangle accurately using ruler and compasses.

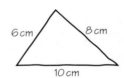

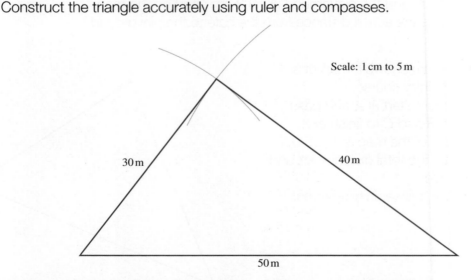

Scale: 1 cm to 5 m

Exercise B

1 The map shows the position of a ship, *P*, and a lighthouse, *L*.
  Scale: 1 cm represents 50 km.

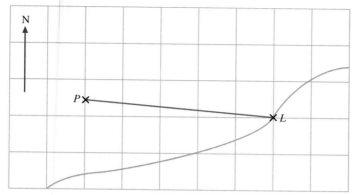

 a Measure and write down the bearing of *P* from *L*.
 b Another ship, *Q*, is 150 km due north of *L*.
   Mark the position of *Q* on a copy of the diagram.
 c Measure and write down the bearing of *Q* from *P*.
 d Use your diagram to work out the actual distance of ship *P* from ship *Q*.

2 A lighthouse, *L*, is on the coast. A ship, *P*, is 5 kilometres due north of *L*.
  Another ship, *Q*, is 8 kilometres due east of *L*.
 a Make an accurate scale drawing to show the positions of *L*, *P* and *Q*.
   Use a scale of 1 cm to 1 km. (It may be helpful to make a sketch first.)
 b Use your scale drawing to work out the distance of ship *P* from ship *Q*.

3 Richard draws a rough sketch of a triangle.
  Using ruler and compasses only, make an
  accurate scale drawing of Richard's triangle.
  Use a scale of 1 cm to represent 50 m.

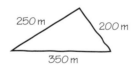

4 The diagram shows the positions of Alex's house, *A*,
  and the youth club, *Y*.
  The diagram is drawn to scale.
  Scale: 1 cm represents 100 m.
 a Use the diagram to calculate the actual
   distance from Alex's house to the
   youth club.
 b Measure and write down the bearing
   of Alex's house from the youth club.
 c Ben's house, *B*, is 450 metres from
   the youth club on a bearing of 120°.
   Trace the diagram and mark the
   position of *B* on it.

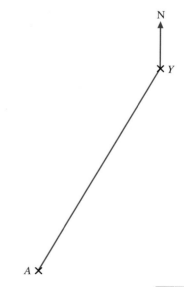

5 The diagram shows the positions of A and B.
The diagram is drawn to scale.
Scale: 1 cm represents 10 km.
  a What is the bearing of A from B?
  b Use the diagram to calculate the actual
    distance of B from A.
  c C is due south of B.
    i Write down the three-figure bearing
      of C from B.
    ii C is also on a bearing of 135° from A.
      Mark the position of C on a copy of the diagram.

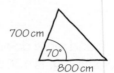

6 Here is a rough sketch of a triangle.
Make an accurate scale drawing
of this triangle.
Use a scale of 1 : 100

700 cm 70° *800 cm*

7 The map shows the position of three villages, A, B and C.
The scale has been missed off the map.

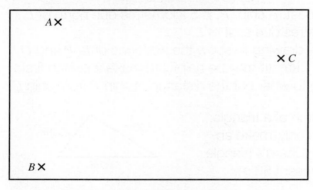

  a The distance from village A to village B is 8 km.
    What is the scale of the map?
  b Peter walks from village A to village B then to village C.
    He then returns directly to village A. Calculate the total distance he walks.

8 A tree is 18.6 m tall. A model of the tree is made to a scale of 2 cm : 3 m.
Calculate the height of the model.

9 An artist's studio is 8.5 m long and 5.5 m wide. A plan is drawn of the studio using
a scale of 3 cm : 5 m. Calculate the length and width of the studio on the plan.

10 The distance between town A and town B on a map is 14.4 cm.
The scale of the map is 2 : 25 000. Calculate the actual distance
from town A to town B. Give your answer in kilometres.

Chapter summary

- A three-figure bearing gives the direction as an angle measured from the north line in a clockwise direction.
- There are two ways to describe a scale.
  Using units:
  - Scale: 1 cm to 2 km or scale: 1 cm represents 2 km
    A length of 1 cm on the scale drawing represents an actual length of 2 km.

  Using ratio:
  - Scale 1 : 50 000
    A length of 1 unit on the map represents an actual length of 50 000 units.

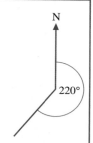

Chapter review

1 **a** The school is east of the church. Copy and complete the sentence. The church is .... of the school.

   b The shop is north-west of the station. Copy and complete the sentence. The station is .... of the shop.

2 Redbrough is on a bearing of 135° from Middleham.
   a Make a sketch of the positions of Redbrough and Middleham.
   b Work out the bearing of Middleham from Redbrough.

3 The diagram shows two points, A and B. Trace the diagram.
   a Measure the bearing of B from A.
   b Point C is due east of A and south-east of B. Mark the position of C on the diagram.

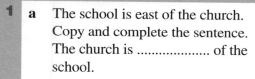

4   A is due north of B.
   The bearing of C from A is 125°.
   The bearing of C from B is 085°.
   Trace the diagram.
   Mark the position of C on the tracing.

A✗

5 The map shows part of a coastline, with a lighthouse and a coastguard station near the coast. The map is drawn to scale.

Scale: 2 cm represent 1 km.

An observer in the lighthouse can see a boat at sea. The boat is on a bearing of 132° from the lighthouse.

At the same time an observer at the coastguard station can see the same boat on a bearing of 065°.

a What is the distance, to the nearest 0.1 km, between the lighthouse and the coastguard station?

b Trace the diagram. Mark, with a cross, the position of the boat on the diagram.

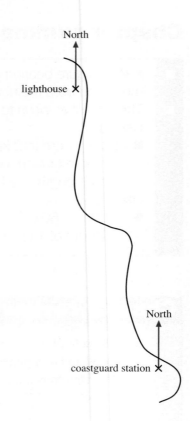

6 The map, which is drawn to scale, shows three towns, Axton, Bixton and Coxton. The towns are joined by straight roads.

a Measure and write down the three-figure bearing of Bixton from Axton.

b Measure and write down the three-figure bearing of Bixton from Coxton.

c A new straight road is to be built from Bixton on a bearing of 165°. Trace the diagram and draw this road as far as the point where it reaches the road between Axton and Coxton.

d A village, Duffield, is 2 km west of Bixton. Mark the position of Duffield with a cross on your tracing of the diagram.

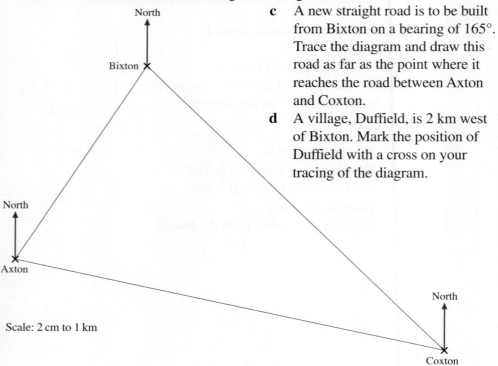

Scale: 2 cm to 1 km

7 A ship is on a bearing of 072° from a lighthouse.
What is the bearing of the lighthouse from the ship?

8 Tom draws a rough sketch of a triangle
with sides 120 m, 160 m and 200 m.
Using a ruler and compasses only, make
an accurate scale drawing of the triangle.
Use a scale of 1 cm to represent 20 m.
You **must** show clearly all your
construction arcs.

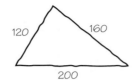

9 The diagram shows the positions of
Ben's house, *B*, and the local shop, *S*.
The map is drawn to scale.

Scale: 1 cm to 100 m

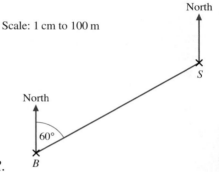

    a Use the diagram to calculate the actual
distance from Ben's house to the shop.

    b Measure and write down the three-figure
bearing of Ben's house from the shop.

    c Rachel's house, *R*, is 550 metres from
the shop on a bearing of 105°.
Trace the diagram and mark the position of *R*.

10 A model of a house is made using a scale of 1 cm to 1.5 m.
The kitchen is 3.6 m wide, 5.1 m long and 2.4 m high.
Work out the dimensions of the kitchen on the model.

Using and comparing data

24.1 Two-way tables

IN THIS SECTION YOU WILL

- Read information from a two-way table.
- Work out missing information in a two-way table.
- Design two-way tables.
- Complete a two-way table using data from a graph.

A *two-way table* shows two linked sets of information.

	Age 14	Age 15
Male	8	9
Female	4	7

For example, the table above shows the gender and age of a class of Year 10 pupils.

- There are eight boys aged 14
- There are nine boys aged 15
- There are four girls aged 14
- There are seven girls aged 15
- There are 17 boys (8 + 9).
- There are 11 girls (4 + 7).
- There are 12 students aged 14 (8 + 4).
- There are 16 students aged 15 (9 + 7).
- There are 28 students altogether (8 + 9 + 4 + 7).

Example 1

200 people are asked which petrol station they usually use.
An equal number of males and females are asked.
Altogether 90 people use station A, but only half that number use station C.

Use this information to complete
the two-way table.

	A	B	C
Males	52	32	
Females			

Solution 1

Total number of males = 100
Number of males who use station C = 100 − 52 − 32 = 16
90 people use station A.
Number of females who use station A = 90 − 52 = 38
Total number who use station C = total number who use station A ÷ 2
$$= 90 \div 2 = 45$$
Number of females who use station C = 45 − 16 = 29
Number of females who use station B = 100 − 38 − 29 = 33

	A	B	C
Males	52	32	16
Females	38	33	29

Exercise A

1 The two-way table shows the year
group and gender of the students
on a trip to France.
How many:
a Year 7 students went to France
b female students went to France
c students in total went to France?

	Year 7	Year 8	Year 9
Male	12	15	13
Female	20	18	12

2 The two-way table shows items sold in the restaurant and take-away sections of a
fish-and-chip shop during a 20-minute period.

	Fish	Sausage	Fishcake	Pie
Restaurant	12	8	5	7
Take-away	23	15	10	11

a Find the total number of pies sold
b Find the number of fish sold in the take-away
c Find the total number of sausages and pies sold in the restaurant.

3 The two-way table shows the destination and gender of 100 travellers.
One of the entries is missing.
a Copy and complete the table.
b How many travellers are female?
c How many travellers are going to the USA?
d Copy and complete this sentence.

	Europe	USA	Other
Female	26	13	4
Male	35	20	

'Seven more .... travellers than .... travellers are going to ....'

469

4 The two-way table shows the numbers of child, adult, home and away supporters at a football match.

	Home	Away
Adult	25 152	3087
Child	8559	231

    a How many home supporters are at the match?
    b How many children are at the match?
    c Charlie said, 'There were over 40 000 people at the match.' Is Charlie correct? Explain your answer.

5 The incomplete two-way table shows information about the visitors to a theme park.

	Young child	Teenager	Adult
Male	2304		565
Female	3121	1143	

    a Copy the table. Use the following information to complete it.
       ■ There are 2010 teenage visitors.
       ■ The total number of adults is half the total number of teenagers.
    b Calculate the total number of visitors.

6 The incomplete two-way table shows the numbers of different vehicles recorded on a local road and a motorway in a 30-minute period.

	Car	Lorry	Bus	Motorbike	Bicycle
Local road		4	6	3	19
Motorway	141		2	4	

    a Copy the table. Use the following information to complete it.
       ■ Bicycles are not allowed on the motorway.
       ■ 61 lorries are recorded in total.
       ■ There are six times more cars than buses on the local road.
    b Calculate the total number of vehicles on:
       i the local road   **ii** the motorway.
    c Copy and complete this sentence.
       'There were .... times more vehicles in total on the motorway than on the local road.'

Example 2

520 people play in a charity golf tournament.
$\frac{3}{4}$ of the players are male.
90% of the male players are professionals.
60% of the female players are professionals.
Design and complete a two-way table to show this information.

Solution 2

Step 1: Identify the headings for the table.
The information given is on male/female and professional players.
The headings are as opposite.

Step 2: Work out the entries
for the table.

	Professional	Non-professional
Male	351	39
Female	78	52

$\frac{3}{4}$ of the 520 players are male. $\frac{3}{4}$ of $520 = \frac{3}{4} \times 520 = 390$

There are 390 male players. So there are $520 - 390 = 130$ female players.
90% of the males are professional. 90% of $390 = 0.9 \times 390 = 351$
So $390 - 351 = 39$ males are non-professional.
60% of the female players are professional. 60% of $130 = 0.6 \times 130 = 78$
So $130 - 78 = 52$ females are non-professional.

Example 3

The dual bar chart shows the data for the number
of people joining a book club over three years.

a Construct a two-way table for the data
shown in the bar chart.

b Describe two patterns in the data.

c Work out the total number of people
joining the book club in the three years.

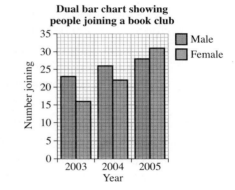

Dual bar chart showing
people joining a book club

Solution 3

a **Step 1:** Identify the headings for the table.
The information is given by year and
by gender.
Step 2: Read the entries for each section
from the bar chart.

	2003	2004	2005
Male	23	26	28
Female	16	22	31

b The numbers of both males and females joining increase each year.
The number of females is increasing at a faster rate than the number of males.

c Total number joining $= 23 + 16 + 26 + 22 + 28 + 31 = 146$

Exercise B

1 Josie travels around different countries. In total she makes 60 journeys, $\frac{1}{4}$ of them
at night.
During the day she travels by aeroplane five times, train 29 times and by boat.
During the night she travels by train for all journeys, except one.
Design and complete a two-way table to show Josie's travel by day and night.

2   The dual bar chart shows the
animals Javed sees in his
garden over three months.

   a   Construct a two-way table for
the data shown in the bar chart.

   b   How many animals does Javed
see in total?

   c   Javed says, 'I saw more cats
than hedgehogs and foxes
put together.'
Explain why Javed is correct.

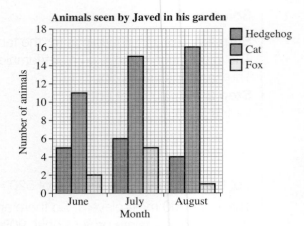

3   In a crowd of 5000 at a rugby match, 10% of the home supporters and 5% of the
away supporters are female. Four fifths of the crowd are home supporters.
Design and complete a two-way table for the data.

4   Jade records the musical tastes of 400 people and whether they are right- or left-
handed. The choices of music are classical, rock or pop.
52 right-handed people choose classical music.
Twice as many right-handed people choose rock music as classical music.
Of the 120 left-handed people, 12 choose classical and the rest choose rock or
pop in equal numbers.
Design and complete the two-way table for the data.

5   The two-way table shows some of the numbers of people from a town and the
country who own no car, one car or more than one car.
200 people from the town are asked which they own.
50 people from the country are asked which they own.

	Do not own a car	Own one car	Own more than one car
Town	24	86	
Country	1		19

   a   Copy and complete this two-way table.

   b   Construct a two-way table showing the **percentage** of people from the town in
each category and the **percentage** of people from the country in each category.

   c   Comment on one similarity and one difference in car ownership between people
from the town and people from the country.

   d   Which of the two two-way tables was more useful when trying to answer part **c**?

6   200 people from Wales, 200 people from England and 200 people from Scotland
are asked if they have visited London, Cardiff or Edinburgh.
The results are shown in the chart.

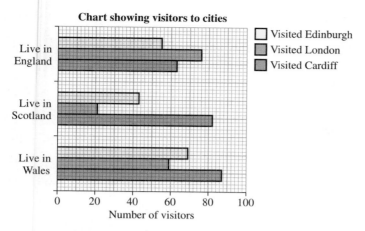

Chart showing visitors to cities

a Design and complete a two-way table for the results.
b Calculate the total number of people from the sample of 600 who have
  i visited Cardiff   **ii** visited London   **iii** visited Edinburgh.
c How many of the people who live in Scotland have visited either Cardiff or London?

24.2 Mean of a discrete frequency distribution

CAN YOU REMEMBER

■ How to find the mean for a set of data?
■ How to collect data into a frequency table?

IN THIS SECTION YOU WILL

■ Learn how to find the mean of a discrete frequency distribution.
■ Understand the meaning of the symbol Σ

A *frequency distribution* shows the number of times particular events have happened.

This frequency distribution table shows the number of times each number occurs when a fair dice is rolled 50 times.

A score of 1 happened 12 times, a score of 2 happened seven times, and so on.
The dice scores are *discrete* data.
They can only take the exact values 1, 2, 3, 4, 5, 6

Dice score	Frequency
1	12
2	7
3	10
4	6
5	5
6	10

Example 1

Find the mean score for this dice from the previous table.

Solution 1

$$\text{Mean} = \frac{\text{Total of all the values}}{\text{Total number of values}}$$

From the table there are:

12 scores of 1	$= 12 \times 1 =$	12
7 scores of 2	$= 7 \times 2 =$	14
10 scores of 3	$= 10 \times 3 =$	30
6 scores of 4	$= 6 \times 4 =$	24
5 scores of 5	$= 5 \times 5 =$	25
10 scores of 6	$= 10 \times 6 =$	60
	Total of all dice scores $=$	165

The total number of values of data $= 12 + 7 + 10 + 6 + 5 + 10 = 50$

Mean $= 165 \div 50 = 3.3$

In the example, the working out can be done in an extended table.

Dice score (x)	Frequency (f)	Frequency $\times$ dice score, fx
1	12	$12 \times 1 = 12$
2	7	$7 \times 2 = 14$
3	10	$10 \times 3 = 30$
4	6	$6 \times 4 = 24$
5	5	$5 \times 5 = 25$
6	10	$10 \times 6 = 60$
	$\Sigma f = 50$	$\Sigma fx = 165$

Add a column for calculating the total of each score.

Add a row at the bottom for calculating: the total number of data values (= total frequency) the total of all the values

Σf is read 'sigma f'. It means the sum of all the f values.

Σfx means the total of all the $f \times x$ values.

For this data $\Sigma fx = 165$

and $\Sigma f = 12 + 7 + 10 + 6 + 5 + 10 = 50$

$$\text{Mean} = \frac{\text{Total of all the values}}{\text{Total number of values}} = \frac{\Sigma fx}{\Sigma f} = \frac{165}{50} = 3.3$$

Example 2

The number of ice creams bought by 20 people during the interval of a theatre show is given in the table.

Number of ice creams	Frequency
0	5
1	11
2	3
3	1

Calculate the mean number of ice creams bought by these people.

Solution 2

Add a third column and an extra row to the table.

Number of ice creams (x)	Frequency (f)	fx
0	5	$5 \times 0 = 0$
1	11	$11 \times 1 = 11$
2	3	$3 \times 2 = 6$
3	1	$1 \times 3 = 3$
	$\Sigma f = 20$	$\Sigma fx = 20$

$$\text{Mean} = \frac{\Sigma fx}{\Sigma f} = \frac{20}{20} = 1$$

Exercise A

1 A spinner has scores 1, 2 and 3 on its sides. The spinner is spun 20 times. The table shows the results.

Number on spinner	Frequency
1	6
2	8
3	6

Find the mean score for this spinner.

2   The numbers of fish caught by some anglers one morning are shown in the table.

Number of fish caught (x)	Frequency (f)	fx
0	3	0
1	12	12
2	21	
3	10	
4	4	
	$\Sigma f =$	$\Sigma fx =$

   a   Copy the table and complete the fx column.
   b   Find Σfx
   c   Find Σf
   d   Find the mean number of fish caught.

3   The number of times the children in a class of 25 are going on holiday in the next year is recorded in the table below.

Number of holidays (x)	Frequency (f)	fx
0	6	
1	14	
2	4	
3	1	

   a   Copy the table and complete the fx column.
   b   Find the mean number of holidays next year for this class.

4   The table shows the number of days of rain per week, for 10 weeks.
   a   Copy and complete the table.
   b   Work out the mean number of days of rain per week.

Days of rain (x)	Frequency (f)	fx
0	1	
1	0	
2	2	
3	3	
4	1	
5	1	
6	2	
7	0	

5 The table shows the number of weddings held per week at a large hotel over several months.

Number of weddings (x)	Frequency (f)	fx
3	2	
4	6	
5	7	
6	4	
7	1	

Find the mean number of weddings held per week at the hotel.

6 This frequency distribution shows Colin's scores for 15 rounds of golf.

Golf score (x)	Frequency (f)
69	1
70	5
71	4
72	2
73	1
74	2

Calculate Colin's mean score for his 15 rounds of golf.

To calculate the mean from a bar chart, write the data in a frequency table.

Example 3

The bar chart shows the number of times Stirling has to stop at traffic lights on his journey from home to work each morning for four weeks.
Find the mean number of times Stirling had to stop.

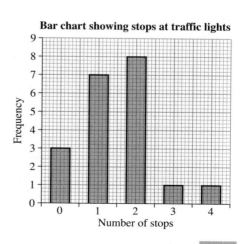

Bar chart showing stops at traffic lights

Solution 3

Write the information on the graph in a frequency distribution table.

Add a third column and an extra row.

$\text{Mean} = \dfrac{\Sigma fx}{\Sigma f} = \dfrac{30}{20} = 1.5$

Number of stops (x)	Frequency (f)	fx
0	3	$3 \times 0 = 0$
1	7	$7 \times 1 = 7$
2	8	$8 \times 2 = 16$
3	1	$1 \times 3 = 3$
4	1	$1 \times 4 = 4$
	$\Sigma f = 20$	$\Sigma fx = 30$

Example 4

The table shows the scores when a fair four-sided spinner is spun 50 times.

a Find y.

b Find the mean score.

Spinner score	Frequency
1	10
2	y
3	8
4	12

Solution 4

a The spinner was spun 50 times.

So $\Sigma f = 10 + y + 8 + 12 = 50$

$30 + y = 50$ Subtract 30 from both sides.

$y = 20$

b Replace y with 20 in the table. Add a third column and a bottom row.

Spinner score	Frequency	fx
1	10	10
2	20	40
3	8	24
4	12	48
	$\Sigma f = 50$	$\Sigma fx = 122$

$\text{Mean} = \dfrac{\Sigma fx}{\Sigma f} = \dfrac{122}{50} = 2.44$

Exercise B

1 The bar chart shows the number of people using taxis on a Saturday night. Find the mean number of people in a taxi.

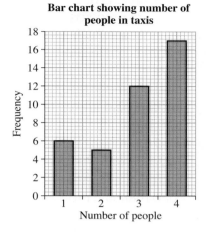

Bar chart showing number of people in taxis

2 a Find the mean of this frequency distribution.
  b If every number is increased by one but the frequencies stay the same, what would the new mean be?
  c Look at this frequency distribution:

Number	Frequency
3	4
4	3
5	2
6	1

Number	Frequency
6	4
8	3
10	2
12	1

  i Predict the mean of this distribution.
  ii Check your prediction by calculating the mean.

3 The numbers of red sweets in 50 mixed bags of sweets are counted. The table shows the results.
  a Find the value of y.
  b Find the mean number of red sweets per packet.
  c What is the range of the number of red sweets per packet?

Number of red sweets	Frequency
3	21
4	15
5	y
6	2
7	1
8	1

4   A shop sells kebabs and pizzas.
The shop opens at 5 pm.
The manager records the
number of each item sold each
hour from 5 pm to 6 pm over
20 days.

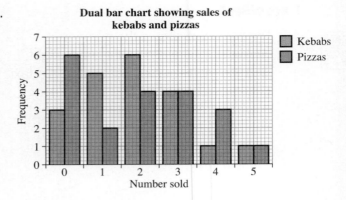

a   Find the mean number of
kebabs sold from 5 pm
to 6 pm.

b   Find the mean number of
pizzas sold from 5 pm to
6 pm.

A kebab makes a profit of 30p. A pizza makes a profit of 50p.

c   Use your answers to parts **a** and **b** to find the mean total profit made on kebabs
and pizzas from 5 pm to 6 pm.

5   The table shows information about the
number of runs scored in a cricket match.

The mean number of runs scored is 2.75

a   Work out Σf and an expression for Σfx.

b   Use your answers to **a** to show that $x = 1$

Number of runs	Frequency
x	2
2	4
3	7
4	2
5	1

6   The frequency distribution shows the number of times per week that Janet goes
swimming over the summer months.

Number of times	Frequency
1	7
2	3
3	1
4	1
n	m

a   The data is recorded over 13 weeks. Find m.

b   The mean of the frequency distribution is 2. Find n.

c   During the following 13 weeks, Janet's average goes down to one swim
per week. She never goes more than twice per week. She goes once per week
nine times.
How many times does she **not** go swimming at all in a week?

24.3 Comparing distributions

IN THIS SECTION YOU WILL

- Interpret the shape of a frequency distribution.
- Compare ranges and averages for frequency distributions, from charts, tables and diagrams.

A frequency distribution can be shown in a *frequency table* or on a *frequency diagram*, such as a bar chart or stem and leaf diagram.

To compare two frequency distributions, compare the range and the averages (mean, median or mode).

Example 1

The bar chart shows the number of goals scored in 50 matches by football team A.

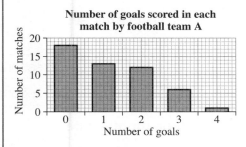

Football team B also played 50 matches.
Here is some information about the number of goals scored by team B.

Range of goals	5
Mean goals per match	1.6

Compare the number of goals scored by the two teams.

Solution 1

From the bar chart for team A:
The range of the number of goals scored by team A = 4 − 0 = 4
The range of the number of goals scored by team B = 5
The range is greater for team B, so team B has a wider spread of goals than team A.

Use the frequency distribution to work out the mean number of goals scored by team A.

Number of goals by football team A (x)	Frequency (f)	fx
0	18	0
1	13	13
2	12	24
3	6	18
4	1	4
	$\Sigma f = 50$	$\Sigma fx = 59$

The total number of goals is 59. The total number of matches is 50

Mean number of goals $= \dfrac{\Sigma fx}{\Sigma f} = \dfrac{59}{50} = 1.18$

The mean number of goals per match for team A is 1.18
The mean number of goals per match for team B is 1.6
The mean number of goals per match is greater for team B, so, on average, team B scored more goals per match than team A.

Exercise A

1 The new members of a gym are timed to complete a set of exercises.

Their results are shown on the right:

Three months later the same members are timed again to complete the same set of exercises.

Their results are also on the right:

Compare the range and the mean of the two sets of times.

New members

Range of times	35 seconds
Mean of times	85 seconds

Three months later

Range of times	22 seconds
Mean of times	68 seconds

2 One day ten students each choose a square metre of grassland at their school.
They count the number of worms in their square metre.
Their results are:

5   8   13   12   15   8   4   7   2   6

  a Write down the range of the number of worms.
  b Work out the mean number of worms.

The same students carry out a similar exercise at night.
Their results are summarised as: range = 18 worms; mean = 11.3 worms.
  c Compare the results for the day and the night.

3 A sample of 20 cars driving into a city centre is observed.
The numbers of people in each car are:

1 3 2 3 2 1 1 2 4 2 1 2 2 1 1 4 2 1 1 2

a Write down the range of the number of people per car.
b Work out the mean number of people per car.

The road is changed so that cars with only one person are only allowed to use one particular lane.
Another observation of the number of people in each car is then carried out.
The results have a range of 4 and a mean number of people per car of 2.2
Compare the results before and after the road change.

4 Each worker in a factory is asked how many hot drinks they have during one day.
The frequency distribution shows the results.

Number of hot drinks	Frequency
0	15
1	19
2	17
3	9

a Write down the range of the number of hot drinks.
b Work out the mean of the number of hot drinks.

The managers at the factory are also asked how many hot drinks they each have that same day. Their results had a range of 5 and a mean of 1.6
c Compare the number of hot drinks of the workers with those of the managers.

5 The frequency distribution shows the maximum daytime temperatures, in °C, in April.
a Write down the range of the maximum daytime temperatures in April.
b Work out the mean of the maximum daytime temperatures in April.

The maximum daytime temperatures in June of the same year have a range of 7 °C and a mean of 19 °C.
Compare the maximum daytime temperatures for these two months.

Maximum daytime temperature (°C)	Frequency
15	3
16	4
17	2
18	10
19	3
20	8

6 The bar chart shows the number of letters in each of the 50 words in a newspaper article.

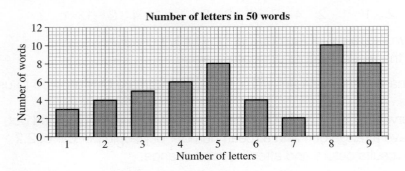

Number of letters in 50 words

a Calculate the range of the number of letters.

b Calculate the mean number of letters per word.

c In a similar article in a magazine it was found that the range of the number of letters was 10 and the mean number of letters per word was 6.4
Compare the lengths of the words in the newspaper with those of the magazine.

When comparing two sets of data, compare the same type of average for each data set. For example, compare the medians, the modes or the means. Do not compare a mean with a median!

The stem and leaf diagram shows the number of GCSE A*– C grades obtained by the pupils from Miss Brown's form.

Key: 0 │ 3 represents 3 A*– C grades

```
0 │ 1  2  3  5  5  7  7  7  8
1 │ 0  0  0  1
```

The number of GCSE A*– C grades obtained by the pupils from Mr Smith's form had a range of 9 and a median of 5
Compare the results for Miss Brown's form with Mr Smith's form.

Solution 2

From the stem and leaf diagram for Miss Brown's form the range of the number of GCSE A*– C grades is $11 - 1 = 10$

The range of the number of GCSE A*– C grades for Mr Smith's form is 9

The numbers of A*– C grades for Miss Brown's form are a little more spread out than for Mr Smith's form.

The median number of GCSE A*– C grades for Miss Brown's form is the middle value of the ordered stem and leaf diagram.

There are 13 pieces of data,

so median $= \dfrac{(13 + 1)}{2}$th = 7th value.

Key: 0 | 3 represents 3 A*– C grades

```
0 | 1  2  3  5  5  7 (7) 7  8
1 | 0  0  0  1
```

The median number of GCSE A*– C grades for Miss Brown's form is 7

The median number of GCSE A*– C grades for Mr Smith's form is 5

This suggests that the average number of GCSE A*– C grades for Miss Brown's form is greater than the average number of GCSE A*– C grades for Mr Smith's form.

Two bar charts or two stem and leaf diagrams can also be compared by looking at the shapes of the distributions.

Example 3

The bar charts show the number of children in each of 50 families taken from a city and each of 50 families taken from the countryside.

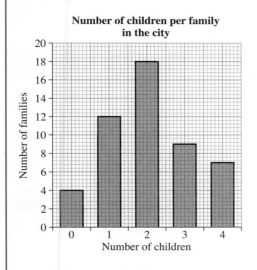

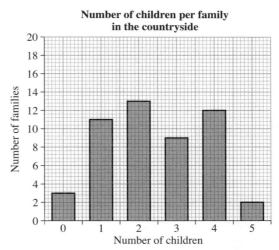

Compare the two distributions.

Solution 3

The range of the number of children per family in the city is $4 - 0 = 4$

The range of the number of children per family in the countryside is $5 - 0 = 5$

The mode for the number of children per family in the city is 2

The mode for the number of children per family in the countryside is 2

The means can also be calculated.

Number of children per family in the city (x)	Frequency (f)	fx
0	4	0
1	12	12
2	18	36
3	9	27
4	7	28
	$\Sigma f = 50$	$\Sigma fx = 103$

The mean number of children per family in the

$$\text{city} = \frac{\Sigma fx}{\Sigma f} = \frac{103}{50} = 2.06$$

Calculating the mean number of children per family in the countryside in the same way

gives $\dfrac{122}{50} = 2.44$

The table summarises these results.

There is a bigger spread of the number of children in the families in the countryside.

	City	Countryside
Range	4	5
Mode	2	2
Mean	2.06	2.44

The most common number of children in a family is 2, both in the city and in the countryside.

The means show that families in the countryside have, on average, more children.

Looking at the shapes of the bar charts, the bar chart for the children in the city families is fairly symmetrical, or balanced.

The bar chart for the number of children in the countryside families is not symmetrical. The bar for four children is quite high when compared with the city bar chart and this is the main cause of the higher mean value.

Exercise B

1 In an experiment divers are asked to hold their breath for as long as they can and record the length of time.

The stem and leaf diagram shows their results.

After practising several techniques to increase the time they can hold their breath, the same experiment is carried out.

```
Key: 5 | 3 represents 53 seconds
5 | 2  3  5  5  5  7  9
6 | 0  0  1  2  2  3  5  9
7 | 0  1  2  3
```

The results are:

After practising techniques

Range of times	15 seconds
Median of times	65 seconds

a Compare the times before and after the practising techniques.

b Has practising the techniques increased the length of time that these divers can hold their breath? Explain your answer.

2 John collects information about the number of cars in each of 70 households selected at random from a town and 70 households selected at random from a village. He summarises his results in two bar charts.

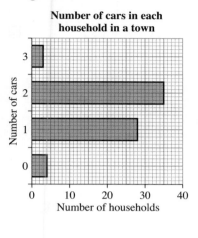

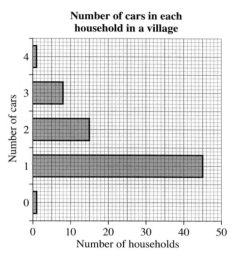

a Compare the number of cars in each household in the town with those from the village.

b John says that the number of cars from the households in the town is greater than the number of cars in the households in the village.
Is John correct? Explain your answer.

3 The stem and leaf diagrams show the number of first-class passengers using two trains from Leeds to London over a period of 15 Saturdays.

Train 1 passengers

> Key: 5 | 9 represents 59 passengers

```
5 | 7   7   8   9
6 | 0   2   2   3   5   5   5   6   8   9
7 | 2
```

Train 2 passengers

> Key: 5 | 2 represents 52 passengers

```
5 | 2   4   6   8   9
6 | 0   1   2   4   5   6
7 | 3   4   5   5
```

a Compare the number of first-class passengers for these two trains.

b A train company spokesman said that the number of first-class passengers is more consistent with train 2 than with train 1
Is he correct?
Explain your answer.

4 The dual bar chart shows the shoe sizes of the girls and the boys in Year 8 at a school.

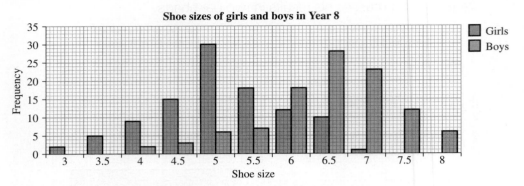

a Compare the girls' and the boys' shoe sizes.

b After another boy's shoe size is added to the data, the boys' range of shoe sizes increases by 0.5

Write down the two possible shoe sizes for this boy.

5 The bar chart shows the arrival times of 30 pupils at school on Monday.

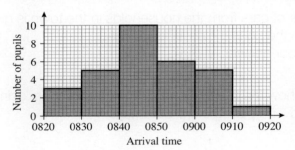

The stem and leaf diagram shows the arrival times of the same 30 pupils at school on Friday.

Key: 082 | 5 represents an arrival time of 0825

082	2	5	8			
083	0	2	5	8	9	
084	0	5	5	7	9	9
085	0	2	4	5	6	8	9
090	0	1	3	7	8	
091	2	5	6			
092	4					

a Explain why the maximum range of arrival times on Monday is 60 minutes.

b Compare Monday's arrival times with Friday's arrival times.

c Is there evidence that the pupils arrive earlier on Mondays than on Fridays? Give a reason for your answer.

d Explain why it is **not** possible to compare the mean arrival times.

Chapter summary

- A *two-way table* shows two linked sets of information.
- A *frequency distribution* shows the number of times particular events have happened.
- The mean of a discrete frequency distribution is found using the formula:

  $$\text{Mean} = \frac{\text{Total of all the values}}{\text{Total number of values}}$$

- To calculate the mean from a frequency table:
  - add a column to calculate fx
  - add a row and calculate Σf and Σfx
  - $\text{mean} = \dfrac{\Sigma fx}{\Sigma f}$

- To calculate the mean from a bar chart, write the data in a frequency table.
- To compare two frequency distributions, compare:
  - the range
  - one or more of the averages (mean, median or mode).
- If distributions are given as a bar chart or stem and leaf diagram, also compare the shapes of the distributions.

Chapter review

1 The two-way table shows information about the people entering a college one morning.

	Male	Female
Sixth-former	34	54
Adult	8	12

a Find the total number of females entering the college.
b How many people in total entered the college?

2 A spinner with numbers 10, 15 and 20 on its sides is spun 20 times.
The frequency distribution shows the results.

Score	Frequency
10	6
15	4
20	10

Find the mean score for this spinner.

3 The frequency table shows the number of games Andrew won in ten sets of tennis.

a Copy and complete the table.

b Find the mean number of games Andrew won.

Number of games (x)	Frequency (f)	fx
1	1	
2	0	
3	0	
4	2	
5	1	
6	5	
7	1	

4 40 families are asked how many adults there are in the family and how many cars the family owns. The two-way table shows the results.

a How many families own two cars?

b How many families have four adults?

c How many households have the same number of cars as adults?

	1 adult	2 adults	3 adults	4 adults
1 car	6	4	2	0
2 cars	1	4	8	1
3 cars	0	1	3	3
4 cars	0	1	1	5

5 The bar chart shows the number of pets owned by the students in a Year 10 class.

a What is the modal number of pets owned?

b Calculate the mean number of pets owned.

c Another student joins the class. The new student owns at least one pet but the mean value is reduced for the class. How many pets does the new student own?

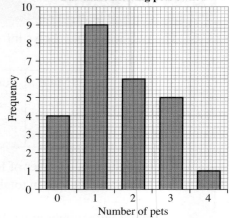

6 The two-way table shows the items Vicky sold over three days on an Internet auction site.

On Saturday she sold twice as many items as on Friday.

	Friday	Saturday	Sunday
CDs	3	6	8
DVDs	7		
Computer games	2	3	

Sunday represented 50% of all her sales over the three days.

Vicky sold five more CDs than computer games. Complete the table.

7 The table shows the salaries of 20 employees at a small firm.

Employee (salary)	Number of this type of employee
Manager (£50 000)	1
Team leader (£20 000)	4
Shift workers (£12 000)	15

a Find the mean salary at this small firm.
b Does the mean fairly represent the data?

8 The incomplete two-way table shows the film certificate of all the films shown at a cinema over three months.

Certificate/Month	June	July	August
U	3	7	15
PG	6	9	21
12	12	10	14
15	18		9
18		16	3

a The same number of films was shown each month.
Copy and complete the table.
b Describe a pattern in the data.
Give a possible explanation for the pattern.

9 A teacher asks pupils how many hours they revised for their GCSE Module 1 exam.
The results for six boys are:

10   13   12   4   18   21

a Work out the range of these numbers.
b Calculate the mean of these numbers.
c The number of hours a sample of girls revised for is summarised in the table.
Write down two comparisons between the number of hours of revision done by the boys and girls.

Range	Mean
12	10

10 Nigel's wine company sells three different volumes of wine in bottles. The table shows their sales yesterday. The average volume per bottle is 640 ml. Find x, the volume of a small bottle.

Size of bottle (volume)	Number sold
Large (1000 ml)	5
Medium (750 ml)	12
Small (x ml)	8

Percentages

25.1 Expressing one quantity as a percentage of another

CAN YOU REMEMBER

- How to express one quantity as a fraction of another?
- How to change from one unit to another?
- How to simplify a fraction (by cancelling common factors)?
- Simple conversions from fractions to percentages, e.g. $\frac{1}{2} = 50\%$, $\frac{1}{3} = 33.3\%$?

IN THIS SECTION YOU WILL

- Learn how to write one number as a percentage of another number.
- Use percentages to compare quantities using the same or different units.
- Learn how to write one quantity as a percentage of another quantity.

In this test, the score was 7 out of 10

7 written as a fraction of 10 is $\frac{7}{10}$

$\frac{7}{10} = \frac{70}{100} = 70\%$

7 written as a percentage of 10 = 70%.

To write a quantity as a percentage of another quantity:

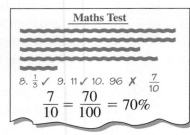

Maths Test

8. $\frac{1}{3}$ ✓ 9. 11 ✓ 10. 96 ✗ $\frac{7}{10}$

$$\frac{7}{10} = \frac{70}{100} = 70\%$$

Method 1
Step 1: Make sure that both quantities have the same units.

Step 2: Write the fraction
$$\frac{\text{first quantity}}{\text{second quantity}}$$ as a fraction
with a denominator of 100

Step 3: Write the fraction as a percentage:
for example, $\frac{55}{100} = 55\%$.

Method 2
Step 1: Make sure that both quantities have the same units.

Step 2: Use the formula:
$$\frac{\text{first quantity}}{\text{second quantity}} \times 100\%$$
For example,
$\frac{7}{10} \times 100\% = 70\%$.

Example 1

a Write 60 as a percentage of 150   **b** Write 3 kg as a percentage of 10 kg.
c Write 70 cm as a percentage of 1 metre.

Solution 1

a **Method 1**

Simplify the fraction $\dfrac{60}{150}$:

$$\frac{60}{150} = \frac{6}{15} = \frac{2}{5}$$

Write $\dfrac{2}{5}$ as a fraction with a denominator of 100

$$\frac{2}{5} = \frac{2 \times 20}{5 \times 20} = \frac{40}{100} = 40\%$$

Method 2

Use the formula:

$$\frac{\text{first quantity}}{\text{second quantity}} = \frac{60}{150}$$

$$\frac{60}{150} \times 100\% = 40\%$$

b **Step 1:** Both quantities have the same units.

Method 1

Step 2: $\dfrac{3\,\text{kg}}{10\,\text{kg}}$ simplifies by cancelling the

common units to $\dfrac{3}{10}$

$$\frac{3}{10} \times 100\% = 30\%$$

Method 2

$$\frac{3}{10} = \frac{3 \times 10}{10 \times 10} = \frac{30}{100} = 30\%$$

c **Step 1:** 1 metre = 100 cm   **Step 2:** $\dfrac{70\,\text{cm}}{1\,\text{metre}} = \dfrac{70\,\text{cm}}{100\,\text{cm}} = \dfrac{70}{100} = 70\%$

Exercise A

1 Copy and complete:

a $\frac{9}{10} = \frac{}{100} = \dots\%$ **b** $\frac{21}{50} = \frac{}{100} = \dots\%$ **c** $\frac{4}{25} = \frac{}{100} = \dots\%$

d $\frac{7}{20} = \frac{}{100} = \dots\%$ **e** $\frac{3}{4} = \frac{}{100} = \dots\%$ **f** $\frac{4}{5} = \frac{}{100} = \dots\%$

2 **a** Write 1 as a percentage of 10   **b** Write 3 as a percentage of 5
c Write 4 as a percentage of 16   **d** Write 8 as a percentage of 20
e Write 1 as a percentage of 4   **f** Write 18 as a percentage of 20
g Write 80 as a percentage of 160   **h** Write 50 as a percentage of 200

3 In each part, remember to simplify by cancelling the common units.
a Write 2 cm as a percentage of 8 cm.
b Write 4 litres as a percentage of 20 litres.
c Write 6 grams as a percentage of 25 grams.
d Write 9 cm³ as a percentage of 90 cm³.
e Write 4 kg as a percentage of 8 kg.
f Write 3 metres as a percentage of 10 metres.

4 In each part, change to common units. Then cancel the common units before converting to a percentage.

   a   Write 40 cm as a percentage of 1 metre (hint: 100 cm = 1 metre).

   b   Write 6 inches as a percentage of 1 foot (hint: 12 inches = 1 foot).

   c   Write 9 inches as a percentage of 3 feet.

   d   Write 20 cl as a percentage of 1 litre (hint: 100 cl = 1 litre).

   e   Write 300 grams as a percentage of 1 kg (hint: 1000 grams = 1 kg).

   f   Write 250 kg as a percentage of 1 tonne (hint: 1000 kg = 1 tonne).

   g   Write 75p as a percentage of £1

   h   Write 500 metres as a percentage of 1 kilometre (hint: 1000 metres = 1 km).

5 In each part, give your answer to one decimal place.

   a   Write 1 as a percentage of 3   **b**   Write 6 as a percentage of 9

   c   Write 5 as a percentage of 7   **d**   Write 9 as a percentage of 11

   e   Write 18 as a percentage of 27   **f**   Write 8 as a percentage of 13

   g   Write 7 as a percentage of 21   **h**   Write 25 as a percentage of 42

6 In each part, give your answer to one decimal place.

   a   Write 6 cm as a percentage of 9 cm.

   b   Write 5 tonnes as a percentage of 15 tonnes.

   c   Write 12 miles as a percentage of 72 miles.

   d   Write £14 as a percentage of £98

   e   Write 8 km as a percentage of 12 km.

   f   Write 25 kg as a percentage of 30 kg.

   g   Write 21 cl as a percentage of 26 cl.

   h   Write 12 cm² as a percentage of 34 cm².

7 Use the fact that 1 mile = 1760 yards to write 440 yards as a percentage of 1 mile.

8 2460 fish are caught in a net. 820 are too small and are thrown back in the sea.
What percentage of the fish is thrown back in the sea?
Write your answer to one decimal place.

9 936 people visit a theatre in London. 104 are from Yorkshire.
What percentage of the total is from Yorkshire?
Write your answer to one decimal place.

10 21 600 people attend a football match. 8640 support the away team.
What percentage of the total attendance supports the away team?

11 Belinda spends £97.62 at the supermarket.
£32.54 of this is on wine.
What percentage of her total bill is spent on wine?
Write your answer to one decimal place.

Exercise B

1 60 children visit a show. 36 are boys.
What percentage of the children are girls?

2 A shape has ten sides. Three of the sides are curved.
The rest are straight. What percentage of the sides is straight?

3 A bag contains 13 red marbles, seven blue marbles
and five yellow marbles.
What percentage of the marbles is **not** yellow?

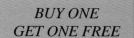

4 In test 1 a student scores 13 out of 20
In test 2 the same student scores 24 out of 30
In which test did the student do better?

5 A CD has 12 tracks. Four of the tracks were Number 1 singles.
What percentage of the tracks were not Number 1 singles?
Write your answer to one decimal place.

6 A shop has two offers.
Which is the better value?
Use percentages to explain
your answer.

> *BUY ONE
> GET ONE FREE*

> *BUY TWO GET
> THE THIRD FREE*

7 In test 1 a student scores 13 out of 15
In test 2 the same student scores 38 out of 45
In which test did the student do better?
Explain your answer by giving the percentage mark for each test.

8 An 800 ml bottle contains 500 ml of water.
Darren says that the bottle is more than 50% but less than 60% full.
Is he correct? Explain your answer.

9 A book contains 750 pages.
300 of the pages have pictures and no writing.
100 pages have pictures and writing.
The rest have just writing.
What percentage of the pages have pictures on them?
Give your answer to one decimal place.

10 A shop has two offers:

> *Spend £5
> Get £1 back*

> *Buy any three items
> of the same value
> Get the fourth free*

Which is the better value? Explain your answer.

25.2 Increasing and decreasing by a percentage

CAN YOU REMEMBER

- How to find a percentage of a quantity?
- How to use mental methods to work out 10%, 5%, 20%, 25%?

IN THIS SECTION YOU WILL

- Learn how to increase or decrease an amount by a percentage.
- Learn how to decrease an amount by a percentage.
- Use the multiplier method to increase or decrease an amount by a percentage.

There are two methods for working out the sale price.

Method 1
Work out the decrease,
10% of £17
Subtract the decrease
from the original price.
10% of £17 = 0.1 × £17
　　　　　　 = £1.70
Sale price = £17 − £1.70
　　　　　　 = £15.30

Method 2
　Original price = 100%,
　　 decrease = 10%
100% − 10% = 90%
90% written as a decimal = 0.9
Sale price = 90% of original price
　　　　　　 = £17 × 0.9 = £15.30
0.9 is called the *multiplier*.
New value = original value × multiplier

Example 1

a Increase 40 kg by 25%.

b Decrease £6.50 by 18%.

Solution 1

a **Method 1**
Work out the increase: 25% of 40 kg = 0.25 × 40 kg = 10 kg
Add on the increase to the original amount.
Increased amount = 40 kg + 10 kg = 50 kg

Method 2
Original = 100%, increase = 25%
100% + 25% = 125%
125% written as a decimal = 1.25, so the multiplier = 1.25
Increased amount = original amount × multiplier = 40 kg × 1.25 = 50 kg

b Use the multiplier method.
Original = 100%, decrease = 18%
100% − 18% = 82%
82% written as a decimal = 0.82, so the multiplier = 0.82
　Decreased amount = original amount × multiplier = £6.50 × 0.82 = £5.33

Exercise A

1 Increase each of the following quantities by 10%.

a	£200	**b**	1000 tonnes	**c**	900 people	**d**	300 buttons
e	80 cm	**f**	70 litres	**g**	40 pence	**h**	20 kg
i	£10	**j**	30 km	**k**	120 minutes	**l**	180°

2 Decrease each of the following quantities by 25%.

a	£400	**b**	800 tonnes	**c**	2000 fish	**d**	100 buttons
e	80 cm	**f**	60 g	**g**	8 litres	**h**	120 m
i	£16	**j**	32 miles	**k**	600 km	**l**	180°

3 Increase each of the following quantities by 5%.

a	£100	**b**	20 tonnes	**c**	500 fish	**d**	12 g
e	70 litres	**f**	£2.20	**g**	18 m	**h**	24 kg
i	£26	**j**	32 miles	**k**	36 km	**l**	90 minutes

4 Decrease each of the following quantities by 20%.

a	£100	**b**	40 people	**c**	50 fish	**d**	80 buttons
e	30 cm	**f**	12 g	**g**	18 m	**h**	24 kg
i	£26	**j**	32 miles	**k**	36 km	**l**	90 minutes

5
  a Increase 75p by 20%.
  b Increase £36 by 15%.
  c Increase 80 grams by 25%.
  d Increase £2.40 by 50%.
  e Decrease £20 by $2\frac{1}{2}$%.
  f Decrease 40 litres by 15%.

6 Write down the multiplier for each of the following percentage increases.
  a 18% **b** 22% **c** 30% **d** 70% **e** 100% **f** 8% **g** 6% **h** 9%

7 Write down the multiplier for each of the following percentage decreases.
  a 19% **b** 24% **c** 40% **d** 60% **e** 5% **f** 7% **g** 9% **h** 2%

8 Match the multipliers to the percentage changes.

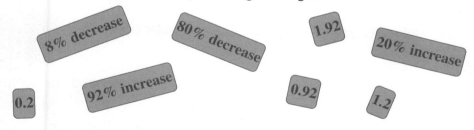

9 Use the multiplier method to work out the following.
  a Increase £4.50 by 12%.
  b Increase 82 cl by 18%.
  c Increase 90 g by 23%.
  d Increase £2.50 by 38%.
  e Increase $94 by 19%.
  f Increase 45 tonnes by 6%.

10 Use the multiplier method to work out the following.
  a Decrease £54 by 22%.
  b Decrease 90 minutes by 17%.
  c Decrease 34 kg by 8%.
  d Decrease 220 g by 53%.
  e Decrease £57 by 14%.
  f Decrease 75 litres by 7%.

Example 2

Calculate the price of the van including VAT.

'£3500 plus VAT at 17.5%'

Solution 2

Original amount = 100%, VAT = 17.5%
100% + 17.5% = 117.5%
117.5% written as a decimal = 1.175, so the multiplier = 1.175
  Price of van including VAT = original amount × multiplier
                = £3500 × 1.175 = £4112.50

Exercise B

1 A new car costs £15 000
After one year the value of the car
has decreased by 35%.
Work out the value of the car
after one year.

2 A meal in a restaurant costs £36
A service charge of 15% is added.
Work out the cost of the meal including
the service charge.

3 A statue is sold at an auction for £800
Commission is charged to the buyer
at 5% of the selling price.
What is the total cost of the statue
including the commission?

4 Amina invests £950 for one year
at 6% interest.
What is the total value of the
investment after one year?

5 Pablo has €750.
He spends 5% on clothes.
How much does he have left?

6 Harriet receives a
gas bill for £70
VAT is added at 5%.
How much is the total bill?

7 A computer costs
£450 plus
VAT at 17.5%.
What is the total cost of the computer?

£450
+ VAT

8 A man who weighed 14 stone
lost 6% of this weight.
Work out his new weight.

9 The area of a football pitch is 7000 m².
This is increased by 0.5%.
What is the new area of the football pitch?

10 A fashion shop sells 250 dresses
in a week. The following week,
sales decrease by 12%.
How many dresses are sold in
the following week?

11 The population of Somalia is 9.9 million.
It is estimated to be increasing at the rate
of 3.3% per year.
Calculate an estimate for the population
next year.

25.3 Finding a percentage change

CAN YOU REMEMBER

- How to express one quantity as a percentage of another?
- How to increase or decrease by a percentage?
- How to simplify a fraction?

IN THIS SECTION YOU WILL

- Learn how to work out an increase as a percentage.
- Learn how to work out a decrease as a percentage.

When a value increases or decreases, the change is often given as a percentage of the original amount.

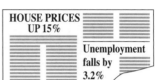

To calculate percentage change, use the formula

$$\text{Percentage change} = \frac{\text{Change (increase or decrease)}}{\text{Original amount}} \times 100\%$$

Example 1

The number of tickets on sale for a concert increases from 5000 to 6000
Calculate the percentage increase.

Solution 1

The increase in the number of tickets is 1000. The original number of tickets on sale was 5000

$$\text{Percentage increase} = \frac{\text{Increase}}{\text{Original amount}} \times 100\% = \frac{1000}{5000} \times 100\% = 20\%$$

Example 2

The weight of bags of potatoes is reduced from 15 kg to 10 kg.
Find the percentage reduction in the weight of the bags.

Solution 2

The reduction in the weight is 5 kg.
The original weight was 15 kg.

$$\text{Percentage reduction} = \frac{\text{Reduction}}{\text{Original amount}} \times 100\% = \frac{5 \text{ kg}}{15 \text{ kg}} \times 100\% = 33\tfrac{1}{3}\%$$

Exercise A

1 Work out the percentage change for each of the following.
    a Increasing 50 by 5
    b Increasing 30 by 6
    c Increasing 100 by 20
    d Decreasing 25 by 20
    e Decreasing 50 by 30
    f Decreasing 44 by 11

2 Work out the percentage change for each of the following.
    a Increasing from 40 to 50
    b Increasing from 100 to 130
    c Increasing from 160 to 200
    d Increasing from 48 to 60
    e Decreasing from 60 to 48
    f Decreasing from 80 to 40
    g Decreasing from 300 to 200
    h Decreasing from 72 to 18

3 Copy and complete the table.

	Initial quantity	Change	Final quantity	Percentage change
a	£20	£2 increase		
b	40 g	8 g increase		
c	36 litres		54 litres	
d	100 minutes	20 minute decrease		
e	18 kg	6 kg decrease		
f	70 km		35 km	

4 Match each statement to the correct percentage change.

In questions **5** to **8** give any decimal answers to one decimal place.

5 Work out the percentage change for each of the following.
    a Increasing £90 by £5
    b Increasing 76 g by 4 g
    c Increasing 84 litres by 24 litres
    d Decreasing 92 cm by 8 cm
    e Decreasing 124 kg by 24 kg
    f Decreasing 750 km by 100 km

6 Work out the percentage change for each of the following.
    a Increasing from 600 mm to 840 mm
    b Increasing from €1200 to €1250
    c Increasing from £185 to £200
    d Decreasing from $844 to $800
    e Decreasing from 580 km to 500 km
    f Decreasing from 72 hours to 50 hours

7 Which of the following statements represent a 30% change?
    a 40 changes to 52
    b 40 changes to 10
    c 40 changes to 28

8 A candle is 40 cm tall. As it burns, it shrinks by 5 cm each hour.
   a Work out the percentage change after one hour.
   b Work out the percentage change after three hours.
   c After how many hours is the percentage change 50%?

Percentage profit or percentage loss can be calculated in the same way as percentage increase or decrease.

$$\text{Percentage profit} = \frac{\text{Profit}}{\text{Original amount}} \times 100\%$$

$$\text{Percentage loss} = \frac{\text{Loss}}{\text{Original amount}} \times 100\%$$

Example 3

Jon buys a car for £1200. He then sells it for £1500. Work out the percentage profit.

Solution 3

Profit = £1500 − £1200 = £300. Original amount = £1200

$$\text{Percentage profit} = \frac{\text{Profit}}{\text{Original amount}} \times 100\% = \frac{£300}{£1200} \times 100\% = 25\%$$

Exercise B

1 A television is bought for £1000 and then sold for £750
Find the percentage loss.

2 A chef makes a meal for £20
The price on the menu is £23
Calculate the percentage profit.

3 Mick buys a toy for £4 and sells it for £5
Work out the percentage profit.

4 There are 250 fish in a lake. 50 of the fish are caught by anglers. Calculate the percentage caught by anglers.

5 The price of fish and chips is increased from £4.00 to £4.40
Work out the percentage increase.

6 Pavel's salary is reduced from £30 000 a year to £21 000 a year. What is the percentage reduction in Pavel's salary?

7 A computer is bought for £450
It is then sold for £400
Calculate the percentage loss.
Give your answer to one decimal place.

8 Matt buys a watch for £80.
He sells it for £50
Calculate his percentage loss.

9 Peter and his son Jack each take two tests.
The results are shown in the table.
Whose test mark has improved by the
greatest percentage?
Show your working.

	Test A	Test B
Peter	60	75
Jack	34	43

10 Terry invests £875 in shares. The value of the shares falls by £150
He says that this is a loss of between 15% and 20%.
Is he correct? Show your working.

11 a Work out the percentage increase when 240 kg is increased to 300 kg.
   b Work out the percentage decrease when 300 kg is decreased to 240 kg.
   c Explain why your answers to parts **a** and **b** are different.

12 The average attendance for a football team last season was 11 500
This season the average has fallen by 800
What is the percentage fall in the average attendance this season?
Give your answer to the nearest whole number.

13 The value of a luxury coach depreciates (decreases) from £240 000 when new to
£160 000 one year later.
Calculate the percentage depreciation.

25.4 Percentages in real life

CAN YOU REMEMBER

- How to work out a percentage of a quantity?
- How to increase or decrease by a percentage?
- How to write one quantity as a percentage of another?

IN THIS SECTION YOU WILL

- Understand the meaning of 'interest', 'inflation' and 'income tax'.
- Learn how to calculate simple interest.
- Learn how to calculate income tax.
- Solve real-life problems using percentages.

Interest is the cost of borrowing or lending money.
Interest is earned when money is invested.
Interest is charged when a loan is taken out.

For this account the interest for one year is 5% of £1000 = £50

In three years the interest = £50 × 3 = £150

This account pays *simple interest*. The amount paid is the same each year.

After three years the value of the investment is
£1000 + £150 = £1150

INVEST £1000
Interest paid annually at a fixed rate of 5% of the initial investment

Simple interest can also be calculated using the formula $I = \dfrac{PRT}{100}$

where I is the interest, P is the amount invested, R is the rate of interest and T is the time invested.

Example 1

Chico borrows £800 for two years. Simple interest is charged at 10% per year. How much does Chico have to pay back altogether?

Solution 1

Method 1

Interest per year = 10% of £800

          = 0.1 × 800 = £80

Interest charged for two years

          = £80 × 2 = £160

Total to pay back = £800 + £160 = £960

Method 2

Using the formula $I = \dfrac{PRT}{100}$

P = £800, R = 10%, T = 2 years

$I = \dfrac{800 \times 10 \times 2}{100} = £160$

Total to pay back = £800 + £160 = £960

Example 2

Tim invests £1000 for 1 year. He earns interest of £75. What is the interest rate?

Solution 2

Method 1

£75 as a percentage of £1000

$= \dfrac{75}{1000} \times 100\%$

$= 7.5\%$

Interest rate = 7.5%

Method 2

Using the formula $I = \dfrac{PRT}{100}$

P = £1000, T = 1 year, I = £75

$75 = \dfrac{1000 \times R \times 1}{100}$ Cancel

$75 = 10R$ Divide both sides by 10

$7.5 = R$

Interest rate = 7.5%

Exercise A

1 Work out the simple interest on each of the following for:
   i 1 year   **ii** 3 years   **iii** 5 years.
   a £500 at 10% per year   **b** £400 at 5% per year   **c** £2000 at 3% per year
   d £1000 at 8% per year   **e** £200 at 2.5% per year   **f** £1500 at 4% per year

2 Work out the value of the following investments after:
   i 1 year   **ii** 2 years.
   a £300 at 10% per year   **b** £500 at 2% per year   **c** £1000 at 5% per year
   d £1200 at 4% per year   **e** £100 at 2.5% per year   **f** £2500 at 7% per year

3 For each of the following loans, use the formula $I = \dfrac{PRT}{100}$ to work out:

   i the simple interest   **ii** the total amount repaid.
   a £250 at 10% per year for 2 years   **b** £400 at 2% per year for 2 years
   c £1000 at 6% per year for 3 years   **d** £500 at 4% per year for 3 years
   e £1500 at 3% per year for 3 years   **f** £800 at 5% per year for 6 years
   g £1000 at 2.5% per year for 5 years   **h** £2000 at 8% per year for 4 years

4 Jo invested £500 at 6% simple interest. She received £90 interest in total.
   For how many years did she invest?

5 Copy and complete this simple interest table.

	Initial Amount	Interest rate per year	Simple interest per year	Simple interest for 5 years	Total amount after 5 years
a	£675	8%			
b	£450	5.5%			
c	£280	3.5%			
d	£520	4.5%			
e	£650	3.2%			

6 Norris invests £2500 in a bond paying 3.8% simple interest.
   He says that in three years his bond will be worth over £3000
   Is he correct? Explain your answer.

7 For each of the following loans work out:
   i the simple interest using the formula $I = \dfrac{PRT}{100}$ **ii** the total amount repaid.

   a £32 000 at 4% per year for 2 years   **b** £1800 at 2.5% per year for 2 years
   c £4500 at 6.2% per year for 3 years   **d** £7200 at 4.8% per year for 3 years
   e £1600 at 3.4% per year for 3 years   **f** £900 at 5.6% per year for 4 years
   g £5000 at 7.5% per year for 5 years   **h** £4000 at 2.1% per year for 10 years

8 Greg takes out a loan of £3500 for 3 years.
He pays £525 simple interest.
Work out the interest rate.

9 Terry lends £2200 to his daughter.
She agrees to pay back 5% of the initial loan each year.
How long will it take her to pay off the loan?

Inflation is the increase in prices or costs.
The *annual rate of inflation* is the percentage increase over one year.

Example 3

The annual rate of inflation is 6% per year. A house is valued at £125 000 this year.
Use the annual rate of inflation to work out the value of the house next year.

Solution 3

6% of £125 000 = 0.06 × 125 000 = £7500
New value = £125 000 + £7500 = £132 500

The government takes a percentage of people's earnings as *income tax.* The rate of income tax paid depends on the total income.

Example 4

A man earns £8000 per year. The first £5000 is tax free.
The remainder is taxed at 20%. How much tax does he pay?

Solution 4

He pays tax on £8000 − £5000 = £3000
20% of £3000 = 0.2 × £3000 = £600
He pays £600 tax.

Exercise B

1 The annual rate of inflation is 5%.
Use the annual rate of inflation to work out the prices after one year of:
   a a car costing £8000 this year
   b a trolley of food costing £50 this year
   c a tank of petrol costing £40 this year
   d a three-piece suite costing £800 this year.

2 Mrs Farthing earns $20 000 per year.
The first $5000 is tax free.
She pays income tax at the rate of 25%.
How much tax does she pay?

3 Mr Shilling earns £10 000 per year.
The first £4800 is tax free.
He pays income tax at the rate
of 20%.
How much tax does he pay?

4 Miss Halfpenny earns £5000 per year.
The first £4000 is tax free.
She pays income tax at the rate
of 10%.
How much does she have left after tax?

5 The annual rate of inflation is 7.5%.
Use the annual rate of inflation to work out the prices after one year of:
   a a house costing £95 000 this year
   b a dress costing £80 this year
   c a shirt costing £17.50 this year
   d a tyre costing £63 this year.

6 Mrs Florin earns £25 000 per year.
The first £4600 is tax free.
She pays income tax at the rate
of 25%.
How much tax does she pay?

7 Mr Crown earns £12 500 per year.
The first £5200 is tax free.
He pays income tax at the rate
of 22%.
How much tax does he pay?

8 The first £4300 of income is tax free.
Income tax is paid at the rate of 10% on £5000
Income tax is paid at the rate of 22% on the remainder.
   a Miss Guinea earns £17 000 per year. How much tax does she pay?
   b Mr Penny earns £15 700 per year. How much tax does he pay?

Chapter summary

- To write a quantity as a percentage of another quantity:
  - **Method 1**
    Step 1: Make sure that both quantities have the same units.
    Step 2: Use the formula $\dfrac{\text{first quantity}}{\text{second quantity}} \times 100\%$
  - **Method 2**
    Step 1: Make sure that both quantities have the same units.
    Step 2: Write the fraction $\dfrac{\text{first quantity}}{\text{second quantity}}$ as a fraction with a denominator of 100
    Step 3: Write the fraction as a percentage.

- There are two methods for working out a percentage increase or decrease.
  - **Method 1**
    Work out the decrease.
    Subtract the decrease
    from the original value.

    Work out the increase.
    Add the increase to the original value.

- **Method 2** – Use a multiplier.
  New value = original value × multiplier

Original value = 100%, decrease = 20%	Original value = 100%, increase = 10%
100% − 20% = 80%	100% + 10% = 110%
80% written as a decimal = 0.8, so the multiplier = 0.8	110% written as a decimal = 1.1, so the multiplier = 1.1

- Percentage change = $\dfrac{\text{Change (increase or decrease)}}{\text{Original amount}} \times 100\%$

- Percentage profit = $\dfrac{\text{Profit}}{\text{Original amount}} \times 100\%$

- Percentage loss = $\dfrac{\text{Loss}}{\text{Original amount}} \times 100\%$

- Interest is the cost of borrowing or lending money.

- With simple interest, the amount of interest is the same each year.

- Simple interest can be calculated using the formula $I = \dfrac{PRT}{100}$, where I is the interest, P is the amount invested, R is the rate of interest and T is the time invested.

- Inflation is the increase in prices or costs.

- The annual rate of inflation is the percentage increase over one year.

- Income tax is the percentage of people's earnings taken by the government.

Chapter review

1 There are 50 members of a rowing club.
  a There are 32 male members.
    What percentage is male?
  b The number of members increases by 20% of the original number of members each year.
    Calculate the number of members in the rowing club after two years.

2 Tara has a weekend job. She earns £4.50 per hour on Saturdays.
  On Sundays her pay per hour is 50% more than it is on Saturdays.
  a What is her pay on Sundays?
  b Last weekend Tara worked for 6 hours on Saturday and for 5 hours on Sunday.
    How much did she earn in the two days?

3 The recommended price of a guitar is £240.
Sanjay discovers that he can order the guitar on the Internet and get a discount of 30% off the recommended price.
Calculate the amount Sanjay would pay if he ordered the guitar on the Internet.

4 Owen receives his gas bill. The bill is for £120 plus VAT at 5%.
  a Calculate the amount of VAT.
  b Find the total amount which Owen has to pay.

5 This year Mr Day attended 50 meetings. Mr Day wants to decrease the number of meetings he attends by 10%. Which calculation should he use to work out the number of meetings he wants to attend?

50×0.1 $\qquad$ 50×0.9 $\qquad$ 50×1.1 $\qquad$ 50×10

Explain your answer.

6 Rosemary and her sister are getting ready for the new term.
They go to Suzie's Stationery to buy paper, pens and pencils.
Paper costs 87 pence per pad.
Pens cost £1.05 each.
Pencils cost 35 pence each.
  a Copy and complete the bill.
  b Because they are students,
     they are given a reduction of 10%
     of the total cost.
     By how much is their bill reduced?

Suzie's Stationery	
8 pads of paper	£ ....
...... pens	£ 12.60
6 pencils	£ ....
Total	£ ....

7 Roy invests £5000 for two years.
Simple interest is paid annually at the rate of 4.5%.
How much is the investment worth after two years?

8 The cost of a camera is £250, plus VAT at 17.5%.
Calculate the amount of VAT charged on the camera.

9 A fish increases in weight from 28 kg to 30 kg.
Calculate the percentage increase in the weight of the fish.

10 An antiques dealer buys a table for £450. He sells the table for 60% more than the price he paid for it.
It costs the dealer £70 to restore the table before he sells it.
  a For how much does the dealer sell the table?
  b Calculate the amount of profit the dealer made.
  c Calculate this profit as a percentage of the price the dealer paid for the table.

More algebra skills

26.1 Indices

CAN YOU REMEMBER

- The square numbers from 1 to 225 and the cube numbers from 1 to 125?
- That x^2 means $x \times x$ and x^3 means $x \times x \times x$?
- How to substitute values into an algebraic expression?
- That $p \times q$ simplifies to pq?

IN THIS SECTION YOU WILL

- Learn the rules for multiplying and dividing index numbers.

The same number multiplied together a number of times can be written in a shorthand form using *powers*.

For example

$3 \times 3 = 3^2$	'3 squared' or '3 to the power 2'
$4 \times 4 \times 4 = 4^3$	'4 cubed' or '4 to the power 3'
$5 \times 5 \times 5 \times 5 \times 5 \times 5 \times 5 = 5^7$	'5 to the power 7'

In the expression 5^7, 5 is the *base number* and 7 is the power or *index*.

The power is the number of times that the base number is multiplied together.

Example 1

a Write each of the following in index form.

  i $3 \times 3 \times 3 \times 3$ **ii** $2 \times 2 \times 2 \times 5 \times 5 \times 5 \times 5 \times 5 \times 5$

  iii $p \times p \times p \times p$ **iv** $q \times q \times q \times r \times r \times r \times r \times r \times r$

b Write each of the following using multiplication symbols.

  i $5^3 \times 7^4$ **ii** $y^5 z^2$

Solution 1

a   **i** $3 \times 3 \times 3 \times 3 = 3^4$

  ii $2 \times 2 \times 2 \times 5 \times 5 \times 5 \times 5 \times 5 \times 5 = 2^3 \times 5^6$

  iii $p \times p \times p \times p = p^4$

  iv $q \times q \times q \times r \times r \times r \times r \times r \times r = q^3 \times r^6 = q^3 r^6$

b   **i** $5^3 \times 7^4 = 5 \times 5 \times 5 \times 7 \times 7 \times 7 \times 7$

  ii $y^5 z^2 = y \times y \times y \times y \times y \times z \times z$

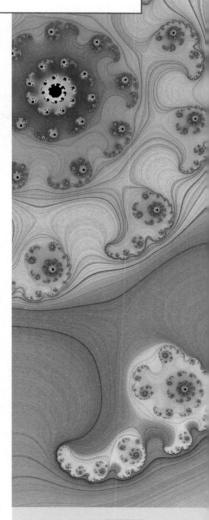

Make sure you know how to work out powers using your calculator.

Example 2

Calculate the value of each of the following expressions when $x = 3$ and $y = 4$

a　x^3　　　　b　y^2　　　　c　$x^5 + y^6$　　　d　$x^5 y^6$

Solution 2

a　$x^3 = x \times x \times x$
　　When　$x = 3$
　　　　$x^3 = 3 \times 3 \times 3 = 27$

b　When　$y = 4$
　　　　$y^2 = 4 \times 4 = 16$

c　$x^5 + y^6 = 3^5 + 4^6$
　　　　$= 4339$

d　$x^5 y^6 = 3^5 \times 4^6$
　　　　$= 995\,328$

Exercise A

1　Write each of the following in index form.
　　a　$3 \times 3 \times 3 \times 3 \times 3 \times 3 \times 3$
　　b　$5 \times 5 \times 5 \times 5 \times 5 \times 5$
　　c　4×4
　　d　$2 \times 2 \times 2 \times 3 \times 3$
　　e　$2 \times 2 \times 5 \times 5 \times 5 \times 5 \times 5 \times 5$
　　f　$2 \times 2 \times 3 \times 3 \times 3 \times 4 \times 4 \times 4 \times 4$
　　g　$3 \times 3 \times 4 \times 4 \times 4 \times 5 \times 5 \times 5 \times 5$
　　h　$7 \times 7 \times 7 \times 9 \times 9 \times 9 \times 11 \times 11 \times 11$
　　i　$4 \times 4 \times 4 \times 4 \times 4 \times 4 \times 4 \times 4 \times 4 \times 4 \times 4 \times 4 \times 4 \times 4 \times 4$
　　j　$2 \times 2 \times 2 \times 2 \times 2 \times 2 \times 2 \times 2 \times 2 \times 2 \times 2 \times 2 \times 2 \times 2 \times 2$

2　Write each of the following in index form.
　　a　$x \times x \times x \times x \times x \times x \times x \times x \times x \times x$
　　b　$y \times y \times y \times y \times y$
　　c　$z \times z$
　　d　$a \times a \times b \times b \times b$
　　e　$p \times p \times p \times q \times q \times q \times q \times q$
　　f　$r \times r \times s \times s \times s \times t$
　　g　$v \times v \times v \times v \times w \times w \times w \times w \times w$
　　h　$a \times a \times a \times b \times b \times b \times c \times c \times c$
　　i　$x \times y \times y \times z \times z \times z \times z \times z \times z \times z$
　　j　$a \times a \times b \times b \times b \times c \times c \times c \times c \times c \times c \times c \times d \times d \times d \times d$

3　Write each of the following using multiplication symbols.
　　a　4^2　　　　b　6^3　　　　c　7^1　　　　d　2^{10}
　　e　$2^2 \times 3^3$　　f　$4^5 \times 6^3$　　g　$4^5 \times 5^4$　　h　$2^2 \times 3^3 \times 4$
　　i　$3 \times 4^3 \times 5^4$　　j　$2^4 \times 3^3 \times 4^2 \times 5$

4   Write each of the following using multiplication symbols.
    a a^3 b a^5 c b^7 d b^9 e a^2b^3
    f x^3y^2 g x^5y^4 h p^3q^7r i pq^2r^5 j $a^5b^4c^2$

5   Copy and complete this table. The first one has been done for you.

	x	y	x^2	y^3	$x^2 + y^3$	x^2y^3
a	3	2	9	8	$9 + 8 = 17$	$9 \times 8 = 72$
b	2	3				
c	10	5				
d	5	10				
e	1	4				
f	4	1				

6   Use your knowledge of squares and cubes to work out the value of each letter
    symbol in the following.
    a $2^a = 4$ b $3^b = 27$ c $4^c = 64$
    d $10^d = 1000$ e $5^e = 125$

7   You are given that $A = x^4 + y^5$ and $B = x^4y^5$
    Find the values of A and B when
    a $x = 4$ and $y = 5$ b $x = 5$ and $y = 4$

8   The letter symbols in the following expressions represent positive integers.
    Use the power button on a scientific calculator to find their values.
    a $5^a = 625$ b $7^b = 343$ c $8^c = 32\,768$
    d $9^d = 729$ e $2^e = 256$

Multiplying index numbers with the same base

$2^5 \times 2^4 = (2 \times 2 \times 2 \times 2 \times 2) \times (2 \times 2 \times 2 \times 2)$
$ = 2 \times 2 \times 2 \times 2 \times 2 \times 2 \times 2 \times 2 \times 2 = 2^9$

So $2^5 \times 2^4 = 2^{5 + 4} = 2^9$

In general, $x^a \times x^b = x^{a + b}$

To **multiply** index numbers with the same base **add** the powers.

Dividing index numbers with the same base

$$7^{10} \div 7^4 = \frac{(7 \times 7 \times 7 \times 7 \times 7 \times 7 \times 7 \times 7 \times 7 \times 7)}{(7 \times 7 \times 7 \times 7)} = 7^6$$

So $7^{10} \div 7^4 = 7^{10 - 4} = 7^6$

In general, $x^a \div x^b = x^{a - b}$

To **divide** index numbers with the same base **subtract** the powers.

Example 3

a   Simplify $x^5 \times x^3 \times x$

b   Simplify $z^3 \times z^2 \div z^2$

Solution 3

a $x^5 \times x^3 \times x = x^{5+3+1} = x^9$

b $z^3 \times z^2 \div z^2 = z^{3+2-2} = z^3$

   x can be written as x^1

When terms include numbers and letters, deal with the numbers and letters separately.

Example 4

Simplify: a $2x^3 \times 3x^2$ b $8y^6 \div 2y^4$

Solution 4

a $2x^3 \times 3x^2 = 2 \times 3 \times x^3 \times x^2 = 6 \times x^{3+2} = 6x^5$

   Multiply the numbers (2×3) and **add** the powers ($3 + 2$).

b $8y^6 \div 2y^4 = \dfrac{(8 \times y^6)}{(2 \times y^4)} = \dfrac{8}{2} \times \dfrac{y^6}{y^4}$

   $\dfrac{8}{2} = 4$ and $\dfrac{y^6}{y^4} = y^{6-4} = y^2$ So $8y^6 \div 2y^4 = 4 \times y^2 = 4y^2$

   Divide the numbers ($8 \div 2$) and **subtract** the powers ($6 - 4$).

Exercise B

1 a   Sadik says that the value of 2^3 is 6
       By working out the correct answer show that Sadik is wrong.

    b   Tom says that the expressions $5x$ and x^5 are the same. Explain why Tom is wrong.

2 Match pairs of equivalent expressions in each set.
    In set **a** one has been done for you.

    a

$3 + 3 + 3 + 3$	3^4
$3 \times 3 \times 3 \times 3$	4^3
$4 + 4 + 4$	3×4
$4 \times 4 \times 4$	4×3

    b

$x + x + x + x$	x^5
$x \times x \times x \times x \times x \times x$	$4x$
$x \times x \times x \times x \times x$	$5x$
$x + x + x + x + x$	x^4

    c

$(a + a + a) + (b + b)$	$a^3 b^2$	$(a \times a \times a) + (b \times b)$	$6ab$
$(a + a + a) \times (b + b)$	$a^3 + 2b$	$(a \times a \times a) \times (b \times b)$	$3a + b^2$
$(a + a + a) + (b \times b)$	$3a + 2b$	$(a \times a \times a) + (b + b)$	$a^3 + b^2$

3 Find the value of the letter symbol in each of the following.

a $2^a = 2^5 \times 2^4$ **b** $3^b = 3^5 \times 3^3$ **c** $5^c = 5^2 \times 5^3 \times 5^4$ **d** $7^d = 7 \times 7^2 \times 7^5$

e $2^e = 2^7 \div 2^4$ **f** $3^f = 3^5 \div 3^3$ **g** $5^g = 5^4 \div 5^3$ **h** $7^h = 7^5 \div 7^4$

i $2^i = 2^4 \times 2^5 \div 2^3$

4 Simplify each of the following.

a $t^2 \times t^3$ **b** $p^5 \times p^4$ **c** $x \times x^5$ **d** $a^4 \times a^7$ **e** $a^2 \times a^4$

f $q^4 \div q$ **g** $y^5 \div y^2$ **h** $d^7 \div d^2$ **i** $z^{12} \div z^9$ **j** $g^9 \div g^2$

5 Simplify each of the following.

a $a^3 \times a^2 \times a$ **b** $b^4 \times b^3 \times b^2$ **c** $c^5 \times c^2 \times c^2$ **d** $d^5 \times d^3 \div d^2$

e $e \times e^3 \div e^2$ **f** $\dfrac{f^5}{(f^2 \times f^2)}$ **g** $\dfrac{(g^7 \div g^2)}{(g \times g^2)}$ **h** $\dfrac{(h^4 \times h^2)}{(h^3 \times h)}$

i $\dfrac{(i^3 \times i^2)}{(i^6 \div i^2)}$ **j** $\dfrac{(j^3 \times j^2 \div j)}{(j^5 \times j^3 \div j^4)}$

6 Emma is asked to simplify $4x^3 \times 7x^5$. She writes down $11x^8$.

a What has Emma done wrong?   **b** Simplify $4x^3 \times 7x^5$ correctly.

7 Simplify each of the following.

a $2x^2 \times 5x^3$ **b** $3x \times 4x^5$ **c** $5x^4 \times 4x^5$ **d** $3x^2 \times 2x^3 \times 2x$

e $7x \times 2x^3 \times 5x^4$ **f** $12x^5 \div 3x^2$ **g** $15x^3 \div 5x$ **h** $16x^9 \div 8x^3$

i $24x \div 3x^2$ **j** $5x^3 \times 4x \div 2x^6$

8 The table shows a list of the powers of 2 up to 2^{12}

2^1	2^2	2^3	2^4	2^5	2^6	2^7	2^8	2^9	2^{10}	2^{11}	2^{12}
2	4	8	16	32	64	128	256	512	1024	2048	4096

a   **i** Write 64 and 32 as powers of 2

     ii Use the table to work out the value of 64×32

b   **i** Write 2048 and 16 as powers of 2   **ii** Use the table to work out $2048 \div 16$

9 Copy and complete this table of the powers of 3

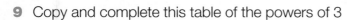

3^1	3^2	3^3	3^4	3^5	3^6	3^7	3^8	3^9	3^{10}	3^{11}	3^{12}

a Use the table to find the value of

     i 81×2187 **ii** 243^2 **iii** $531\,441 \div 19\,683$

     You **must** show your working.

b Use the table to show that   **i** $243 \times 2187 = 729^2$

     ii $243 \times 177\,147 = 6561^2$ **iii** $(531\,441 \div 2187)^2 = 59\,049$

     You **must** show your working.

10 Use the powers of 5 to show that $9\,765\,625 = 5 \times 25 \times 125 \times 625$

26.2 Expanding brackets and simplifying expressions

IN THIS SECTION YOU WILL

- Reinforce and extend skills in simplifying expressions.
- Learn how to multiply an expression in brackets by a single term.
- Learn how to simplify expressions that include brackets.

Each bag contains $x + 2$ marbles.

The total number of marbles in the three bags can be written as:

$3 \times (x + 2)$ or $3(x + 2)$ or $x + 2 + x + 2 + x + 2$ or $3 \times x + 3 \times 2$ or $3x + 6$

This shows that $3(x + 2) = 3 \times x + 3 \times 2$

This can also be shown using the *grid method*.

$3(x + 2)$

So $3 \times (x + 2) = 3 \times x + 3 \times 2$
$\qquad\qquad\quad = 3x + 6$

$\times$	x	2	
3	$3 \times x$	3×2	$3 \times x + 3 \times 2 = 3x + 6$

$a(b + c)$

In general, $a(b + c) = a \times b + a \times c$
$\qquad\qquad\qquad = ab + ac$

$\times$	b	c	
a	$a \times b = ab$	$a \times c = ac$	$ab + ac$

Multiplying $3(x + 2)$ to get $3x + 6$ is called *expanding* or multiplying out the brackets.

Example 1

a Use the grid method to expand $-4(y - 5)$.
b Expand $3(x + y)$.

Solution 1

a $-4(y - 5)$

$\times$	y	-5	
-4	$-4 \times y = -4y$	$-4 \times -5 = 20$	$-4y + 20$

So $-4(y - 5) = -4 \times y + -4 \times -5 = -4y + 20$

b $3(x + y) = 3 \times x + 3 \times y = 3x + 3y$

When an expression contains brackets and other terms, expand the brackets and then collect like terms.

Example 2

a   Expand and simplify $3(4x + 2y) + 5y$.
b   Expand $3(2a + 3b - 4c)$.
c   Expand and simplify $-4(3p - 2) - 5$

Solution 2

a   Expand the brackets.
$$3(4x + 2y) + 5y = 3 \times 4x + 3 \times 2y + 5y = 12x + 6y + 5y$$
Collect like terms
$$12x + 6y + 5y = 12x + 11y$$

b $3(2a + 3b - 4c) = 3(2a + 3b + -4c)$
$$= 3 \times 2a + 3 \times 3b + 3 \times -4c = 6a + 9b - 12c$$

c $-4(3p - 2) - 5 = -4(3p + -2) - 5$
$$= -4 \times 3p + -4 \times -2 - 5 = -12p + 8 - 5 = -12p + 3$$

Exercise A

1   Copy and complete this table.

a	$2(a + 6)$	$(a + 6) + (a + 6)$	$2a + 12$
b	$3(b + 4)$	$(b + 4) + (b + 4) + (b + 4)$	
c	$2(4c - 5)$		$8c - 10$
d	$4(d + 2)$		
e		$(e + 1) + (e + 1) + (e + 1)$	
f			$5f + 10$
g	$6(g - 3)$		
h	$4(2h + 7)$		
i		$(3i - 2) + (3i - 2) + (3i - 2) + (3i - 2)$	
j		$(2j + 3) + (2j + 3) + (2j + 3) + (2j + 3) + (2j + 3)$	
k			$6k - 12$
l	$7(3l - 1)$		

2   Copy and complete the grids to expand the expressions given.
The first one has been done for you.

a $5(x + 4)$

×	x	4	
5	$5 \times x = 5x$	$5 \times 4 = 20$	$5x + 20$

b $3(x + 6)$

×	x	6
3		

c $2(4x + 3)$

×	$4x$	3
2		

d $3(2x - 7)$

×	$2x$	-7
3		

e $-3(-2x + 3y - 4)$

×			

3   Match the pairs of equivalent expressions in these boxes.

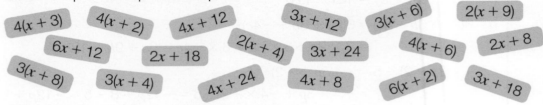

$4(x + 3)$ $4(x + 2)$ $4x + 12$ $3x + 12$ $3(x + 6)$ $2(x + 9)$
$6x + 12$ $2(x + 4)$ $3x + 24$ $4(x + 6)$ $2x + 8$
$3(x + 8)$ $3(x + 4)$ $4x + 24$ $4x + 8$ $6(x + 2)$ $3x + 18$
$2x + 18$

4   Match the pairs of equivalent expressions in these boxes.

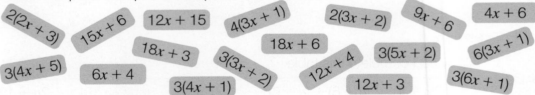

$2(2x + 3)$ $15x + 6$ $12x + 15$ $4(3x + 1)$ $2(3x + 2)$ $9x + 6$ $4x + 6$
$18x + 3$ $3(3x + 2)$ $18x + 6$ $3(5x + 2)$ $6(3x + 1)$
$3(4x + 5)$ $6x + 4$ $12x + 4$ $12x + 3$ $3(6x + 1)$
$3(4x + 1)$

5   Expand each of these expressions.
   a $2(a + 4)$ **b** $3(b + 7)$ **c** $4(c + 3)$ **d** $5(d + 1)$
   e $4(e - 1)$ **f** $7(f - 2)$ **g** $3(g + 9)$ **h** $4(h - 3)$
   i $3(2 - i)$ **j** $4(5 - j)$ **k** $-4(2 - k)$ **l** $-2(l + 9)$
   m $-5(m - 6)$ **n** $5(x + y - 1)$ **o** $3(x - y + 1)$ **p** $-2(x - y - 1)$

6   Expand each of these expressions.
   a $2(3a + 5)$ **b** $3(2b + 1)$ **c** $4(3c + 2)$ **d** $5(3d + 7)$
   e $3(4e - 1)$ **f** $5(4f - 3)$ **g** $3(5g + 3)$ **h** $4(4h - 3)$
   i $2(6 - 5i)$ **j** $3(4 - 3j)$ **k** $-3(1 - 5k)$ **l** $-6(2l + 7)$
   m $-3(5m - 2)$ **n** $3(2x + 3y - 1)$ **o** $3(3x - 2y + 4)$ **p** $-5(2x - 4y - 3)$

7   Multiply out the brackets and simplify each of the following expressions.
   a $3(a + 5) + 7$ **b** $2(b + 1) + 3$ **c** $4(c + 3) - 3$
   d $5(d + 3) + 2d$ **e** $3(e + 1) + 4e$ **f** $6(2f + 1) + 5$
   g $4(2g - 3) + 5g$ **h** $5(2h - 3) + 4$ **i** $3(6 - 5i) + 15i$
   j $3(2 - 5j) - 6$ **k** $-4(1 - 2k) + 4$ **l** $-5(2l + 1) + 11l$
   m $-2(4m - 2) + 6$ **n** $3(4x + 2y - 1) + 3x + 3$
   o $2(5x - 3y + 1) + 6y - 2$ **p** $-5(x - 2y + 3) + 5x - 10y$

8 Sakshi expands $3(2a + 4)$. Her answer is $6a + 4$. Explain what Sakshi has done wrong.

9 Sue and Bill use different methods to show that $8x + 14 = 4(2x + 3) + 2$

Sue's method

$$8x + 14 = (2x + 3) + (2x + 3) +$$
$$(2x + 3) + (2x + 3) + 2$$
$$= 4(2x + 3) + 2$$

Bill's method

$$4(2x + 3) + 2 = 4 \times 2x + 4 \times 3 + 2$$
$$= 8x + 12 + 2$$
$$= 8x + 14$$

  a Use both Sue's and Bill's methods to show that:

   i $6(x + 2) + 3 = 6x + 15$ **ii** $3(x + 5) + 3x = 6x + 15$

  b **i** Use Sue's method to show that $6a - 10b = 6(a - 2b) + 2b$

   ii Use Bill's method to show that $5(a - 2b) + a = 6a - 10b$

10 a **i** Work out $8 \times 70 + 8 \times 9$

   ii Work out $8 \times (70 + 9)$.   **iii** What do you notice?

  b **i** Work out $9 \times 200 + 9 \times 70 + 9 \times 6$

   ii Work out $9 \times (200 + 70 + 6)$.   **iii** What do you notice?

  c **i** Work out $6 \times 400 + 6 \times 80 + 6 \times 9 + 7 \times 90 + 7 \times 8$

   ii Work out $6 \times (400 + 80 + 9) + 7 \times (90 + 8)$.   **iii** What do you notice?

Example 3

Use the grid method to expand   **a** $x(x + 4)$ **b** $2x(3x + 2)$

Solution 3

a $x(x + 4)$

$\times$	x	4	
x	$x \times x = x^2$	$x \times 4 = 4x$	$x^2 + 4x$

So $x(x + 4) = x \times x + x \times 4 = x^{1+1} + 4x = x^2 + 4x$

b $2x(3x + 2)$

$\times$	$3x$	2	
$2x$	$2x \times 3x = 6x^2$	$2x \times 2 = 4x$	$6x^2 + 4x$

So $2x(3x + 2) = 2x \times 3x + 2x \times 2$
$$= 2 \times 3 \times x \times x + 2 \times 2 \times x = 6x^2 + 4x$$

Example 4

Expand and simplify: **a** $2(x + 5) + 3(x - 2)$ **b** $3(4x - 5) - 3(2x - 1)$

Solution 4

a $2(x + 5) = 2 \times x + 2 \times 5$
$$= 2x + 10$$
$3(x - 2) = 3 \times x + 3 \times -2$
$$= 3x + -6 = 3x - 6$$
$2(x + 5) + 3(x - 2)$
$$= 2x + 10 + 3x - 6$$
$$= 5x + 4$$

b $3(4x - 5) - 3(2x - 1)$
$$= 3(4x + -5) + -3(2x + -1)$$
$$= 3 \times 4x + 3 \times -5 + -3 \times 2x + -3 \times -1$$
$$= 12x + -15 + -6x + 3$$
$$= 6x - 12$$

Two expressions in brackets can be multiplied together.
- Multiply **all** terms in the first bracket by **all** terms in the second bracket.
- Simplify by collecting like terms.

Example 5

a　Expand and simplify $(x + 5)(x + 2)$.
b　Multiply out the brackets and simplify $(x - 4)(x + 1)$.

Solution 5

a　$(x + 5)(x + 2)$

Method 1
$$= x \times (x + 2) + 5 \times (x + 2)$$
$$= x \times x + x \times 2 + 5 \times x + 5 \times 2$$
$$= x^2 \times 2x + 5x + 10$$
$$= x^2 + 7x + 10$$

Method 2

×	x	5
x	x^2	$5x$
2	$2x$	10

$$= x^2 + 2x + 5x + 10$$
$$= x^2 + 7x + 10$$

b　$(x - 4)(x + 1)$

Method 1
$$= x \times (x + 1) - 4 \times (x + 1)$$
$$= x \times x + x \times 1 - 4 \times x - 4 \times 1$$
$$= x^2 + x - 4x - 4$$
$$= x^2 - 3x - 4$$

Method 2

×	x	−4
x	x^2	$-4x$
1	x	−4

$$= x^2 + x - 4x - 4$$
$$= x^2 - 3x - 4$$

Exercise B

1　Expand each of these expressions.

a　$a(a + 5)$　　　b　$b(b + 1)$　　　c　$c(c - 2)$　　　d　$d(2d + 3)$
e　$e(3e - 1)$　　f　$f(2f - 5)$　　g　$g(3g + 7)$　　h　$h(5h - 2)$
i　$i(3 - 2i)$　　j　$j(1 - j)$　　　k　$-k(3 - 2k)$　　l　$x(x + y)$
m　$x(5x - 2y)$　n　$x(2x + 3y - 1)$　o　$-x(2x - 3y)$　p　$-x(2x - 4y - 3)$

2　Expand each of these expressions.

a　$2a(4a + 3)$　　　　　b　$5b(2b + 3)$　　　　　c　$3c(4c + 1)$
d　$7d(2d + 3)$　　　　　e　$3e^2(2e - 5)$　　　　f　$4f^2(2f - 1)$
g　$3g^2(5g^2 + 2)$　　　　h　$4h^3(4h^2 - 3)$　　　i　$2i(6 - 5i + i^2)$
j　$3j^2(4j^2 - 3j + 1)$　　k　$-3k^4(1 - 3k^2)$　　l　$x^4(2x + 3y)$
m　$3x^3(x - 2y)$　　　　n　$3x(2x^2 + 3xy - y^2)$　o　$xy(x - y + 1)$
p　$5xy(3x^2 - 2xy - 4y^2)$

3　Multiply out the brackets and simplify each of the following expressions.

a　$4(a + 3) + 7(a + 4)$　　　　　b　$3(b + 1) + 3(b + 5)$
c　$4(2c + 3) + 3(3c - 1)$　　　　d　$7(3d + 3) - 2(4d - 3)$
e　$e(5e + 4) - 4e(e + 1)$　　　　f　$f(4f + 3) - 3f(f + 1)$

g $2g(2g - 5) + 5g(g + 2)$ h $5h(3h - 2) + 2h(3h + 5)$

i $2i(4 - 5i) + 5i(3i + 4) + i(i + 1)$ j $3j(1 - 5j) - 2j(1 - 4j) + 7j^2$

k $-4k(1 - 2k) + 4k(2 - 3k)$ l $x(x + y) + x(x - y)$

m $x(x + y) - x(x - y)$ n $xy(x + y) + xy(x - y)$

o $2x^3(3x^2 + 4x - 1) + x^2(3x^3 - 8x^2 + 2x + 1)$

p $3x^2(2x^2 + x - 3) - 2x(3x^3 - x^2 + 2x + 1)$

4   Look at Ben's homework.

1 $2(5x + 3) = 2 \times 5x + 2 \times 3$ ✓		**1 mark**
$= 10x + 6$ ✓		**1 mark**

2 $x(x + 3)$

$\times$	x	3	
x	$x \times x = x^2$	$x \times 3 = 3x$	$x^2 + 3x$

$x(x + 3) = x \times x + x \times 3$

$\qquad\qquad = 2x + x3$

3 $3(a - b) + 4(a + 2b) = 3 \times a + 3 \times -b + 4 \times a + 4 \times 2b$

$\qquad\qquad\qquad\qquad\quad = 3a - 3b + 4a + 8b$

$\qquad\qquad\qquad\qquad\quad = 7a - 11b$

4 $4(p + q) + 4(p - q) = 4 \times p + 4 \times q + 4 \times p + 4 \times -q$

$\qquad\qquad\qquad\qquad\quad = 4p + 4q + 4p - 4q$

$\qquad\qquad\qquad\qquad\quad = 8p$

5 $4x(3x^2 + 2x) = 4x \times 3x^2 + 4x \times 2x$

$\qquad\qquad\qquad = 7x^3 + 6x^2$

a   Ben scores one mark for using the right method to expand the brackets.
He scores another mark if he gets the correct answer.
The first question has been marked.
Check the rest of Ben's homework and show that he scores 7 out of 10

b   Correct Ben's mistakes.
Write some notes to help Ben work out what he has done wrong.

5   In each row of the table one expression is not equivalent to the other three.
Which expression is the odd one out in each row?
Give a reason for each of your answers.

a	$3(2a + 4)$	$2(3a + 6)$	$6a + 12$	$2(3a + 5)$
b	$5(4b - 3)$	$2(10b - 8) + 1$	$4(5b - 4) - 1$	$10(2b - 1) - 5$
c	$6(1 - 3b)$	$9(1 - 2b) + 3$	$3(2 - 5b) - 3b$	$18(1 - b) - 12$
d	$6d^2 + 8d$	$6d(d + 1) + 2d$	$2d(3d + 4)$	$3d(3d + 4) - 3d^2 - 4$
e	$2(3e + 5) + 3(e - 2)$	$3(3e + 1)$	$9(e + 2) - 15$	$3(3e + 5) - 12$

6 Show that $3(2x + 7) + 5(2x - 1) = 16(x + 1)$.

7 Show that $3x(4x + 3y) - 6x(2x - y) = 15xy$

8 Jim, Kay and Emma try to expand $3x^2(4x^5 + 2y^3)$.
Jim gets $7x^{10} + 5xy^6$
Kay gets $12x^7 + 6x^2y^3$
Emma gets $12x^7 + 3x^2$
a Who is correct?
b Describe the mistakes that the other two have made.

9 Multiply out the brackets and simplify.
    a $(x + 4)(x + 3)$ **b** $(x + 2)(x + 7)$ **c** $(x + 1)(x + 5)$
    d $(x - 3)(x + 5)$ **e** $(x + 1)(x - 4)$ **f** $(x + 7)(x + 8)$
    g $(x + 7)(x - 8)$ **h** $(x - 7)(x - 8)$

10 Expand and simplify.
    a $(a + 2)(a - 5)$ **b** $(b - 2)(b - 4)$ **c** $(c + 8)(c - 3)$
    d $(d - 1)(d - 2)$ **e** $(e + 9)(e - 5)$ **f** $(f + 1)(f - 1)$
    g $(g - 2)(g - 5)$ **h** $(h + 2)(h - 5)$

26.3 Factorising simple expressions

CAN YOU REMEMBER

- How to find the factors of a number?
- How to find the common factors of two numbers?
- How to expand or multiply out brackets?

IN THIS SECTION YOU WILL

- Learn how to factorise simple algebraic expressions with common factors.
- Extend skills in simplifying expressions.

The factors of a number can be found using multiplication facts.
For example, the factors of 6 are found from $6 = 1 \times 6$ and $6 = 2 \times 3$
The factors of an algebraic expression can be found in the same way.
For example, $10x = 1 \times 10x$, $10x = 2 \times 5x$, $10x = 5 \times 2x$, $10x = 10 \times x$

So

Factors of 6	**1**, **2**, 3 and 6
Factors of $10x$	**1**, **2**, 5, 10, x, $2x$, $5x$ and $10x$

1 and **2** are the common factors of 6 and $10x$

The common factors of $10x$ and 6 can be used to *factorise* $10x + 6$
Factorise means 'write an expression as the *product* of its factors'.

Using the common factor 2

$10x + 6 = \mathbf{2} \times 5x + \mathbf{2} \times 3 = \mathbf{2} \times (5x + 3) = \mathbf{2}(5x + 3)$

So $10x + 6$ factorises to $2(5x + 3)$.

Check by *expanding* the brackets.
$2(5x + 3) = 2 \times 5x + 2 \times 3 = 10x + 6$

Factorising is the inverse of *expanding* brackets.

To factorise an expression completely:
Step 1: Find the common factors of the terms of the expression.
Step 2: Choose the highest of the common factors.
Step 3: Write the expression as a product of its factors.

Example 1

Factorise completely $12a - 16b$

Solution 1

Step 1: The common factors of $12a$ and $16b$ are 2 and **4**
Step 2: The highest of the common factors is **4**
Step 3: $12a + 16b = \mathbf{4} \times 3a + \mathbf{4} \times 4b = \mathbf{4} \times (3a + 4b) = \mathbf{4}(3a + 4b)$
Check: $\qquad\qquad 4(3a + 4b) = 4 \times 3a + 4 \times 4b = 12a + 16b$ ✓

Exercise A

1 a Copy and complete the following to find the factors of 20 and $12x$

1×20	$2 \times \ldots$	$4 \times \ldots$			
$1 \times 12x$	$2 \times 6x$	$3 \times \ldots$	$4 \times \ldots$	$6 \times \ldots$	$12 \times \ldots$

Factors of 20	1, 2, 4, …, … and …
Factors of $12x$	1, 2, 3, 4, 6, 12, …, …, …, …, … and $12x$

b What is the highest of the common factors of $12x$ and 20?
c Factorise $12x + 20$

2 a i Copy and complete the following to find the factors of $18p$

$1 \times \ldots$	$2 \times \ldots$	$\ldots \times 6p$	$\ldots \times 3p$	$\ldots \times \ldots$	$18 \times \ldots$

ii Write a similar list of the factors of $12q$

b Copy and complete this table.

Factors of $18p$	1, 2, …, …, …, 18, …, …, $3p$, $6p$, … and …
Factors of $12q$	

c Factorise   **i** $18p + 12q$ **ii** $12p + 18q$

3 **a** Write a list of the factors of   **i** $8a$ **ii** $20b$
   b Factorise   **i** $8a + 20b$ **ii** $20a + 8b$

4 $6x$ 1 $3x$ x 9 $2x$ 3 $9x$ 6 $4x$ 2

   a Which of the cards above show the factors of
     i 3   **ii** 6   **iii** 9?
   b Which of the cards above show the factors of
     i $3x$ **ii** $6x$ **iii** $9x$?
   c Factorise
     i $6x + 3$ **ii** $3x + 9$ **iii** $9x + 6$ **iv** $6x + 9$

5 The diagram on the left shows the relation 'is a factor of'.
   a Copy and complete the diagram on the right.

The arrow says, '8 is a factor of $16x$'

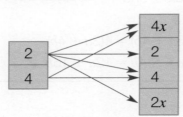

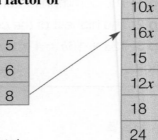

   b Use the diagram to help you factorise completely
     i $10x + 15$ **ii** $16x + 24$ **iii** $12x + 18$

6 Copy and complete this table.

a	$2a + 4$	$2(a + 2)$	**b**	$2b - 6$	$2(b - …)$
c	$4c + 6$	$2(2c + …)$	**d**	$4d - 10$	$2(… - 5)$
e	$6e + 18$	$6(… + …)$	**f**	$12f - 18$	$6(… - …)$
g	$18g + 12$	$6(… + …)$	**h**	$21h - 14$	$…(3h - 2)$
i	$26i + 8$	$…(13i + 4)$	**j**	$16j - 24$	$…(2j - 3)$
k	$4x + 6y$	$2(… + …)$	**l**	$8x - 2y$	$2(… - …)$
m	$12x + 30y$	$6(… + …)$	**n**	$12x - 9y$	$…(… - …)$
o	$14x + 8y$	$…(… + …)$			

7 Factorise completely

a $18a + 24$	b $18b - 27$	c $25c + 15$
d $21d - 35$	e $32e + 16$	f $32f - 24$
g $32g + 20$	h $18h - 45$	i $33i + 22$
j $40x - 60y$	k $26x + 39y$	l $24x - 60y$
m $4x + 6y$	n $6x - 8y$	o $12x + 40y$
p $60x - 90y$	q $56x + 48y$	r $48x - 72y$
s $50x + 75y$	t $80x - 32y$	

Example 2

a Factorise $a^2 + a$

b Factorise completely $b^3 - 2b^2$

Solution 2

a **Step 1:** Find the common factors of a^2 and a:

$a^2 = 1 \times a^2, a^2 = a \times a$
$a = 1 \times a$

Step 2: a is the highest common factor of a and a^2

Step 3:

Factors of a^2	**1**, a and a^2
Factors of a	**1** and a

$a^2 + a = a \times a + a \times 1 = a \times (a + 1) = a(a + 1)$

So $a^2 + a = a(a + 1)$

Check: $a(a + 1) = a \times a + a \times 1 = a^2 + a$ ✓

b **Step 1:**

$b^3 = 1 \times b^3 = b \times b^2$		
$2b^2 = 1 \times 2b^2$	$= 2 \times b^2$	$= b \times 2b$

Step 2: b^2 is the highest common factor of b^3 and $2b^2$

Factors of b^3	**1**, b, b^2 and b^3
Factors of $2b^2$	**1**, 2, b, $2b$, b^2 and $2b^2$

Step 3:

$b^3 - 2b^2 = b^2 \times b - b^2 \times 2 = b^2 \times (b - 2) = b^2(b - 2)$

So, $b^3 - 2b^2 = b^2(b - 2)$

Check: $b^2(b - 2) = b^2 \times b + b^2 \times -2 = b^3 - 2b^2$ ✓

Exercise B

1 **a** Dave is asked to **completely** factorise $20x + 40$
He gives the answer $10(2x + 4)$. Explain why he is wrong.

    b Melanie is asked to factorise $3x^2 + 2x$
She gives the answer $x(3x + 1)$. Explain why she is wrong.

2 Two of the expressions in the boxes are factors of the given expression.
In each case find the two factors.

a $75x + 100$ | 15 | $3x + 4$ | 50 | $5x + 2$ | 25 |

b $36x + 54$ | 18 | $9x + 2$ | 27 | $2x + 3$ | 4 |

c $80x + 60$ | 40 | $4x + 3$ | 20 | $2x + 5$ | 12 |

d $75x + 30$ | 25 | $5x + 2$ | 30 | $3x + 1$ | 15 |

3 a Copy and complete the diagram to show the factors of $20x + 30$

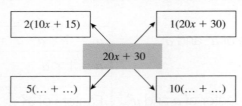

b Copy and complete the diagram to show the factors of $40x - 60y$

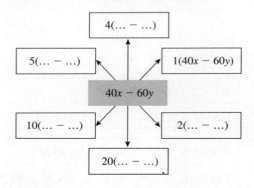

c Copy and complete the diagram to show the factors of $x^3 - 2x^2$

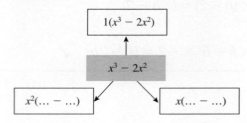

4 Find the value of a in each of the following.
a $16x + 8 = a(2x + 1)$ b $25x - 15 = 5(ax - 3)$
c $12x + 20y = a(3x + 5y)$ d $18p - 27q = 9(2p - aq)$
e $35p + 63q = a(5p + 9q)$

5 Find the values of b and c in each of the following.
  a $35x + 45 = b(cx + 9)$ **b** $42x + 70 = b(3x + c)$ **c** $30p - 48q = b(5p - cq)$
  d $20x + 55y = b(4x + cy)$ **e** $84p - 60q = b(cp - 5q)$

6 a **i** Write down all the factors of x^2.   **ii** Write down all the factors of $5x$.
    iii Factorise $x^2 + 5x$
  b **i** Write down all the factors of xy.   **ii** Write down all the factors of $2x^2$.
    iii Factorise $2x^2 - xy$

7 Copy and complete this table.

a	$a^2 + 2a$	$a(a + 2)$	**b**	$b^2 - 4b$	$b(\ldots - \ldots)$
c	$e^2 + 6e$	$\ldots(e + \ldots)$	**d**	$5f^2 - 2f$	$\ldots(5f - \ldots)$
e	$7g^2 + 6g$	$g(\ldots + \ldots)$	**f**	$4h^3 - h$	$h(\ldots - \ldots)$
g	$i^3 + 6i^2$	$i^2(\ldots + \ldots)$	**h**	$5j^4 - j^2$	$\ldots(\ldots - 1)$
i	$x^2 + xy$	$\ldots(\ldots + y)$	**j**	$4x^4 - 3xy$	$x(\ldots - \ldots)$

8 Factorise **completely**
  a $a^2 + 4a$ **b** $5b^2 - b$ **c** $c^2 + 8c$ **d** $8d^2 + d$
  e $4e - 3e^2$ **f** $ax + bx$ **g** $x - 6xy$ **h** $2x + 3xy$
  i $4x - xy$ **j** $12x^2 + 8y^2$ **k** $75x^2 - 50y^2$ **l** $56x^2 + 63y^2$
  m $x^3 - x$ **n** $x^3 + x^2$ **o** $x^3 - 3x^2$ **p** $x^5 + 5x^2$
  q $ax^6 - bx^3$ **r** $x^5 + 5xy$ **s** $3x^5 - 7x^3$ **t** $x^5 + xy^3$

9 a You are given that $6(3x - 5) + 3(4x - 5) = 15(ax + b)$.
    Find the values of a and b.
  b You are given that $5(4x - 5y) - 2(3x - 2y) = c(2x + dy)$.
    Find the values of c and d.

10 Factorise **completely**
  a **i** $6x + 12y - 30z$ **ii** $14x - 21y + 70z$ **iii** $25p + 35q + 50r$
  b **i** $24x - 60y - 72z$ **ii** $16x - 48y - 144$ **iii** $36p + 54q - 144$
  c **i** $x^4 + x^3 + x^2$ **ii** $2x^4 + 4x^3 + 6x^2$ **iii** $24x^4 - 60x^3 - 72x^2$

Chapter summary

- In the expression b^a, b is called the *base* and a the *power*.
- b^a is shorthand for multiplying b by itself a times.
- x^a is 'x to the power a'.
- To multiply and divide powers with **the same base** follow these rules
  - to multiply **add** the powers: $x^a \times x^b = x^{a+b}$
  - to divide **subtract** the powers: $x^a \div x^b = x^{a-b}$
- When multiplying terms that include both numbers and letters, deal with the numbers and letters separately.

- Expanding or multiplying out brackets:
  $a(b + c) = a \times b + a \times c = ab + ac$
- When an expression contains brackets and extra terms, first expand the brackets and then collect like terms.
- To multiply two expressions in brackets together, multiply **all** terms in the first bracket by **all** terms in the second bracket.
- Factorising is the inverse of expanding brackets.
  To factorise an expression completely:
  - Find the common factors of the terms in the expression.
  - Choose the highest common factor.
  - Write the expression as a product of its factors.
  - **Check** by expanding the factorised expression.

Chapter review

1 Work out the value of $2^7 \div 2^4$

2 Simplify
  a $x^5 \times x^2$ **b** $y^5 \div y^2$ **c** $w^6 \times w^2$ **d** $x^5 \div x^3$

3 Simplify
  a $c \times c \times c \times c$ **b** $d^5 \times d^3 \times d$ **c** $\dfrac{e^8}{e}$

4 Simplify
  a $5y^3 \times 3y^5$ **b** $2a^5 \times 3a^2$ **c** $8y^6 \div 4y^2$ **d** $\dfrac{36a^6}{9a^2}$

5 Expand
  a $4(m - 1)$ **b** $3(4y + 1)$ **c** $p(p + 3)$ **d** $s(s^2 + 6)$ **e** $4(p + 3q - r)$

6 Expand and simplify
  a $4(x + 1) + 3(2x - 5)$ **b** $5(2a - c) + 3(4a + 2c)$
  c $5(2a - 1) - 3(a - 4)$ **d** $3(5x - 4) - 5(2 - x)$

7 **a** Simplify   **i** $x + x + 2x$ **ii** $x \times 2x$
  b Multiply out the brackets and simplify $12 - 3(x + 2)$

8 Factorise
  a $9x + 18$ **b** $4c + 12$ **c** $10a + 5$ **d** $x^2 + 5x$ **e** $4a^2 + a$

9 Factorise completely
  a $12y - 54$ **b** $2a^2 - 4a$ **c** $3xy - 6y^2$

10 **a** Expand $4x(x^2 + 5)$ **b** Expand and simplify $4(x - 2) + 3(x + 2)$
   c Factorise $c^2 - 5c$ **d** Factorise completely $3x^2 - 9x$

11 **a** Calculate the value of $6^4 - 2^{10}$ **b** x is a positive integer.
                                       $4^x = 1\,048\,576$
                                       Find the value of x.

Angles, triangles and polygons

27.1 Parallel lines

CAN YOU REMEMBER

- That parallel lines are lines which are always the same distance apart?
- That angles at a point add up to 360°?
- That angles on a straight line add up to 180°?
- That vertically opposite angles are equal?

IN THIS SECTION YOU WILL

- Understand and use the terms 'alternate', 'corresponding' and 'allied angles'.
- Calculate the sizes of angles between parallel lines.

The diagram shows two *parallel* lines cut by a third line.
The arrowheads indicate that the lines are parallel.
The third line is called a *transversal*.

Several equal pairs of angles are formed.

Alternate angles form a Z-shape a usingthe parallel lines.

The angles are on opposite sides of the transversal.

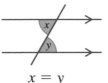 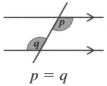

$x = y$ $p = q$

Alternate angles are always equal.

Corresponding angles are formed within an *F*-shape. These angles are in similar positions on the same side of the transversal.

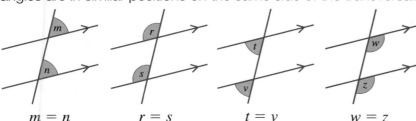

$m = n$ $r = s$ $t = v$ $w = z$

Corresponding angles are always equal.

Allied angles are inside a pair of parallel lines as shown.

Allied angles always add up to 180°.

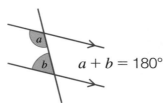

$a + b = 180°$

Example 1

Work out the value of the angles marked by letters. Give reasons for your answers.

a 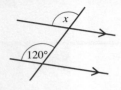   **b** 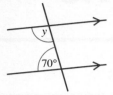   **c**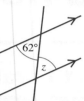

Solution 1

a $x = 120°$ (corresponding angles)
b $y = 180° - 70° = 110°$ (allied angles)
c $z = 62°$ (alternate angles)

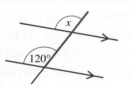

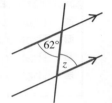

Exercise A

In the following exercise the diagrams are not drawn accurately.

1 Write down the value of angle x in each of these diagrams.

a 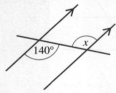   **b**   **c**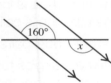

d 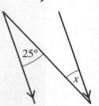   **e** 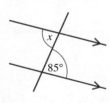   **f**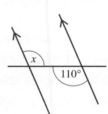

2 Write down the value of angle y in each of these diagrams.

a 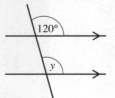   **b** 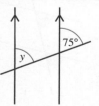   **c**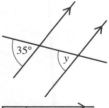

d 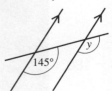   **e** 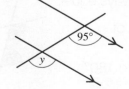   **f**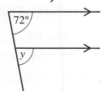

3 Work out the value of the angles marked by letters.

a
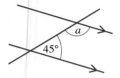

b
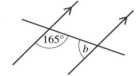

c
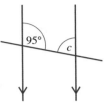

d
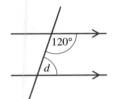

e
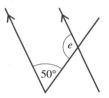

f
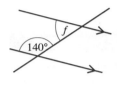

4 Calculate the value of each of the angles marked by letters.
Give reasons for your answers.

a
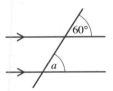

b
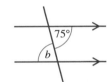

c
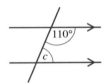

d

e
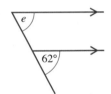

f
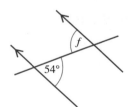

5 Calculate the value of each of the angles marked by letters.
Give reasons for your answers.

a
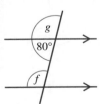

b
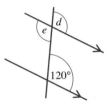

c
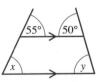

d
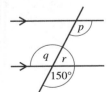

e
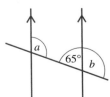

6   Work out the size of each angle marked by a letter in the following diagrams.
Give reasons for your answers.

a 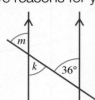   **b** 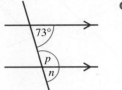   **c** 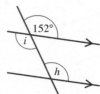   **d**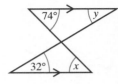

Example 2

Calculate the values of the marked
angles in this diagram.
Give reasons for your answers.

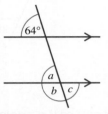

Solution 2

$a = 64°$ (corresponding angles)
$b = 180° - 64° = 116°$ (angles on a straight line total 180°)
$c = 64°$ (vertically opposite to a)

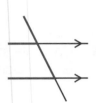

Exercise B

In the following exercise the diagrams are not drawn accurately.

1   In each part, work out the values of the angles marked by letters.

a 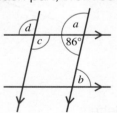   **b** 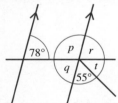   **c**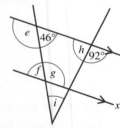

d 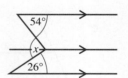   **e** 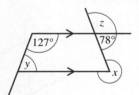   **f**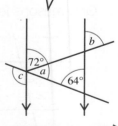

g 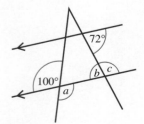   **h** 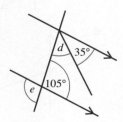   **i**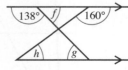

2 In the diagram AB is parallel to CD.
  a Write down the value of x.
  Give a reason for your answer.
  b Find the value of y.

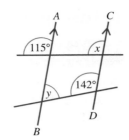

3 Work out the values of angles x, y and z.
  a

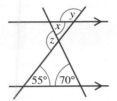

  b

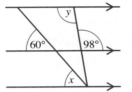

4 Find the size of p and q.
  Give reasons for your answer.
  a

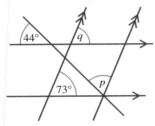

  b

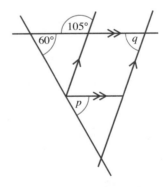

5 a Write down the size of angle a.
  b Work out the size of angle b.

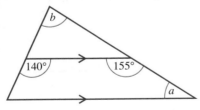

6 Work out the sizes of angles p, q, r and s.

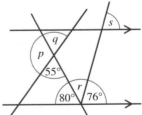

8 Look at these diagrams. Give reasons for your answers.
  a Are lines AB and CD parallel?
  b Are lines PQ and RS parallel?

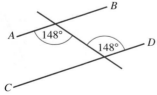

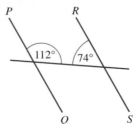

27.2 Angles in quadrilaterals

IN THIS SECTION YOU WILL

- Use your knowledge of triangles to show that the angles in any quadrilateral add up to 360°.
- Understand and use the angle properties of a trapezium, parallelogram and rhombus.
- Calculate the interior angles of any quadrilateral.

Any quadrilateral can be divided into two triangles by drawing a diagonal.

The angles in each triangle add up to 180°.

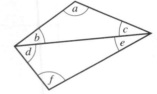

$a + b + c = 180°$ $\qquad d + e + f = 180°$

So $a + b + c + d + e + f = 180° + 180° = 360°$.

The angles in any quadrilateral add up to 360°.

Example 1

Calculate the size of angle x.

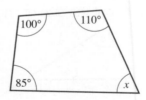

Solution 1

$110° + 100° + 85° = 295°$
The angles in any quadrilateral add up to 360°.
$x = 360° - 295° = 65°$

These quadrilaterals have one or two pairs of parallel sides.

rectangle 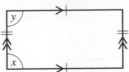   parallelogram 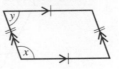   rhombus   trapezium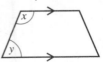

In each diagram x and y are allied angles between parallel lines.
So $x + y = 180°$.

Example 2

ABCD is a trapezium.
Calculate the size of angles *a* and *b*.
Give reasons for your answers.

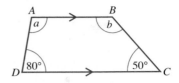

Solution 2

AB and *CD* are parallel.
So $a + 80° = 180°$ (allied angles), $a = 100°$
  $b + 50° = 180°$ (allied angles), $b = 130°$

Exercise A

1 Calculate the size of angle *x* in each of these quadrilaterals.

a
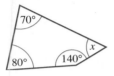

b

c

2 Each diagram shows a trapezium.
Calculate the sizes of the angles marked by letters.

a
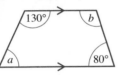

b
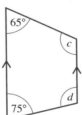

c
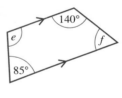

3 Each diagram shows a rhombus.
Calculate the sizes of the angles marked by letters.

a

b

4 Each diagram shows a kite. Calculate the sizes of the angles marked by letters.

a
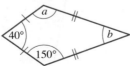

b
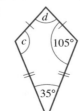

5 Each diagram shows a parallelogram.
Calculate the sizes of the angles marked by letters.

a

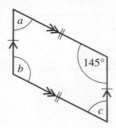

b

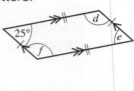

In each of the questions below calculate the size of the angles marked by letters.

6 a

b

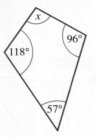

c

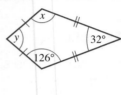

7 a

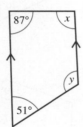

b

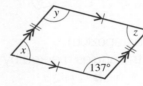

c

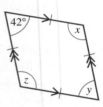

8 a

b

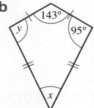

c

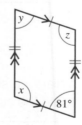

Example 3

Calculate the size of the angles marked by letters in
the diagram. Give a reason for each answer.

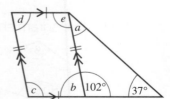

Solution 3

$a + 102° + 37° = 180°$ (angles in a triangle add up to 180°)
$a = 180° - 139° = 41°$
$b = 180° - 102°$ (angles on a straight line add up to 180°)
$b = 78°$

$b + c = 180°$ (allied angles)
$c = 180° - 78° = 102°$
$e = c = 102°$ (opposite angles of a parallelogram are equal)
$d = b = 78°$ (opposite angles of a parallelogram are equal)

Exercise B

1 Calculate the values of the angles marked by letters. Give a reason for each answer.

a

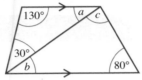

b

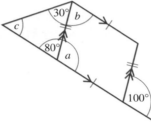

2 The diagram shows a kite.
Calculate the size of the angle marked x.
(Hint: other angles may need to be
worked out first.)

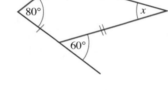

3 The diagram shows a rhombus with
one diagonal drawn in.
Calculate the size of angle x.

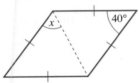

4 The diagram shows a trapezium.
Calculate the values of x and y.
Hence write down the four angles of
the trapezium.

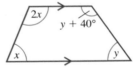

5 Calculate the
  a size of angle x **b** value of y.

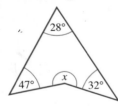

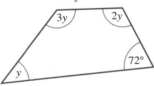

6 Find the values of angles x and y.

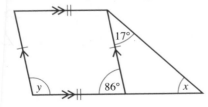

7 The diagram shows a quadrilateral.
Find the value of p.

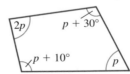

8 *ABCD* is a quadrilateral.
Find the value of *q* and hence write
down the size of each angle.

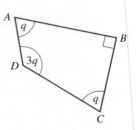

27.3 Properties of polygons

CAN YOU REMEMBER

- That angles on a straight line total 180°?
- That there are 360° in a full turn?
- How to draw lines of symmetry?
- How to find the order of rotational symmetry of a 2-D shape?

IN THIS SECTION YOU WILL

- Recognise and name polygons.
- Understand the symmetry of regular polygons.
- Learn how to calculate interior and exterior angles of polygons.

A *polygon* is a two-dimensional shape made by straight lines.
A triangle is a polygon with three sides.
A quadrilateral is a polygon with four sides.

Other polygons include:

pentagon – five sides	*hexagon* – six sides	regular hexagon
heptagon – seven sides	*octagon* – eight sides	
nonagon – nine sides	*decagon* – ten sides	regular octagon

A *regular polygon* has all sides equal and all angles equal.

The number of lines of symmetry of a regular polygon is equal to the number of sides.

regular pentagon
five lines of symmetry

regular hexagon
six lines of symmetry

The order of rotational symmetry of a regular polygon is equal to the number of sides.

order 5   order 6

A regular polygon can be drawn using a circle.

Example 1

Example 1

Use the circle method to draw a regular hexagon.

Solution 1

Step 1: Use compasses to draw a circle.
Step 2: Divide 360° by the number of sides of a hexagon.

$360° \div 6 = 60°$

Step 3: Use a protractor to divide the circle into
six equal *sectors*, each with angle 60° at the centre.
Step 4: Join the points where the sector
lines meet the circle, to form the hexagon.

Exercise A

1 Write down the name of each of these polygons.

a   b   c

d   e   f

2 Copy and complete this table.

Name of regular polygon	Number of sides	Number of lines of symmetry	Order of rotational symmetry
pentagon	5	5	5
hexagon			
heptagon			7
octagon			
nonagon		9	
decagon			

3 Copy each of these regular polygons and draw in all the lines of symmetry.

a   b   c

4 Use the circle method to draw:
  a a regular pentagon   **b** a regular octagon.

5 A regular icosagon has 20 sides.
How many lines of symmetry does the icosagon have?

6 Use the circle method to draw a regular decagon.

7 A regular dodecagon has 12 sides.
Write down the order of rotational symmetry of a regular dodecagon.

8 Write down the number of lines of symmetry of
  a a regular polygon with 15 sides.   **b** a regular polygon with 18 sides.

9 Use the circle method to draw a regular nonagon.

Angles inside a polygon at the vertices are called *interior angles*.
If a side of the polygon is extended, the angle formed
outside the polygon is called an *exterior angle*.
Interior and exterior angles form a straight line.
So at each vertex
interior angle + exterior angle = 180°

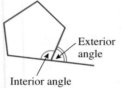

In any regular polygon:
■ interior angles are all equal
■ exterior angles are all equal.

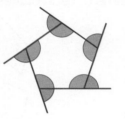

Example 2

A regular polygon has exterior angles of 36°.
Find the size of an interior angle of this polygon.

Not drawn accurately

Solution 2

Interior angle + exterior angle = 180°
Interior angle + 36° = 180°
So interior angle = 144°

Exercise B

1 The exterior angle of a regular polygon is 60°.
Find the size of the interior angle of this polygon.

Not drawn accurately

2 Here are the exterior angles of some polygons.
Work out the interior angles.
  a 50°   **b** 30°   **c** 45°   **d** 80°   **e** 75°   **f** 110°

3 The interior angle of a regular polygon is 160°.
Work out the size of the exterior angle.

Not drawn accurately

4 Here are the interior angles of some polygons.
Work out the exterior angles.

    a 65°   **b** 120°   **c** 55°   **d** 95°   **e** 140°   **f** 25°

5 Here are the exterior angles of some polygons.
Work out the interior angles.

    a 40°   **b** 72°   **c** 36°   **d** 120°

6 Here are the interior angles of some polygons.
Work out the exterior angles.

    a 108°   **b** 135°   **c** 168°   **d** 150°

7 Each interior angle of a regular pentagon is 108°.
Calculate the total sum of all the interior angles of
a regular pentagon.

8 Each exterior angle of a regular hexagon is 60°.

    a How many exterior angles does
a hexagon have?

    b Calculate the total sum of the exterior
angles of a hexagon.

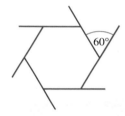

9 Each exterior angle of an octagon is 45°.
Calculate the sum of the exterior angles of an octagon.

27.4 Angles in polygons

CAN YOU REMEMBER

- That angles in a triangle total 180° and that angles in a quadrilateral total 360°?
- That in any polygon the interior angle + the exterior angle = 180°?
- That a regular polygon has all sides equal and all angles equal?

IN THIS SECTION YOU WILL

- Learn how to calculate the sum of the interior angles of any polygon.
- Use a formula to calculate the exterior angle of a regular polygon.
- Use angle properties to work out the number of sides of a given polygon.

The sum of the angles of a quadrilateral is 360° because
the quadrilateral can be divided into two triangles.

$2 \times 180° = 360°$

All polygons can be divided into triangles by drawing the diagonals from one vertex.
A pentagon divides into three triangles.
So the sum of the interior angles in a pentagon is $3 \times 180° = 540°$

The five exterior angles on this pentagon
fit together round a point.

$a + b + c + d + e = 360°$

The same is true for any polygon.

For any polygon:
■ the sum of the exterior angles of the polygon is equal to 360°
■ the number of exterior angles = the number of sides.

In a regular polygon all exterior angles are equal.
Each exterior angle can be found using the formula:

$$\text{Exterior angle} = \frac{360°}{\text{Number of sides}}$$

The number of sides of a regular polygon can be found using the formula:

$$\text{Number of sides} = \frac{360°}{\text{Exterior angle}}$$

Example 1

By drawing the diagonals from one vertex, work out the sum of the interior angles in a hexagon.

Solution 1

A hexagon divides into four triangles.
So the sum of the interior angles in a hexagon is $4 \times 180° = 720°$

Example 2

A regular polygon has an exterior angle of 36°.
How many sides has the polygon?

Not drawn accurately

Solution 2

$$\text{Number of sides} = \frac{360°}{\text{Exterior angle}} = \frac{360°}{36°} = 10$$

The polygon has ten sides.

Exercise A

1 Draw an octagon. By drawing the diagonals from one vertex, work out the sum of the interior angles of an octagon.

2 Copy these diagrams. By drawing the diagonals from one vertex, work out the sum of the angles of each polygon.

a   **b**

3 A regular polygon has 12 sides.
Calculate the size of each exterior angle of the polygon.

4 A regular polygon has nine sides. Find the size of:
   a   each exterior angle   **b**   each interior angle.

5 Each exterior angle of a regular polygon is 60°.
How many sides has this polygon?

6 A regular polygon has 18 sides.
Calculate the size of the exterior angle.

7 Each interior angle of a regular polygon is 162°.
How many sides has this polygon?

8 A regular polygon has an interior angle of 135°.
   a   Calculate the size of each exterior angle.
   b   How many sides has this polygon?
   c   Write down the name of this polygon.

9 A regular polygon has 15 sides.
What is the size of each exterior angle?

10 Calculate the value of each missing exterior angle in these polygons.

   a   **b**

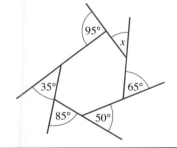 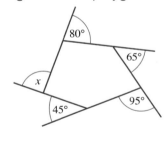

The table shows the sum of the interior angles of some polygons.

Each time the number of sides increases by 1 the sum of the angles increases by 180°.

With **3** sides the sum is $1 \times 180°$

With **4** sides the sum is $2 \times 180°$

With **n** sides the sum is $(n - 2) \times 180°$

Sum of the interior angles of a polygon
$= (n - 2) \times 180°$, where n is the
number of sides.

Polygon	Number of sides	Sum of interior angles
Triangle	3	180°
Quadrilateral	4	360°
Pentagon	5	540°
Hexagon	6	720°

Example 3

The diagram shows a hexagon. Calculate the size of angle x.

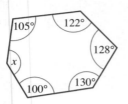

Solution 3

Sum of the interior angles of a hexagon
$= (n - 2) \times 180° = (6 - 2) \times 180° = 4 \times 180° = 720°$
So $105° + 122° + 128° + 130° + 100° + x = 720°$
$$585° + x = 720°$$
$$x = 135°$$

Exercise B

1 Calculate the sum of the interior angles of a decagon.

2 A polygon has 22 sides.
Calculate the sum of the interior angles.

3 Work out the size of the missing angle in each of these polygons.

a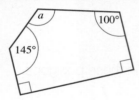

b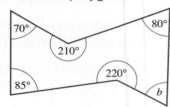

4 The sum of the interior angles of a polygon is 1800°.
How many sides has the polygon?

5 The diagram shows an octagon.

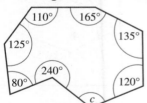

Calculate the size of the angle marked c.

6 Calculate the size of the angle marked with a letter in each of these polygons.

a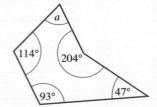

b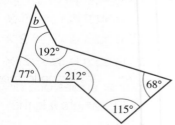

c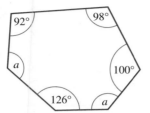

d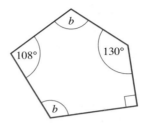

e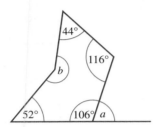

f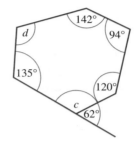

9 A regular hexagon and a regular pentagon are joined together as shown.
Calculate the size of angle x.

10 This diagram shows three regular polygons.
Calculate the size of angle x.

27.5 Pythagoras' theorem

CAN YOU REMEMBER

- That a right-angled triangle has one angle of 90°?
- The square numbers up to $15^2 = 225$?
- How to find squares and square roots using a calculator?

IN THIS SECTION YOU WILL

- Use Pythagoras' theorem to calculate the lengths of sides of right-angled triangles.
- Use Pythagoras' theorem to work out whether a triangle is right-angled.

In a right-angled triangle the longest side of the triangle is opposite to the right angle. This side is called the *hypotenuse*.

hypotenuse

The diagram shows a right-angled triangle with sides of length 3 cm, 4 cm and 5 cm. Squares have been constructed on each side of the triangle.

The areas of these squares are 9, 16 and 25 cm².

The area of the large square is equal to the sum of the areas of the other two squares.
$9 + 16 = 25$ so $3^2 + 4^2 = 5^2$

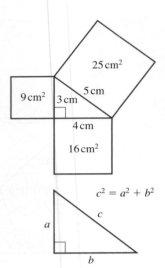

Pythagoras, an ancient Greek mathematician, found that this was true for all right-angled triangles.
Pythagoras' theorem: In any right-angled triangle the square of the hypotenuse is always equal to the sum of the squares of the two shorter sides.

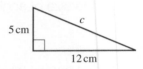

Example 1

Calculate the missing length on this triangle.

Solution 1

The triangle is right-angled so use Pythagoras' theorem.
$c^2 = a^2 + b^2 = 5^2 + 12^2 = 25 + 144$
$c^2 = 169$ Take the square root of each side.
$c = \sqrt{169} = 13$ cm

Example 2

Calculate the length of side c.

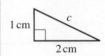

Give your answer
a   as a square root   **b**   to one decimal place.

Solution 2

The triangle is right-angled so use Pythagoras' theorem.
$c^2 = a^2 + b^2 = 1^2 + 2^2 = 1 + 4$
$c^2 = 5$ Take the square root of each side.
a $c = \sqrt{5}$ **b** $c = 2.23606\ldots = 2.2$ (to 1 d.p.)

Exercise A

1 Find the length of the hypotenuse in each of these triangles.

a
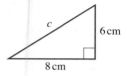
6 cm
c
8 cm

b
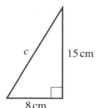
c
15 cm
8 cm

c
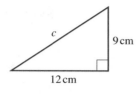
c
9 cm
12 cm

2 Find the length of the hypotenuse, marked *c*, in each of these triangles.
Leave each answer as a square root.

a
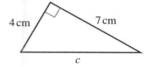
4 cm
7 cm
c

b
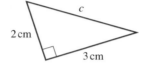
2 cm
c
3 cm

c
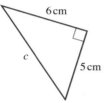
6 cm
c
5 cm

3 Calculate the length of the missing side, marked *x*, in each of these triangles.

a
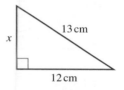
13 cm
x
12 cm

b
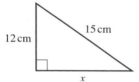
12 cm
15 cm
x

c

5 cm
x
3 cm

d

8 cm
10 cm
x

4 Calculate the length of the missing side, marked *x*, in each of these triangles.
Leave each answer as a square root.

a
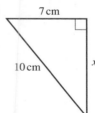
7 cm
10 cm
x

b
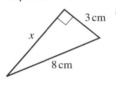
3 cm
x
8 cm

c
10 cm
x
2 cm

d
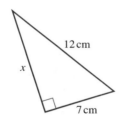
12 cm
x
7 cm

5 A rectangle has a length of 9 cm and a width of 5 cm.
Calculate the length of the diagonal.
Leave your answer as a square root.

5 cm
9 cm

6 Calculate the length of the diagonal of each of these rectangles.
Give your answers to one decimal place.

a
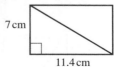
7 cm
11.4 cm

b

21 cm
16 cm

c
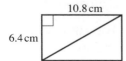
10.8 cm
6.4 cm

7 Calculate the length of the hypotenuse in each of these right-angled triangles.
Give your answers to one decimal place.

a

3.2 cm

c

5.4 cm

b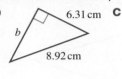

4.5 cm

5.7 cm

c

c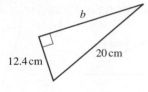

25.2 cm

17.6 cm

c

d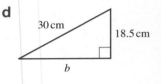

20.7 cm

c

14.9 cm

8 Calculate the length of side b in each of these triangles.
Give your answers to two decimal places.

a

6.5 cm

b

13.4 cm

b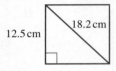

6.31 cm

b

8.92 cm

c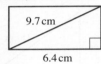

b

12.4 cm

20 cm

d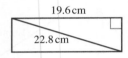

30 cm

18.5 cm

b

9 Calculate the width of each of these rectangles.
Give your answers to two decimal places.

a

12.5 cm

18.2 cm

b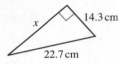

9.7 cm

6.4 cm

c

19.6 cm

22.8 cm

10 Calculate the length of the missing side in each of these triangles.

a

x

14.3 cm

22.7 cm

b

2.4 cm

x

8.9 cm

c

4.5 cm

x

4.5 cm

d

17.5 cm

x

12.2 cm

e

13.6 cm

x

9.8 cm

Example 3

An equilateral triangle has sides 8 cm long.
What is its vertical height?

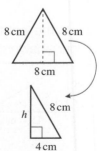

8 cm 8 cm

8 cm

h 8 cm

4 cm

Solution 3

The vertical height divides the equilateral triangle
into two right-angled triangles of equal size.
Pythagoras' theorem can be used with one of these
right-angled triangles to find the vertical height (h).

$h^2 + 4^2 = 8^2$

$h^2 + 16 = 64$ Subtract 16 from both sides.

$h^2 = 64 - 16 = 48$

$h = \sqrt{48} = 6.9$ cm (1 d.p.)

Example 4

A ladder 5 m long stands against a vertical wall. The foot of the ladder is 1 m away from the wall. How far up the wall does the ladder reach?

Solution 4

Draw a sketch.

$h^2 + 1^2 = 5^2$

$h^2 + 1 = 25$

$h^2 = 25 - 1 = 24$

$h = \sqrt{24} = 4.9$ m (1 d.p)

The ladder reaches 4.9 m up the wall.

5 m

Exercise B

1 Calculate the vertical height, h, of this equilateral triangle.

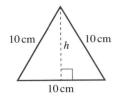

10 cm h 10 cm

10 cm

2 Copy the tables.
Use the patterns in the tables to complete them.
Check your answers using Pythagoras' theorem.

a

Side a	Side b	Hypotenuse c
3	4	5
6	8	10
9	12	15
12		

b

Side a	Side b	Hypotenuse c
5	12	13
0.5	1.2	
50		130
	1200	1300

3 A man walks 6.7 km due south and then turns to walk 3.8 km due west.
How much shorter would the distance be if he walked straight from his starting point to his finishing point?

4 Check whether each of these triangles is right-angled. Show your working.
  a Side lengths 2 cm, 3 cm and 4 cm.
  b Side lengths 12 cm, 16 cm and 20 cm.
  c Side lengths 6 cm, 9 cm and 12 cm.
  d Side lengths 9 cm, 40 cm and 41 cm.
  e Side lengths 7 cm, 24 cm and 25 cm.

5 An isosceles triangle has two sides 9.2 cm
long and a third side which is 7.4 cm long.
Calculate the height of the triangle.

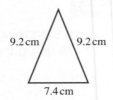

6 A ladder 8.4 m long rests against a wall.
The foot of the ladder is 1.7 m away from the wall.
How high up the wall does the ladder reach?

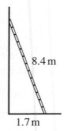

7 A flagpole 9.8 m high is held firm by a wire fixed to its top
and to a point on the ground 6.4 m from the foot of the pole.
How long is the wire?

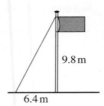

8 Find the length of AB.

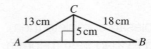

9 Calculate the lengths of x and y in these diagrams.

  a 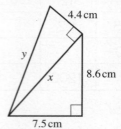   **b** 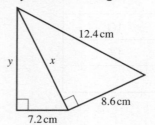   **c**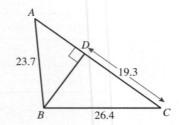

Chapter summary

- When two parallel lines are cut by a third line:

    Alternate angles are equal.

    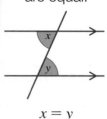

    $x = y$

    Corresponding angles are equal.

    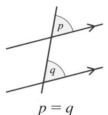

    $p = q$

    Allied angles add up to 180°.

    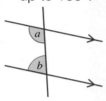

    $a + b = 180°$

- The angles in any quadrilateral add up to 360°.
  $120° + 50° + 130° + 60° = 360°$

    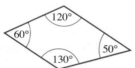

- Quadrilaterals with parallel sides have pairs of allied angles.

    rectangle   parallelogram   rhombus   trapezium

      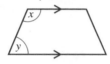

    In each diagram $x + y = 180°$.

- A polygon is a two-dimensional shape made by straight lines.

    pentagon − five sides   hexagon − six sides   heptagon − seven sides
    octagon − eight sides   nonagon − nine sides   decagon − ten sides

- A regular polygon has all sides equal and all angles equal.

- The number of lines of symmetry of a regular polygon is equal to the number of sides.

- The order of rotational symmetry of a regular polygon is equal to the number of sides.

- At each vertex of any polygon the sum of the exterior and interior angles is 180°.

    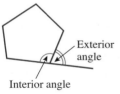

    Exterior angle

    Interior angle

- In any regular polygon:
    - interior angles are all equal
    - exterior angles are all equal.

    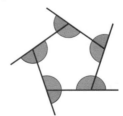

- The sum of the exterior angles of any polygon is equal to 360°.

- An exterior angle of a regular polygon can be found using the formula:

$$\text{Exterior angle} = \frac{360°}{\text{Number of sides}}$$

- The number of sides of a regular polygon can be found using the formula:

  Number of sides $= \dfrac{360°}{\text{Exterior angle}}$

- Sum of the interior angles of a polygon $= (n - 2) \times 180°$, where n is the number of sides.

- Pythagoras' theorem: In any right-angled triangle the square of the hypotenuse is always equal to the sum of the squares of the two shorter sides.

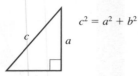

Chapter review

1 The diagram shows a kite.

  a Write down the value of p.
     Give a reason for your answer.

  b Work out the value of q.

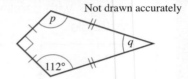

Not drawn accurately

2 Two sides of a regular pentagon have been drawn in the circle.
Trace the circle and lines.
Complete the regular pentagon.

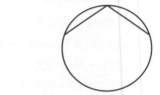

3 **a** ABC is a right-angled triangle.
    Angle $B = 63°$.
    Work out the size of angle A.

  b The diagram shows a regular decagon.

    Calculate the size of the exterior angle,
    marked x on the diagram.

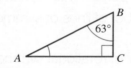

Not drawn accurately

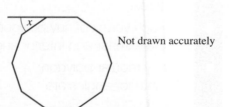

Not drawn accurately

4 The diagram shows a trapezium.

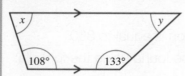

Not drawn accurately

Calculate the values of x and y.

5 **a** The diagram shows a regular hexagon.
     i How many axes of symmetry does
        a regular hexagon have?
     ii Calculate the size of the exterior angle x.
  b Work out the value of y in the triangle below.

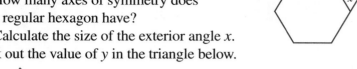

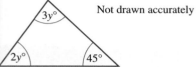

Not drawn accurately

6 The diagram shows a field.
The length of the field, $AB = 130$ m.
The width of the field, $AD = 85$ m.
Calculate the length of the diagonal BD.
Give your answer to one decimal place.

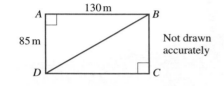

7 The triangle ABC has angles $3x°$, $4x°$ and $5x°$.
Form an equation and solve it to find the
value of x.

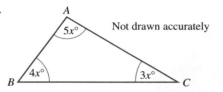

8 Each exterior angle of a regular polygon is 18°.
  a How many sides does the polygon have?
  b Calculate the sum of the interior angles of the polygon.

9 ABC is a right-angled triangle.
$AC = 29$ cm and $AB = 19$ cm.
Calculate the length of BC.

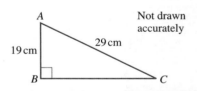

Ratio and proportion

28.1 Ratio

IN THIS SECTION YOU WILL

■ Use ratio notation.
■ Write ratios in their simplest form.
■ Divide quantities in a given ratio.

A *ratio* compares two or more quantities.

The ratio of red beads to blue beads on this necklace is $3 : 1$

For every 3 red beads on the necklace there is 1 blue bead.
The numbers in a ratio can be multiplied or divided by the same number to get an *equivalent ratio*.

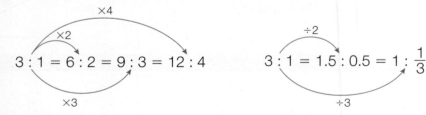

$$3 : 1 = 6 : 2 = 9 : 3 = 12 : 4$$

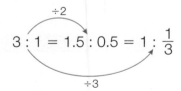

$$3 : 1 = 1.5 : 0.5 = 1 : \frac{1}{3}$$

The simplest form of a ratio has whole numbers with no common factors apart from 1
For example $3 : 1$ and $5 : 2$
The ratio $6 : 4$ is not in simplest form because 6 and 4 have a common factor of 2

$1 : \frac{1}{3}$ is not in simplest form because $\frac{1}{3}$ is not a whole number.

To write a ratio in its simplest form:
■ if the ratio includes fractions or decimals, multiply to make both parts whole numbers
■ divide both parts by their common factors.

Write each ratio in its simplest form.

a 9 : 6   **b** 12 : 15 : 18   **c** 1.6 : 2.4   **d** $\frac{1}{2}$: 7

Solution 1

a 9 : 6 = 3 : 2 (dividing both parts by 3)
b 12 : 15 : 18 = 12 ÷ 3 : 15 ÷ 3 : 18 ÷ 3 = 4 : 5 : 6
c Write the ratio 1.6 : 2.4 using whole numbers, by multiplying each value by 10
   1.6 : 2.4 = 1.6 × 10 : 2.4 × 10 = 16 : 24
   Divide by the common factor 8
   16 : 24 = 16 ÷ 8 : 24 ÷ 8 = 2 : 3
d Write the ratio $\frac{1}{2}$: 7 using whole numbers, by multiplying each value by 2
   $\frac{1}{2}$: 7 = $\frac{1}{2}$ × 2 : 7 × 2 = 1 : 14

Example 2

The ratio of green counters to yellow counters in a bag is 3 : 5
There are 45 green counters.
How many yellow counters are there?

Solution 2

For every three green counters there are five yellow counters.
45 ÷ 3 = 15
45 green counters = 15 lots of three green counters
15 lots of five yellow counters = 15 × 5 = 75 yellow counters

Exercise A

1 Copy and complete the following equivalent ratios.
   a 1 : 4 = 2 : …   **b** 3 : 1 = … : 2
   c 1 : 5 = 3 : …   **d** 4 : 1 = 16 : …
   e 2 : 3 = … : 9   **f** 6 : 1 = 18 : …
   g 3 : 2 = … : 8   **h** 5 : 3 = … : 9

2 Each set of cards shows four equivalent ratios and a different ratio.
   Which is the odd one out?
   a   **b**

   c   **d**

3 a Which of these ratios are equivalent to 3 : 2?

b Which of these ratios are equivalent to 5 : 3?

4 Here are some necklaces with blue and white beads.

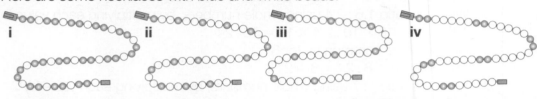

i   ii   iii   iv

a Match the necklaces to the ratios of blue to white beads.

b One necklace is missing. Draw the necklace.

5 Write each ratio in its simplest form.

a 3 : 6	**b** 8 : 4	**c** 9 : 3	**d** 2 : 6
e 15 : 10	**f** 21 : 7	**g** 4 : 24	**h** 20 : 25
i 24 : 32	**j** 25 : 40	**k** 36 : 48	**l** 40 : 48
m 60 : 45			

6 Write each ratio in its simplest form.

a 1.2 : 2.4	**b** 0.5 : 1.5	**c** 3.2 : 1.6	**d** 1.5 : 4.5
e 1.6 : 0.8	**f** 2.1 : 1.4	**g** 2.5 : 5	**h** 7.5 : 2.5
i 0.4 : 1.6	**j** 3.5 : 0.5	**k** 4.8 : 3.6	**l** 1.2 : 6
m 2.7 : 1.8	**n** 3.2 : 3.6	**o** 3.6 : 7.2	**p** 4.2 : 2.8

7 Write each ratio in its simplest form.

a $1\frac{1}{2} : 3$	**b** $\frac{1}{2} : 4$	**c** $5 : \frac{1}{3}$	**d** $2\frac{1}{2} : 5$
e $1\frac{1}{4} : 2\frac{1}{2}$	**f** $5 : 1\frac{1}{4}$	**g** $\frac{1}{5} : 1$	**h** $2 : \frac{1}{3}$
i $\frac{2}{3} : 1$	**j** $4 : \frac{3}{4}$	**k** $1\frac{1}{4} : 2\frac{3}{4}$	**l** $1\frac{1}{3} : 2\frac{1}{4}$

8 A waiter pours out two glasses of juice in the ratio 2 : 3
The larger glass contains 180 ml of juice.
How much does the smaller glass contain?

9 The numbers of apples and pears on a fruit stall are in the ratio 3 : 2
There are 360 apples. How many pears are there?

10 The perimeters of two squares are in the ratio 1 : 4
The perimeter of the smaller square is 20 cm.
What is the perimeter of the larger square?

11 Write each ratio in its simplest form.

a 15:12:9	**b** 24:36:48	**c** 20:40:30	**d** 9:3:12
e 12:8:16	**f** 20:36:24	**g** 18:32:40	**h** 10:90:28
i 14:21:35	**j** 36:48:24	**k** 72:36:18	**l** 100:20:25
m 84:72:60	**n** 40:50:70	**o** 27:81:9	**p** 48:36:72

12 The area of a garden is made up of lawns and plants in the ratio 2:3
The area of plants is 85 hectares. What is the area of the lawns?

13 The ratio of soft sweets to hard sweets in a bag is 3:1
There are 16 hard sweets. How many soft sweets?

14 Mr and Mrs Khan share the driving in the ratio 4:5
Mr Khan drives 60 miles. How many miles does Mrs Khan drive?

Example 3

Divide £24 in the ratio 1:3

Solution 3

The money is divided into lots of £1 and £3
£1 + £3 = £4
£24 ÷ £4 = 6   There are six lots of £4 in £24
6 lots of £1 = £6   6 lots of £3 = £18
£24 divided in the ratio 1:3 = £6:£18   Check: £6 + £18 = £24

Example 4

Matt and Viki share £72 in the ratio 2:7 with Viki having the larger share.
How much more is Viki's share than Matt's share?

Solution 4

For every £2 that Matt gets, Viki gets £7   £2 + £7 = £9
£72 ÷ £9 = 8   There are eight lots of £9 in £72

Method 1
8 lots of £2 = £16
8 lots of £7 = £56
£72 divided in the ratio 2:7 = £16:£56
Matt gets £16 and Viki gets £56
So Viki's share = £40 more than Matt's share.

Method 2
For each £2 that Matt gets, Viki gets £5 more.
8 lots of £5 = £40
So Viki's share = £40 more than Matt's share.

Exercise B

1 **a** Divide £21 in the ratio 6 : 1
    b Divide 25 metres in the ratio 1 : 4
   c Divide $40 in the ratio 7 : 1
    d Divide €18 in the ratio 1 : 5
   e Divide £36 in the ratio 5 : 4
    f Divide 20 litres in the ratio 3 : 5
   g Divide 48 sweets in the ratio 5 : 3
   h Divide £28 in the ratio 4 : 3
   i Divide £28 in the ratio 3 : 2 : 2
   j Divide 75 litres in the ratio 2 : 3 : 5
   k Divide $100 in the ratio 5 : 2 : 3
   l Divide €48 in the ratio 2 : 3 : 3

2 In each part find the smaller share when:
   a £80 is divided in the ratio 3 : 2
    b 70 cm is divided in the ratio 2 : 5
   c $30 is divided in the ratio 2 : 3
    d €27 is divided in the ratio 4 : 5

3 In each part find the larger share when:
   a 36 g is divided in the ratio 4 : 5
    b 42 sweets are divided in the ratio 3 : 4
   c £110 is divided in the ratio 7 : 4
    d 130 cm is divided in the ratio 5 : 8

4 **a** Divide $100 in the ratio 5 : 2 : 3
    b Divide 70 sweets in the ratio 2 : 2 : 3
   c Divide £120 in the ratio 4 : 3 : 5
   d Divide 40 cm in the ratio 2 : 3 : 3

5 Jack and Jill share 24 litres of water in the ratio 5 : 3
How much more water does Jack have than Jill?

6 **a** Divide £96 in the ratio 1 : 7
    b Divide 144 metres in the ratio 1 : 15
   c Divide $108 in the ratio 8 : 1
    d Divide €180 in the ratio 1 : 8
   e Divide £550 in the ratio 4 : 1
    f Divide 2424 cm in the ratio 1 : 11

7 In each part find the smaller share when:
   a £120 is divided in the ratio 4 : 1
    b 480 m is divided in the ratio 1 : 15
   c $750 is divided in the ratio 9 : 1
    d €1200 is divided in the ratio 1 : 7
   e 3600 g is divided in the ratio 5 : 3 : 1
  f £840 is divided in the ratio 3 : 3 : 1

8 In each part find the larger share when:
   a 300 m is divided in the ratio 1 : 14
    b $500 is divided in the ratio 9 : 1
   c €1024 is divided in the ratio 1 : 7
    d 189 g is divided in the ratio 3 : 5 : 1
   e £560 is divided in the ratio 5 : 1 : 1
   f 400 cm is divided in the ratio 1 : 1 : 2

9 Juice is made by mixing orange and water in the ratio 2 : 5
   a If 280 litres of juice are mixed, how much orange is required?
   b Bill says that to mix 105 litres of juice he uses 30 litres of water.
     Is he correct? Explain your answer.
   c Ben mixes 20 litres of orange with 55 litres of water. Is this correct?
     Explain your answer.

10 Tom travels 290 miles. His journey is made up of walking, taxi and train in the
ratio 3 : 10 : 45
Work out the distances for each part of his journey.

11 A garage has three models of car for sale.
The manager says "We have sold 45 of the cars in the
ratio 7 : 6 : 5"
Is this possible? Explain your answer.

12 David and Dawn share £75 in the ratio 11 : 4
David says that he received £35 more than Dawn.
Is he correct? Show your working.

28.2 Proportion and best value

Proportion compares parts of a quantity to the whole quantity.
Proportions can be written in words, fractions, percentages or decimals.

For example, 1 out of 4, 1 in 4, $\frac{1}{4}$, 25% or 0.25 are different ways of writing the same
proportion.

Example 1

There are 120 visitors to a park. 90 are female and 30 are male.
What proportion of the visitors is female?

Solution 1

There are 90 female visitors out of a total of 120 visitors.
The proportion of female visitors is 90 out of 120, or 9 out of 12, or 3 out of 4, or $\frac{3}{4}$,
or 75%, or 0.75

A bar of chocolate costs 50 pence.
So two bars of chocolate cost £1, three bars cost £1.50 and so on.
The total cost is *proportional* to the number of bars bought.
For each extra bar, the cost increases by 50 pence.

When two values are in proportion, as one changes, the other changes at a steady rate. To solve problems using proportional reasoning, start by working out the cost or amount for one item.

Example 2

Four ice-creams cost £1.20
What is the cost of:
a   one ice-cream   b   five ice-creams?

Solution 2

Four ice-creams cost £1.20
a   One ice-cream costs 30 pence   Dividing by 4
b   Five ice-creams cost 5 × 30 pence = £1.50

Example 3

Here is a recipe for white sauce for two people.
How many grams of plain flour does a recipe for three people need?

25 g butter
30 g plain flour
300 ml of milk

Solution 3

30 g flour for two people.
15 g flour for one person.   Dividing by 2
15 × 3 = 45 g for three people.   Multiplying by 3

Exercise A

1   A bag contains 20 coloured counters – five red, ten green, one blue and four yellow.
    Find the proportion of:
    a   red counters   b   green counters   c   blue counters
    d   counters that are **not** yellow.

2   A toolbox contains five spanners, two wrenches, one hammer and four screwdrivers.
    Write down the proportion of tools that are:
    a   screwdrivers   b   wrenches   c   spanners
    d   **not** wrenches or a hammer.

3   1 litre of juice contains 250 ml of grapefruit juice.
    How much grapefruit juice is there in 5 litres of juice?

4   5 miles is approximately equal to 8 kilometres.
    Find the number of kilometres in:
    a   1 mile   b   30 miles   c   300 miles.

5 Three tins of paint cost £10.50. Find the cost of:
   a one tin   **b** five tins   **c** 15 tins.

6 Here is a recipe for Yorkshire pudding to serve four people. Find the number of grams of flour for a recipe for:
   a eight people   **b** six people.

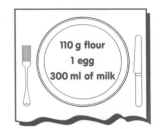

110 g flour
1 egg
300 ml of milk

7 Shaheen has £45. She spends two thirds and saves the rest.
   a What proportion does she save?
   b How much does she save?

8 Making 10 litres of orange paint uses 7 litres of yellow paint and 3 litres of red paint. How many litres of yellow paint and red paint are needed to make:
   a 15 litres of orange paint   **b** 25 litres of orange paint?

9 There are seven soft sweets out of every nine sweets in a tin. Altogether there are 72 sweets in the tin.
   a What proportion are soft sweets?   **b** How many are soft sweets?
   c How many are **not** soft sweets?

10 At a party there are 57 children. There are twice as many girls as boys.
   a What proportion are girls?   **b** How many girls are there?
   c How many boys are there?

11 At an athletics meeting the number of competitors and the number of spectators are recorded. Show that the proportion of male to female is the same for both competitors and spectators.

	Competitors	Spectators
Male	35	245
Female	15	105

Two small boxes contain 160 tea bags, the same as one large box.

80 Golden Tea Bags   £1.41

160 Golden Tea Bags   £2.95

Two small boxes cost 2 × £1.41 = £2.82
One large box costs £2.95
The small box is better value.
To decide which pack is the better value, work out the cost of each for the same quantity.

Example 4

Which packet is the better value?

Solution 4

Method 1 – Cost per gram

Cost of 1 g of small packet = £1.78 ÷ 750
= 178 ÷ 750 pence = 0.237… pence
Cost of 1 g of large packet = £2.28 ÷ 1000
= 228 ÷ 1000 pence = 0.228 pence
The large packet is better value.

Method 2 – Number of grams per penny

Number of grams for one penny in small packet = 750 ÷ 178 = 4.21… g
Number of grams for one penny in large packet = 1000 ÷ 228 = 4.38… g
The large packet is better value.

Method 3 – Scaling

Work out the cost of 250 g for each packet.
Small packet: 750 g cost £1.78
250 g cost £1.78 ÷ 3 = 59.3 pence
Large packet: 1000 g cost £2.28
250 g cost £2.28 ÷ 4 = 57 pence
The large packet is better value.

Exercise B

1 Show that both offers
are the same value.

2 Are four fish for £10 better
value than ten fish for £25?
Explain your answer.

3 Which is the better value?
Show your working.

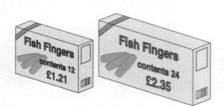

4 40 tea bags cost 71 pence.
80 tea bags cost £1.43
Which is the better value?

5 Two cogs, A and B, are connected as shown.
The number of turns made by the small cog
is proportional to the number of turns made by
the large cog.
When cog A makes nine turns, cog B makes
two turns.
Cog A makes 360 turns.
How many turns does cog B make?

6 The table shows the number of male and female
relatives for Pavel and Andy.
Who has the greater proportion of male relatives?
Show your working.

	Male	Female
Pavel	17	20
Andy	22	25

7 In a large hotel, the manager estimates that the proportion of light bulbs not working
is 1 out of 30
If 29 870 lights are working, estimate the number of lights there are altogether.

8 Zanib and Tracey went fishing.
The table shows the number of days that
each of them went fishing and the number
of fish caught.
Who caught the highest proportion
of fish per day?

	Number of days fishing	Number of fish caught
Zanib	140	253
Tracey	85	151

9 Which bottle is the better value?
Show your working.

10 5 miles = 8 km
Which is further, 60 miles or 88 km?
Show your working

75 cl
£3.00

1 litre
£3.75

5 litres
£19.00

Chapter summary

- A *ratio* compares two or more quantities.
  The simplest form of a ratio has whole numbers with no common factors apart from 1
- To write a ratio in its simplest form:
  - if the ratio includes fractions or decimals, multiply to make both parts whole numbers
  - divide both parts by their common factors.
- *Proportion* compares parts of a quantity to the whole quantity.
- Proportions can be written in words, fractions, percentages or decimals,
  e.g. 1 out of 4, 1 in 4, $\frac{1}{4}$, 25% or 0.25
- When two values are in proportion, as one changes, the other changes at a steady rate.
- To solve problems using proportional reasoning, start by working out the cost or amount for one item.
- To decide which pack is the better value, work out the cost of each for the same quantity.

Chapter review

1 Four apples cost £1.40. How much will five apples cost?

2 In Class 3B, the ratio of City supporters to United supporters is 4 : 1
There are 30 students in Class 3B. How many are City supporters?

3 Rosie and Sophie share some chocolates in the ratio 3 : 2
Sophie gets 12 chocolates. How many does Rosie get?

4 Danny and Richard share £49 in the ratio 4 : 3
How much is the smaller share?

5 Pietro walks 9 miles in 3 hours. Adriana walks 8 miles in 2 hours.
Who is the slower walker? You **must** show your working.

6 A shop sells milk in different sizes.
Which size is the best value for money?
You **must** show your working.

7 Packets of sausages are sold in two sizes

Which packet is the better value?
You **must** show your working.

8 A business spends £387 000 in one year.
£9 out of every £10 is spent on salaries.
How much is spent on salaries?

9 1250 people watch a school concert.
The numbers of teachers, pupils and visitors are in the ratio 1 : 6 : 3
  a How many pupils watched the concert?
  b How many visitors watched the concert?

10 At an auction the number of cars and vans for
sale is recorded on two days.
Is the proportion of cars for sale greater on
Wednesday or Friday?
You **must** show your working.

	Cars	Vans
Wednesday	180	32
Friday	85	17

11 Making 5 litres of tree green paint uses 3.5 litres of yellow paint and 1.5 litres of blue
paint. How many litres of yellow paint and blue paint are needed to make:
  a 10 litres of tree green paint   **b** 3 litres of tree green paint?

Using formulae

29.1 Substituting into expressions and formulae

CAN YOU REMEMBER

- The difference between an 'algebraic expression' and a 'formula'?
- The order of operations (BODMAS or BIDMAS)?
- How to calculate with negative numbers, fractions and decimals, using written methods and a calculator?
- How to solve equations using the balance method?

IN THIS SECTION YOU WILL

- Substitute values into algebraic expressions and formulae.
- Evaluate formulae.

To substitute numbers into an algebraic expression (or formula):
- replace the letter symbols with numbers and insert all the operation symbols
- work out the value of the expression, using the correct order of operations.

Example 1

a If $a = 3$ and $b = 4$, work out the value of: **i** $2ab + 5$ **ii** $2a(b + 5)$.

b Find the value of $5x - \dfrac{8}{y}$ when $x = 3$ and $y = -2$

Solution 1

a **i** When $a = 3$ and $b = 4$
$$2ab + 5 = 2 \times 3 \times 4 + 5 = 24 + 5 = 29$$
ii When $a = 3$ and $b = 4$
$$2a(b + 5) = 2 \times 3 \times (4 + 5) = 2 \times 3 \times 9 = 54$$

b When $x = 3$ and $y = -2$
$$5x - \frac{8}{y} = 5 \times 3 - 8 \div -2$$
$$= 15 - -4$$
$$= 15 + 4 = 19$$

> Dividing a positive by a negative gives a negative.

> Subtracting a negative is the same as adding a positive.

Example 2

You are given the formula $S = 3p^2 + \dfrac{q}{5}$ and the formula $T = \dfrac{c + 4d}{e^3}$

a   Work out S when $p = -5$ and $q = 15$
b   Work out T when $c = -12$, $d = 7$ and $e = -2$

Solution 2

a   When $p = -5$ and $q = 15$
$$S = 3 \times (-5)^2 + 15 \div 5$$
$$= 3 \times 25 + 15 \div 5$$
$$S = 75 + 3 = 78$$

> A negative number squared is always positive.

b   When $c = -12$, $d = 7$ and $e = -2$
$$T = \frac{-12 + 4 \times 7}{(-2)^3}$$
$$= \frac{-12 + 28}{-8}$$

> A negative number cubed is always negative.

$$= \frac{16}{-8}$$
$$T = -2$$

Example 3

$$P = \frac{2x^2}{y^3}$$

Find the value of P when $x = 8$ and $y = \frac{2}{5}$

Solution 3

When $x = 8$ and $y = \frac{2}{5}$, $P = \dfrac{2 \times 8^2}{\left(\frac{2}{5}\right)^3} = 2 \times 8^2 \div \left(\tfrac{2}{5}\right)^3$

Using a calculator, $P = 2000$
Make sure you know how to work out fractions using your calculator.

Exercise A

1   a   If $p = 4$ and $q = 2$ work out:

  i $6pq$ ii $\dfrac{p}{q} + 6$ iii $pq + 6$ iv $p(q - 5)$ v $\dfrac{p}{q - 5}$

  vi $5p + 4q$ vii $2p - 3q$ viii $3pq - \dfrac{2p}{q}$ ix $\dfrac{8}{p} + q$ x $\dfrac{30}{p - q}$

   b   Repeat **a** for the values $p = 10$ and $q = -5$

2   **a**   If $a = 10$, $b = 4$ and $c = 2$ work out:

   i abc **ii** $ab - c$ **iii** $\dfrac{ab}{c}$ **iv** $a(b - c)$ **v** $a - bc$

   vi $\dfrac{a}{b} - c$ **vii** $\dfrac{a}{b - c}$ **viii** $a - \dfrac{b}{c}$ **ix** $\dfrac{a - b}{c}$ **x** $\dfrac{a}{\left(\dfrac{b}{c}\right)}$

   b   Repeat **a** for the values $a = 20$, $b = -5$ and $c = -10$

3   **a**   If $w = 12$, $x = 4$, $y = 8$ and $z = 2$ work out:

   i $wx + yz$ **ii** $w(x + y + z)$ **iii** $\dfrac{w}{x} + \dfrac{y}{z}$ **iv** $\dfrac{w(x + y)}{z}$ **v** $\dfrac{wx}{yz}$

   vi $\dfrac{wxy}{z}$ **vii** $\dfrac{w}{y - x} + z$ **viii** $\dfrac{w}{x + y - z}$ **ix** $(w + x)(y + z)$ **x** $\dfrac{w + x}{y + z}$

   b   Repeat **a** for the values $w = 12$, $x = -3$, $y = -6$ and $z = 3$

4 $P = x^2 + y^2$ $Q = x^3 + y^3$ $R = \sqrt{(x^2 + y^2)}$ $S = 2x^2 + 3y^2$ $T = (2x)^2 + (3y)^2$
   Work out the values of P, Q, R, S and T when:
   a $x = 3$ and $y = 4$ **b** $x = -3$ and $y = -4$
   c $x = 3$ and $y = -4$ **d** $x = -3$ and $y = 4$

5   **a** $A = \dfrac{5x^3}{4}$ $B = \dfrac{4x^2(x - 5)}{8x}$ $C = 2x^3(x - 1)^2$ $D = 2\dfrac{x + 15}{(x - 15)^2}$

   Find the values of A, B, C and D when $x = 10$

   b   Work out the value of $\dfrac{2ab^2}{(a - b)^3}$ when $a = 5$ and $b = -5$

6   If $r = 0.7$, $s = 2.75$ and $t = \frac{3}{4}$ work out:
   a rs^2 **b** $(r + s)^3$ **c** $2r(s - t)(r + t)$ **d** $rs(1 + 2t)^3$

   e $\dfrac{15(5s + 1)}{rt}$ **f** $\dfrac{1}{r} + \dfrac{1}{s} + \dfrac{1}{t}$ **g** $\left(\dfrac{1}{r}\right)^2 + \left(\dfrac{2}{s}\right)^2 + \left(\dfrac{3}{t}\right)^2$ **h** $\dfrac{1}{r^2} + \dfrac{1}{s^2} + \dfrac{1}{t^2}$

   i $r^3 + s^4 + t^5$ **j** $2r^3 + (3s)^3$

Sometimes substituting into a formula leads to an equation to solve.

Example 4

The formula $l = 30 + 0.2W$ gives the length, l cm, of a spring when a weight, W grams, is added to it.
   a   Find l when $W = 100$ g.   **b**   Find W when $l = 36$ cm.

Solution 4

a When $W = 100$

$l = 30 + 0.2 \times 100 = 30 + 20 = 50$ cm

b When $l = 36$

$36 = 30 + 0.2 \times W$ | Solve this equation using the balance method.

$36 - 30 = 30 - 30 + 0.2 \times W$ | Subtract 30 from both sides.

$6 = 0.2 \times W$

$6 \div 0.2 = 0.2 \div 0.2 \times W$ | Divide both sides by 0.2

$\dfrac{6}{0.2} = W$

$W = \dfrac{6 \times 10}{0.2 \times 10}$ | Multiply numerator and denominator by 10

$= \dfrac{60}{2} = 30$ g

Exercise B

1 This formula is used to convert temperatures from °C to °F.

$F = \dfrac{9C}{5} + 32$

Work out F when C is:

a 30   b 0   c −5   d 8

2 This formula is used to convert temperatures from °F to °C.

$C = \dfrac{5(F - 32)}{9}$

Work out C when F is:

a 41   b 212   c 68   d −4

3 The formula $f = \dfrac{uv}{u + v}$ is used in the study of light.

Calculate f when:

a $u = 2$ and $v = 8$ b $u = 5$ and $v = -3$
c $u = 80$ and $v = 20$ d $u = 0.3$ and $v = 0.7$

4 The area of a trapezium is given by the formula $A = \frac{1}{2}(a + b)h$

a Find A when:

i $a = 5$, $b = 7$ and $h = 6$
ii $a = 3$, $b = 12$ and $h = 10$
iii $a = 4.8$, $b = 15.2$ and $h = 6.375$
iv $a = 0.55$, $b = 1.45$ and $h = 17.5$

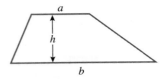

b i Find h when $A = 250$, $a = 7$ and $b = 18$
ii Find h when $A = 250$, $a = 21$ and $b = 29$
iii Find values of a, b and h for another trapezium with $A = 250$

5   The formula $v = u + at$ is used in the study of motion.
  a   Work out v when:
     i $u = 12$, $a = 4$ and $t = 5$ **ii** $u = 1.2$, $a = 0.4$ and $t = 20$
  b   Work out u when:
     i $v = 16$, $a = 0.4$ and $t = 5$ **ii** $v = 34.2$, $a = 2.38$ and $t = 10$
  c   Work out t when:
     i $v = 18$, $u = 3$ and $a = 3$ **ii** $v = 22$, $u = 4$ and $a = 10$
  d   Work out a when:
     i $v = 26.5$, $u = 2.5$ and $t = 60$ **ii** $v = 102$, $u = 27$ and $t = 7.5$

6   Another formula used in the study of motion is $s = ut + \frac{1}{2}at^2$
  a   Work out s when:
     i $u = 11$, $a = 4$ and $t = 5$ **ii** $u = 4.5$, $a = 2$ and $t = 20$
  b   Work out u when:
     i $s = 200$, $a = 4$ and $t = 8$ **ii** $s = 27.2$, $a = 0.36$ and $t = 10$
  c   Work out a when:
     i $s = 32$, $u = 5$ and $t = 4$ **ii** $s = 180$, $u = 6.5$ and $t = 20$

7   **a**   Copy and complete this table of values for $a^2 + a$ and $a(a + 1)$ for the values
        of a given.

a	$a^2 + a$	$a(a + 1)$
2	$4 + 2 = 6$	$2 \times 3 = 6$
5		
-2		
-5		
$\frac{1}{2}$		

  b   What do you notice? Give a reason for your answer.

8   The volume of this solid is given by
     the formula $V = \frac{4}{3}a^3$
  a   Work out V when a is:
     i 9
     ii 15
  b   Work out a when V is 36

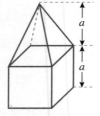

9 R is given by the formula $R = \dfrac{xyz}{xy + xz + yz}$

  Work out R when:
  a $x = 5$, $y = 2$ and $z = 10$
  b $x = 8.6$, $y = 3.7$ and $z = 9.8$
  c $x = 12.5$, $y = 32.7$ and $z = 19.8$
  d $x = 0.465$, $y = 0.326$ and $z = 1.072$

10 x is a positive integer.

Terry says that $(x + 1)^3 - x^3$ is *always* a prime number.

He gives this example:

> *When $x = 2$*
> $(2 + 1)^3 - 2^3 = 3^3 - 2^3 = 27 - 8 = 19$
> *19 is a prime number*

Find a counter example to show that Terry is wrong.

11 $P = \dfrac{x^2 + y^2}{x - y}$ $Q = \dfrac{x^2 - y^2}{x + y}$

$R = P^2Q + Q^2P$ $S = PQ(P + Q)$

a Work out R and S when:

    i $x = 8$ and $y = 6$ **ii** $x = 14$ and $y = 4$

b What do you notice about your answers for **a**?

Give a reason for this.

29.2 Writing expressions, formulae and equations

CAN YOU REMEMBER

- The difference between an algebraic expression and a formula?
- How to expand brackets in expressions like $3(2x + 1)$?
- How to simplify expressions by collecting like terms?
- How to find the perimeter and area of a rectangle?

IN THIS SECTION YOU WILL

- Understand the difference between an equation and a formula.
- Write expressions, formulae and equations using letter symbols.

The *formula* for the area, A, of a trapezium is $A = \frac{1}{2}(a + b)h$

The letter symbols a, b and h represent lengths and can take **any** value.

Given the values of a, b and h, the value of A can be calculated.

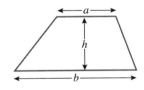

A formula always includes an '$=$' symbol.

In a formula the letter symbols can take **any** value.

An *equation* also includes an '$=$' symbol.

In an equation, the letter symbols have fixed values.

For example, $3x + 2 = 11$ is an equation with one letter symbol, x.

There is only **one** fixed value of x that fits this equation, $x = 3$

Example 1

Bags labelled X each contain x counters.   Bags labelled Y each contain y counters.

a   Write an expression for the number of counters in:
  i   A bag labelled X with three counters taken out.
  ii A bag labelled Y with half the counters taken out.
  iii Three bags labelled X.
  iv Three bags labelled X and two bags labelled Y.
b   Write a *formula* for T, the total number of counters in a bags labelled X and b bags labelled Y.
c   There are two bags labelled X.
  Five counters are removed.
  The total number of counters left is 15
  Use this information to write an *equation* in terms of x.

Solution 1

a   **i** $x - 3$ **ii** $\dfrac{y}{2}$ or $\dfrac{1}{2}y$ **iii** $3x$
  iv Three bags labelled X contain $3x$ counters.
    Two bags labelled Y contain $2y$ counters.
    So an expression for the total number of counters is $3x + 2y$
b a bags labelled X contain ax counters.
    b bags labelled Y contain by counters.
    So the formula for T, the total number of counters in the bags, is $T = ax + by$
c   Two bags labelled X contain $2x$ counters.
    When five counters are removed there are $2x - 5$ counters left.
    So the equation is $2x - 5 = 15$

Exercise A

1   Boxes of matches each contain b matches.
  a   Write an expression for the number of matches in three boxes.
  b   Write an expression for the number of matches in three boxes when one match has been removed.
  c   James uses half the matches in one box and five matches from another box. Write a formula for T, the total number of matches that James uses.

2   Michael is m years old.
  Naomi is n years old.
  a   Andrew is five years older than Michael. Write an expression for Andrew's age.
  b   Ben is three years younger than Naomi. Write an expression for Ben's age.
  c   Peter's age, p, is the sum of Andrew's age and Ben's age. Write a formula giving p in terms of m and n.

3   Afzal saves £5 each week.
   a   Write an expression for the amount that Afzal saves in w weeks.
   b   After saving for w weeks Afzal spends £8
        Write an expression for the amount that Afzal has left.

4   Billy is using building blocks to build towers and walls.
   Each tower contains five blocks.
   Each wall contains eight blocks.

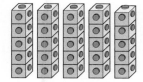 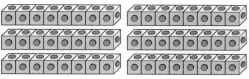 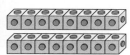

   a   Write an expression for the number of blocks that Billy uses to build:
        i t towers   **ii** w walls.
   b   Write a formula for B, the number of blocks that Billy uses to build t towers and
        w walls.

5   Tickets for the school play cost £5 for adults and £3 for children.
   a   Write an expression for the cost of:
        i x adult tickets   **ii** y children's tickets.
   b   Write a formula for £T, the total cost of x adult tickets and y children's tickets.

6   A window cleaner charges £5 for visiting a house and £3 for each window
   he cleans.
   Write a formula for £A, the total amount of money that the window cleaner charges
   for visiting h houses and cleaning w windows.

7   Amy has p packets each containing x sweets.
   Jade has b bags each containing y sweets.
   Amy has more sweets than Jade.
   How many more?
   Give your answer as an algebraic expression in terms of p, x, b and y.

8   Sally buys five chocolate bars costing c pence each.
   She pays with a £10 note and gets £6 change.
   Use this information to write an equation in terms of c.

9   Zack buys three boxes of sweets each containing x sweets.
   He also has seven sweets left in an opened box.
   a   How many sweets does Zack have in total?
        Give your answer as an expression in terms of x.
   b   Altogether Zack has 55 sweets.
        Use this information to write an equation in terms of x.

Example 2

The diagram shows a white square inside a shaded rectangle.
a   Write an expression for the shaded area in terms of x.
b   The shaded area is 20 cm².
     Use this information to write an equation in terms of x.
c   Solve the equation to find the value of x.

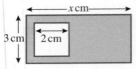

Solution 2

a   Area of rectangle $= x \times 3 = 3x$ cm²
       Area of square $= 2 \times 2 = 4$ cm²
     So shaded area $= 3x - 4$ cm²

b $3x - 4 = 20$

c $3x - 4 = 20$

     $3x - 4 + 4 = 20 + 4$ Add 4 to both sides.

             $3x = 24$

       $3x \div 3 = 24 \div 3$ Divide both sides by 3

             $x = 8$

Exercise B

1   The diagram shows a rectangle with length $(x + 3)$ cm
     and width $(3x - 5)$ cm.

     a   Write an expression for the perimeter of the
          rectangle in terms of x.
     b   The perimeter of the rectangle is 20 cm.
          i Write an equation in terms of x.
          ii Solve the equation to find the value of x.

2   A list of consecutive integers starts x, $x + 1$, $x + 2$
     a   i Copy the list and continue it up to six consecutive integers starting with x.
          ii Write down the list when $x = 8$
     b   The sum of four consecutive integers starting with x is 14
          i Use this information to write an equation in terms of x.
          ii Solve the equation to find the value of x.
     c   The sum of six consecutive integers starting with y is 39
          i Use this information to write an equation in terms of y.
          ii Solve the equation to find the value of y.

3   Sally buys x chocolate bars costing y pence each.
     She pays with a £10 note.
     a   Write an expression for the change that Sally gets in pence.
     b   Write a formula for C, the change that Sally gets in pounds.
     c   Write an equation for working out y when $x = 5$ and $C = £8$

4 The diagram shows a shape made up of two rectangles.

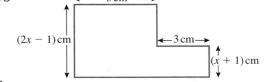

   a Show that the area of this shape, A cm², is given by the formula $A = 13x - 2$

   b Write an equation to find x when $A = 37$

   c Solve the equation to find x.

5 The diagram shows a path of width x metres surrounding a rectangular lawn.

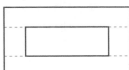

The lawn has length L metres and width W metres.

   a Use each of the following methods to write down a possible formula for P, the area of the path.

     i Subtract the area of the lawn from the area of the lawn and path.

     ii Split the path up into the sections shown in the diagram and add the area of each section.

   b By splitting the path up into different sections find another possible formula for P.

   c Use $L = 5$, $W = 3$ and $x = 2$ to show that all of the formulae you have found give the same value of P. You **must** show your working.

6 Look at the number machines A and B below.

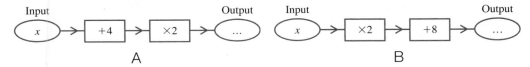

   a Write an expression in terms of x for the output of each machine.

   b Show that the output for machine A equals the output for machine B when the input value, x, is:

     i 2   **ii** −2   **iii** 0   **iv** 0.5   **v** −0.5

   c Repeat **b** for some other values of x.

   d Explain your answers to **b** and **c**.

   e Find some other pairs of number machines that have equal output for the same input.

7 In the year 2000 Tim was x years old. Mary was 3 years older than Tim. John was twice Tim's age.

   a Write an expression in terms of x for the sum of Tim's, Mary's and John's ages in 2000. Write the expression as simply as possible.

   b Write an expression in terms of x for:

     i Tim's age in 2005   **ii** Mary's age in 2005   **iii** John's age in 2005

   c In 2005 the sum of Tim's, Mary's and John's ages is twice the sum of their ages in 2000

     i Show that $4x + 18 = 8x + 6$

     ii Is this a formula or an equation? Explain your answer.

8 The table shows the number of marbles in six bags labelled A, B, C, D, E and F.

Bag	Number of marbles
A	x
B	y
C	Three more than in bag A
D	Four times the number in bag B
E	Twice as many as bag C
F	Five less than in bag D

Find a formula for the total number of marbles, M, in all of bags A to F.

9 Shape A and shape B are made up of rectangles with dimensions as shown.

In parts **a** and **b** write your answers as simply as possible.

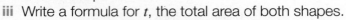

A   B

a　**i** Write a formula for a, the total area of shape A.

　　ii Write a formula for b, the total area of shape B.

　　iii Write a formula for t, the total area of both shapes.

b　**i** Write an equation to find x when $a = 30$ and $y = 3$

　　ii Write an equation to find x when $b = 30$ and $y = 3$

c Tom is told that $t = 70$ and $x = 6$

Explain clearly how Tom can work out a and b.

29.3 Changing the subject of a formula

CAN YOU REMEMBER

- That a formula is a rule for working out the value of one quantity from the value of other quantities?
- How to construct number machines and inverse number machines?
- How to solve equations using the balance method?

IN THIS SECTION YOU WILL

- Learn how to change the subject of a formula.

The formula $F = 1.8C + 32$ can be used to change temperatures in degrees Celsius (°C) to degrees Fahrenheit (°F).

The *subject* of this formula is F.

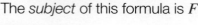

The subject of a formula is the single letter symbol on one side of the equals sign. The formula can be *rearranged* to make C the subject. Then it can be used to change temperatures in degrees Fahrenheit (°F) to degrees Celsius (°C).

One method of changing the subject of a formula uses inverse number machines. The formula $F = 1.8C + 32$ can be written using number machines:

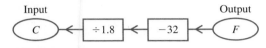

The inverse number machine is:

The output of the inverse number machine is
$C = (F - 32) \div 1.8$
This is the rearranged formula with C as the subject.

Example 1

For each formula:
  i draw the number machine and inverse number machine
  ii rearrange the formula to make x the subject.

a $y = x + 3$
b $y = \dfrac{x}{4}$
c $y = 2x - 5$

Solution 1

a $y = x + 3$ $x = y - 3$

b $y = \dfrac{x}{4}$ $x = 4y$

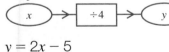

c $y = 2x - 5$ $x = (y + 5) \div 2$

Example 2

Use number machines to make:
  a b the subject of the formula $a = \dfrac{b}{c} - d$
  b r the subject of the formula $p = q(r - 3)$

Solution 2

a
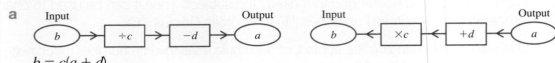

$$b = c(a + d)$$

b
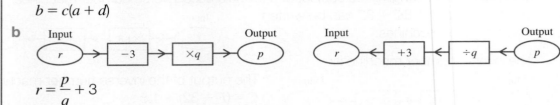

$$r = \frac{p}{q} + 3$$

Exercise A

1 Make w the subject of:
   a $a = w + 4$ b $b = w + 9$ c $c = w + t$ d $d = w - 4$
   e $e = w - 1$ f $f = w - t$ g $g = 5 - w$ h $h = t - w$

2 Make x the subject of:
   a $a = 5x$ b $b = 6x$ c $c = px$ d $d = -2x$

   e $e = -px$ f $f = \dfrac{x}{2}$ g $g = \dfrac{x}{5}$ h $h = \dfrac{x}{q}$

3 Make y the subject of:
   a $a = 2y + 8$ b $b = 3y + 2$ c $c = 5y + t$ d $d = my + 2$
   e $e = ny + p$ f $f = 5y - 3$ g $g = py - 5$ h $h = qy - s$

4 Make z the subject of:

   a $a = \dfrac{z}{2} + 4$ b $b = \dfrac{z}{8} - 5$ c $c = \dfrac{z}{8} - r$

   d $d = \dfrac{z}{m} + 2$ e $e = \dfrac{z}{a} + b$ f $f = \dfrac{z}{p} - q$

5 Make p the subject of:
   a $a = 2(p + 3)$ b $b = x(p + y)$ c $c = r(p - q)$
   d $d = p(a + 1)$ e $e = p(a - 5)$ f $f = p(a - b)$

6 Make q the subject of:

   a $a = \dfrac{q + 3}{2}$ b $b = \dfrac{q - 3}{5}$ c $c = \dfrac{q + x}{10}$

   d $d = \dfrac{q - x}{y}$ e $e = \dfrac{q + a}{b}$ f $f = \dfrac{2q - c}{d}$

The subject of a formula can be changed using the *balance method.*

Example 3

Use the balance method to make x the subject of:

a $y = px + q$ **b** $y = \dfrac{x}{a} - b$ **c** $y = p(x + q)$ **d** $y = \dfrac{x - b}{a}$

Solution 3

a $y = px + q$ | Subtract q from both sides.

$y - q = px$ | Divide both sides by p.

$\dfrac{y - q}{p} = x$

So $x = \dfrac{y - q}{p}$

b $y = \dfrac{x}{a} - b$ | Add b to both sides.

$y + b = \dfrac{x}{a}$ | Multiply both sides by a.

$a(y + b) = x$

So $x = a(y + b)$

c $y = p(x + q)$ | Divide both sides by p.

$\dfrac{y}{p} = x + q$ | Subtract q from both sides.

$\dfrac{y}{p} - q = x$

So $x = \dfrac{y}{p} - q$

d $y = \dfrac{x - b}{a}$ | Multiply both sides by a.

$ay = x - b$ | Add b to both sides.

$ay + b = x$

So $x = ay + b$

Example 4

The volume, V, of the square-based cuboid shown in the diagram is given by the formula $V = x^2 h$
A square-based cuboid has volume 900 cm³ and height 4 cm.
Calculate the length of the base of the cuboid.

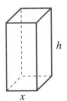

Solution 4

Substitute values into the formula and solve the equation.

$$900 = x^2 \times 4$$

$$900 \div 4 = x^2 \times 4 \div 4 \qquad \boxed{\text{Divide both sides by 4}}$$

$$225 = x^2$$

$$\sqrt{225} = x \qquad \boxed{\text{Take the square root of both sides.}}$$

So $\quad x = 15$ cm

Exercise B

1 Repeat **Exercise A** using the balance method to rearrange each formula.
   You **must** show your working.

2 A rectangle has length l and width w.
   The perimeter, P, of the rectangle is given by the formula
   $P = 2l + 2w$
   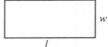
   The area, A, of the rectangle is given by the formula $A = lw$
   a Rearrange $P = 2l + 2w$ to make l the subject.
   b A rectangle has width 7.5 cm and perimeter 31 cm.
      i Work out l.   ii Work out A.
   c Find A when $w = 4$ cm and $P = 25$ cm.

3 The area of a trapezium is given by the formula $A = \frac{1}{2}(a + b)h$
   This formula can also be written in the form $A = \dfrac{(a + b)h}{2}$
   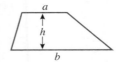
   a Calculate A when $a = 12$ cm, $b = 18$ cm and $h = 20$ cm.
   b Rearrange the formula to make a the subject.
   c   i Calculate a when $A = 500$ cm^2, $b = 6.5$ cm and $h = 40$ cm.
      ii Calculate a when $A = 165$ cm^2, $b = 20.2$ cm and $h = 7.5$ cm.
   d Calculate h when $A = 12$ cm^2, $a = 6.3$ cm and $b = 3.7$ cm.

4 The surface area, A, of the square-based cuboid shown
   in the diagram is given by the formula $A = 2x^2 + 4hx$
   a Rearrange this formula to make h the subject.
   b Work out h when $A = 250$ cm^2 and $x = 5$ cm.

5 a Rearrange the formula $v = u + at$ to make:
      i u the subject   ii a the subject   iii t the subject.
   b Rearrange the formula $v^2 = u^2 + 2as$ to make:
      i a the subject   ii s the subject.

6 $X = ab + c \qquad Y = b + ac$
   a By rearranging each of these formulae to make b the subject show that
      $$\frac{(X - c)}{a} = Y - ac$$
   b Hence show that $X = a(Y - ac) + c$

7 The letter symbols a, b and c are connected by the formula $a = \sqrt{b^2 + c^2}$
  a Calculate a when $b = 14$ and $c = 48$
  b Calculate b when $a = 17$ and $c = 15$
  c Calculate c when $a = 1.23$ and $b = 0.27$

8 A triangle has sides of length a, b and c.
  The area, A, of the triangle is given by the formula

  $A = \sqrt{s(s - a)(s - b)(s - c)}$ where $s = \dfrac{a + b + c}{2}$

  a Rearrange the formula $s = \dfrac{a + b + c}{2}$ to make c the subject.
  b Work out the area of a triangle when $a = 6$ cm, $b = 8$ cm and $s = 12$ cm.

Chapter summary

- To substitute numbers into an algebraic expression (or formula):
  - replace the letter symbols with numbers and insert all the operation symbols
  - work out the value of the expression, using the correct order of operations.
- A *formula* always includes an '=' symbol. For example, $A = l \times w$
  In a formula the letter symbols can take **any** value.
- An *equation* also includes an '=' symbol.
  In an equation the letter symbols have fixed values. For example, $x + 5 = 12$
- The subject of a formula is the single letter symbol on one side of the equals sign.
  The subject of a formula can be changed using inverse number machines or the balance method.

Chapter review

1 a Find the value of $x^2 + 5xy$ when $x = -6$ and $y = 2$
  b You are given that $m = \frac{3}{4}$, $p = \frac{1}{2}$ and $t = 2$
  Find the value of: **i** $mp + t$ **ii** $t(m + p)$

2 Tara buys x rulers at 25 pence each and y pens at 60 pence each.
Write down an expression for the total cost of the rulers and the pens.

3 The diagram shows an isosceles triangle.
Write down an expression, in terms of x,
for the size of angle B.

4 Make x the subject of the formula $5x + 2y = 12y - 5$
Simplify your answer as much as possible.

5 Make q the subject of the formula $p = \dfrac{q}{5} + 3$

6 **a** Make p the subject of the formula $r = \dfrac{4(p + 3)}{q}$

    b Hence find the value of p when $r = -5$ and $q = 8$

7 You are given the formula $t = \sqrt{\dfrac{r}{s}}$

    Calculate t when $r = 720$ and $s = 20$

8 Bill makes x cakes. He puts them into packs of four.
He has n packs of cakes and three cakes left over.
Write down the value of x in terms of n.

9 A small paving slab weighs x kilograms.
A large paving slab weighs $(2x + 3)$ kilograms.
    a Show that the total weight of 16 small slabs and four large slabs is $12(2x + 1)$.
    b The total weight of the slabs is 132 kilograms. Write down an equation in x.

10 A cuboid has a square base of side x cm.
The volume of the cuboid is V cm^3 and the height is h cm.
    a Write down an expression for x in terms of V and h.
    b Find the value of x when $V = 150$ and $h = 24$

11 The formula used to calculate Jenny's electricity bill is
    $A = F + 0.08N$
£A stands for the amount of the bill. £F represents a fixed charge, and N is the
number of units of electricity used.
Calculate the amount of Jenny's bill if the fixed charge is £13.60 and she uses 830 units.

12 You are given the formula $a = bc + d$
    a Calculate a when $b = \frac{2}{5}$, $c = 3$ and $d = -0.8$
    b Rearrange the formula to give b in terms of a, c and d.

Experimental probability

30.1 Relative frequency

CAN YOU REMEMBER

- How to calculate the probability of an event using equally likely outcomes?
- How to convert a fraction to a decimal?
- How to multiply whole numbers by fractions and decimals?

IN THIS SECTION YOU WILL

- Learn the meaning of 'trial' and 'relative frequency'.
- Learn how to use relative frequency to estimate probabilities from the results of experiments or surveys.
- Learn that the reliability of relative frequency as a measure of probability increases with the number of trials or observations.

For some events, the probability cannot be calculated using equally likely outcomes.

For example, for the probability of a train from Newcastle to Manchester being late, 'being late' and 'being on time' may not be equally likely.

In cases like this, the probability can be estimated using the results of an experiment or a survey and the *relative frequency*.

$$\text{The relative frequency of an event} = \frac{\text{number of times the event occurs in an experiment (or survey)}}{\text{total number of } trials \text{ in the experiment (or observations in the survey)}}$$

Relative frequency is usually written as a fraction or a decimal. It can also be written as a percentage.

Probability based on relative frequency is called *experimental probability*.

Probability calculated from equally likely outcomes is called *theoretical probability*.

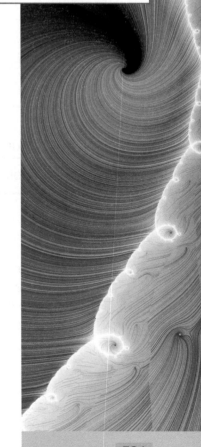

Example 1

2000 children take a cycling proficiency test.
1860 of these children pass the test.
Estimate the probability that a child passes the test.

Solution 1

Relative frequency $= \dfrac{1860}{2000} = 0.93$

An estimate for the probability that a child passes the test $= 0.93$

Example 2

Eric throws a dart at a dartboard 100 times. The table shows his results.

Result	Hits treble	Hits double	Hits single	Misses board
Frequency	12	5	80	3
Relative frequency				

a Complete the table.
b Use the answer to part **a** to estimate the probability that Eric throws a double.

Solution 2

a Total number of trials $= 100$

Result	Hits treble	Hits double	Hits single	Misses board
Frequency	12	5	80	3
Relative frequency	$\frac{12}{100}$	$\frac{5}{100}$	$\frac{80}{100}$	$\frac{3}{100}$

b The estimated probability that Eric hits a double $= \frac{5}{100}$ or 5% or 0.05

Exercise A

1   100 vehicles are observed passing the school gate.
14 of the vehicles are vans.
What is the relative frequency of a van passing the school gate?

2   Chandra drops a drawing pin and records whether it lands point up or point down.
She repeats this trial 100 times.
The number of times the drawing pin lands point up is 28
a   What is the relative frequency of the drawing pin landing point up?
b   Estimate the probability that the drawing pin lands point down.

3 A gardener plants 50 bulbs.
45 of the bulbs grow into healthy plants.
  a What is the relative frequency of a bulb growing into a healthy plant?
  b Estimate the probability of a bulb not producing a healthy plant.

4 Some students do this experiment with a bag of coloured counters.
  ■ Take a counter from the bag.   ■ Put the counter back in the bag.
  ■ Record its colour.   ■ Repeat this trial a number of times.
Their results are shown in this table.

Name of student	Number of trials	Colour of counter		
		Red	White	Blue
David	50	22	15	13
Suki	100	48	32	20
Leon	200	102	60	38

  a What is the relative frequency of David taking a red counter from the bag?
  b What is the relative frequency of Suki taking a white counter from the bag?
  c Estimate the probability of Leon taking a blue counter from the bag.

5 In an experiment a marble is picked from a bag at random.
Its colour is recorded and it is replaced in the bag.
This trial is repeated ten times.
The results of the experiment are
Copy and complete this table for the results.

Colour	Blue	Yellow	Red	Green
Frequency				
Relative frequency				

6 A four-sided spinner is spun 20 times.
The results are shown in the table.

Number on spinner	1	2	3	4
Frequency	4	7	3	6

Use the results to calculate the relative frequency of each number.

7 A supermarket records the amount of money spent by 50 shoppers.
The results are shown in the table.

Amount spent	Less than £10	£10–£19.99	£20–£29.99	£30 or more
Frequency	2	10	25	13

  a Work out the relative frequency of a shopper spending:
    i less than £10   **ii** between £10 and £30
  b Estimate the probability that a shopper chosen at random will spend £30 or more.

8 In a survey, James records the colours of 25 cars on a motorway as either red (R), silver (S) or other (O). Here are his results.

S S R S O R S S O R O O R S S S S R R O S R S S O

Copy and complete the table.

Colour	R	S	O
Frequency			
Relative frequency			

9 Pavel is a footballer. His scoring record for attempts at goal with his left foot, his right foot and his head are shown below.

Left foot: ✓ ✗ ✗ ✓ ✓ ✓ ✓ ✗ ✓ ✗
Right foot: ✓ ✓ ✗ ✓ ✗ ✓ ✓ ✓ ✓ ✓
Head: ✗ ✗ ✗ ✓ ✗ ✓ ✓ ✓ ✗ ✓

a Work out the relative frequency of Pavel scoring:
   i with his right foot   **ii** with his left foot.
b Estimate the probability of Pavel scoring with his head.
c If you were Pavel's coach, what advice would you give him?

Relative frequency gives a more reliable estimate of probability when its value is based on a large number of trials or observations.

Example 3

A bead is taken from a bag of coloured beads and then replaced.
This trial is repeated 200 times.
The number of red beads taken from the bag every 20 trials is recorded.
This table shows the relative frequency of the number of red beads after each 20 trials.

Total number of beads	20	40	60	80	100	120	140	160	180	200
Number of red beads	2	7	14	18	21	26	28	33	37	40
Relative frequency	$\frac{2}{20}$	$\frac{7}{40}$	$\frac{14}{60}$	$\frac{18}{80}$	$\frac{21}{100}$	$\frac{26}{120}$	$\frac{28}{140}$	$\frac{33}{160}$	$\frac{37}{180}$	$\frac{40}{200}$
	0.1	0.175	0.233	0.225	0.21	0.217	0.2	0.206	0.206	0.2

a Show the relative frequencies on a graph.
b Describe the pattern shown in the graph.
c Estimate the probability of picking a red bead from the bag.

Solution 3

a

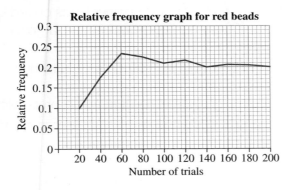

Relative frequency graph for red beads

b At first, when the number of trials is small, the relative frequency changes a lot. As the number of trials increases the relative frequency changes less.

c The best estimate of the probability is 0.2, the relative frequency for the largest number of trials in the experiment.

For a large number of trials the relative frequency gives a reliable estimate of the theoretical probability.

Example 4

Adrian carries out an experiment with this spinner.
He spins the spinner 100 times and calculates the relative frequency of the spinner landing on red after every 20 spins.
Some of the results are shown on the graph.

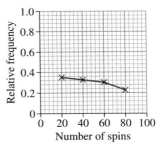

a Use the graph to find the number of times the spinner lands on red:
  i after 20 spins
  ii after 40 spins.
b After 100 spins red had appeared 24 times.
  Calculate the relative frequency.
c What is the most reliable estimate of the spinner landing on red? Explain your answer.
d Assuming the spinner is fair, work out the theoretical probability of the spinner landing on red. Compare this with your answer to part **c**.

Solution 4

a Relative frequency $= \dfrac{\text{number of times spinner lands on red}}{\text{total number of spins}}$

  i When the total number of spins is 20, the relative frequency is 0.35

  $0.35 = \dfrac{\text{Number of times spinner lands on red}}{20}$

  Number of times spinner landed on red $= 0.35 \times 20 = 7$
  The spinner lands on red seven times.

  ii When the total number of spins is 40, the relative frequency is 0.325
  Number of times spinner lands on red $= 0.325 \times 40 = 13$

b Relative frequency $= \frac{24}{100} = 0.24$

c The most reliable estimate of the probability that the spinner lands on red is 0.24
This is the relative frequency of the spinner landing on red for the largest number of trials in the experiment.

d The theoretical probability = number of successful outcomes ÷ total number of outcomes $= \frac{1}{4} = 0.25$
The experimental probability, 0.24, is very close to the theoretical probability.

Exercise B

1 Tom takes a counter from a bag, records its colour and then replaces it.
He does this for 50 trials.

a Copy and complete this table.

Number of trials	10	20	30	40	50
Number of red counters	3	10	15	18	20
Relative frequency of a red counter	$\frac{3}{10}$ 0.3		$\frac{15}{30}$	$\frac{18}{40}$ 0.45	

b Copy and complete the graph to show how the relative frequency changes as the number of trials increases.

c Describe the pattern shown in the graph.

d What is the best estimate of the probability of taking a red counter from the bag?

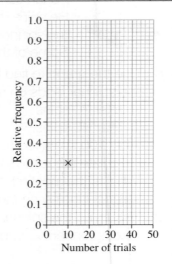

2 The diagram shows the number of trials and the relative frequency of a head when a coin is thrown 100 times.

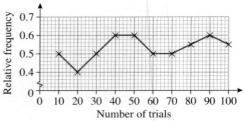

a Copy and complete the table.

Number of trials	10	20	30	40	50	60	70	80	90	100
Relative frequency	0.5	0.4								
Number of heads	5									

b Write down the best estimate of the probability of throwing a head.
Explain your answer.
c Assuming the coin is fair, work out the theoretical probability of throwing a head.
Compare this with the estimated probability.

3 The diagram shows the number of
trials and the relative frequency of
a spinner landing on green
when it is spun 100 times.
a Copy and complete the table.

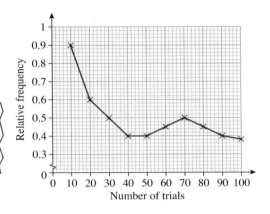

Number of trials	10	20	30	40
Relative frequency	0.9	0.6	0.5	
Frequency of green				

b What is the best estimate of the
probability of the spinner landing
on green?
Explain your answer.

4 The diagram shows the number of trials
and the relative frequency of a dice
landing on an even number.
a After 400 trials the dice has landed
on an even number 200 times. After
500 trials the dice has landed on
an even number 250 times.
Copy the graph and plot the relative
frequencies at 400 and 500 trials.

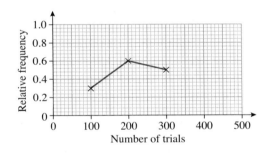

b Estimate the probability that the dice lands on an even number.
c How does the answer to **b** compare with the theoretical probability?

5 Paul records the number of left-handed students he meets at regular intervals.
The table shows his results.

Number of students	20	50	80	100	120
Number of left-handed students	3	9	15	18	21

a Draw a graph to show the relative frequency of a student being left-handed.
b Estimate the probability of a student being left-handed.

6  Shania spins the spinner 50 times and calculates the relative
frequency of blue after every ten spins.
The results are shown on the graph.

a Use the graph to calculate the number of times that the spinner lands on blue:
  i after the first ten spins
  ii after the first 50 spins.
b What is the best estimate of the theoretical probability that the spinner lands on blue?

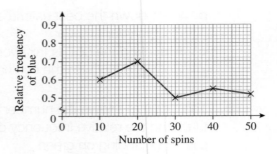

7 The table shows the results of a survey of the number of red cars passing a school. The results are running totals after every 25 cars.

Number of cars	25	50	75	100	125	150
Number of red cars	4	12	20	25	32	38
Relative frequency of red						

a Copy and complete the table of relative frequencies.
b Show the information on a relative frequency graph.

8 Jo and Owen are trying to estimate the probability of their team winning a football match. Jo says that so far this season the team have won nine of their 20 games. Owen says that the team have won 84 of their 420 games in the previous ten seasons before this season.
a **i** Using Jo's figures, what is the team's relative frequency of winning?
   ii Using Owen's figures, what is the team's relative frequency of winning?
b Give a reason why Jo's figures may provide a better estimate of the probability of the team winning.
c Give a reason why Owen's figures may provide a better estimate of the probability of the team winning.

30.2 Using relative frequency

CAN YOU REMEMBER

- How to calculate the probability of an event using equally likely outcomes?
- How to use relative frequency to estimate probability for an experiment or survey?
- How to multiply whole numbers by fractions and decimals?
- How to round to the nearest integer?

IN THIS SECTION YOU WILL

- Use theoretical probability and relative frequency to estimate the result of an experiment or survey.
- Use theoretical probability and relative frequency to judge whether a situation is fair or biased.

In an experiment a coin is thrown 1000 times. The theoretical probability of throwing a head is: $\dfrac{\text{number of successful outcomes}}{\text{total number of outcomes}} = \dfrac{1}{2}$

1000 is a large number of trials. For a large number of trials, the relative frequency is close to the theoretical probability.

So for 1000 trials: $\dfrac{\text{Number of heads}}{1000} = \dfrac{1}{2}$

Number of heads $= \frac{1}{2} \times 1000 = 500$

500 is a good estimate for the number of heads when the coin is thrown 1000 times.
Estimated number of successful outcomes = probability × total number of trials

Relative frequency and theoretical probability can be used to estimate the result of an experiment.

The larger the number of trials in the experiment, the more accurate the estimate.

Example 1

The probability of scoring 1 on a four-sided dice is $\frac{1}{4}$
The dice is rolled 20 times.
a Estimate the number of times a 1 is likely to occur.
b How reliable is this estimate? Give a reason for your answer.

Solution 1

a Estimated number of results = probability × total number of trials
Estimated number of 1s $= \frac{1}{4} \times 20 = 5$
b The estimate is not reliable because the number of trials is small.

If a situation is fair, the relative frequency for a large number of trials is close to the theoretical probability.
If the relative frequency for a large number of trials is not close to the theoretical probability, the situation could be unfair or biased.

Example 2

A coin is spun 500 times and shows heads 160 times.
Is the coin fair? Explain your answer.

Solution 2

The relative frequency of a head $= \frac{160}{500} = 0.32$. This is lower than the theoretical probability of 0.5
The number of trials is large, so the relative frequency is a reliable estimate of probability.
So it is likely that the coin is biased.

Example 3

Dan spins a coin 10 times and gets three heads.

Is the coin biased?

Solution 3

The relative frequency of a head $= \frac{3}{10} = 0.3$

The relative frequency is lower than the theoretical probability of 0.5. But 0.3 is not a reliable estimate of probability, because the number of trials is small.

So it is not possible to say whether the coin is biased.

Exercise A

1 An ordinary fair dice is thrown 60 times.
   Estimate the number of times that a 6 is likely to be thrown.

2 An ordinary dice is thrown 600 times.
   The dice lands on a square number 120 times.
   Is the dice fair?
   Give a reason for your answer.

3 The probability of winning a game is 0.4
   Steve plays the game 20 times.
   a Estimate the number of times Steve is likely to win.
   b How reliable is this estimate?
      Explain your answer.

4 a Jenny throws a coin 200 times.
      She gets 107 heads and 93 tails.
      Is the coin fair? Give a reason for your answer.
   b Tim throws two coins 400 times.
      He gets two heads 112 times and two tails 88 times.
      He says that the coins are biased towards heads.
      Give a reason why he might be wrong.

5 A survey of 100 men is carried out in a town. 30 of the men are married.
   a Estimate the probability that a man selected at random in the town is married.
   b The population of men in the town is 5000
      Estimate the number of married men in the town.

6 An ordinary fair dice is thrown. A score is given according to these rules:

   If the dice lands on an odd number, | score = 2 × number on the dice

   If the dice lands on an even number, | score = number on the dice

   a Complete the table to show the possible scores.

Number on dice	1	2	3	4	5	6
Score	2	2				

b Write down the probability of a score of:
    i 1   **ii** 2   **iii** less than 6

c The dice is thrown 120 times.
Estimate the number of scores of 2 that is likely to be obtained.

d A different dice is thrown 120 times.
Scores are given in the same way.
57 scores of 2 are obtained.
Is this dice fair? Give a reason for your answer.

7 A fish farmer measures the lengths of 200 fish in a pond.
32 of the fish are longer than 20 cm.
Altogether, there are approximately 2500 fish in the pond.
Estimate the number of fish in the pond that are longer than 20 cm.

8 Two fair five-sided spinners are spun.
A score is obtained by adding the numbers
on each spinner.

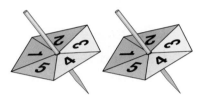

a Copy and complete the table of scores.

+	1	2	3	4	5
1	2	3	4		
2	3	4			
3					
4					
5					

b Write down the probability of a score of: **i** 3   **ii** 8 or more.

c The spinners are spun 500 times.
Estimate the number of times that a score of 8 or more is likely to occur.

9 In a game, a fair coin is thrown and an ordinary fair dice is rolled.
A score is given according to these rules:

If the coin lands on heads,   score = 2 × number on the dice

If the coin lands on tails,   score = number on the dice +1

a Copy and complete the table of scores.

	1	2	3	4	5	6
Head			6			
Tail		3				

b Write down the probability of a score of: **i** 3   **ii** more than 4

c The game is played 120 times.
Estimate the number of times that a score more than 4 is likely to be obtained.

d The same game is played 500 times using a different coin and dice.
A score of more than 4 was obtained 320 times.
Is this game fair? Explain your answer.

10 A group of 2500 people were asked which party they would vote for in an election.
The group were typical of the people who vote in the election.
1360 of the people said they would vote for the Democrats.
  a What is the probability that a person chosen at random will vote Democrat?
  b 55 000 000 people are expected to vote in the election.
     Estimate the number of people who are likely to vote for the Democrats.

Example 4

The probability that a clover has four leaves is 0.02
Sally picks 1000 clovers.
Estimate the number she is likely to find that do **not** have four leaves.

Solution 4

Method 1
The probability of **not** getting a four-leaf clover $= 1 - 0.02 = 0.98$
$0.98 \times 1000 = 980$

Method 2
$0.02 \times 1000 = 20$
The estimated number of clovers with four leaves $= 20$
$1000 - 20 = 980$
The estimated number of clovers that do not have four leaves is 980

Example 5

Here are some instructions for an experiment.
Bill and Sally both complete this experiment.
Their results are shown in the table.

Take a bead at random from a bag containing 500 beads.

Record the colour of the bead and then put it back in the bag.

Repeat this trial a number of times.

Student	Number of trials	Number of red beads obtained
Bill	35	8
Sally	300	78

  a **i** What is the relative frequency of Bill taking a red bead from the bag?
     ii What is the relative frequency of Sally taking a red bead from the bag?
  b **i** Use Bill's results to estimate the number of red beads in the bag.
     ii Use Sally's results to estimate the number of red beads in the bag.
  c Whose experiment should give the more accurate estimate of the number of red beads in the bag?
     Explain your answer.

Solution 5

a   **i** $\dfrac{8}{35}$ or 0.229   **ii** $\dfrac{78}{300}$ or 0.26

b   Theoretical probability $= \dfrac{\text{number of red beads in bag}}{500}$

     i Estimated probability $= \dfrac{8}{35}$

     $\dfrac{\text{Number of red beads}}{500} = \dfrac{8}{35}$

     Number of red beads $= \dfrac{8}{35} \times 500 = 114.28\ldots$

     From Bill's experiment, the estimated number of red beads $= 114$

     ii $\dfrac{\text{Number of red beads}}{500} = \dfrac{78}{300}$

     Estimated number of red beads $= \dfrac{78}{300} \times 500 = 130$

     From Sally's experiment, the estimated number of red beads $= 130$

c   Sally's experiment should give a more accurate estimate of the number of red beads in the bag.
The relative frequency from Sally's experiment is a more reliable estimate of the probability of taking a red bead from the bag.

Exercise B

1   A fair dice is thrown thousands of times.
Estimate the relative frequency of throwing a six.
Explain your answer.

2   **a**   The probability that Daisy wins a game is 0.2
     She plays the game 20 times.
     How many times would you expect Daisy **not** to win?

    b   The probability that a number 289 bus is late is 0.1
     Over one week the number 289 bus makes 80 journeys.
     How many times would you expect the bus **not** to be late?

3   The diagram shows a fair spinner.
The results of the first 20 spins are shown below.

     A   B   C   D   B   C   A   A   D   E
     E   E   B   C   D   C   D   E   A   A

    a   What is the relative frequency of the letter A for these results?
    b   The results of the next ten spins are:
       B   C   D   C   A   B   C   D   B   E
     What is the relative frequency of the letter A after 30 spins?
    c   The spinner is spun some more times.
     Estimate the number of times the letter A will occur after 1000 spins.

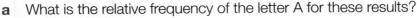

4 The table shows the probabilities of four players playing for a team.

Paul	Andy	Danny	Nathan
$\frac{1}{2}$	$\frac{3}{4}$	$\frac{1}{10}$	$\frac{2}{3}$

The team plays 60 games.
Andy and Danny never play in the same team.
Estimate the number of times that neither Andy nor Danny play.

5 A sack contains a number of gold and silver discs.
A disc is taken from the sack at random and its colour is recorded.
The disc is then replaced.
This trial is repeated a number of times.
The table shows the results.

Number of trials	10	50	100	150	200
Number of gold discs	3	8	23	30	38

a On a copy of this grid draw a graph to show how the relative frequency of a gold disc changes as the number of trials increases.

b Write down an estimate of the probability of taking a gold disc from the sack. Give a reason for your answer.

c The sack contains 1000 discs. Estimate the number of gold discs in the sack.

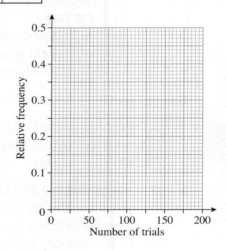

6 Bags A, B and C each contain coloured counters.
Counters are taken at random from each bag and then replaced.
This trial is repeated a different number of times for each bag.

a The relative frequency of taking a blue counter from bag A is shown in the graph.
Explain why this graph is unlikely to give a reliable estimate of the probability of taking a blue counter from bag A.

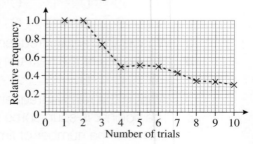

b Bag B contains 80 counters.

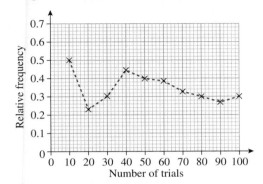

The relative frequency of taking a blue counter from bag B is shown on this graph.
Estimate the number of blue counters in bag B.

c Bag C contains 120 counters.
72 of the counters are blue.
Complete this graph to show possible relative frequencies of taking a blue counter from bag C.

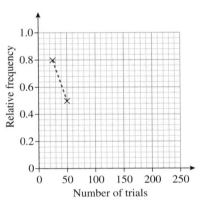

7 A survey of the age groups of 170 rail passengers is shown.

Age	16 or under	17–59	60 or over
Number of passengers	38	72	60

Estimate the number of passengers aged 17 or over on a train carrying 1000 passengers.

8 An internet shop has the following delivery charges:

Delivery	Super saver (5 days)	Saver (3 days)	Express (next day)
Charge	Free	£3.50	£5

Customer records show the following probabilities.
Probability that a customer chooses Super saver = 0.8
Probability that a customer chooses Saver = 0.15
On average, the company makes 2320 deliveries per month.
a Estimate the average number of Express deliveries each month.
b Estimate the average amount the company receives in delivery charges each month.

9 Matthew throws darts at a target. His results are shown in this table.

Total number of throws	10	25	50	100
Total number of hits	4	6	14	24

   a Work out the relative frequency that Matthew hits the target after:

     i 10 throws   **ii** 25 throws   **iii** 50 throws   **iv** 100 throws.

   b On a copy of this grid draw a graph to show how the relative frequency of a hit changes as the total number of throws increases.

   c Write down the best estimate of the probability that Matthew hits the target. Give a reason for your answer.

   d During one week Matthew throws darts at the target 1000 times. Estimate the number of hits he gets.

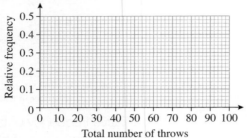

Chapter summary

- Probabilities can be estimated from the results of an experiment or a survey using relative frequency.
- The relative frequency of an event is:

$$\frac{\text{number of times the event occurs in an experiment (or survey)}}{\text{total number of trials in the experiment (or observations in the survey)}}$$

- Relative frequency can be written as a fraction, decimal or a percentage.
- Probability based on relative frequency is called experimental probability. Probability calculated from equally likely outcomes is called theoretical probability.
- Relative frequency gives a more reliable estimate of probability when its value is based on a large number of trials or observations.
- For a large number of trials the relative frequency gives a reliable estimate of the theoretical probability.
- Estimated number of successful outcomes = probability × total number of trials
- Relative frequency and theoretical probability can be used to estimate the result of an experiment.
- The larger the number of trials in the experiment, the more accurate the prediction.
- If a situation is fair, the relative frequency for a large number of trials is close to the theoretical probability.
- If the relative frequency for a large number of trials is not close to the theoretical probability, the situation could be unfair or biased.

Chapter review

1 The diagram shows a fair spinner.
The results of the first ten spins are:

A   B   C   A   B   D   C   C   D   B

  a What is the relative frequency of the letter C?

  b Describe what will happen to the relative frequency of the letter C as the number of spins increases.

2 Twenty-five students each shuffle a pack of cards labelled A, B, C and D and choose a card at random.
A list of the cards chosen is shown.

A   B   B   C   D   C   D   B   A   A   B   D   A
A   B   A   A   C   D   B   C   A   B   A   D

  a Work out the relative frequency of each letter.

  b Estimate the number of times that a letter A is likely to be chosen if 100 students choose a letter at random.

3 James takes a bead at random from a box of coloured beads.
He records its colour and then puts the bead back in the box.
He repeats this trial 300 times.
The table shows his results.

Colour	Red	Blue	Green	White
Frequency	81	90	114	15

  a What is the relative frequency of James taking a red bead from the box?

  b There are 500 beads in the box.
Estimate the number of red beads in the box.

4 Kali has a spinner with coloured sections of equal size.
She does an experiment to find the probability that her spinner lands on blue.
In her experiment Kali spins the spinner 100 times.
She works out the relative frequency of a blue after every ten spins.
Her results are shown on the graph.

  a Use the graph to work out the number of times that the spinner lands on blue:

     i after the first ten spins

     ii after the first 50 spins.

  b Estimate the probability of the spinner landing on blue.

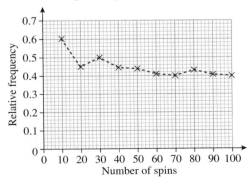

5 A circular spinner has a red sector (R)
and a blue sector (B).
The arrow is spun 1000 times.

a The results for the first ten spins are:

R   R   B   B   B   R   B   B   B   R

Work out the relative frequency of the spinner landing on red after ten spins.

b The table shows the relative frequency of the spinner landing on red after
different numbers of spins.

Number of spins	Relative frequency of a red
50	0.42
100	0.35
200	0.36
500	0.3
1000	0.31

   i How many times did the spinner land on red after 500 spins?

  ii Give an estimate of the probability of a red.
Explain your answer.

6 A circular spinner has sections coloured red (R),
white (W) and blue (B).
The spinner is spun 20 times.
The results are shown below.

R	R	B	W	W	R	B
W	W	R	W	B	W	B
W	R	W	B	W	B	

a Copy and complete the relative frequency table.

Colour	Red (R)	White (W)	Blue (B)
Relative frequency			

b The table shows the relative frequencies after the spinner has been spun
200 times.

Colour	Red (R)	White (W)	Blue (B)
Relative frequency	$\frac{42}{200}$	$\frac{102}{200}$	$\frac{56}{200}$

Tom wants to estimate the probability of the spinner landing on red.
Which of the two relative frequencies for red should he use?
Give a reason for your answer.

7 Serena and Venus play a game of cards.
They have played 150 times before.
15 of their games were drawn.
a Estimate the probability that their next game will be drawn.
Serena is twice as likely to win as Venus.
b What is the probability that Venus wins?

8 It is suspected that a dice is unfair.
Here are the results of 20 throws.

3	4	2	3	1	5	6	2	4	3
4	3	1	1	6	2	5	6	5	3

a Work out the relative frequency of each score.
b Use the relative frequency of a 3 to estimate the number of scores of 3 you are likely to obtain with 60 throws of the dice.
c Compare the answer to **b** with the most likely number of scores of 3 you obtain with 60 throws of a fair dice.

9 Matthew has a dice with three red faces, two blue faces and one green face.
He throws the dice 300 times and gets:

153 reds   98 blues   49 greens

a What is the relative frequency of throwing red?
b Is the dice fair?
Explain your answer.
c Emmie has a dice with four red faces and two blue faces.
She throws the dice ten times and gets two reds.
Emmie says the dice is biased.
Explain why Emmie could be wrong.

10 Tim, Sam and Joe carry out this experiment with the same bag of ten counters.

> **1** Take a counter from the bag at random.
> **2** Record its colour.
> **3** Replace the counter in the bag.
> **4** Repeat this trial a number of times.

Their results are shown in this table.
Estimate the number of each different coloured counter in the box.
State the set of results that you use to make the estimate.
Give a reason for your choice.

Name of pupil	Number of trials	Colour of counters		
		Black	White	Green
Tim	10	0	7	3
Sam	40	4	17	19
Joe	200	23	78	99

Perimeter and area

31.1 Area of parallelograms and triangles

CAN YOU REMEMBER

- The formula for the area of a rectangle: area = length × width?
- That area is measured in square units, e.g. cm^2, mm^2, m^2, km^2?

IN THIS SECTION YOU WILL

- Understand how the formulae for the area of a parallelogram and area of a triangle can be worked out from the formula for the area of a rectangle.
- Learn the meaning of 'base' and 'perpendicular height'.
- Calculate the area of triangles and parallelograms.
- Use area formulae to work out lengths in triangles and parallelograms.

The diagram shows a rectangle drawn on centimetre-squared paper.
There are ten squares in the rectangle.
Area of rectangle = length × width = 10 cm²

This parallelogram is drawn on centimetre-squared paper.

The shaded triangle is cut from one end of the parallelogram. It fits onto the other end to form a rectangle.
Area of parallelogram = area of rectangle = 10 cm²

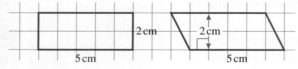

The *base* of the parallelogram is 5 cm.
The *perpendicular height* is at right angles to the base.
The perpendicular height of this parallelogram is 2 cm.
The area of the parallelogram can be calculated using the formula

area = base × perpendicular height

Example 1

Find the area of each of these parallelograms.

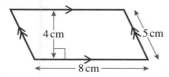
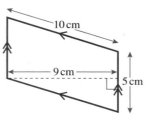

Solution 1

a base = 8 cm,
perpendicular height = 4 cm
(The 5 cm measurement is not used.)
area = base × perpendicular height
= 8 × 4 = 32 cm²

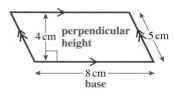

b The base must be at right angles to the height.
So base = 5 cm, perpendicular height = 9 cm.
(The 10 cm measurement is not used.)
area = base × perpendicular height
= 5 × 9 = 45 cm²

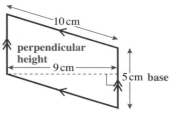

In the diagram, a diagonal has been drawn on the rectangle and the parallelogram.

The diagonal divides each shape into two triangles of the same size and area.
The area of each triangle is half the area of the rectangle or parallelogram.
This gives the formula for the area of a triangle:

area of triangle = $\frac{1}{2}$ × base × perpendicular height

$$A = \frac{1}{2}bh$$

Example 2

Calculate the area of this triangle.

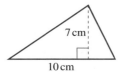

Solution 2

base = 10 cm, perpendicular height = 7 cm
area = $\frac{1}{2}$ × base × perpendicular height
= $\frac{1}{2}$ × 10 × 7 = 35 cm²

Exercise A

1 Work out the area of each of these parallelograms.

a 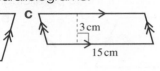 b 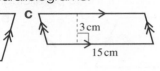 c 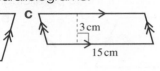 d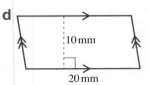

2 Find the area of each of these parallelograms.

a 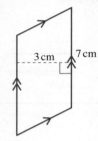 b 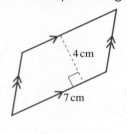 c 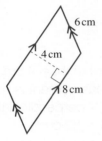 d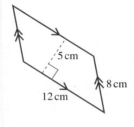

3 Find the area of each of these triangles.

a 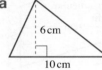 b 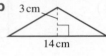 c 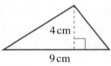 d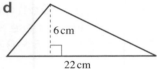

4 Find the area of each of these triangles.

a 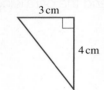 b 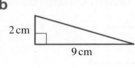 c 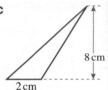 d

5 Find the area of each of these shapes.

a 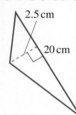 b 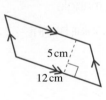 c 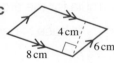 d

6 Calculate the area of each of these parallelograms.

a 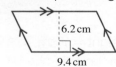 b 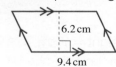 c 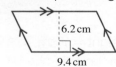 d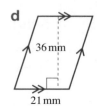

7 Calculate the area of each of these parallelograms.

a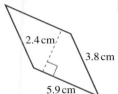

b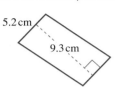

c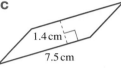

d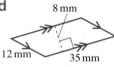

8 Calculate the area of each of these triangles.

a

b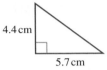

c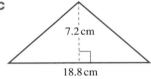

d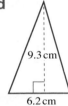

9 Calculate the area of each of these triangles.

a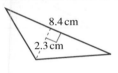

b

c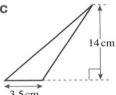

d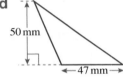

10 Calculate the area of these shapes.

a

b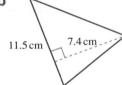

c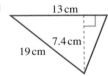

d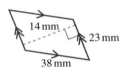

Example 3

Calculate the area of the parallelogram.
Give your answer in square centimetres.

Solution 3

The base is 36 mm.
The perpendicular height is 2.5 cm.
The two measurements are given in different units.
Convert 36 mm to centimetres: 10 mm = 1 cm

$$36 \text{ mm} = 36 \div 10 = 3.6 \text{ cm}$$

Area = base × perpendicular height = $3.6 \times 2.5 = 9 \text{ cm}^2$

Example 4

A parallelogram of base 20 cm has an area of 280 cm²
Calculate the perpendicular height of the parallelogram.

Solution 4

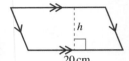

Area = base × perpendicular height
$280 = 20 \times h$
$280 \div 20 = h$ Dividing both sides by 20
$14 = h$
The perpendicular height is 14 cm.

Example 5

The area of this triangle is 24 cm²
Calculate the length of the base, b, of the triangle.

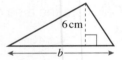

Solution 5

Area = $\frac{1}{2}$ base × perpendicular height
$24 = \frac{1}{2} \times b \times 6$
$24 \div 6 = \frac{1}{2} \times b$ Dividing both sides by 6
$4 = \frac{1}{2} \times b$
$4 \times 2 = b$ Multiplying both sides by 2
$b = 8$ cm

Exercise B

1 Calculate the area of each of these shapes.
Give your answers in square centimetres.

a 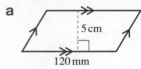 b 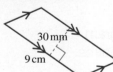 c 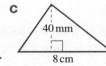 d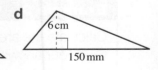

2 Which of the following shapes has the largest area?
Show your working.

a 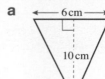 b 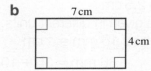 c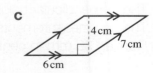

3 Three of these shapes have the same area. Which is the odd one out? Show your working.

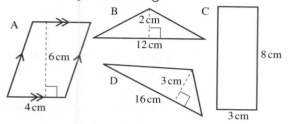

4 A parallelogram has an area of 75 cm². If the base of the parallelogram is 25 cm, what is the perpendicular height?

5 A triangle has a base of 14 cm. The area of the triangle is 70 cm². Calculate the perpendicular height of the triangle.

6 A parallelogram of base 14.6 cm has an area of 124.1 cm²
Calculate the perpendicular height of the parallelogram.

7 A triangle of base 10 cm and perpendicular height 8.5 cm is cut from a rectangle of length 14 cm and width 12 cm.
What area of the rectangle is left?

8 A triangle has a perpendicular height of 26 cm. If the area of the triangle is 447 cm², what is the length of the base of the triangle? Give your answer to one decimal place.

9 An arrowhead is made from two parallelograms of the same size. Calculate the area of the arrowhead.

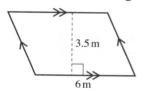

10 Mr Green's lawn is in the shape of a parallelogram.
Mr Green sows each square metre with 40 grams of grass seed. The seed costs £1.05 for 140 grams. Calculate the cost of the grass seed.

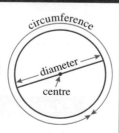

31.2 Circle definitions and circumference

CAN YOU REMEMBER

- That perimeter is the distance around a shape?
- That the circumference of a circle is the distance around the edge or the perimeter of the circle?
- That the centre of the circle is an equal distance from every point on the circumference?
- That the diameter is a line across the circle passing through the centre?

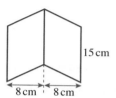

IN THIS SECTION YOU WILL

- Recognise and name parts of a circle.
- Calculate the circumference of a circle or part of a circle.

The *radius* is a straight line from the centre to any point on the circumference. So the length of the radius is half the length of the diameter. The plural of radius is *radii*.

A *tangent* is a straight line outside the circle that touches the circle at only one point.

A *chord* is a straight line that joins any two points on the circumference.

An *arc* is a section of the circumference.

A *segment* is an area between a chord and an arc.

A *sector* is an area between two radii and an arc.

Circumference of a circle

The circumference of a circle can be calculated accurately using the formulae:

$$C = \pi d \qquad \text{or} \qquad C = 2\pi r$$

where d is the diameter, r is the radius and π (pi) is the Greek letter which represents a value of 3.1415 ...

To **estimate** the area use $\pi = 3$

To **calculate** the area use $\pi = 3.14$ or the π button on a calculator.

Example 1

Estimate the circumference of a circle with diameter 5 cm.
Take the value of π to be 3

Solution 1

Using $C = \pi d$ Using $C = 2\pi r$

$\qquad C = 3 \times 5 = 15 \, \text{cm}$ $d = 5 \, \text{cm}, \text{ so } r = 2.5 \, \text{cm}$

$\qquad\qquad\qquad\qquad\qquad\qquad\qquad C = 2 \times 3 \times 2.5 = 15 \, \text{cm}$

An estimate for the circumference is 15 cm.

Example 2

Find the circumference of a circle of radius 8 cm.
Leave your answer in terms of π.

Solution 2

$C = 2\pi r = 2 \times \pi \times 8 = 16\pi \, \text{cm}$

Example 3

Calculate the circumference of a circle of radius 5 cm.
Take the value of π to be 3.14

Solution 3

Using $C = 2\pi r$
$\quad d = 10\,\text{cm}$ so $r = 5\,\text{cm}$
$\quad C = 2 \times 3.14 \times 5 = 31.4\,\text{cm}$

Using $C = \pi d$
$\quad r = 5\,\text{cm}$ so $d = 10\,\text{cm}$
$\quad C = 3.14 \times 10 = 31.4$

The circumference is 31.4 cm.

Exercise A

1 Copy each diagram and write the names of the parts of the circle in the boxes.

a

i

ii

iii

b

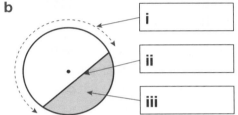

i

ii

iii

2 Copy and complete these statements with the correct word.
   a The .... is a special name for the perimeter
      of a circle.
   b The shaded area between a chord and an arc is called
      a ....
   c A straight line from the centre of a circle to a point on the
      edge of the circle is called a ....

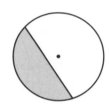

3 Estimate the circumference of these circles.
   Take the value of π to be 3

a
6 cm

b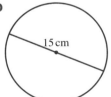
15 cm

c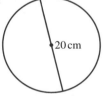
20 cm

d
2.5 cm

e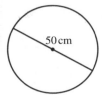
50 cm

f
10 cm

g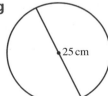
25 cm

h
1.2 cm

4 Estimate the circumference of these circles. Take the value of π to be 3

a 4 cm

b 1.5 cm

c  25 cm

d 10 cm

e 16 mm

f 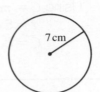 7 cm

g 50 mm

h 11 cm

5 Calculate the circumference of each of the following circles.
Leave your answers in terms of π.

		i	ii	iii
a	diameter =	12 cm	17 cm	35 cm
b	radius =	4.5 cm	22 cm	7.1 cm

6 Calculate the circumference of each of these circles.
Take the value of π to be 3.14

a 4.9 cm

b 15.7 cm

c 11.5 cm

d 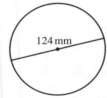 124 mm

e 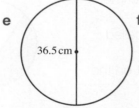 36.5 cm

f 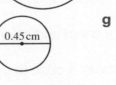 0.45 cm

g 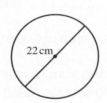 22 cm

h 13.6 cm

7 Calculate the circumference of each of these circles.
Take the value of π to be 3.14

a 3.4 cm

b  9.6 cm

c 0.8 cm

d 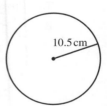 10.5 cm

e  12.5 mm

f  105 mm

g 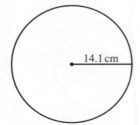 14.1 cm

h 0.3 cm

In questions **8–10** use the π button on a calculator.

8 Calculate the circumference of each of these circles.
Give your answers to one decimal place.

a

5.6 cm

b

12.2 cm

c

14.6 cm

d
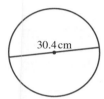
30.4 cm

e

2.3 cm

f
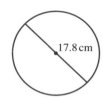
17.8 cm

9 The radius of a bicycle wheel is 56 cm.
What is the circumference of the wheel?
Give your answer to the nearest whole number.

10

A ten-pence piece has a diameter of 2.8 cm.
Work out the circumference of the
ten-pence piece.
Give your answer to one decimal place.

Example 4

A doormat is in the shape of a semicircle of
diameter 75 cm.
Calculate the perimeter of the mat.
Give your answer to the nearest centimetre.

Solution 4

Perimeter of the mat = circumference of half a circle + straight side of 75 cm

So $P = \dfrac{\text{circumference}}{2} + 75$

Circumference of circle diameter 75 cm = $\pi \times 75 = 235.619\,449$ cm

Perimeter of the mat = $\dfrac{235.619\,449}{2} + 75 = 192.809\,724\,5$

$= 193$ cm (to the nearest cm)

Example 5

Calculate the perimeter of this shape.

4 cm

4 cm

Solution 5

The shape is one quarter of a circle of radius 4 cm.
Perimeter = circumference of quarter circle + the lengths of the two straight sides

So perimeter = $\dfrac{\text{circumference}}{4} + 4 + 4$

Circumference of a circle of radius 4 cm = $2 \times \pi \times 4 = 25.132\ 741$ cm

Perimeter of the shape = $\dfrac{25.132\ 741}{4} + 8 = 14.283\ 185 = 14.3$ cm (to 1 d.p.)

Example 6

The circumference of a circle is 36 cm. Calculate the diameter of this circle.

Solution 6

$C = \pi d$, so $36 = \pi \times d$

$\dfrac{36}{\pi} = d$ Dividing both sides by π.

$11.459\ 155 = d$
The diameter is 11.46 cm (to 2 d.p.).

Example 7

The circumference of a circle is 40.84 cm. Calculate the radius of this circle.

Solution 7

$C = 2\pi r$, so $40.84 = 2 \times \pi \times r$

$\dfrac{40.84}{\pi} = 2 \times r$ Dividing both sides by π.

$12.999\ 775 = 2 \times r$

$6.499\ 888 = r$ Dividing both sides by 2

The radius is 6.5 cm (to 1 d.p.).

Exercise B

1   Estimate the diameter of each of the circles with the following circumferences.
Take π to be 3

   a   21 cm   **b**   333 cm   **c**   96 mm   **d**   0.6 m

2 Estimate the radius of each of the circles with the following circumferences.
Take π to be 3
  a 66 cm   **b** 12.6 cm   **c** 186 mm   **d** 0.9 m

3 A wheel of diameter 70 cm makes five complete revolutions.
How far does the wheel travel? Leave your answer in terms of π.

4 Ann has four circular pillowcases and a roll of ribbon. Each pillowcase has a radius
of 11 cm. Ann sews ribbon around the circumference of each pillowcase.
How many centimetres of ribbon does she need? Leave your answer in terms of π.

In questions **5–10** use the π button on your calculator.

5 Find the perimeter of these shapes. Give your answers to two decimal places.

a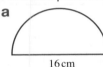
16 cm

b
3 cm

c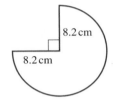
8.2 cm
8.2 cm

d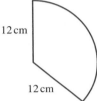
12 cm
12 cm

    semicircle   quarter circle   three-quarter circle $\frac{1}{3}$ of a circle

6 Calculate the diameter of each of the circles with the following circumferences.
Give your answers to one decimal place.
  a 13.7 cm   **b** 46.8 cm   **c** 804 mm   **d** 2.85 m

7 Calculate the radius of each of the circles with the following circumferences.
Give your answers to two decimal places.
  a 4.72 cm   **b** 112 mm   **c** 0.475 m   **d** 76.45 cm

8 A circular sweet tin has a diameter of 14.2 cm.
The lid is sealed with tape. The ends of the tape overlap by 2 cm.
Calculate the length of tape needed to seal the tin.

9 A cycling track has two straight sections of length
150 m and two semicircular ends of diameter 65 m.
Jacob says that three times round the track is greater
than 1500 metres.
Is he correct? Show your working.

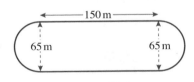
150 m
65 m   65 m

10 A bicycle wheel has a diameter of 30 cm.
Calculate the number of complete revolutions made by the wheel when the bicycle
travels 50 metres.

31.3 Area of a circle

IN THIS SECTION YOU WILL

- Use a formula to calculate the area of circles, semicircles and quarter circles.
- Calculate the area of shapes made from parts of circles and rectangles.

The area of a circle can be found using the formula

area = $\pi \times$ (radius)^2 or $A = \pi r^2$

Example 1

Work out the area of a circle of radius 4 cm.
Leave your answer in terms of π.
Remember to state the units in your answer.

Solution 1

$A = \pi r^2 = \pi \times 4^2 = \pi \times 4 \times 4 = 16\pi$
Area of circle = 16π cm^2

Example 2

Calculate the area of a circle of diameter 5.6 mm.

Solution 2

Diameter = 5.6 mm, so radius = 5.6 mm $\div$ 2 = 2.8 mm
$A = \pi r^2 = \pi \times 2.8^2 = \pi \times 2.8 \times 2.8$
  = 24.630 086 | Using the π button on a calculator. |
Area of circle = 24.63 mm^2 (to 2 d.p.)

Exercise A

For questions **1** and **2**, take π to be 3

1 Estimate the area of each of the following circles.

a

3 cm

b

10 cm

c

2 cm

2 Estimate the area of each of the following circles.

a

10 cm

b

16 cm

c

12 cm

For questions **3** and **4**, leave your answers in terms of π.
State the units of your answers.

3 Work out the area of each of the circles with the following radii.
  a 7 cm **b** 11 mm **c** 8 km **d** 15 cm **e** 9 m **f** 6 mm

4 Work out the area of each of the circles with the following diameters.
  a 2 km **b** 8 cm **c** 24 mm **d** 6 m **e** 20 cm **f** 26 mm

For questions **5–7**, use $\pi = 3.14$ or the π button on a calculator.

5 Calculate the area of each of the following circles.
Give your answers to the nearest whole number.
  a radius = 4.5 mm **b** radius = 17.4 cm **c** radius = 7.36 cm

6 Calculate the area of each of the following circles.
Give your answers to one decimal place.
  a diameter = 26.2 cm **b** diameter = 4.06 cm **c** diameter = 104 mm

7 Calculate the area of each of the following circles.
Give your answer to two decimal places.

a

5.6 cm

b

12.2 cm

c

14.6 cm

d
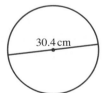
30.4 cm

e

2.3 cm

f
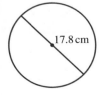
17.8 cm

g
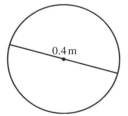
0.4 m

h

27 mm

i
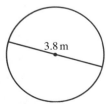
3.8 m

8 A circular rug has a diameter of 1.6 m.
Calculate the area covered by the rug.
Give your answer to the nearest square metre.

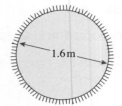

9 A circular window has a diameter of 34 cm.
Calculate the area of glass needed for the window.
Give your answer to the nearest square centimetre.

10 A two-pence piece has a diameter of 2.5 cm.
Find the total area of both faces of the coin.
Give your answer to one decimal place.

Example 3

A plate has a radius of 6 cm.
a Calculate the area of the plate. Leave your answer in terms of π.
b How many plates will fit side by side on a tray of length
50 cm and width 25 cm?

Solution 3

a $A = \pi r^2 = \pi \times 6 \times 6 = 36\pi$
Area of the plate $= 36\pi$ cm^2

b Each plate has radius 6 cm, so diameter $2 \times 6 = 12$ cm.
Length of tray $= 50$ cm
  4×12 cm $= 48$ cm
so four plates will fit along the length of the tray.
  Width of tray $= 25$ cm
  2×12 cm $= 24$ cm
so two plates will fit along the width of the tray.
  $2 \times 4 = 8$ plates will fit on the tray.

Example 4

A shape is made up of a semicircle of diameter
8 cm and a square of side 8 cm.
Calculate the total area of this shape.

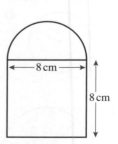

Solution 4

Diameter of semicircle $= 8$ cm so radius $= 4$ cm
Area of circle of radius 4 cm $= \pi \times 4^2 = 50.265$ cm^2
Area of semicircle $= 50.265$ cm$^2 \div 2 = 25.133$ cm^2
Area of square $= 8 \times 8 = 64$ cm^2
So total area of shape $= 25.133 + 64 = 89.1$ cm^2 (to 1 d.p.)

Exercise B

1 A semicircular rug has a radius of 20 cm.
Calculate the area covered by the rug.
Leave your answer in terms of π.

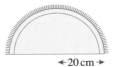

2 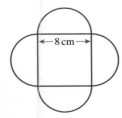 A shape is made from a square
of side 8 cm surrounded by four semicircles
of diameter 8 cm as shown.
Estimate the area of the shape.
Take the value of π to be 3

3 Calculate the area of each of the following shapes.
Give your answers in terms of π.

a

b

4 The diagram shows a circle of diameter 10 cm
inside a square of side 10 cm.
Estimate the area of the square not covered by the circle.
Take the value of π to be 3

5 A mug has a radius of 4 cm.
   a Calculate the area of the base of the mug.
   Give your answer in terms of π.
   b How many of these mugs will fit on a tray
   of length 40 cm and width 24 cm?

6 A circular flower bed has a radius of 1.5 metres.
   a Calculate the area of the flower bed.
   Give your answer to the nearest square metre.

Six plants can be grown in each square metre.
   b Calculate the number of plants that can be grown
   in this flower bed.

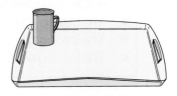

7 The diagram shows a solid wooden gate which is
made up of a rectangle and a semicircle.
   a Write down the height of the gate.
   b Calculate the area of wood needed to
   make the gate.

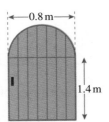

8 A badge is made out of two semicircles as shown. The diameter of each semicircle is 2.5 cm.

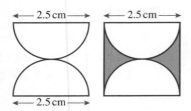

  a Calculate the area of the badge.

  b The badge is cut from a square piece of metal of side 2.5 cm.
Calculate the amount of metal wasted.

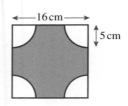

9 A quadrant (quarter circle) is cut from each side of a square piece of card as shown in the diagram.
The square has side length 16 cm.
Each quadrant has a radius of 5 cm.
Calculate the area of card remaining (shown shaded).
Give your answer to one decimal place.

10 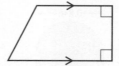 A circular flower bed of radius 1.2 m is surrounded by a path 55 cm wide.
Calculate the area of the path in square metres.
Give your answer to one decimal place.

31.4 Composite shapes

CAN YOU REMEMBER

- That the perimeter is the distance all the way round a shape?
- The properties of a parallelogram and a trapezium?
- That for a rectangle $A = lw$, for a parallelogram $A = bh$, and for a triangle $A = \frac{1}{2}bh$?

IN THIS SECTION YOU WILL

- Work out the perimeter of shapes made from rectangles and triangles.
- Use a formula to calculate the area of a trapezium.
- Calculate the area of shapes made from rectangles and triangles.

This shape is formed from a rectangle and a triangle.

 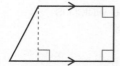 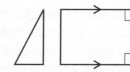

The perimeter of a shape is the total length of the sides of the shape.

Area of the shape = area of rectangle + area of triangle

Example 1

Calculate
a the perimeter
b the area of this shape.

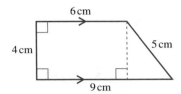

Solution 1

a Perimeter = $6 + 4 + 9 + 5 = 24$ cm
b The shape is made from a rectangle A and a triangle B.

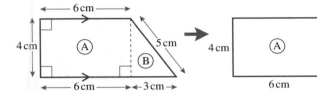

Area of rectangle A = $6 \times 4 = 24$ cm²
Area of triangle B = $\frac{1}{2} \times 3 \times 4 = 6$ cm²
Total area of shape = $24 + 6 = 30$ cm²

The shape in Example 1 is a trapezium.

The area of a trapezium can also be found by using the formula
area = $\frac{1}{2}(a + b)h$

where a and b are the lengths of the parallel sides
and h is the perpendicular height.

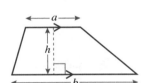

Example 2

Find the area of this trapezium.

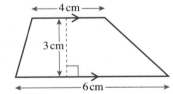

Solution 2

Area of trapezium = $\frac{1}{2}(a+b)h$
$a = 4$ cm, $b = 6$ cm, $h = 3$ cm
Area of trapezium = $\frac{1}{2} \times (4 + 6) \times 3 = \frac{1}{2} \times 10 \times 3 = 15$ cm²

Exercise A

1 Work out the perimeter of these shapes.

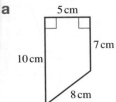

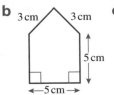

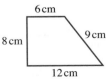

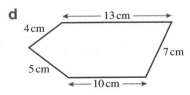

2   Work out the area of these shapes.

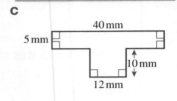
Divide them into rectangles.

a
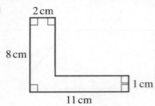
2 cm
8 cm
11 cm
1 cm

b
6 cm   6 cm
9 cm
15 cm
20 cm

c
40 mm
5 mm
10 mm
12 mm

3   Calculate the area of each of these shapes.

a
5 cm
4 cm
40 cm

b
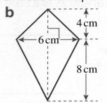
4 cm
6 cm
8 cm

c
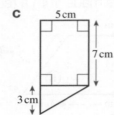
5 cm
7 cm
3 cm

d
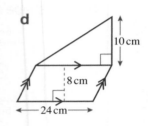
10 cm
8 cm
24 cm

4   Calculate the area of each of these shapes.

a
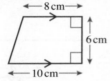
8 cm
6 cm
10 cm

b
15 cm
3 cm   3 cm
10 cm

c
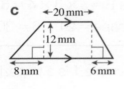
20 mm
12 mm
8 mm   6 mm

d
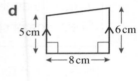
5 cm   6 cm
8 cm

5   Calculate the area of each trapezium.

a

7 cm
5 cm
11 cm

b
20 cm
3 cm
10 cm

c
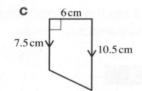
6 cm
7.5 cm   10.5 cm

d
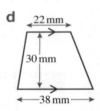
22 mm
30 mm
38 mm

6   Calculate the perimeter of these shapes.

a
22 cm   22 cm
7.5 cm
4.5 cm   4.5 cm
38.6 cm

b
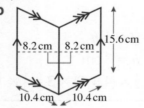
8.2 cm   8.2 cm   15.6 cm
10.4 cm   10.4 cm

c
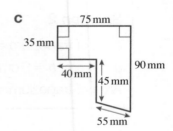
75 mm
35 mm
40 mm   90 mm
45 mm
55 mm

7   Each of the following shapes is a trapezium. Calculate the area of each shape.

a
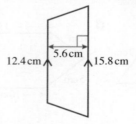
12.4 cm   5.6 cm   15.8 cm

b
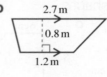
2.7 m
0.8 m
1.2 m

c
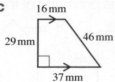
16 mm
29 mm   46 mm
37 mm

d
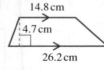
14.8 cm
4.7 cm
26.2 cm

8 Calculate the area of the shapes given in question **6**.

9 This shape is made from a square of side 2.5 cm and four isosceles triangles of base 2.5 cm and perpendicular height 1.8 cm.
Calculate the area of the shape.

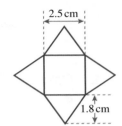

10 Calculate the area of these shapes.

a

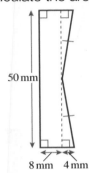

50 mm

8 mm   4 mm

b

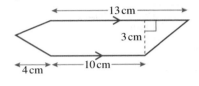

13 cm

3 cm

4 cm   10 cm

Example 3

Find the area of the shaded part of this diagram.

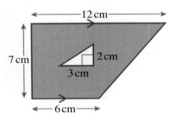

12 cm

7 cm   2 cm

3 cm

6 cm

Solution 3

Shaded area shown
= area of trapezium – area of unshaded triangle

Area of trapezium $= \frac{1}{2}(a+b)h$

$= \frac{1}{2}(12 + 6) \times 7 = \frac{1}{2} \times 18 \times 7 = 63\ \text{cm}^2$

Area of triangle $= \frac{1}{2}bh = \frac{1}{2} \times 3 \times 2 = 3\ \text{cm}^2$

Shaded area $= 63\ \text{cm}^2 - 3\ \text{cm}^2 = 60\ \text{cm}^2$

Example 4

This trapezium has area 90 cm².
The parallel sides of the trapezium measure 11 cm and 19 cm.
Calculate the perpendicular height of the trapezium.

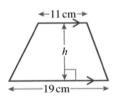

11 cm

h

19 cm

Solution 4

Area of a trapezium $= \frac{1}{2}(a+b)h$

$90 = \frac{1}{2} \times (11 + 19) \times h$

$90 = \frac{1}{2} \times 30 \times h$

$90 = 15 \times h$

$\frac{90}{15} = h = 6$

| Dividing both sides by 15 |

The perpendicular height of the trapezium is 6 cm.

Exercise B

1   Find
   a   the perimeter
   b   the area of this shape.

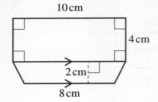

2   Calculate the area of each of these shapes.

   a

   b

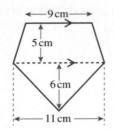

3   A small square of side 6 cm is cut from a large square
   of side 8 cm as shown. Calculate the shaded area.

4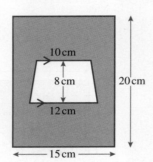

   A trapezium is cut from a rectangular
   piece of card as shown.
   Calculate the shaded area.

5   A trapezium has parallel sides of 14 cm and 26 cm.
   The area of the trapezium is 160 cm²
   Calculate the perpendicular height of
   the trapezium.

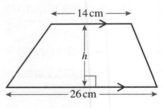

6   Calculate the shaded area of the following shapes.

   a   **b**

   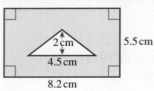   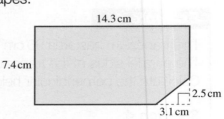

   c   **d**

   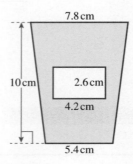   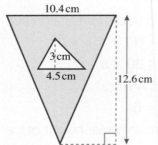

7 Which of the following shapes has the smallest area?
Show your working.

a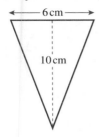

b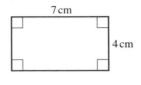

c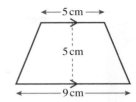

8 Here is a sketch of an L-shaped lawn.
Turf is bought in rolls. Each roll covers
1 square metre and costs £2.50.
Calculate the cost of turfing the lawn.

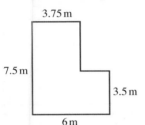

9 The diagram shows a trapezium
ABCD of area 245.68 mm²
AB = 22.4 mm and *CD* = 36.8 mm.
Calculate the perpendicular height,
h, of the trapezium.

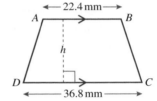

10 A field is in the shape of a trapezium.
There is a gate, 3 m wide, in the longest side of the field.
  a Calculate the area of the field.
  b The farmer wants to build a new fence to
  enclose the field, leaving the gate in the same place.
  He has £2000 to spend. The cost of the fencing is
  £8.50 per metre.
  Does the farmer have enough money to complete the fence?
  Show your working

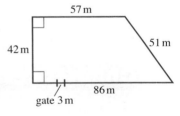

Chapter summary

■ Area of a parallelogram = base × perpendicular height
$A = bh$

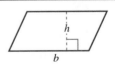

■ Area of a triangle = $\frac{1}{2}$ × base × perpendicular height
$A = \frac{1}{2}bh$

621

■ The names given to parts of a circle are shown below.

 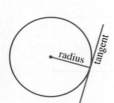 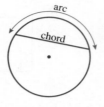 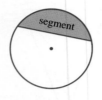

■ The diameter (d) of a circle is twice the length of the radius (r).
■ The circumference of a circle $C = \pi d$ or $C = 2\pi r$
■ The area of a circle $A = \pi r^2$
■ The perimeter of a shape is the total length of the sides of the shape.
■ The area of a trapezium can sometimes be found by dividing the trapezium into a rectangle and triangles.
■ The area of a trapezium can also be found using the formula area $= \frac{1}{2}(a+b)h$ where a and b are the lengths of the parallel sides and h is the perpendicular height.

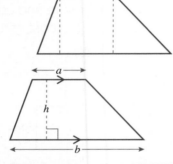

Chapter review

1 Here is a list of words that are connected with circles.

arc   chord   diameter   radius   sector   segment   tangent

Label the lettered parts on the diagram, by choosing the correct words from the list.

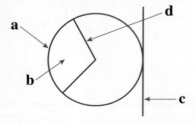

2 A parallelogram is drawn on a centimetre-square grid.
Calculate the area of the parallelogram.

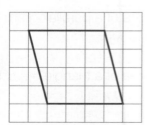

3 PQR is a right-angled triangle.
Calculate the area of triangle PQR.

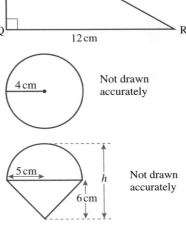

4 **a** The diagram shows a circle of radius 4 cm.
Work out the area of the circle.
Give your answer in terms of π.

b A badge is made out of a semicircle and
an isosceles triangle as shown.
The radius of the semicircle is 5 cm.
The height of the isosceles triangle is 6 cm.
  i Work out the area of the badge.
     Give your answer in terms of π.
  ii Write down the height of the badge,
     marked h on the diagram.
  iii The badge is cut from a strip of metal.
     The metal strip is 10 cm wide and 1 metre long.
     How many badges can be cut from the strip?
     Show your working.

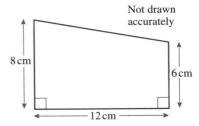

5 The diagram shows a trapezium.
Calculate the area of the trapezium.

Not drawn
accurately

8 cm

6 cm

12 cm

6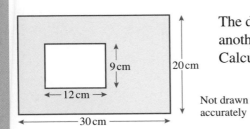

9 cm   20 cm

12 cm

30 cm

Not drawn
accurately

The diagram shows one rectangle drawn inside
another rectangle.
Calculate the area of the shaded region.

7 Calculate the value of πr^2 when $r = 5.4$
Give your answer correct to two decimal places.

8 **a** A circle has a diameter of 6 cm. Write down the length of the radius.
b Draw a circle. On the circle:
  i draw a radius   **ii** draw a chord
  iii mark with a cross a point on the circumference.

9 **a** Calculate the area of a circle with diameter 3 metres.

b A semicircular table has a radius of 0.8 metres.
Calculate the perimeter of the table.

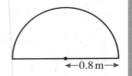

←0.8 m→

10 Hazel's back garden is in the shape of a trapezium.
In the middle of the garden there is a circular pond
of diameter 2 m. The rest of the garden is covered
with grass.
Calculate the area of grass in the garden to the
nearest square metre.

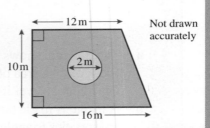

Not drawn
accurately

Equalities and inequalities

32.1 Linear equations

CAN YOU REMEMBER

- How to use the balance method to solve simple equations?
- How to expand brackets and simplify algebraic expressions by collecting like terms?
- How to write statements in words as algebraic expressions?

IN THIS SECTION YOU WILL

- Use the balance method to solve equations with the unknown on both sides of the equation.
- Learn how to solve equations with brackets.
- Set up equations from given situations.

These scales are balanced so the weights on the left-hand side (LHS) equal the weights on the right-hand side (RHS).

This gives the equation

$5x + 200 = 3x + 800$

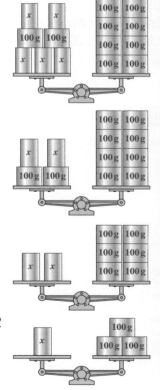

Three x gram weights are removed from the RHS of the scales, so three x gram weights must be removed from the LHS to keep the scales balanced.

The equation changes to $2x + 200 = 800$

Now take two 100 gram weights from both sides.

The equation changes to $2x = 600$

Now divide the weights on both sides by 2
The equation changes to $x = 300$
The *solution* of the equation
$5x + 200 = 3x + 800$ is $x = 300$

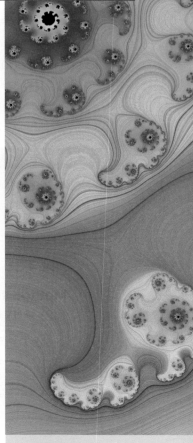

Example 1

Solve each of the following equations.

a $\frac{1}{2}a + 8 = 5$ b $8b - 3 = 6b + 7$

Solution 1

a $\frac{1}{2}a + 8 = 5$

$\qquad \frac{1}{2}a = -3$ | To remove the number term from the LHS subtract 8 from both sides.

$\qquad \frac{1}{2}a \times 2 = -3 \times 2$ | To remove the fraction ($\frac{1}{2}$) term on the LHS multiply both sides by 2

$\qquad a = -6$

Check: When $a = -6, \frac{1}{2}a + 8 = \frac{1}{2} \times -6 + 8 = -3 + 8 = 5$ ✓

b $8b - 3 = 6b + 7$

$\qquad 2b - 3 = 7$ | To remove the b term from the RHS subtract $6b$ from both sides.

$\qquad 2b = 10$ | To remove the number term from the LHS add 3 to both sides.

$\qquad \dfrac{2b}{2} = \dfrac{10}{2}$ | Divide both sides by 2

$\qquad b = 5$

Check: When $b = 5, 8b - 3 = 8 \times 5 - 3 = 40 - 3 = 37$

$\qquad\qquad\qquad\quad 6b + 7 = 6 \times 5 + 7 = 30 + 7 = 37$ ✓

To solve an equation with brackets, first *expand* the brackets and then, if necessary, *simplify*. Then solve the resulting equation using the balance method.

Example 2

Solve the following equations.

a $3(2x + 1) = 9$ b $3(5y - 2) + 5 = 7y + 3$ c $\dfrac{3 - 2c}{4} = 5$

Solution 2

a $3(2x + 1) = 9$

Method 1

$3(2x + 1) = 6x + 3$

$\qquad 6x + 3 = 9$ | Expand brackets.

$\qquad\quad 6x = 6$ | Subtract 3 from both sides.

$\qquad \dfrac{6x}{6} = \dfrac{6}{6}$ | Divide both sides by 6

$\qquad\quad x = 1$

Method 2

$$3(2x + 1) = 9$$

$$\frac{3(2x + 1)}{3} = \frac{9}{3}$$ | Divide both sides by 3

$$2x + 1 = 3$$

$$2x = 2$$ | Subtract 1 from both sides.

$$\frac{2x}{2} = \frac{2}{2}$$ | Divide both sides by 2

$$x = 1$$

Check: When $x = 1$, $3(2x + 1) = 3 \times (2 \times 1 + 1) = 3 \times 3 = 9$ ✓

b $3(5y - 2) + 5 = 7y + 3$

$$3(5y - 2) + 5 = 15y - 6 + 5 = 15y - 1$$

$$15y - 1 = 7y + 3$$ | Expand brackets and simplify.

$$8y - 1 = 3$$ | Subtract $7y$ from both sides.

$$8y = 4$$ | Add 1 to both sides.

$$y = \frac{4}{8} = \frac{1}{2}$$ | Divide both sides by 8

Check: When $y = \frac{1}{2}$, $3(5y - 2) + 5 = 3 \times (5 \times \frac{1}{2} - 2) + 5 = 3 \times \frac{1}{2} + 5 = 6\frac{1}{2}$

$7y + 3 = 7 \times \frac{1}{2} + 3 = 3\frac{1}{2} + 3 = 6\frac{1}{2}$ ✓

c $$\frac{3 - 2c}{4} = 5$$

$$3 - 2c = 20$$ | Multiply both sides by 4

$$-2c = 17$$ | Subtract 17 from both sides.

$$-2c \div 2 = 17 \div -2$$ | Divide both sides by -2

$$c = -8.5$$

$$y = \frac{4}{8} = \frac{1}{2}$$

Check: When $c = -8.5$, $\dfrac{3 - 2c}{4} = \dfrac{3 - 2x - 8.5}{4} = \dfrac{3 + 17}{4} = \dfrac{20}{4} = 5$ ✓

Exercise A

1 a These scales balance.

   i Write an equation to show this situation.

   ii Solve the equation to find x.

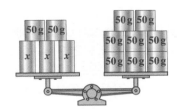

b Repeat for each of the following scales.

i   ii   iii

2 Solve each of the following equations

  a $5a - 2 = 8$ **b** $3b + 1 = 10$ **c** $2c + 6 = 0$ **d** $4d - 3 = -7$

  e $4e + 1 = -5$ **f** $-5f - 2 = -12$ **g** $4g - 1 = -7$ **h** $-3h + 5 = -7$

3 Solve each of the following equations.

  a $\dfrac{a}{3} + 1 = 2$ **b** $\dfrac{b}{2} - 12 = 0$ **c** $\dfrac{c}{2} + 14 = 2$ **d** $\dfrac{d}{2} - 2 = -2$

  e $5 - \dfrac{g}{3} = 6$ **f** $-2 - \dfrac{h}{4} = 3$ **g** $\dfrac{2}{3}e = 4$ **h** $\dfrac{3}{5}f = 9$

  i $\dfrac{i + 7}{5} = 2$ **j** $\dfrac{5 - k}{4} = 2$ **k** $\dfrac{2(l + 3)}{7} = 3$

4 Solve each of the following equations.

  a $4a + 7 = 2a + 3$ **b** $5b - 3 = 3b + 5$ **c** $9c + 1 = 4c + 11$

  d $6d - 4 = 3d + 11$ **e** $8e - 12 = 3e - 2$ **f** $5f - 8 = 2f + 1$

  g $5g - 2 = 10 - g$ **h** $9h - 5 = 5h + 7$ **i** $7i - 15 = 5 - 3i$

  j $-3j + 2 = 10 - 5j$

5 Solve each of the following equations.

  a $5a + 12 = 3a + 5$ **b** $6b - 5 = 4b - 13$ **c** $5c - 2 = 3c - 5$

  d $8d + 14 = 3d - 1$ **e** $11e - 9 = 3e - 2$ **f** $6f + 1 = 2f + 8$

  g $-8g + 6 = -3g + 2$ **h** $-i + 7 = 5 - 3i$ **i** $3j + 7 = 6 - 2j$

6 Solve each of the following equations.

  a $4(a + 1) = 8$ **b** $5(4b - 1) = 25$ **c** $3(5c - 7) = 9$

  d $2(6d - 1) = 4$ **e** $7(2e - 3) = 14$

7 Solve each of the following equations.

  a $4(a + 2) = 2a - 6$ **b** $2(3b - 4) = 4b - 7$ **c** $5(3c + 2) = 5c + 1$

  d $4(3d - 7) = 2 - 3d$ **e** $2(5e - 2) = e + 2$ **f** $3(4f - 5) = 8f + 9$

  g $7(3h - 1) = 5 - 4h$ **h** $4(3i + 1) = 7(i + 2)$ **i** $3(2j + 11) = 2(5 - 2j)$

8 Solve each of the following equations.

  a $14a + 249 = -73$ **b** $23b - 325 = -26$ **c** $46c + 171 = 12c - 373$

  d $12(13e - 2) = 15$ **e** $8(14f + 5) = 432$ **f** $-5(12g - 7) = -13$

  g $7(4h - 5) + 12h = -7$ **h** $6(5 - 3i) - 6i = 81$ **i** $7(11j - 9) = 3(9j + 7)$

Equations are often used to solve problems.
Step 1: Use the information given to set up an equation.
Step 2: Solve the equation using the balance method.

Example 3

The two rectangles shown are equal in area.
a Write down an equation in x.
b Solve the equation to find the value of x.
c Work out the area of the rectangles.

Rectangle A

3 cm

$(2x + 1)$ cm

Solution 3

Rectangle B

4 cm

$2x$ cm

a Area of rectangle A $= 3(2x + 1)$
   Area of rectangle B $= 4 \times 2x = 8x$
   The areas are equal so $8x = 3(2x + 1)$

b $\qquad 8x = 3(2x + 1)$

   $3(2x + 1) = 3 \times 2x + 3 \times 1 = 6x + 3$ Expand the brackets.

   $\qquad 8x = 6x + 3$

   $\qquad 2x = 3$ Subtract $6x$ from both sides.

   $\qquad \dfrac{2x}{2} = \dfrac{3}{2}$ Divide both sides by 2

   $\qquad x = 1.5$

c Rectangle A: area $= 3 \times (2 \times 1.5 + 1) = 3 \times (3 + 1) = 3 \times 4 = 12$ cm^2
   So rectangle B: area $= 12$ cm^2

Example 4

The diagram shows a triangle with angles $x°$, $(x + 30)°$
and $(2x - 10)°$.
Show that the triangle is an isosceles triangle.

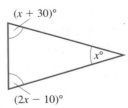

$(x + 30)°$

$x°$

$(2x - 10)°$

Solution 4

The sum of the angles in the triangle $= x + (x + 30) + (2x - 10)$
$= 4x + 20$
The sum of the angles of a triangle is $180°$.
So $\quad 4x + 20 = 180$

   $\qquad 4x = 160$ Subtract 20 from both sides.

   $\qquad x = 40$ Divide both sides by 4

So the angles of the triangle are
$x = 40°$, $x + 30 = 70°$, $2x - 10 = 70°$
The triangle has two equal angles and, therefore, is isosceles.

Exercise B

1 **a** A triangle has angles $x°$, $2x°$ and $(x + 20)°$.

     i Write down an equation in x.

     ii Solve the equation to find x.

  b Repeat **a** for these triangles.

     i

     ii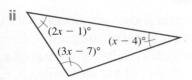

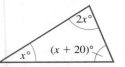

2 For each of the following diagrams

  a Write down an equation in y.

  b Solve the equation to find the value of y.

     i

     ii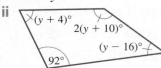

3 Sally has a piece of ribbon 1 metre long.

    She cuts the ribbon into eight pieces each of length x cm.

    She has exactly 8 cm of ribbon left over.

    Write down and solve an equation to find x.

4 **a** **i** Explain why the three consecutive integers starting with x are

       x, $x + 1$ and $x + 2$

    ii The sum of three consecutive integers starting with x is 24

       Write down and solve an equation to find the three integers.

  b The sum of five consecutive integers is 60

    Find the median of the five integers.

5 Tom and Sally investigate the numbers they can make using different rules.

  a **Tom**

    Use x to stand for the number
that Tom thinks of.
Write down and solve an
equation to find x when
Tom's answer is 12

  b **Sally**

    Use y to stand for the number
that Sally thinks of.
Write down and solve an
equation to find y when
Sally's answer is 28

  c Both Tom and Sally think of the same number, z.
They both get the same answer.
Write down and solve an equation to find z.

6 **a** Here are two number machines.
There is a value of x that gives the **same** value of y for **both** machines.
Write the output for each machine in the format $y = \dots$
Hence write down and solve an equation to find this value of x.

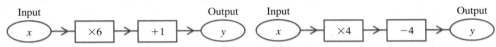

b Repeat **a** for each of the following pairs of number machines.

i

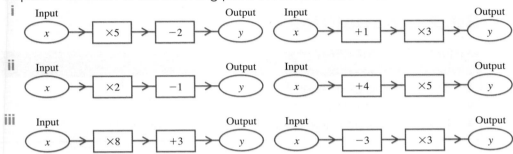

ii

iii

7 **a** Rectangle A has sides of length 4 cm and $(3x - 2)$ cm.
Work out x if the perimeter of rectangle A is 16 cm.
b Rectangle B has sides of length 5 cm and $(2y + 1)$ cm.
Work out y if the area of rectangle B is 50 cm²
c Rectangle C has sides of length 3 cm and $(4z - 1)$ cm.
Rectangle D has sides of length 5 cm and $(3z - 2)$ cm.
Work out z if the area of rectangle C equals the area of rectangle D.

8 **a** Show that this triangle is equilateral. **b** This triangle is also equilateral.

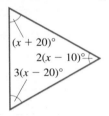

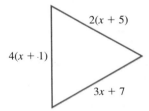

Work out the value of x.

9 **a** A rectangle has the measurements
shown on the diagram.

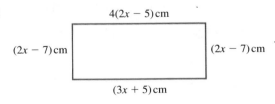

  i Explain why
$4(2x - 5) = 3x + 5$
  ii Solve the equation
$4(2x - 5) = 3x + 5$
  iii Show that the area of the rectangle is 60 cm²
b Show that this rectangle has
a perimeter of 54 cm.

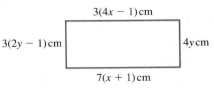

10 In bag A there are x counters.

In bag B there are 4 fewer counters than in bag A.

In bag C there are twice as many counters as there are in bag B.

In bag D there are 5 times as many counters as there are in bag A.

Afzal says that the number of counters in bag C equals the number of counters in bag D.

Explain why this is impossible.

32.2 Inequalities

CAN YOU REMEMBER

- The meaning of 'integer'?
- How to use a number line?
- How to solve an equation using the balance method?

IN THIS SECTION YOU WILL

- Learn how to represent an inequality on a number line.
- Learn how to use the balance method to solve a simple inequality.

An *inequality* is written using one of these symbols $< \leqslant > \geqslant$

$x < 2$ means that the value of the letter symbol x is *less than* 2

$x > -3$ means that the value of the letter symbol x is *greater than* -3

$x \leqslant -1$ means that the value of the letter symbol x is *less than or equal to* -1

$x \geqslant 3$ means that the value of the letter symbol x is *greater than or equal to* 3

Inequalities can be shown on a number line.

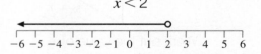
         or   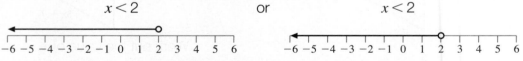

The values covered by the solid line are the values of x that fit the inequality.

The hollow circle at 2 means that 2 is **not** included in the inequality.

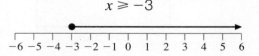
         or   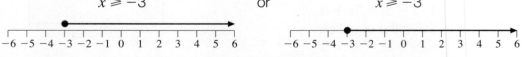

The values covered by the solid line are the values of x that fit the inequality.

The full circle at -3 means that -3 **is** included in the inequality.

x is greater than 2 means the same as
2 is less than x.
So $x > 2$ and $2 < x$ are equivalent.

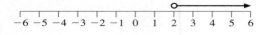

Example 1

Write down the inequality shown on each of these number lines.

a

b

Solution 1

a $\quad x \geqslant -5$ or $-5 \leqslant x$

b $\quad x < 2$ or $2 > x$

The balance method can be used to solve simple linear inequalities.
The solution can be written as an inequality or shown on a number line.

For example

$$3x + 4 \geqslant -2 \qquad \boxed{\text{Subtract 4 from both sides.}}$$

$$3x \geqslant -6 \qquad \boxed{\text{Divide both sides by 3}}$$

$$x \geqslant -2$$

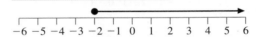

Example 2

Solve the inequalities:

a $\quad 5x \leqslant 10$

b $\quad \frac{1}{2}x - 4 < -1$

c $\quad 4x < 2x - 5$

Solution 2

a $\quad 5x \leqslant 10 \qquad \boxed{\text{Divide both sides by 5}}$

$\quad\quad x \leqslant 2$

b $\quad \frac{1}{2}x - 4 < -1 \qquad \boxed{\text{Add 4 to both sides.}}$

$\quad\quad \frac{1}{2}x < 3 \qquad \boxed{\text{Multiply both sides by 2}}$

$\quad\quad x < 6$

c $\quad 4x < 2x - 5 \qquad \boxed{\text{Subtract } 2x \text{ from both sides.}}$

$\quad\quad 2x < -5 \qquad \boxed{\text{Divide both sides by 2}}$

$\quad\quad x < -2.5$

Exercise A

1 Rewrite each of the following statements using inequality symbols.

    a w is greater than 4   b x is less than or equal to -1

    c y is greater than or equal to -5 d z is less than 7

2 Decide whether each of the following statements is true or false.

    a $6 < 6$ b $6 \leqslant 6$ c $6 > 6$ d $6 \geqslant 6$

    e $-5 > -3$ f $-5 < -3$ g $0 > 2$

3 Show the following inequalities on a copy of this number line.

$$-6\ -5\ -4\ -3\ -2\ -1\ \ 0\ \ 1\ \ 2\ \ 3\ \ 4\ \ 5\ \ 6$$

Use a different number line for each inequality.

a $x < 4$ b $x \geqslant 1$ c $x > -3$ d $x \leqslant -1$

e $-5 > x$ f $-5 \leqslant x$ g $3 \geqslant x$ h $3 < x$

4 The number lines show values of x.
Write down each of the inequalities.

a
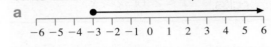

b
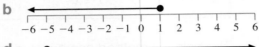

c
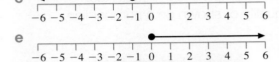

d
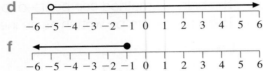

e
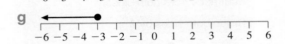

f
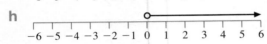

g

h

5 The smallest integer that satisfies the inequality $x \geqslant 2$ is $x = 2$
Write down the smallest integer that satisfies each of these inequalities.

a $a > 3$ b $b > 7$ c $c \geqslant -1$ d $d \geqslant -6$

e $e > -1$ f $f > -4$ g $g \geqslant -4$ h $h \geqslant -2$

i $i > 1\frac{1}{4}$ j $j > 2\frac{5}{8}$ k $k \geqslant 1\frac{1}{4}$ l $l \geqslant 2\frac{5}{8}$

m $m \geqslant -3\frac{4}{5}$ n $n \geqslant -1\frac{1}{3}$ o $o \geqslant -7.964$ p $p \geqslant -1.007$

6 The largest integer that satisfies the inequality $x < 2$ is $x = 1$
Write down the largest integer that satisfies each of these inequalities.

a $a < 3$ b $b < 7$ c $c \leqslant -1$ d $d \leqslant -6$

e $e < -1$ f $f < -4$ g $g \leqslant -4$ h $h \leqslant -2$

i $i < 1\frac{1}{4}$ j $j < 2\frac{5}{8}$ k $k \leqslant 1\frac{1}{4}$ l $l \leqslant 2\frac{5}{8}$

m $m \leqslant -3\frac{4}{5}$ n $n \leqslant -1\frac{1}{3}$ o $o \leqslant -7.964$ p $p \leqslant -1.007$

7 Solve each of the following inequalities.

a $a + 2 \leqslant 1$ b $b - 5 > -1$ c $4c \geqslant 12$ d $\frac{1}{4}d < -3$

e $2e + 3 \leqslant -1$ f $4f < 2f + 12$ g $5g - 3 \geqslant -8$ h $3(h - 6) \geqslant h$

i $3i - 3 \leqslant i - 5$ j $10j - 15 \geqslant 4j - 24$

8 Solve each of the following inequalities. Show your answers on a number line.

a $a - 3 > -7$ b $b - 5 \leqslant -2$ c $3c < -12$ d $\frac{1}{3}d \geqslant -1$

e $3e - 2 \leqslant -5$ f $6f > 2f - 8$ g $\frac{1}{5}g - 3 \geqslant -2$ h $\frac{1}{2}(h - 4) < -4$

i $5i - 6 \leqslant 2i - 3$ j $3(2j + 1) \geqslant 2j - 5$

Two single inequalities can be combined into a double inequality.
For example, the values of x that fit both of the inequalities $-4 < x$ and $x \leqslant 2$ can be described by the double inequality $-4 < x \leqslant 2$
The integers that satisfy this double inequality are $-3, -2, -1, 0, 1$ and 2

Example 3

Show each of the following double inequalities on a number line.

a $-4 \leqslant x < 3$ b $-4 < x \leqslant 3$ c $-3 \geqslant x$ and $x > 4$

Solution 3

a   The values of x that fit the inequality $-4 \leqslant x < 3$ fit **both** $-4 \leqslant x$ and $x < 3$

$-4 \leqslant x$ (or $x \geqslant -4$)

$x < 3$

So the values of x that fit $-4 \leqslant x < 3$ are

b $-4 < x \leqslant 3$ c $-3 \geqslant x$ and $x > 4$

The balance method can be used to solve double inequalities.
Separate the double inequality into two inequalities and solve each using the balance method. Then combine the two solution inequalities.

Example 4

a   Solve the inequality $1 \leqslant x + 4 < 5$
b   Find the integer values that satisfy $-4 \leqslant 2x \leqslant 8$

Solution 4

a   Separating $-1 \leqslant x + 4 < 5$ into two inequalities gives

$-1 \leqslant x + 4$ $x + 4 < 5$ | Subtract 4 from both sides.
$-5 \leqslant x$ $x < 1$

Combining the single inequalities gives the double inequality $-5 \leqslant x < 1$

b   Separating $-4 \leqslant 2x \leqslant 8$ into two inequalities gives

$-4 \leqslant 2x$ $2x \leqslant 8$ | Divide both sides by 2
$-2 \leqslant x$ $x \leqslant 4$

So the solution is the double inequality $-2 \leqslant x \leqslant 4$

On a number line the solution is:

So the integer values satisfying $-4 \leqslant 2x \leqslant 8$ are $-2, -1, 0, 1, 2, 3, 4$

Exercise B

1   Tim says that the integers $-2, -1, 0, 1$ and 2 fit the double inequality $-3 \leqslant x < 2$
Explain why Tim is wrong.

2   Sally says that the integers $-1, 0$ and 1 fit the inequalities $-1 \geqslant x$ and $x \geqslant 1$
Explain why Sally is wrong.

3   Find the values of each of the integers p, q, r, s, t and u where
   a   the integers $-3, -2, -1, 0, 1, 2$ and 3 fit the inequality $p < x \leqslant q$
   b   the integers $-2, -1, 0, 1, 2, 3$ and 4 fit the inequality $r \leqslant x \leqslant s$
   c   the integers $-5, -4, -3, -2$ and -1 fit the inequality $t < x < u$.

4   You are given the following inequalities:
   A $-4 \leqslant x < 1$ B $-1 < x \leqslant 3$
   C $2 > x$ and $x \geqslant 4$ D $1 > x$ and $x > 3$
   a   Show each of inequalities A, B, C and D on a number line.
   b   Write down the integers that fit both A and B.
   c   Write down the integers that fit both A and C.
   d   Write down the integers that fit all of A, B, C and D.

5   Write down the inequalities shown on each of these number lines.
   a 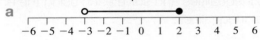   **b**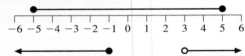

   c 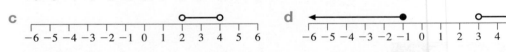   **d**

   e 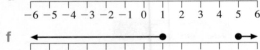   **f**

6 **a**   Write the following pairs of inequalities as a single inequality.
       i $-2 \leqslant x$ and $x < 5$ **ii** $-3 \leqslant x$ and $x \leqslant 2$ **iii** $0 < x$ and $x \leqslant 3$
       iv $-1 \leqslant x$ and $x \leqslant 2$ **v** $-6 < x$ and $x < 3$
   b   Write down two separate inequalities that are equivalent to each of these double inequalities.
       i $-1 \leqslant x < 2$ **ii** $-4 \leqslant x \leqslant 6$ **iii** $-4 < x \leqslant 0$
       iv $1 \leqslant x \leqslant 2$ **v** $-1 < x < 1$
   c   List the integers that fit each of the inequalities in **a** and **b**.

7   Solve each of these inequalities.
   a $-1 < x + 3 < 1$ **b** $-3 \leqslant x - 1 < 2$ **c** $-2 < x + 4 \leqslant 3$
   d $-5 \leqslant x - 2 \leqslant -1$ **e** $-4 < 2x \leqslant 8$ **f** $-8 < 4x < 4$
   g $-1 \leqslant \frac{1}{2}x \leqslant 3$ **h** $-2 \leqslant \frac{1}{4}x < 1$

8   Write down the integer values that satisfy each of these inequalities.
   a $2 < x + 5 < 8$ **b** $-5 \leqslant x - 2 < -1$ **c** $-1 < x + 4 \leqslant 4$
   d $-8 \leqslant x - 6 \leqslant -4$ **e** $-20 < 5x \leqslant 5$ **f** $-9 < 3x < 3$
   g $-1 \leqslant \frac{1}{3}x \leqslant 1$ **h** $-2 \leqslant \frac{1}{2}x < 0$

32.3 Trial and improvement

CAN YOU REMEMBER

- How to substitute values into expressions involving squares and cubes?
- The meaning of 'one decimal place', 'two decimal places', etc.?
- How to round values to one decimal place?

IN THIS SECTION YOU WILL

- Learn how to solve equations using the method of trial and improvement.

Simple equations like $3x + 2 = 11$, $5y - 2 = 4 + y$ and $5(z + 7) = 12$ can always be solved using the balance method.

However, it is **not** possible to use the balance method to solve equations involving powers and roots like $x^3 + 2x = 12$, $y^2 - \dfrac{1}{y} = 17$ and $\sqrt{y} + y = 11$

One way of solving these equations is the method of *trial and improvement*.

Estimate a solution, try it in the equation, and use the result to improve the estimate.

Trial and improvement can take a lot of time. It should only be used to solve equations that cannot easily be solved by other methods.

Example 1

The equation $x^3 + 2x = 33$ has a solution that is a whole number.
Use the method of trial and improvement to find this solution.

Solution 1

Trial value of x	$x^3 + 2x$	Comment	Conclusion
2	$2^3 + 4 = 8 + 4 = 12$	Too small	$x > 2$, x is bigger than 2
4	$4^3 + 8 = 64 + 8 = 72$	Too big	$x < 4$, x is smaller than 4
3	$3^3 + 6 = 27 + 6 = 33$	Correct	$x = 3$

The solution of $x^3 + 2x = 33$ is $x = 3$

Example 2

Use the method of trial and improvement to solve the equation $x^3 - x = 30$
Give your answer to two decimal places.

Solution 2

Step 1: Try whole numbers.

x	$x^3 - x$	Comment	Conclusion
2	$2^3 - 2 = 6$	Too small	$x > 2$, x is bigger than 2
3	$3^3 - 3 = 24$	Too small	$x > 3$, x is bigger than 3
4	$4^3 - 4 = 60$	Too big	$3 < x < 4$, x is between 3 and 4

The solution lies between $x = 3$ and $x = 4$

Step 2: Try numbers between 3 and 4, with one decimal place.

x	$x^3 - x$	Comment	Conclusion
3.5	$3.5^3 - 3.5 = 39.375$	Too big	$3 < x < 3.5$, x is between 3 and 3.5
3.2	$3.2^3 - 3.2 = 29.568$	Too small	$3.2 < x < 3.5$, x is between 3.2 and 3.5
3.3	$3.3^3 - 3.3 = 32.637$	Too big	$3.2 < x < 3.3$, x is between 3.2 and 3.3

The solution lies between $x = 3.2$ and $x = 3.3$

Step 3: Try numbers between 3.2 and 3.3, with two decimal places.

x	$x^3 - x$	Comment	Conclusion
3.25	$3.25^3 - 3.25 = 31.078$	Too big	$3.2 < x < 3.25$, x is between 3.2 and 3.25
3.22	$3.22^3 - 3.22 = 30.166$	Too big	$3.2 < x < 3.22$, x is between 3.2 and 3.22
3.21	$3.21^3 - 3.21 = 29.866$	Too small	$3.21 < x < 3.22$, x is between 3.21 and 3.22

The solution lies between $x = 3.21$ and $x = 3.22$

Step 4: Try 3.215

x	$x^3 - x$	Comment	Conclusion
3.215	$3.215^3 - 3.215 = 30.016$	Too big	$3.21 < x < 3.215$

The solution lies between 3.21 and 3.215
All numbers between 3.21 and 3.215 round to 3.21 to two decimal places.
The solution of $x^3 - x = 30$ is $x = 3.21$ to two decimal places.

Exercise A

1 Each of the following equations has a solution that is a whole number.
Use the method of trial and improvement to find the exact solution.
You **must** show your trials.

  a $a^2 + a = 56$ **b** $b^2 + b = 210$ **c** $c^2 - c = 210$ **d** $d^2 - d = 156$

  e $e^2 + 2e = 99$ **f** $f^3 + f = 130$ **g** $g^3 + 3g = 36$ **h** $h^2 + \sqrt{h} = 84$

  i $i^2 + \dfrac{1}{i} = 16.25$ **j** $j^3 - j^2 = 100$ **k** $k + \sqrt{k} = 20$

2 Lara, Bill and Sunita are solving an equation in x using trial and improvement.

  a Lara finds that the solution lies between $x = 3.5$ and $x = 4$
  What is the solution to the nearest whole number?

  b Bill finds that the solution lies between $x = 3.6$ and $x = 3.65$
  What is the solution to one decimal place?

  c Sunita finds that the solution lies between $x = 3.63$ and $x = 3.64$
  i Write this information as an inequality.
  ii What value of x should Sunita try so that she can give the solution to two decimal places?

3 **a** The solution of the equation $x^3 - x = 20$ lies between $x = p$ and $x = q$ where p and q are consecutive whole numbers.

  i Find the values of p and q. **ii** Write this information as an inequality.

  b Repeat **a** for

  i $x^3 + x^2 = 60$ **ii** $x^3 + x^2 - x = 100$ **iii** $x^3 - x^2 + x - \dfrac{1}{x} = 52$

4 **a** Use trial and improvement to solve the equation $x^3 = 16$
  Give your answer to an accuracy of two decimal places.
  Use a starting trial value of $x = 2$ You **must** show your trials.

  b James wants to find the cube root of 1100
  i What equation should James solve?
  ii Find the cube root of 1100 to two decimal places using trial and improvement.
    You **must** show your trials.

  c Use trial and improvement to find the cube root of 425 to an accuracy of two decimal places. You **must** show your trials.

5 Copy and complete the following to solve the equation $x^3 + x = 20$ using the method of trial and improvement.
Give your answer to an accuracy of one decimal place.

Trial value of x	$x^3 + x$	Comment	Conclusion
2	$2^3 + 2 = \dots$	Too …	$x > 2$
3	…	…	$\dots < x < \dots$

The solution lies between $x = \ldots$ and $x = \ldots$

Trial value of x	$x^3 + x$	Comment	Conclusion
2.5	$2.5^3 + 2.5 = \ldots$	$\ldots$	$\ldots < x < \ldots$
$\ldots$	$\ldots$	$\ldots$	$\ldots < x < \ldots$

The solution lies between $x = \ldots$ and $x = \ldots$

Trial value of x	$x^3 + x$	Comment	Conclusion
$\ldots$	$\ldots$	$\ldots$	$\ldots < x < \ldots$

So to one decimal place the solution of $x^3 + x = 20$ is $x = \ldots$

6 Copy and complete the following to solve the equation $x^3 - x^2 = 95$ using the method of trial and improvement.
Give your answer to two decimal places.

Trial value of x	$x^3 - x^2$	Comment	Conclusion
4	$4^3 - 4^2 = \ldots$	Too $\ldots$	$x > 4$
5	$\ldots$	$\ldots$	$\ldots < x < \ldots$

The solution lies between $x = \ldots$ and $x = \ldots$

Trial value of x	$x^3 - x^2$	Comment	Conclusion
4.5	$4.5^3 - 4.5^2 = \ldots$	$\ldots$	$\ldots < x < \ldots$
4.9	$\ldots$	$\ldots$	$\ldots < x < 5$

The solution lies between $x = \ldots$ and $x = \ldots$

Trial value of x	$x^3 - x^2$	Comment	Conclusion
4.95	$\ldots$	$\ldots$	$\ldots < x < \ldots$
4.92	$\ldots$	$\ldots$	$\ldots < x < \ldots$
$\ldots$	$\ldots$	$\ldots$	$\ldots < x < \ldots$

The solution lies between $x = \ldots$ and $x = \ldots$

Trial value of x	$x^3 - x^2$	Comment	Conclusion
$\ldots$	$\ldots$	$\ldots$	$\ldots < x < \ldots$

So to two decimal places the solution of $x^3 - x^2 = 95$ is $x = \ldots$

7 Use trial and improvement to solve each of the following equations.
Use the starting values given. Give each of your answers to one decimal place.
You **must** show your trials.
a $a^2 + a = 60$ (start with $a = 7$)   b $b^2 - b = 250$ (start with $b = 16$)
c $c^3 + 3c = 42$ (start with $c = 3$)

Example 3

Use trial and improvement to complete the table to find a solution to the equation
$x^2 + \sqrt{x} = 90$
Give your answer to one decimal place.

x	$x^2 + \sqrt{x}$	Comment
9	$9^2 + \sqrt{9} = 84$	Too small, $x > 9$, x is bigger than 9
10	$10^2 + \sqrt{10} = 103.162\ldots$	Too big, $9 < x < 10$, x is between 9 and 10

Solution 3

x	$x^2 + \sqrt{x}$	Comment
Try one decimal place numbers between $x = 9$ and $x = 10$		
9.5	$9.5^2 + \sqrt{9.5} = 93.332\ldots$	Too big, $9 < x < 9.5$ x is between 9 and 9.5
9.4	$9.4^2 + \sqrt{9.4} = 91.425\ldots$	Too big, $9 < x < 9.4$ x is between 9 and 9.4
9.3	$9.3^2 + \sqrt{9.3} = 89.539\ldots$	Too small, $9.3 < x < 9.4$ x is between 9.3 and 9.4
Try $x = 9.35$		
9.35	$9.35^2 + \sqrt{9.35} = 90.480\ldots$	Too big, $9.3 < x < 9.35$ x is between 9.3 and 9.35

The solution lies between 9.3 and 9.35
All numbers between 9.3 and 9.35 round to 9.3 to one decimal place.
So the solution of $x^2 + \sqrt{x} = 90$ is $x = 9.3$ (to 1 d.p.).

Exercise B

1   Use trial and improvement to solve each of the following equations.
Use the starting values given. Give each of your answers to one decimal place.
You **must** show your trials.

   a $d^2 + \sqrt{d} = 95$ (start with $d = 9$)   b $e^2 + \dfrac{1}{e} = 43$ (start with $e = 6$)

   c $f^3 - f^2 = 286$ (start with $f = 7$)   d $g + \sqrt{g} = 4$ (start with $g = 2$)

   e $h^3 - h^2 + h - \dfrac{1}{h} = 200$ (start with $h = 6$)

2   a   Derek uses trial and improvement to
solve an equation. He finds that the
solution lies between 3.731 and 3.734
Derek makes three statements.
Which statements are true?
Write a correct statement to
replace any false statement.

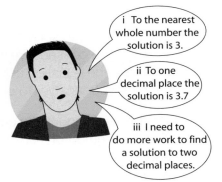

i To the nearest whole number the solution is 3.

ii To one decimal place the solution is 3.7

iii I need to do more work to find a solution to two decimal places.

b Derek finds that the solution of another equation is between 4.73 and 4.78
Derek gives the solution as 4.8. Explain why he is wrong.

3 John is trying to solve the
equation $x^3 + 2x = 45$ using
trial and improvement.
He has been asked for the
solution to an accuracy of
one decimal place.
John's work is shown
opposite.

Write down three (or more)
pieces of advice for John.
Point out where he has gone
wrong and how he could
improve his method.

x	$x^3 + 2x$	Comment
3.5	$3.5^3 + 7 = 50$	Too big
3	$3^3 + 6 = 33$	Too small
3.25	$3.25^3 + 6.5 = 40$	Too small
3.24	$3.24^3 + 6.48 = 40$	Too small
3.28	$3.28^3 + 6.56 = 42$	Too small
3.32	$3.32^3 + 6.64 = 43$	Too small
3.325	$3.325^3 + 6.65 = 43$	Too small
3.4	$3.4^3 + 6.8 = 46$	Too big
3.35	$3.35^3 + 6.7 = 44.29$	Too small
3.36	$3.36^3 + 6.72 = 44.65$	Too small
3.37	$3.37^3 + 6.74 = 45.01$	Too big
3.369	$3.369^3 + 6.738 = 44.98$	Too small
3.3695	$3.3695^3 + 6.739 = 44.994 \ldots$	Too small

Answer 44.994 ...

4 Megan is using trial and improvement to solve this problem.

Number $\times 2.7 = 6.2$

Megan shows her working in this table.
Copy the table and continue Megan's
work until you know the number
correct to two decimal places.

Try	Result	Comment
2	$2 \times 2.7 = 5.4$	Too small
2.5	$2.5 \times 2.7 = 6.75$	Too big

5 Copy the table. Use trial and
improvement to complete it to find a
solution to the equation $x^3 + 5x = 167$

Give your answer to one decimal place.

x	$x^3 + 5x$	Comment
5		

6 Copy the table. Use trial and
improvement to complete it to find a
solution to the equation $x^3 - 2x = 50$

Give your answer to one decimal place.

x	$x^3 - 2x$	Comment
3		

7 You are asked to solve the equation $x(x + 1)(x + 2) = 3$
a Find two consecutive whole numbers between which x must lie.
b Solve the equation using the method of trial and improvement.
Give your answer to one decimal place. You **must** show your trials.

8 The following equations each have two solutions, some of which are negative.
Use the method of trial and improvement to find both the solutions for each
equation to an accuracy of one decimal place.
a $x^2 + x = 55$ **b** $x^2 - 5x = 7$ **c** $x^2 + 6x = 24$

9 Use the method of trial and improvement to solve each of these equations. Give your answer to one decimal place. You **must** show your trials.

a $a^3 + 3a = 82$ b $b^3 - 2b = 147$ c $c^3 + 3c = 75$

d $d^3 + 4d = 94$ e $e^3 + 2e^2 = 1055$ f $f^3 - 3f^2 = 170$

g $3g^3 - 4g = 60$ h $h^3 - 2h^2 + 3h = 54$

Chapter summary

- The balance method can be extended to solve equations with the unknown on both sides and/or containing brackets.
- Equations are often used to solve problems.
  Step 1: Use the information given to set up an equation.
  Step 2: Solve the equation using the balance method.
- An inequality is written using one of these symbols $< \leqslant > \geqslant$
- Inequalities can be shown on a number line.

  The hollow circle indicates that 4 is **not** included in the inequality.

  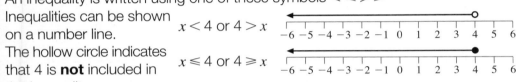

  $x < 4$ or $4 > x$

  $x \leqslant 4$ or $4 \geqslant x$

  The full circle indicates that 4 **is** included in the inequality.
- The balance method can be used to solve simple inequalities.
- Two single inequalities can be combined into a double inequality.
- The balance method can be used to solve double inequalities.
  Separate the double inequality into two inequalities and solve each using the balance method. Then combine the two solution inequalities.
- One way of solving equations involving powers and roots is the method of trial and improvement.

Chapter review

1 a Solve the equation, giving your answer as a mixed number.
   $3x - 2 = 8$
   b Solve the equation $6x + 1 = 3 + 2x$

2 Solve these equations.

   a $8s + 2 = 6s + 3$ b $\dfrac{20 - y}{3} = 5.5$

3 Solve these equations.
   a $2(y + 3) = 24$ b $8z + 2 = 9 - 2z$

4 Solve these equations.

   a $9x - 4 = 8 + x$ **b** $2(z - 3) = 5 - 3z$ **c** $2(3x + 7) = 14$

5 The angles of a quadrilateral are $71°$, $x°$, $4x°$ and $104°$.

   a   Write down an equation in x.

   b   Use your equation to find the smallest angle in the
       quadrilateral.

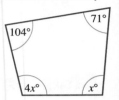

Not drawn accurately

6 The diagram shows a triangle with the lengths of its
   sides given in centimetres.

   a   Write down an expression for the
       perimeter of the triangle.
       Give your answer in its simplest form.

   b   The perimeter of the triangle is 22 cm.
       By forming an equation, find the value of y.

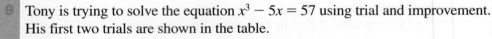

Not drawn accurately

7 Solve the inequalities.

   a $4x + 9 < 1$ **b** $9y < 5y + 6$

8 List the values of x, where x is an integer, such that $-1 \leqslant 3x + 2 < 8$

9 Tony is trying to solve the equation $x^3 - 5x = 57$ using trial and improvement.
   His first two trials are shown in the table.

x	$x^3 - 5x$	Comment
4	44	Too small
5	100	Too big

Find the solution of the equation. Give your answer to one decimal place.

10 Cathy is solving the equation $x + \dfrac{1}{x} = 6$ using trial and improvement.

    The table shows her first two trials.
    Find the solution of the equation.
    Give your answer to one decimal place.

x	$x + \dfrac{1}{x}$	Comment
5	5.2	Too small
6	6.17	Too big

Accuracy and speed

33.1 Accuracy and measures

IN THIS SECTION YOU WILL

- Learn the meaning of approximation, lower bound and upper bound.
- Estimate solutions to problems using approximate data.
- Write numbers to an appropriate level or degree of accuracy.

An *approximation* is a rounded value.

For example, an approximation for the number of people at a party is 120 people to the nearest ten.

There could be as few as 115 people, because 115 rounds up to 120 to the nearest ten.

There could be as many as 124 people, because 124 rounds down to 120 to the nearest ten.

This can be shown on a number line, as on the right.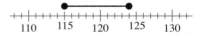

110   115   120   125   130

The approximation, 120, lies between the *lower bound* 115 and the *upper bound* 124.

The smallest possible value is called the lower bound or *lower limit*.

The largest possible value is called the upper bound or *upper limit*.

For example, the cost of a car journey is £9 to the nearest pound.

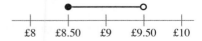

£8   £8.50   £9   £9.50   £10

£8.50 ≤ cost < £9.50

The lower bound is £8.50

The upper bound is £9.49   £9.50 is not included as it rounds to £10

Here are some statements using continuous data.

A car is travelling at 30 miles per hour to the
nearest whole number.

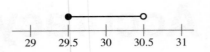

The approximate speed, 30 mph, lies between the lower
bound 29.5 mph and the upper bound 30.5 mph.

The greatest possible speed is actually 30.499 99… mph, as this is the greatest value
that rounds down to 30 mph. 30.499 99… mph is very close to 30.5 mph.
It is more convenient to give the maximum possible speed as 30.5 mph.

Example 1

The River Don is 70 miles long to the nearest 10 miles.
Write down the smallest and largest possible lengths of the river.

Solution 1

Smallest possible length = 65 miles

Largest possible length = 74.999 999 9 = 75 miles

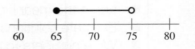

Example 2

On a shopping trip Mrs Senior spent £50 to the nearest £5
What is the most that she could have spent?

Solution 2

£47.50 ⩽ spent < £52.50

Most she could have spent = £50 + £2.49 = £52.49

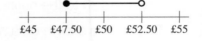

The answer is not £52.50 as this would round up to £55

Exercise A

1 Each of the following values is given to the nearest whole number. Write down the
largest and smallest possible values.

    a   £5   **b**   £12   **c**   £20   **d**   £100

    e   30 kg   **f**   25 miles   **g**   17 km   **h**   30 seconds

2 Write down the minimum and maximum values of each of the following.

    a   £10 given to the nearest pound   **b**   60 pence given to the nearest 10 p

    c   £1.40 given to the nearest 10 p   **d**   85 pence given to the nearest 5 p

    e   £5.55 given to the nearest 5 p   **f**   80 pence given to the nearest 20 p

    g   £4.60 given to the nearest 20 p   **h**   £25 given to the nearest £5

    i   £70 given to the nearest £5   **j**   £90 given to the nearest £10

    k   £130 given to the nearest £10

3 Write down the minimum and maximum values of each of the following.
    a 30 miles to the nearest mile   **b** 14 miles to the nearest mile
    c 16 kg to the nearest kg   **d** 25 kg to the nearest kg
    e 27 seconds to the nearest second   **f** 60 seconds to the nearest second

4 Write down the minimum and maximum values of each of the following.
    a 50 miles to the nearest 10 miles   **b** 180 kg to the nearest 10 kg
    c 30 tonnes to the nearest 10 tonnes   **d** 80 km to the nearest 10 km
    e 25 metres to the nearest 5 metres   **f** 70 grams to the nearest 5 grams
    g 120 cm to the nearest 5 cm   **h** 175 cl to the nearest 5 cl

5 The signpost is accurate to the nearest mile.
What is the shortest possible distance to Todwick?

Todwick 12 miles

6 Lawrence is working out his salary on his calculator.
He says that his salary is £83 000 to the nearest thousand pounds.
    a What is the least possible value of his salary?
    b What is the highest possible value of his salary?

7 A car is for sale. The advertisement says that the car has travelled 65 000 miles, to the nearest thousand miles.
What is the smallest possible mileage the car could have travelled?

8 A television commentator said that the attendance at Old Trafford was 53 000 to the nearest thousand. What was the largest possible attendance?

Here are three statements.
The height of the Empire State Building is 1453 feet, $8\frac{9}{16}$ inches – very accurate.
The height of the Empire State Building is 1450 feet – accurate but rounded sensibly.
The height of the Empire State Building is 1500 feet – not very accurate, rounded to the nearest 100 feet.

To write answers to an appropriate or suitable degree of accuracy, round the number to a value that would be used in conversation.

Example 3

Write each of the following values to a suitable degree of accuracy.
    a The average salary of a consultant is £82 147.34
    b The number of units of electricity that the average household uses in winter is 1678
    c The average speed on a motorway is 63.2143 mph.

> *Solution 3*
>
> **a** Write to the nearest thousand → £82 000
> **b** Write to the nearest 50 → 1700
> **c** Write to the nearest whole number → 63 mph or to the nearest 10 mph → 60 mph.

For a calculation, a suitable degree of accuracy often means giving the answer to the same number of decimal places as the values in the question.

> ### Example 4
>
> A rectangle has length = 3.1 cm and width = 4.7 cm.
> Calculate the area, giving your answer to a suitable degree of accuracy.
>
> *Solution 4*
>
> Area = $l \times w$ = 3.1 × 4.7 = 14.57 cm^2
> The values in the question are to one decimal place.
> So the answer should be given to the same degree of accuracy, one decimal place:
> area = 14.6 cm^2

Exercise B

1 Write each of the following values to a suitable degree of accuracy, giving a reason for your answer.
    a An average wage of £187.50 per week
    b An average attendance at a football ground of 34 127
    c The height of a mountain 1203.1 metres
    d The distance between two towns is 32.157 miles
    e The average number of patients per dentist is 971.2

2 Match the most appropriate degree of accuracy to each measurement.

Distance between planets and the sun	to the nearest km	Distance between British towns
Diameter of planets	to the nearest 1 000 000 km	to the nearest 1000 km

3 The length of a rectangle is 11.3 cm. The width of the rectangle is 7.1 cm.
Each length is approximate.
Work out the perimeter of the rectangle.
Give your answer to a suitable degree of accuracy.

4 Daniel says he lives 472 metres from school. Give this distance to a suitable degree of accuracy and state the degree of accuracy used.

5 The radius of a circle is 4.2 cm.
Find the area of the circle. Give your answer to a suitable degree of accuracy.

6 Megan is 5 feet 3 inches tall. Use
1 foot = 12 inches = 30 centimetres
to calculate Megan's height in
centimetres. Give your answer to an
appropriate degree of accuracy.

7 The radius of a circle is 10.42 cm.
Calculate the circumference.
Give your answer to a suitable degree of
accuracy.

8 A 70 cl bottle of wine costs £2.99
Work out the cost of 1 litre.

9 A man is paid at the rate of
£7.125 per hour.
He works 15 hours.
How much is he paid?

10 Paul travels 6.7 km in
4.15 minutes.
He works out his speed using
6.7 ÷ 4.15
He says his speed is
1.614 457 831 km/min.
Explain why this is not an
appropriate degree of accuracy.

11 $f = \dfrac{u + v}{uv}$

Work out the value of f given that $u = 3.4$
and $v = 7.2$, where u and v are given to
one decimal place.
a Write down the full calculator display.
b Write your answer to a suitable
degree of accuracy.

33.2 Speed

CAN YOU REMEMBER

- How to convert fractions of an hour into minutes, e.g. 20 minutes = $\frac{1}{3}$ of an hour?
- Units for distance, e.g. metres (m), kilometres (km), miles?
- That there are 60 seconds in a minute and 60 minutes in an hour?
- How to divide by fractions?

IN THIS SECTION YOU WILL

- Learn the units for speed.
- Use fractions of an hour to work out speed.
- Use a formula to work out average speed.

Speed measures how fast or slow something is travelling. *Constant speed* means the
speed does not increase or decrease.
A constant speed of 15 metres per second (m/s) means that a distance of 15 metres is
travelled in every second.
In a journey, speed is not usually constant. A car may slow down for traffic, or speed up
on a clear stretch of road. If a car travels 30 miles in 1 hour, its *average speed* is
30 miles per hour or 30 mph.
Average speed = total distance ÷ time taken

Example 1

A car travels 80 miles in 2 hours.
What is the average speed of the car? Give the answer in miles per hour.

Solution 1

Average speed $= \dfrac{\text{total distance}}{\text{time taken}} = \dfrac{80}{2} = 40$ miles per hour or 40 mph

Example 2

A boy travels 10 miles in 15 minutes.
What is his speed? Give the answer in miles per hour.

Solution 2

To calculate speed in miles per hour, the time needs to be in hours.

15 minutes $= \dfrac{15}{60}$ hours $= 0.25$ hours

Average speed $= \dfrac{10}{0.25} = \dfrac{1000}{25} = 40$

His speed is 40 miles per hour.

Example 3

A girl runs 12 kilometres in 1 hour 30 minutes.
Work out her average speed. Give your answer in kilometres per hour.

Solution 3

1 hour 30 minutes $= 1.5$ hours

Average speed $= \dfrac{12}{1.5} = \dfrac{120}{15} = 8$

Her average speed is 8 km/h.

Exercise A

1   Write the following times as fractions of an hour.
    The first one has been done for you.

    a   30 minutes $= \frac{30}{60}$ hours $= \frac{1}{2}$ hour

    b   15 minutes   **c**   45 minutes   **d**   20 minutes

    e   40 minutes   **f**   10 minutes   **g**   6 minutes

    h   12 minutes   **i**   1 hour 30 minutes   **j**   2 hours 15 minutes

2 Work out the average speed for these journeys in miles per hour.
    a 60 miles in 2 hours   **b** 30 miles in 3 hours   **c** 45 miles in 5 hours

3 Work out the average speed for these journeys in kilometres per hour.
    a 24 km in 2 hours   **b** 36 km in 4 hours   **c** 28 km in 7 hours

4 Work out the average speed for these journeys in metres per second.
    a 40 metres in 20 seconds   **b** 60 metres in 15 seconds

5 Work out the average speed for these journeys.
    a 60 miles in $\frac{1}{2}$ hour   **b** 30 miles in 15 minutes
    c 20 miles in $\frac{1}{4}$ hour   **d** 36 miles in 45 minutes
    e 44 km in $\frac{1}{2}$ hour   **f** 25 km in 30 minutes
    g 40 km in 20 minutes   **h** 60 km in 15 minutes

6 A cheetah runs 90 metres in 3 seconds.
What is its average speed in
metres per second?

7 Work out the average speed for these journeys.
    a 30 miles in $1\frac{1}{2}$ hours   **b** 50 miles in 2 hours 30 minutes
    c 30 miles in $\frac{3}{4}$ hour   **d** 24 miles in 15 minutes
    e 45 km in $1\frac{1}{2}$ hours   **f** 90 km in 1 hour 30 minutes
    g 40 km in 1 hour 20 minutes   **h** 105 km in 3 hours 30 minutes

8 Sushma walks to Silkstone.
It takes her 20 minutes.
At what speed does she walk?

The formula Average speed $= \dfrac{\text{Total distance}}{\text{Time taken}}$ can be rearranged to give

$$\text{Total distance} = \text{average speed} \times \text{time taken}$$

$$\text{Time} = \frac{\text{Total distance}}{\text{Average speed}}$$

This can be remembered by using the diagram. $D = s \times t$

Example 4

A person travels 45 miles in 2 hours and then a further 30 miles in 1 hour.
Calculate the average speed for the whole journey.

Solution 4

Total distance = 45 miles + 30 miles = 75 miles
Time taken = 2 hours + 1 hour = 3 hours

$$\text{Average speed} = \frac{\text{Total distance}}{\text{Time taken}} = \frac{75}{3} = 25\,\text{mph}$$

Example 5

The average speed of a train on a journey is 120 km/h.
The time taken is 2.5 hours. How far is the journey?

Solution 5

Average speed = 120 km/h   Time taken = 2.5 hours
Distance = average speed × time = 120 × 2.5 = 300 km

Example 6

A woman drives at an average speed of 60 km/h.
How long will it take her to travel 75 km? Give your answer in hours and minutes.

Solution 6

$$D = s \times t$$

$$\frac{D}{s} = t$$

> To make *t* the subject, divide both sides by *s*.

$$\text{Time taken} = \frac{75}{60} = \frac{15}{12} = \frac{5}{4}$$

> Dividing by 5 and then by 3

$$= 1\tfrac{1}{4} \text{ hours} = 1 \text{ hour } 15 \text{ minutes}$$

Exercise B

1   Work out the distance travelled at an average speed of:
   a   30 mph for 2 hours   **b**   25 mph for 3 hours   **c**   32 km/h for 2 hours
   d   56 km/h for 3 hours   **e**   40 m/s for 6 seconds   **f**   60 m/s for 8 seconds.

2   Work out the distance travelled at an average speed of:
   a   40 mph for 30 minutes   **b**   60 mph for 15 minutes
   c   30 mph for 10 minutes   **d**   33 mph for 20 minutes
   e   48 km/h for 30 minutes   **f**   48 km/h for 45 minutes
   g   90 km/h for 20 minutes   **h**   60 km/h for 12 minutes.

3 Work out the time taken, in minutes, to travel:
  a 5 miles at 10 mph   **b** 30 miles at 30 mph   **c** 20 miles at 60 mph
  d 10 miles at 40 mph   **e** 20 km at 40 km/h   **f** 30 km at 40 km/h
  g 25 km at 100 km/h   **h** 20 km at 30 km/h.

4 Use a formula to work out the time taken, in minutes, to travel:
  a 70 miles at 35 mph   **b** 35 miles at 70 mph   **c** 10 miles at 60 mph
  d 25 miles at 75 mph   **e** 16 km at 64 km/h   **f** 20 km at 80 km/h
  g 45 km at 15 km/h   **h** 30 km at 6 km/h.

5 A sprinter runs 100 metres in 10 seconds.
  a Work out his average speed.
  b Explain why his top speed is greater than his average speed.

6 Fred drives his taxi on two journeys. The first journey is 8 miles and takes 35 minutes.
  The second journey is 17.5 miles and takes 55 minutes.
  Calculate the average speed for the two journeys combined.
  Give your answer in miles per hour.

7 A bus drives 2500 km in a week. Its average speed is estimated at 30 km/h.
  Estimate how long the bus spends driving in the week.
  Give your answer to the nearest hour.

8 You are given that 5 miles = 8 kilometres.
  A car travels 45 miles in 1 hour 30 minutes. A lorry travels 50 kilometres in 1 hour.
  Which vehicle has the greater average speed? Show your working.

9 The distance between two towns is 30 miles on the motorway or 25 miles on other
  roads. At rush hour, the average speed on the motorway is 36 mph and the average
  speed on other roads is 37.5 mph.
  Which is the quicker journey? You **must** show your working.

Chapter summary

- An *approximation* is a rounded value that lies between two values.
- The smallest possible value is called the *lower bound* or *lower limit*.
- The largest possible value is called the *upper bound* or *upper limit*.
- *Speed* measures how fast or slow something is travelling. *Constant speed* means the speed does not increase or decrease.
- The formula Average speed $= \dfrac{\text{Total distance}}{\text{Time taken}}$ can be rearranged to give

  Total distance = average speed $\times$ time taken

- Time $= \dfrac{\text{Total distance}}{\text{Average speed}}$

Chapter review

1 Two towns X and Y are connected by a country lane of length 30 miles and motorway of length 40 miles as shown.

A tractor travels down the country lane at an average speed of 20 mph.

A car travels on the motorway at an average speed of 60 mph.

Which vehicle gets from X to Y in the shortest time?

What is the difference in their journey times?

Give your answers in minutes.

2 A packet of biscuits weighs 250 grams to the nearest 10 grams.
What is the minimum possible weight of this packet of biscuits?

3 A hockey pitch is 91 metres long to the nearest metre.
Write down the least and greatest possible length of the pitch.

4 A book costs £8 to the nearest pound. Write down:
a the maximum possible price of the book
b the minimum possible price of the book.

5 Wales High School has 1500 students to the nearest hundred.
a What is the least possible number of students?
b What is the greatest possible number of students?

6 A train journey is 125 miles.
a The journey takes 2 hours 30 minutes.
What is the average speed of the train in miles per hour?
b The average speed of another train on the same journey is 100 mph.
How long does the journey take?

7 A 15 mile journey takes 20 minutes.
What is the average speed for the journey in miles per hour?

8 Mr Day travels 60 miles in 2 hours. Mrs Thompson travels 98 miles in 3.5 hours.
Who has the fastest average speed? You **must** show your working.

9 Mike runs 3 km in 15 minutes.
Calculate his average speed in kilometres per hour.

10 A cycle route is 20 miles long. Paul completes the route in 1 hour 15 minutes.
Norris completes the route at an average speed of 15 mph. Who is quicker?
You **must** show your working.

11 Nicola drives 183 miles at an average speed of 42 mph. Work out how long it takes her. Give your answer in hours and minutes to a suitable degree of accuracy.

Collecting data

34.1 Questionnaires and surveys

CAN YOU REMEMBER

- How data is often arranged in groups?

IN THIS SECTION YOU WILL

- Learn how to design and improve questions for a questionnaire.
- Learn the different methods of carrying out a survey.
- Learn the difference between a sample and a census.

A *questionnaire* is a set of questions. Questionnaires are often used in a *survey* to collect data on people's opinions on a particular topic.

A questionnaire needs to be carefully planned to make sure that the information obtained is appropriate and relevant.

The following checklist should be considered when producing a questionnaire:

- Use simple language that is easily understood.
- Keep the questionnaire short and to the point.
- Avoid *open questions*, where there is no restriction on possible answers.
- Use *closed questions*, which give a choice of answer. Use a *response section* containing tick boxes. Restricting the choice of answer makes analysing the results much easier.
- If giving options or tick boxes for answers, make sure they are exclusive. This means that every possible answer can only go in **one** box.
- Avoid *leading questions* like 'Don't you agree ...?' or 'Do you agree ...?' which encourage a particular answer. *Biased questions* like these make the questionnaire invalid.
- Unless it is essential, avoid personal questions such as 'How old are you?'
- Test the questions on a small number of people before carrying out the full survey. This is called carrying out a *pilot survey.*

A pilot survey may show up problems with the questionnaire.

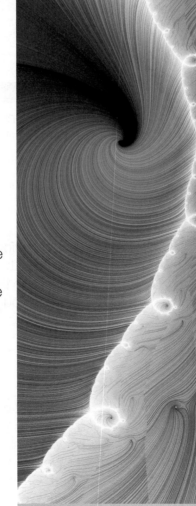

Example 1

Here are two possible questions for a questionnaire.

   1 How old are you?

   2 Tick the box which indicates your age.

     Under 10 ☐   11–20 ☐   20 or over ☐

a Criticise these questions.   **b** Write a better question to find out age.

Solution 1

a Question 1 is an open question. The answers will be lots of different numbers and it will be difficult to process the data.

    Question 2 is better as it is a closed question with a response section but:
- there is overlap – someone aged 20 would not know which box to tick
- there is a gap in the ages – someone aged 10 has no option to tick
- more age groups above 20 are needed.

b How old are you? Tick one box.

     under 10 ☐   10–19 ☐   20–29 ☐   30–39 ☐

     40–49 ☐   50–59 ☐   60 and over ☐

Example 2

In her questionnaire about school Dana asked:

'Don't you think it's about time they got rid of school uniform?'

    Yes, definitely ☐   Yes, probably ☐   No ☐

a Criticise this question.   **b** Rewrite the question.

Solution 2

a The question is biased – it gives away Dana's own opinion.

    There are two response boxes for Yes and only one for No. It is better to have balance in the boxes. It is not possible to answer 'Don't know'.

b What is your opinion on school uniform? Tick the box for your answer.

    Keep it ☐   Get rid of it ☐   Unsure/Don't know ☐

Exercise A

1 The school caterers decide to ask students these questions.

    a What is your age?

    b We think it would be great to offer Chinese food on the school dinner menu. Do you agree?

      i Criticise each question.

      ii Write a better version of each question.

2 For each of the following questions, say whether it is suitable, leading or biased. For each question that is not suitable, write a new question.

    a Smoking kills people and should be totally banned. What do you think?

    b How far do you travel to school?

       Less than 3 miles ☐   More than 3 miles ☐

    c Name the country of your birth.   **d** What is your favourite type of music?

3 Write a question which would effectively find out the following. Remember to give a response section where appropriate.

    a The total number of brothers and sisters a person has.

    b The time it takes for a student to get home from school.

    c Whether people think that footballers are paid too much.

    d Where a person went on holiday last year.

4 **a** Design a short questionnaire on a topic of your choice.

    b Use your questionnaire in a pilot survey of about five people.

    c If necessary, improve your questionnaire based on the results of your pilot.

    d Give your questionnaire to about 30 people. Collect the results and write two sentences to explain what they show.

5 **a** Explain what a pilot survey is in the context of a questionnaire.

    b Why might it be useful to use a pilot survey?

A survey finds out information about a topic or situation. Most surveys use a questionnaire. They can be carried out by face-to-face or telephone interviews, or the questionnaire can be sent out by post.

Surveys may also be carried out by observation, for example recording the gender of people using a shop.

Surveys need to be carried out in a fair way to avoid *bias*.

For example, if a school wants to find out about students' eating habits, it is not a fair survey if only the students who use the school canteen are included. All the students who have other lunch arrangements will be omitted from the survey and the results will be biased.

The group of people a survey is interested in is called the *population*. For example, the population for a survey on school lunches is the students at the school.

If a survey asks the views of the whole population, this is called a *census*. A census will find out more accurate information but can be expensive and time-consuming. For example, the UK National Census takes place every ten years. Every household in the UK is sent a questionnaire.

A survey about a large population uses a sample of the population. A *sample* is a small group selected from the larger population.

A sample needs to be *representative* – this means that it should reflect the population fairly. For example, for a survey on uniform, a representative sample will include students from each year.

Example 3

Mushtaq is finding out about the cost of new computers. He goes to a supermarket near his home and records the cost of every computer on sale there.
a Is this a survey or a census? Explain your answer.
b Is this a fair way of finding out the cost of new computers? Explain your answer.

Solution 3

a Mushtaq is interested in the cost of new computers and so the population is all new computers.
He has only recorded costs from one shop, a sample. This is a survey not a census.
b No, he should go to a range of different shops that sell computers and obtain a sample of prices from each.

Exercise B

1 Two schools are considering merging their sports teams to try to win the National Finals.
School A asks 10% of its staff and students whether they think this is a good idea.
School B asks all of its staff and students the same question.
  a Which school is carrying out a survey? Explain your answer.
  b Give one advantage and one disadvantage of school A's approach.
  c Give one advantage and one disadvantage of school B's approach.

2 Pauline is interested in finding out who uses the launderette she owns.
She decides to ask everyone who comes into the launderette about their age, family and job one Monday from 9 am to 11 am.
  a Explain why this is not a good method.
  b Suggest how Pauline might find her information in a better way.

3 A company wants to test the lifetime of the new light bulbs it has developed.
It produces 1000 light bulbs each hour.
  a Explain why the company must test a sample and not the population.
  b The company suggests three possible methods of choosing the light bulbs to be tested.
    Method 1: Take the first light bulb produced every day for one month.
    Method 2: Take 30 light bulbs produced on 1 March.
    Method 3: Take every 50th light bulb produced each day for three months.
    Comment on each suggested method.

4 Search on the Internet to answer the following questions about the UK National Census.
  a How often is there a National Census in the UK?
  b When is the next National Census?
  c Who has to respond to the National Census?
  d Find out five pieces of information which the National Census asks about.

5 Imagine you are going to find out information about the amount of homework the average Year 10 student does each evening.

    a Write down some questions you would ask.

    b Describe how you could choose a sample of people for your survey.

34.2 Observation sheets and data logging

CAN YOU REMEMBER

- How to construct a two-way table?
- How to construct a tally chart?

IN THIS SECTION YOU WILL

- Learn the meaning of the phrase 'observation sheet'.
- Learn how to construct an observation sheet.
- Learn the meaning of data logging.
- Interpret data from an observation sheet.

An *observation sheet* or *data collection sheet* is a chart or table for recording data from a survey or experiment or from observation.

Tally charts and two-way tables are types of observation sheet.
An observation sheet should be drawn before the data is collected.
It is a good idea to test the sheet using a pilot survey and then improve it as necessary.

Example 1

Billy says that primary school pupils eat chips more often than secondary school pupils. Design an observation sheet to investigate Billy's claim.
Invent the first 20 possible responses.

Solution 1

A time period needs to be stated even though this was not mentioned in the question: for example, 'number of times chips are eaten per week'.
The first category is age of pupil – primary or secondary.
The second category is the number of times chips are eaten per week.

Number of times chips are eaten per week School	0	1	2	3	4 or more
Primary		||	||||	|||			
Secondary			JH|			||		

Data logging is when data is collected automatically by a machine. For example, the numbers of cars entering and leaving a car park are logged by a machine, so that no cars can enter when the car park is full.

Exercise A

1 Javed wants to know whether his friends prefer pizza, burgers or fish and chips. He wants to know if this is different for boys and girls.
Design an observation sheet to collect this information.

2 The observation sheet below is designed to collect data about the number of visits abroad made by children of different ages.

Visits Age	0	1 or 2	4 or 5	7 or 8	More than 10
Under 10					
11–14					
Older teenagers					

    a Criticise the observation sheet.   **b** Design a better observation sheet.

3 Julian thought that his teacher gave tests much more often in the afternoon than in the morning and did practical work much more often in the morning than the afternoon.
    a Design an observation sheet to collect data to test Julian's ideas.
    b Invent the first 20 entries.

4 **a** Describe how data logging might be used to collect data about the number of people entering a shop at different times.
    b How might this data be useful to the owners of the shop?

5 **a** Design an observation sheet which would collect data for the following question. 'Does it rain more often at weekends than during the week?'
    b **i** Invent data for four weeks. Try to make the data realistic.
       ii Use the invented data to answer the question 'Does it rain more often at weekends than during the week?'
       What extra factor should be considered to make the question fair?

6 **a** Criticise and improve on the observation sheet below for a survey on pocket money of boys and girls in Year 10.

Pocket money Gender	£1	£2–£5	£5–£10	£10–£20
Boys				
Girls				

    b Ask a sample of students for their responses and fill in the improved observation sheet.

Example 2

This observation sheet is designed to collect data about the preferred method of transport of adults and children.

	Car	Bus	Train	Plane
Adults				
Children				

a What problems may arise in the use of this observation sheet?
b Suggest an improved version of the observation sheet.

Solution 2

a There is no definition of adults and children, e.g. which box does a 17 year-old go into?
There are other transport methods apart from those listed.
It may also be fair to say that there is not enough space to collect much data.
b An improved observation sheet is:

	Car	Bus	Train	Plane	Boat	Other
Age 16 or over						
Age under 16						

Example 3

Look at this completed version of the observation sheet from Example 3 and determine whether the statements about it are true or false. Explain your answers.

	Car	Bus	Train	Plane	Boat	Other
Age 16 or over	ⵘ	|||	ⵘ ⵘ		||			||
Age under 16	||	||||	ⵘ ||	ⵘ ||||	|||		

a More under-16s prefer planes than 16s or over.
b The same number of people in each age category were asked.
c 10% of under-16s preferred cars.

Solution 3

a True, nine under-16s prefer planes whereas only two 16s or over do.
b False, 24 people aged 16 or over were asked whereas 26 under-16s were asked.
c False, as there were 26 under-16s, 10% of 26 is not 2.

Exercise B

1 This observation sheet was designed to collect data about the favourite fruit of people of different ages.

	Apple	Banana	Strawberry	Peach
Under 10				
Under 20				
Under 40				
Over 40				

a Explain two distinct problems with this observation sheet.

b Design an improved version of this observation sheet.

2 This observation sheet shows data collected on favourite colour.

	Red	Blue	Purple	Green	Yellow	Other
Boys	JHT III	JHT JHT JHT III	IIII	II	I	JHT II
Girls	JHT IIII	III	JHT JHT II	III	JHT II	I

State whether each of these statements about the observation sheet is true or false. Give a reason each time.

a More girls than boys preferred purple.

b Green was the least favourite colour overall.

c 20% of boys chose red as their favourite colour.

3 A data logging machine recorded this table of information about the numbers of vehicles in a car park at different times.

a How many extra vehicles entered the car park between 9 am and 10 am?

b 17 vehicles left the car park between 10 am and 11 am.
How many vehicles entered the car park between 10 am and 11 am?

c How many spaces are there for vehicles in the car park?
Give a reason for your answer.

Time	Number of vehicles
9 am	36
10 am	125
11 am	170
12 pm	170
1 pm	156
2 pm	168
3 pm	170
4 pm	152
5 pm	87

4 Jodie asked a sample of 60 people, two thirds of whom were men, to name a city in the USA.
Half of the women and ten of the men named New York.
20% of the women and 40% of the men named Washington.
Three women and six men named San Francisco.
The rest of the sample named various other US cities.
Jodie collected all of this information on an observation sheet.
Given that she had predicted the responses well, draw a suitable observation sheet and complete it with her data.

5 This observation sheet was used to record the number of goals scored by home teams and goals scored by away teams in 100 football fixtures. The tallies have been converted into figures.

Number of goals scored	0	1	2	3	4	5	6	7
Goals scored by home team	18	37	20	14	8	2	0	1
Goals scored by away team	32	38	16	8	4	1	1	0

a Compare the goals scored by the home teams and away teams by looking at the figures on the observation sheet.
b **i** Calculate the mean and range of both sets of data.
  ii Do these measures confirm your observations in part **a**?
c Illustrate the data using a suitable graph.

6 The data logging equipment on the doors at a nightclub keeps a record of the number of people inside the nightclub.
The data for each night is recorded every hour. The table shows one night's data.

Time	Number of people inside nightclub
9 pm	120
10 pm	246
11 pm	287
12 am	378
1 am	X
2 am	367
3 am	112

a The club opened at 8 pm. On average how many people per minute entered the club in the first hour?
b 87 people left the nightclub between 11 pm and 12 am. How many people entered the nightclub between 11 pm and 12 am?
c According to safety inspectors the nightclub is full when 400 people are inside.
At 1 am the nightclub was full.
Only five people entered the nightclub between 1 am and 2 am.
How many people left the nightclub between 1 am and 2 am?

34.3 Social statistics

CAN YOU REMEMBER

- How to draw and interpret time series graphs?
- How to calculate with percentages?

IN THIS SECTION YOU WILL

- Learn the meaning of 'index number'.
- Use and interpret data collected by the Government.

The Government's Office for National Statistics (ONS) collects and publishes a vast amount of information about the population of the UK and patterns of spending.

For example, the Retail Prices Index (RPI) measures the changing cost of selected items. The information is given as an *index number*. An index number represents a value by giving it as a percentage of an original value or *base value*.

For example, using January 2003 as the base value (100%), the RPI for September 2005 was 114.

Month	January 2003	September 2005
RPI	100	114

This means that, on average, prices were 14% higher in September 2005 than in January 2003.

Example 1

The cost of a banana in January 2004 was 40 pence.
Using January 2004 as a base, the index number for the cost in January 2006 was 105. Find the cost of a banana in January 2006

Solution 1

The index number of 105 indicates that the January 2006 cost is 5% higher than the January 2004 cost.
January 2006 cost = 105% of January 2004 cost
105% written as a decimal = 1.05, so the multiplier is 1.05
January 2006 cost = January 2004 cost × multiplier = 40 pence × 1.05 = 42 pence
The cost in January 2006 was 42 pence.

Example 2

A car was bought for £8000 in January 2005 and sold for £6000 in September 2006. Find the index number for September 2006 using January 2005 as the base.

Solution 2

The price has decreased from the original, so the index number will be less than 100
The calculation is equivalent to finding the new value as a percentage of the old value.

$$\text{Index number} = \frac{\text{new value}}{\text{old value}} \times 100 = \frac{6000}{8000} \times 100 = 0.75 \times 100 = 75$$

Government data is also presented as time series, such as unemployment rates, and in graphs and charts, such as data from the National Census about the number of people living in each house.

Example 3

The time series below shows the car and commercial vehicle production figures for the United Kingdom for 1999–2004 with 2000 as base.

Year	1999	2000	2001	2002	2003	2004
Index	108.8	100.0	90.9	99.3	101.0	100.3

(Source: www.statistics.gov.uk)

a Explain why this data is a time series.
b In which year from this period was the car and commercial vehicle production:
   i lowest   **ii** highest?
c In which years were the production figures lower than the previous year?

Solution 3

a This data is a time series as the values are recorded over a period of time.
b **i** 2001   **ii** 1999
c 2000, 2001, 2004

Exercise A

1 The cost of a loaf of bread in 1990 was 30 pence.
   The index value for 2006 using 1990 as base year is 150
   Find the cost of a loaf of bread in 2006

2 The cost of a litre of petrol in 2000 was 60 pence.
   The cost of a litre of petrol in 2012 is predicted to be £1.50
   Find the predicted index number for 2012 using 2000 as the base year.

3 The price of an item doubles.
   Write down the index value of the new price compared to the old price.

4 The time series data shows the numbers (in thousands) of self-employed people for the period 1995–2005

Year	1995	1996	1997	1998	1999	2000	2001	2002	2003	2004	2005
Number of people	3820	3777	3724	3588	3614	3517	3526	3585	3801	3860	3840

(Source: www.statistics.gov.uk)

a Draw a time series graph for the data.
b Describe any patterns in the data.
c In which year was the greatest increase in the number of self-employed?

5 The average cost of a CD in 2000 was £12.40
The index number for 2006 using 2000 as the base year was 81
Find, to the nearest penny, the average cost of a CD in 2006

6 In 1980 a field was valued at £12 500
In 2005 the same field was valued at £230 000
Find the index number for this field in 2005 using 1980 as the base year.

7 The graph shows the percentages of households with Internet access according to Government surveys for 2000 to 2005

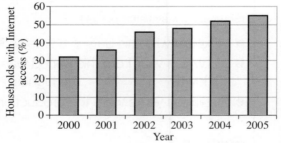

(Source: www.statistics.gov.uk)

a In which year did the value first rise above 50%?
b Use the graph to estimate the index number for 2005 with 2000 as base year.
c If 2005 were taken as the base year, approximately what would the index number for 2000 be?

8 The time series graph shows the percentage change in the Retail Prices Index (RPI) and the Consumer Prices Index (CPI) compared with the same month one year before, for September 2003–September 2005

(Source: www.statistics.gov.uk)

a In which month and year was the change in the:
  i RPI at its highest for this period
  ii CPI at its lowest for this period?
b Estimate the difference between the changes in the two indices for June 2004

Exercise B

The table shows the percentage change for the average cost of items from September 2004 to September 2005

Use the data in the table to answer questions **1–7**

Sections	Percentage change September 2004–September 2005
All items	6.9
Food and non-alcoholic beverages	23.1
Alcoholic beverages and tobacco	2.7
Clothing and footwear	−1.3
Housing, water, electricity, gas and other fuels	1.8
Home ownership	1.6
Rent	6.1
Water, electricity, gas and other fuels	0.5
Furnishings, household equipment and routine maintenance of the house	1.4
Health	4.6
Transport	2.1
Communication	−9.1
Recreation and culture	11.1
Education	4.0
Hotels, cafés and restaurants	7.0
Miscellaneous goods and services	2.3

1 **a** Which items showed the greatest percentage increase in price?

   b Use the answers to part **a** to work out the index number for September 2005, using September 2004 as a base.

2 **a** Which items decreased in price during the period?

   b Give the September 2005 index numbers for these items using September 2004 as a base.

3 Which item had the smallest percentage change in price during the period?

4 Display the data in the table using a suitable graph.

5 In September 2004, a room in Green's hotel cost £71 per night. If Green's hotel's prices moved in line with the average for that sector, how much did the room cost in September 2005?

6 **a** Calculate the mean of all the values in the table excluding the 'All items' value.

   b Explain why the 'All items' value of 6.9 is different from your answer to part **a**.

7 Which would cost more in September 2005?
   ■ A pair of shoes that cost £40 in September 2004 or
   ■ A small piece of household equipment that cost £39 in September 2004
   You may assume that each item's price moved in line with the average for its sector.

Chapter summary

- A *questionnaire* is a set of questions. Questionnaires are often used in a *survey* to collect data on people's opinions on a particular topic.
- An observation sheet or data collection sheet is a chart or table for recording data from a survey or experiment or from observation.
- Tally charts and two-way tables are types of observation sheet.
- *Data logging* is when data is collected automatically by a machine.
- The Retail Prices Index (RPI) measures the changing cost of selected items. The information is given as an *index number*. An index number represents a value by giving it as a percentage of an original value or *base value*.
- Government data is also presented as time series, such as unemployment rates, and in graphs and charts, for example data from the National Census.

Chapter review

1 Justin is asking for opinions on the quality of the local bus service.
   He wants to find out the age of each person he asks.
   a Give two reasons why he should not ask 'What is your age?'
   b One of his questions asks, 'Are you fed up with being let down by the local bus service?' Explain what is wrong with this question.

2 April wants to collect data about the numbers of cats and dogs owned by her friends. Design an observation sheet for this purpose. Use a two-way table with headings 'cats' and 'dogs'.

3 Nitin is investigating where people go on holiday.
   He thinks of three possible ways of finding out information for his survey.
   Method 1: Stand outside a travel agent and ask the people who enter.
   Method 2: Ask all his family and friends where they went on holiday.
   Method 3: Put questionnaires through some letter boxes in a range of houses around his town.
   a Give one disadvantage of each method.
   b Which of the three methods is likely to produce the best data?

4 The table shows the index values for service industries' costs for some months of 2005, using January 2002 as the base.

Month in 2005	March	April	May	June	July	August
Index value	108.0	108.3	108.4	109.0	108.9	109.2

   a By what percentage are the March 2005 service industry costs higher than in January 2002?
   b Which of the given months in 2005 had the highest costs?
   c Find the cost in May 2005 of an item that cost £50 in January 2002

5 A consumer magazine is investigating the cost of washing machines.
A reporter for the magazine visits an electrical shop in the town centre and records
the cost of all the washing machines in the shop.
  a Explain whether this is a census or a sample.
  b Give reasons why the reporter's choice of survey method may not be ideal.

6 a What is a pilot survey?   **b** Why might a pilot survey be useful?

7 Zarina is writing a questionnaire about people's choice of supermarket.
One of the questions is about the distance people travel to their favourite
supermarket. The question states,
'How far do you travel to your favourite supermarket?
1 mile   2 miles   3 miles   more'
  a Comment on Zarina's response section.   **b** Write an improved response section.

8 The table shows the number of registrations (in thousands) for new vehicles from
1991 to 2002

Year	1991	1992	1993	1994	1995	1996	1997	1998	1999	2000	2001	2002
Registrations	1921.5	1901.5	2073.9	2249.0	2306.5	2410.1	2597.7	2740.3	2765.8	2870.9	3136.6	3229.5

  a What is the name given to this type of data which changes over time?
  b Show the data on an appropriate graph.
  c Comment on the trend in the data.

9 A company which manufactures fireworks wishes to test the performance of their
new rocket.
  a Explain why the company must test a sample and not the population.
  b They propose to test the first five rockets produced the following day.
      Give two reasons why this is not an ideal way to take the sample.

10 The graph shows the voting
intentions of the people who
responded to surveys in the
run-up to the 2005 General
Election.

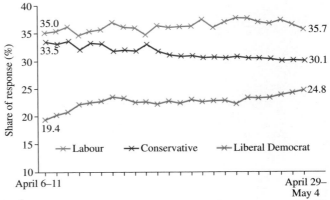

  a Which party always had
the greatest share of the
vote?
  b Which party's support
increased the most over
the period?
  c **i** For each party, calculate the
index number of the final value, using the first value as base.
     ii Which party showed the greatest percentage increase in popularity?
  d Explain why the percentages at the end of the time series do not add to 100%.

Three-dimensional shapes

35.1 Plans and elevations

CAN YOU REMEMBER

■ The area of a rectangle can be found by counting squares or by using the formula area = length × width?
■ The volume of a cuboid can be found by counting cubes or by using the formulae volume = length × width × height or volume = area of base × height?

IN THIS SECTION YOU WILL

■ Draw 2-D views of 3-D objects.
■ Draw 3-D objects from 2-D projections.
■ Calculate the surface area of 2-D views.
■ Calculate volumes of 3-D objects made from cubes.

This picture shows the roof, front and side of a garage.

The roof, front and side can be drawn as three separate two-dimensional views.

Plan

Side   Front

The view from above is called the *plan view*.

The view from the front is called the *front elevation*.

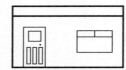

The view from the side is called the *side elevation*.

The side elevation is from one side of the garage. The side elevation from the other side may be different.
For example, there may be no door or window on the other side.

Example 1

A solid is made from a cube of side 2 cm and
two cubes of side 1 cm. Draw on square grids:
a   the front elevation
b   the side elevation from the direction shown
c   the plan view of this solid.

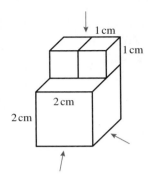

Solution 1

Colour the faces for each view.

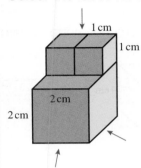

a
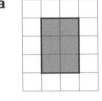
Front elevation

b
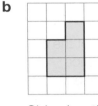
Side elevation

c

Plan view

Example 2

The plan view, front elevation and side elevation of a 3-D solid made up of cubes are
shown below.

plan view

front
elevation

side
elevation

Draw the solid on isometric paper.

Solution 2

The plan view shows how the
cubes are arranged on the base.
The front and side elevations show
that the tallest parts of the solid
are two cubes high.
The side elevation shows a gap in the centre.
If only one side elevation
is shown then the views
from both sides
are the same.
This is the solid.

plan view

front
elevation

side
elevation

Exercise A

1 Here are some pictures of solid objects together with the plan view of each.
Match the object with its plan view.

a   b    c   d   e

i   ii    iii   iv   v

2 The diagram shows a clock tower.
Draw a sketch of:
  a the plan view of the clock tower
  b the front elevation
  c the side elevation.

3 Draw the plan view of each shape accurately on centimetre-squared paper.

a
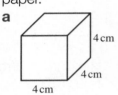

b
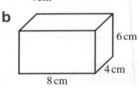

4 Draw the plan view of each solid on squared paper.

a 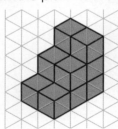   b 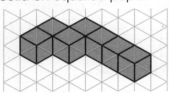   c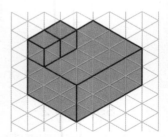

5 The plan view, front elevation and side elevation of a 3-D solid made from cubes are shown.
Draw the solid on isometric paper.

plan view	front elevation	side elevation

6 Each solid is made from centimetre cubes.
For each solid, draw on centimetre-squared paper:
  i the plan view   **ii** the front elevation   **iii** the side elevation.

a   **b**   **c**   **d**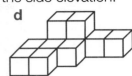

7 The plan view, front elevation
and side elevation of a 3-D solid
made from cubes are shown.
Draw the solid on isometric paper.

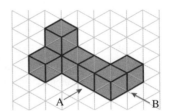

8 The diagram represents a solid made from
seven small cubes.
On squared paper, draw the view
of the solid:
a from direction A
b from direction B.

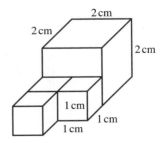

9

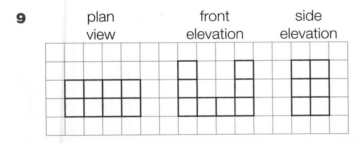

The plan view, front elevation and
side elevation of a 3-D solid
made from cubes are shown left.
Draw the solid on isometric
paper.

The surface area of a solid is the total area of all the faces in the solid.
The plan view, side and front elevations of the solid can be used to work out the surface
area and the volume of a solid.

Example 3

A solid is made from a cube of side 2 cm
and three cubes of side 1 cm as shown.
a Draw the plan view, front elevation and side elevation
of the solid, on centimetre-squared paper.
b Work out the surface area of the solid.
c Calculate the volume of the solid.

Solution 3

a

plan view   front elevation   side elevation

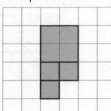 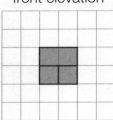 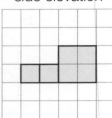

b The plan view shows the surface area of the top and the base of the solid.
The front elevation shows the surface area of the front and the back of the solid.
The side elevation shows the surface area of each side of the solid.
By counting squares,
Area of plan view $= 7\ \text{cm}^2$
Area of front elevation $= 4\ \text{cm}^2$
Area of side elevation $= 6\ \text{cm}^2$
Total surface area $= (2 \times 7) + (2 \times 4) + (2 \times 6) = 14 + 8 + 12 = 34\ \text{cm}^2$

c Volume of the cube with side 2 cm $= 2 \times 2 \times 2 = 8\ \text{cm}^3$
Volume of each cube with side 1 cm $= 1 \times 1 \times 1 = 1\ \text{cm}^3$
So total volume = volume of 2 cm cube + volume of three 1 cm cubes
$= 8 + 1 + 1 + 1 = 11\ \text{cm}^3$

Exercise B

1 This solid is made from cubes of side 1 cm.
a Draw the plan view, front elevation and side elevation of the solid on centimetre-squared paper.
b Calculate the surface area of the solid.

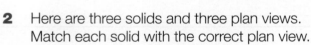

2 Here are three solids and three plan views.
Match each solid with the correct plan view.

A 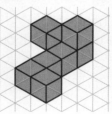   **B** 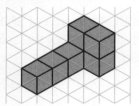   **C**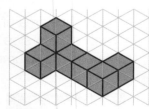

① ② ③

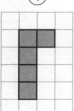 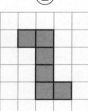 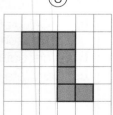

3 Here are three views of a solid made from centimetre cubes.

    a Draw the solid on isometric paper.

    b Calculate the volume of the solid.

plan view   front elevation   side elevation

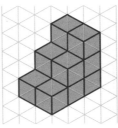
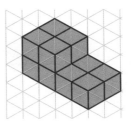

4 These solids are built from cubes of side 1 cm.
Work out the volume of each solid.

a 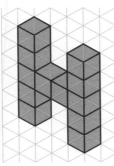   **b**   **c**

Some of the cubes are not visible in the drawing.

5 These solids are made from cubes of side 1 cm.
Calculate the surface area of each solid.

a 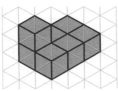   **b**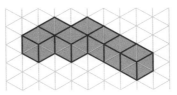

6 The solid shown is made up of a cuboid and two cubes of side 1 cm.

    a Draw the plan view, front elevation and side elevation of this solid.

    b Calculate the volume of this solid.

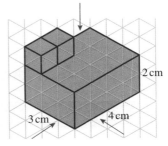

2 cm

3 cm   4 cm

7 A stage is made from one cube of side 3 metres and two cubes of side 2 metres as shown.

    a Draw the plan view of the stage.

    b Calculate the area of the plan view of the stage.

    c Calculate the volume of the stage.

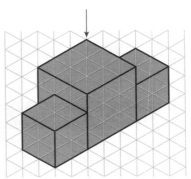

8 The diagrams show the plan view, front elevation and side elevation of a cuboid drawn on centimetre-squared paper.
Calculate the volume of the cuboid.

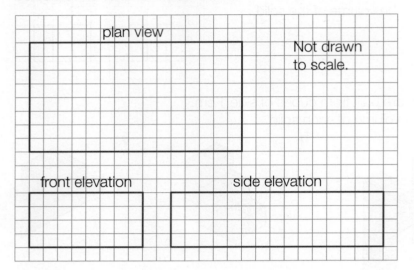

9 Each diagram shows a solid. For each diagram:
draw the front elevation and calculate its area.

a

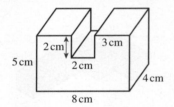

b

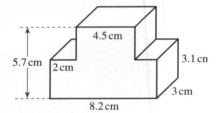

35.2 Surface area of prisms

CAN YOU REMEMBER

- How to sketch nets of cubes, cuboids and triangular prisms?
- Area of a rectangle = length × width, area of a triangle = $\frac{1}{2}$ × base × perpendicular height?
- Area of a circle = πr^2, circumference of a circle = $2\pi r$?
- Metric conversions for lengths: 1 m = 100 cm, 1 cm = 10 mm?

IN THIS SECTION YOU WILL

- Calculate the surface area of cubes, cuboids, triangular prisms and cylinders.
- Convert between area measures, e.g. cm^2 to m^2

The total surface area of a three-dimensional shape is the sum of the areas of all the faces of the shape.

The diagram shows a cube of side 5 cm and its net.

Each face of the cube is a square of side 5 cm.

The net is made from six squares.

The area of each face is $5 \times 5 = 25 \, \text{cm}^2$

So the total surface area $= 6 \times 25 = 150 \, \text{cm}^2$

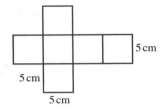

Example 1

Work out the total surface area of this cuboid.

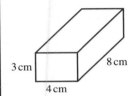

Solution 1

Draw the net.

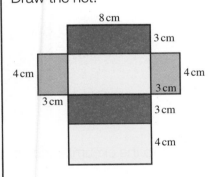

Two blue faces (front and back) are rectangles of length 4 cm and width 3 cm.

The total area of these rectangles is
$2 \times (4 \times 3) = 24 \, \text{cm}^2$

Two yellow faces (top and base) are rectangles of length 4 cm and width 8 cm.

The total area of these rectangles is
$2 \times (4 \times 8) = 64 \, \text{cm}^2$

Two red faces (sides) are rectangles of length 8 cm and width 3 cm.

The total area of these rectangles is
$2 \times (8 \times 3) = 48 \, \text{cm}^2$

Total surface area $= 24 + 64 + 48 = 136 \, \text{cm}^2$

Example 2

Calculate the total surface area of this triangular prism.

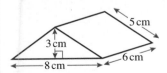

Solution 2

Draw the net.

Two blue faces are triangles.

Area of each triangle

$= \frac{1}{2} \times$ base $\times$ perpendicular height

$= \frac{1}{2} \times 8 \times 3 = 12\,\text{cm}^2$

Two yellow faces (sides) are rectangles.

Area of each rectangle $= 6 \times 5 = 30\,\text{cm}^2$

One red face (base) is a rectangle.

Area $= 6 \times 8 = 48\,\text{cm}^2$

Total surface area $= (2 \times 12) + (2 \times 30) + 48 = 24 + 60 + 48 = 132\,\text{cm}^2$

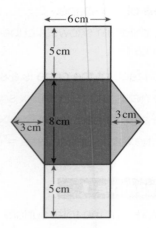

Surface area of a cylinder

The diagram shows a hollow cylinder. It has no base or top.

This is called an *open cylinder*.

The area of the surface is called the *curved surface area*.

The net of the curved surface is a rectangle.

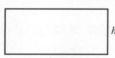

The length of the rectangle is equal to the circumference of the circular end.

So length $= 2\pi r$

The area of the curved surface $= 2\pi r \times h = 2\pi rh$

Example 3

Calculate the curved surface area of a cylinder of radius 4 cm and height 10 cm.

Leave your answer in terms of π.

Solution 3

$r = 4\,\text{cm}, h = 10\,\text{cm}$

Curved surface area $= 2\pi rh = 2 \times \pi \times 4 \times 10 = 80\pi\,\text{cm}^2$

Exercise A

1 Calculate the total surface area of the cubes with the following sides.

  a 3 cm   **b** 7 cm   **c** 10 cm   **d** 2 cm

2 For each of these cuboids:

  i sketch a net   **ii** calculate the total surface area of the cuboid.

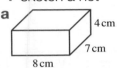 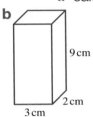 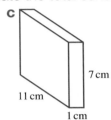 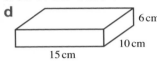

3 Calculate the total surface area of the following cuboids.

Cuboid	Length	Width	Height
a	3 cm	9 cm	5 cm
b	7 cm	2 cm	4 cm
c	4 m	4 m	10 m
d	5 cm	8 cm	12 cm

4 Here is a triangular prism.

  a Sketch a net of the prism.

  b Calculate the total surface area of the prism.

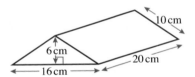

5 Calculate the curved surface area of these open cylinders.
Leave your answers in terms of π.

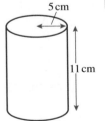 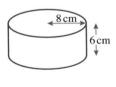 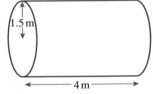 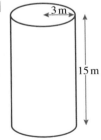

6 Calculate the total surface area of the cubes with the following sides.

  a 2.4 cm   **b** 3.1 cm   **c** 27 cm   **d** 8.7 m

7 Calculate the total surface area of each cuboid.

a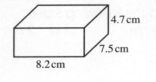

4.7 cm

7.5 cm

8.2 cm

b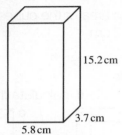

15.2 cm

3.7 cm

5.8 cm

c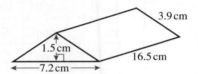

16 mm

21 mm

37 mm

8 Calculate the total surface area of the following cuboids.

Cuboid	Length	Width	Height
a	1.7 cm	0.9 cm	2.1 cm
b	14 cm	46 cm	52 cm
c	3.2 m	2.5 m	4.1 m
d	12.5 cm	8 cm	12.5 cm

9 Here is a triangular prism.

   a   Sketch a net of this prism.

   b   Calculate the total surface area of the prism.

3.9 cm

1.5 cm

7.2 cm

16.5 cm

10 Calculate the curved surface area of each cylinder. Take the value of π to be 3.14 or use the π button on a calculator. Give each answer to one decimal place.

a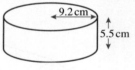

9.2 cm

5.5 cm

b

12 mm

46 mm

c

1.2 cm

9.5 cm

d

39 m

2.3 m

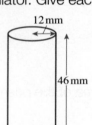 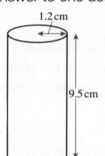 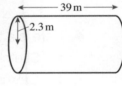

This square has side 1 metre.
The area of the square is 1 m²

1 m²   1 m

1 m

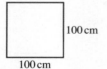

100 cm

100 cm

Here is the same square with the units given in centimetres.
Each side is 100 cm.
The area of the square is 100 cm × 100 cm = 10 000 cm²
So 1 m² = 10 000 cm²

Other units of area can be converted using this method.
For example, 1 cm = 10 mm
         1 cm² = 10 mm × 10 mm = 100 mm²

Example 4

a Work out the number of square centimetres there are in: **i** 3 m² **ii** 4.2 m²
b Convert 15 500 cm² to square metres.

Solution 4

a 1 m² = 10 000 cm²
To convert m² to cm² multiply by 10 000
   i 3 m² = 3 × 10 000 cm² = 30 000 cm²
  ii 4.2 m² = 4.2 × 10 000 cm² = 42 000 cm²
b To convert cm² to m² divide by 10 000
    15 500 cm² = 15 500 ÷ 10 000 cm² = 1.55 m²

A closed cylinder has a circular top and a circular base.
The net of a closed cylinder is shown on the right.

The total surface area
             = curved surface area + area of top + area of base
             = $2\pi rh + \pi r^2 + \pi r^2$
Surface area = $2\pi rh + 2\pi r^2$

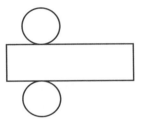

Example 5

The diagram shows a closed cylinder.
Calculate the total surface area of the cylinder.
Give your answer:
a to the nearest cm²
b in square metres to one decimal place.

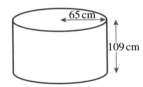

Solution 5

Curved surface area = $2\pi rh$ = 2 × π × 65 × 109 = 44 516.3679 cm²
Area of top **and** base = 2 × πr^2 = 2 × π × 65 × 65 = 26 546.457 92 cm²
a Total surface area = 44 516.3679 + 26 546.457 92 = 71 062.825 = 71 063 cm²
b Dividing by 10 000
    Total surface area = 71 062.825 ÷ 10 000 cm² = 7.1 m² (to 1 d.p.)

Exercise B

1 Convert the following areas to square metres.
   a 34 500 cm²   **b** 200 000 cm²   **c** 4563 cm²   **d** 97 480 cm²

2 Convert the following areas to square centimetres.
   a 7 m²   **b** 3.4 m²   **c** 0.75 m²   **d** 13.8 m²

3 A cuboid measures 12 mm by 9 mm by 11 mm.
Calculate the total surface area of the cuboid.
  a Give your answer in mm^2
  b Convert your answer to part **a** into cm^2

4 A circular cake tin has a base radius of 11 cm and a depth of 6 cm.
The sides and the base of the tin are to be lined with paper.
Work out the area of paper needed to line the tin.
Leave your answer in terms of π.

5 Sam makes wooden toy boxes.
The boxes are cuboids measuring
50 cm by 30 cm by 25 cm and have no lid.
Sam paints the outside of each box.
A tin of paint covers an area of 5.5 m^2
How many toy boxes can Sam complete
with one tin of paint?

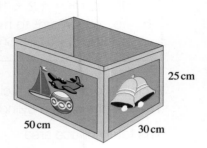

6 Which of the following has the largest surface area?
  a A cube of side 25 cm.
  b A cuboid measuring 30 cm by 26 cm by 18 cm.
Show your working.

7 A tent is in the form of a triangular prism as shown.
The ends of the prism are equilateral triangles of
side 80 cm.
Calculate the total surface area of the tent
not including the groundsheet.
Give your answer in square metres.

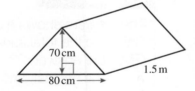

8 Calculate the total surface area of the following closed cylinders.
Give each answer to two decimal places.
  a radius 7.2 cm, height 12.8 cm   **b** radius 0.7 m, height 3.6 m
  c diameter 12.4 cm, height 20 cm

9 The diagram shows a wooden wedge.
Calculate the total surface area of the wedge.

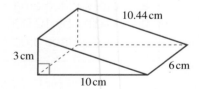

10 Two cylindrical pipes are shown below.

  a
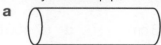

  b

    radius 0.5 m, length 37 m   radius 1.2 m, length 15 m

Which pipe has the smallest curved surface area? Show your working.

35.3 Volumes of prisms

CAN YOU REMEMBER

- A prism is a three-dimensional shape which has the same cross-section all the way through the shape?
- Volume is measured in cube units: mm^3, cm^3, m^3?
- 1 litre = 1000 cm^3?

IN THIS SECTION YOU WILL

- Learn how to calculate the volume of prisms.
- Learn how to convert between volume measures, e.g. cm^3 to m^3

In these prisms the cross-sections are shaded.

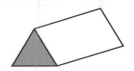 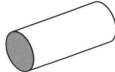 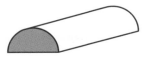

The formula for calculating the volume of a prism is:
volume of a prism = area of cross-section × length
Remember that you should always state the units of your answer.

Example 1

Work out the volume of this triangular prism.

Solution 1

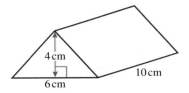

The cross-section is a triangle.
Area of cross-section $= \frac{1}{2} \times$ base $\times$ height
$= \frac{1}{2} \times 6 \times 4 = 12\ cm^2$
Volume = area of cross-section × length = 12 × 10 = 120
Volume of the prism = 120 cm^3

Example 2

A cylinder has a base radius of 3 cm and a height of 8 cm.
Calculate the volume of the cylinder. Leave your answer in terms of π.

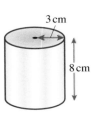

Solution 2

The cross-section is a circle.
Area of cross-section $= \pi r^2 = \pi \times 3^2 = \pi \times 3 \times 3 = 9\pi\ cm^2$
Volume of the cylinder = area of cross-section × length = $9\pi \times 8 = 72\pi\ cm^3$

Example 3

Here is a prism.

a Calculate the area of the cross-section.
b Calculate the volume of the prism.
c Calculate the weight of the prism.

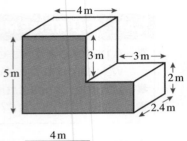

Solution 3

a Divide the cross-section into rectangles
Area of cross-section = $(5 \times 4) + (3 \times 2)$
$= 20 + 6 = 26 \, m^2$

b Volume of prism = area of cross-section × length
$= 26 \times 2.4 = 62.4 \, m^3$

c $1 \, m^3$ weighs 250 kg
Weight of prism = $62.4 \times 250 = 15\,600$ kg

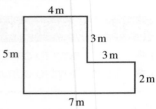

Exercise A

1 For each triangular prism:
   i sketch the cross-section   **ii** work out the area of the cross-section
   iii work out the volume of the prism.
State the units of your answer.

a
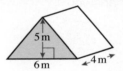

b
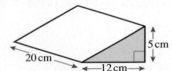

c
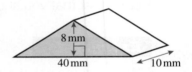

2 Calculate an estimate of the volume of each cylinder. Take the value of π to be 3

a
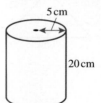

b

c
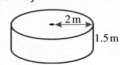

d
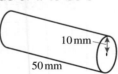

3 For each prism shown:
   i sketch the cross-section   **ii** work out the area of the cross-section
   iii work out the volume of the prism.

a
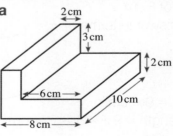

b
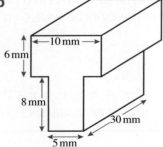

c
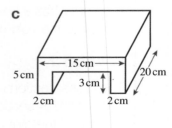

4 Work out the volume of each of these triangular prisms.

a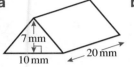

b

c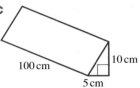

d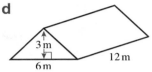

5 Work out the volume of each cylinder. Leave your answer in terms of π.

a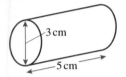

b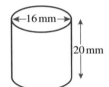

c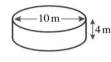

6 a Calculate the area of the cross-section of this prism.

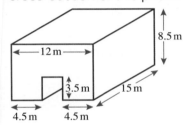

b Calculate the volume of the prism.

7 a Calculate the volume of the prism below.

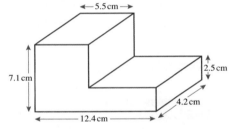

b 1 cm weighs 30 grams. How much does the prism weigh?

8 The prism below has a cross-section in the shape of a right-angled triangle.

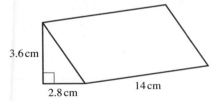

Calculate the volume of the prism.

9 A drinks can is in the shape of a cylinder of radius 3.5 cm and height 12 cm.
Calculate the volume of the can.
Give your answer to the nearest cm^3

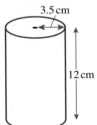

10 Calculate the volume of each of these semicircular prisms.
Give each answer to one decimal place.

a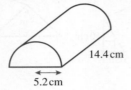

14.4 cm

5.2 cm

b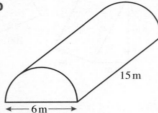

15 m

6 m

c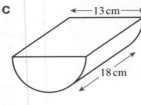

13 cm

18 cm

This cube has side 1 metre.
The volume of the cube is 1 m³

1 m

1 m

1 m

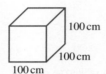

100 cm

100 cm

100 cm

Here is the same cube with the units given in centimetres.
Each side is 100 cm.
The volume of the cube is
100 cm × 100 cm × 100 cm = 1 000 000 cm³
So 1 m³ = 1 000 000 cm³

Other units of volume can be converted using this method.

For example, 1 cm = 10 mm

1 cm³ = 10 mm × 10 mm × 10 mm = 1000 mm³

Remember also that 1000 cm³ = 1 litre

Example 4

a Work out the number of cubic centimetres (cm³) there are in:
   i 4 m³   **ii** 2.7 m³
b Convert 2 350 000 cm³ to cubic metres (m³).

Solution 4

a 1 m³ = 1 000 000 cm³
To convert m³ to cm³ multiply by 1 000 000
   i 4 m³ = 4 × 1 000 000 cm³   **ii** 2.7 m³ = 2.7 × 1 000 000 cm³
         = 4 000 000 cm³   = 2 700 000 cm³
b To convert cm³ to m³ divide by 1 000 000
   2 350 000 cm³ = 2 350 000 ÷ 1 000 000 cm³ = 2.35 m³

Example 5

a Shaun says that length × width is the formula for the volume of a cuboid.
   Is he correct?
b Which is the correct unit for volume: cm², cm³ or cm

Solution 5

a No he is not correct as length × width is the formula for **area** of a rectangle.
(Volume of a cuboid = length × width × height)

b Volume is measured in cube units so cm³ is correct. (cm² = area, cm = length)

Example 6

The diagram shows a cylinder of volume 80π cm³
The radius of the base of the cylinder is 4 cm.
Calculate the height of the cylinder.

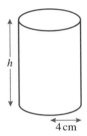

Solution 6

Volume of a cylinder = $\pi r^2 h$
Substitute volume = 80π and $r = 4$ into the formula:

$80\pi = \pi \times 4 \times 4 \times h$

$80 = 4 \times 4 \times h$ Divide both sides by π

$80 = 16 \times h$ Divide both sides by 16

$5 = h$

The height of the cylinder is 5 cm.

Exercise B

1 Convert the following to cubic metres (m³).
     a 1 940 000 cm³   **b** 31 000 000 cm³   **c** 826 700 cm³

2 Convert the following to cubic centimetres (cm³).
     a 8 m³   **b** 7.9 m³   **c** 0.25 m³   **d** 37.4 m³

3 Match the words to the units.

     Length   Area   Volume

     cm   m²   mm   km²   cubic foot   mile   mm³   square inch

     m   cm³

4 A vase is a cuboid with a square base of side 8 cm and a height of 30 cm.
The vase is half full of water.
One litre of water is added. Will the water overflow?
Show your working.

5 The diagram shows a cylinder.
The volume of the cylinder is 100π cm³
The radius of the cylinder is 5 cm.
Calculate the height of the cylinder.

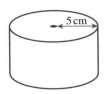

6 Here is a list of formulae.
Copy these headings and write each formula in the correct column.

length × width 2πr   Area of cross section × length ½base × height

2l + 2w length × width × height   πr²h

Length	Area	Volume

7 Pete says that πr² is the formula for circumference of a circle. Is he correct?
Give a reason for your answer.

8

A farmer has a water trough in the shape of a triangular prism.
a Calculate the volume of the trough.
b How many litres of water will the trough hold when full?

1 m³ = 1000 litres

9 A carton holds 2 litres of apple juice.
Cylindrical glasses of height 8 cm and
radius 3.5 cm are to be filled from the carton.
How many glasses can be filled?
Show your working.

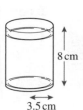

10 A metal girder is 4 metres long.
Its cross-section is L-shaped.
Calculate the volume of the girder.
State the units of your answer.

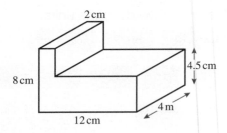

Chapter summary

- Solids can be represented by two-dimensional views.
- The views are plan view, front elevation and side elevation.
- The surface area of a solid is the total area of all the faces in the solid.
- The plan view, side and front elevations of the solid can be used to work out the surface area and the volume of a solid.

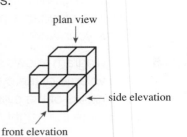

- The total surface area of a three-dimensional shape is the sum of the areas of all the faces of the shape.
- The curved surface area of a cylinder $= 2\pi rh$
- A closed cylinder has a circular top and a circular base.
  The total surface area
  = curved surface area + area of top + area of base
  $= 2\pi rh + \pi r^2 + \pi r^2 = 2\pi rh + 2\pi r^2$
- To convert units of area, e.g.
  $1\,m^2 = 100\,cm \times 100\,cm = 10\,000\,cm^2$
- $1\,cm^2 = 10\,mm \times 10\,mm = 100\,mm^2$
- Volume of a prism = area of cross-section $\times$ length
- Conversion of units of volume:
  $1\,m^3 = 100\,cm \times 100\,cm \times 100\,cm = 1\,000\,000\,cm^3$
  $1\,cm^3 = 10\,mm \times 10\,mm \times 10\,mm = 1000\,mm^3$
  $1\,litre = 1000\,cm^3$

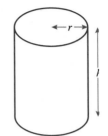

Chapter review

1 The diagram opposite shows a solid.
On a grid, draw the elevation of this solid
as seen from the direction of the arrow.

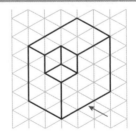

2 The diagram shows an isometric
representation of a house.
On a grid, draw the plan of the house.
The plan is the view from above the house.

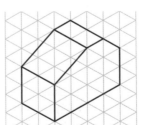

3 The diagram shows a triangular prism.
The cross-section of the prism is a
right-angled triangle.
Calculate the volume of the prism.

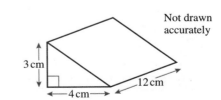

Not drawn
accurately

3 cm

4 cm

12 cm

4 The diagram shows a cylinder.
The volume of the cylinder is 540π cm^3
The radius of the cylinder is 10 cm.
Calculate the height of the cylinder.

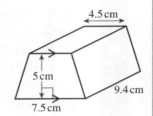

5 A child's swimming pool is in the shape of a cuboid.
The area of the floor of the swimming pool is 50 m^2
Calculate the number of litres of water needed to fill the pool to a height of 1.2 m.

6 The diagram shows a gold bar.
The cross-section of the gold bar is a trapezium.

      a   Calculate the area of the cross-section.
      b   Calculate the volume of the gold bar.

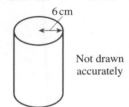

7 A cylinder has a radius of 6 cm.
  a Calculate the circumference of a circular
      end of the cylinder.
  b The cylinder has a volume of 950 cm^3
      Calculate the height of the cylinder.

Not drawn
accurately

8 A metal girder is 5.6 m long
and has an L-shaped cross-section
as shown.
Calculate the volume of the girder:
  a in cm^3
  b in m^3
Give each answer correct to two
significant figures.

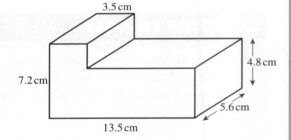

9 The diagram shows a cylindrical tin of fruit.
The height of the tin is 5.1 cm.
The radius of the base is 4.2 cm.
Calculate the **total** surface area of the tin.
Give your answer correct to one decimal place.

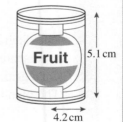

10 The diagram shows a ridge tent
which is 3.6 m long.
Calculate the volume of the ridge tent.

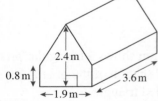

Sequences

36.1 Generating sequences using nth term rules

IN THIS SECTION YOU WILL

- Learn how to use *position-to-term rules* to generate sequences.

Sequences can be generated using a *term-to-term rule* provided that one term in the sequence is known.

For example: The 1st term in a sequence is 5

         The term-to-term rule is   add 4

         1st term $= 5$

         2nd term $= 5 + 4 = 9$

         3rd term $= 9 + 4 = 13$

         4th term $= 13 + 4 = 17$

So the first four terms of the sequence are 5, 9, 13, 17

Sequences can also be generated using *position-to-term* rules.

The nth term of a sequence is a *position-to-term* rule where n represents the position of a term in the sequence.

Example 1

Find the first three terms of the sequences with the following nth terms.

Describe each sequence in words.

a $3n$ **b** $3n - 1$

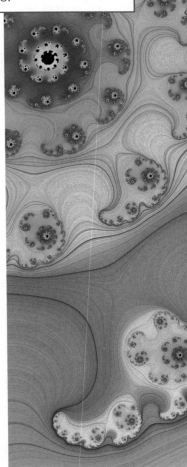

Solution 1

a nth term $= 3n$, where n stands for the term number or the position of the term in the sequence.

Term number	**1**st term	**2**nd term	**3**rd term
n	1	2	3
$3n$	$3 \times \mathbf{1} = 3$	$3 \times \mathbf{2} = 6$	$3 \times \mathbf{3} = 9$
Sequence	3	6	9

The first three terms are 3, 6, 9
The sequence with nth term $3n$ consists of the multiples of 3

b nth term $= 3n - 1$

Term number	**1**st term	**2**nd term	**3**rd term
n	1	2	3
$3n - 1$	$3 \times \mathbf{1} - 1 = 2$	$3 \times \mathbf{2} - 1 = 5$	$3 \times \mathbf{3} - 1 = 8$
Sequence	2	5	8

The first three terms are 2, 5, 8
The terms in the sequence are one less than the multiples of 3

Example 2

Find the first three terms and *term-to-term* rule of the sequences with these nth terms. Describe each sequence in words.

a $5n$ b $5n + 2$

Solution 2

a nth term $= 5n$

Term number	**1**st term	**2**nd term	**3**rd term
n	1	2	3
$5n$	$5 \times \mathbf{1} = 5$	$5 \times \mathbf{2} = 10$	$5 \times \mathbf{3} = 15$
Sequence	5	10	15

The first three terms are 5, 10, 15. Term-to-term rule   add 5
The sequence with nth term $5n$ consists of the multiples of 5

b nth term $= 5n + 2$

Term number	**1**st term	**2**nd term	**3**rd term
n	1	2	3
$5n + 2$	$5 \times \mathbf{1} + 2 = 7$	$5 \times \mathbf{2} + 2 = 12$	$5 \times \mathbf{3} + 2 = 17$
Sequence	7	12	17

The nth term can be used:

■ to work out the terms in a sequence
■ to check whether a given term is in a sequence
■ to find the position of a given term in a sequence.

Example 3

A sequence has nth term $3n + 5$
a Is 145 a term in the sequence?
b What is the position of the term 80 in the sequence?

Solution 3

a $3n + 5 = 145$ | Subtract 5 from both sides.

$\quad\quad 3n = 140$ | Divide both sides by 3

$\quad\quad\quad n = 140 \div 3 = 46\frac{2}{3}$

There is no $46\frac{2}{3}$ term (n must be a positive integer), so 145 is not a term in the sequence.

b $3n + 5 = 80$ | Subtract 5 from both sides.

$\quad\quad 3n = 75$ | Divide both sides by 3

$\quad\quad\quad n = 75 \div 3 = 25$

So 80 is the 25th term in the sequence.

Exercise A

1 Write down the first five terms of the sequences with nth terms given below.

a $2n$	b $3n + 5$	c $5n - 2$	d $2n - 3$	e $5n + 3$
f $3n - 3$	g $5n - 3$	h $2n + 5$	i $3n - 2$	j $5n + 2$

2 Write down the first five terms of the sequences with nth terms given below. Describe each sequence in words.

a i $4n$ ii $4n - 1$ iii $4n + 3$ iv $4n - 5$ v $4n + 9$
b i $10n$ ii $10n - 3$ iii $10n + 7$ iv $10n - 11$ v $10n + 6$

3 a A sequence has nth term $2n - 5$
   i Find the fifth term of this sequence.
   ii Find the tenth term of this sequence.
   iii Find the 15th term of this sequence.
   b Find the second, fourth and sixth terms of the sequence with nth term $3n$.
   c Find the third, fifth and seventh terms of the sequence with nth term $6n - 1$
   d Find the 10th, 20th and 30th terms of the sequence with nth term $5n + 1$
   e Find the 100th, 200th and 300th terms of the sequence with nth term $4n + 1$

4 **a**   A sequence has nth term $7 - 2n$.

    i Find the first three terms of this sequence.

    ii How many terms of the sequence are positive integers? Work out as many terms as you need to find out.

  b   A sequence has nth term $10 - 4n$.

    i Find the fourth term of this sequence.

    ii How many terms of this sequence are positive integers?

5   The cards below give the nth terms of some sequences.

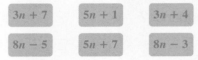

| $3n + 7$ | $5n + 1$ | $3n + 4$ |
| $8n - 5$ | $5n + 7$ | $8n - 3$ |

  a   Which two sequences have a term equal to 11?

  b   Which three sequences have a first term equal to a prime number?

  c   Which two sequences have a third term equal to a square number?

  d   Which three sequences have a term equal to 13?

  e   Which three sequences have the term 16 in common?

  f   Which two sequences have the term-to-term rule   add 8 ?

6 **a**   A sequence has nth term $2n - 5$

    Find the first term and *term-to-term* rule of this sequence.

  b   Repeat part **a** for the sequence with nth term:

    i $4n + 3$ **ii** $3n - 7$ **iii** $8 - 3n$ **iv** $20 - 5n$

7 **a**   Match the nth term rules with the sequences.

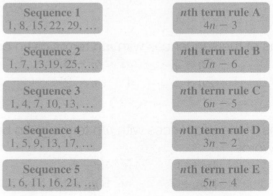

Sequence 1	nth term rule A
1, 8, 15, 22, 29, …	$4n - 3$
Sequence 2	nth term rule B
1, 7, 13, 19, 25, …	$7n - 6$
Sequence 3	nth term rule C
1, 4, 7, 10, 13, …	$6n - 5$
Sequence 4	nth term rule D
1, 5, 9, 13, 17, …	$3n - 2$
Sequence 5	nth term rule E
1, 6, 11, 16, 21, …	$5n - 4$

  b   Write the nth term rule for the sequence 1, 9, 17, 25, 33, …

8 **a**   This number machine gives the nth term of a sequence

Term number, $n \longrightarrow \boxed{\times 2} \longrightarrow \boxed{+7} \longrightarrow$ nth term

    i Use the number machine to complete this table.

Term number, n	1	2	3	4	5
Term					

  ii Write down the term-to-term rule for the sequence.

  iii Find the nth term rule for the sequence.

b Repeat part **a** for the sequences given by these number machines.

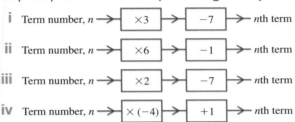

i Term number, n → ×3 → −7 → nth term

ii Term number, n → ×6 → −1 → nth term

iii Term number, n → ×2 → −7 → nth term

iv Term number, n → × (−4) → +1 → nth term

9 Match each of these nth terms with the term-to-term rule for its sequence.

nth terms	Term-to-term rules
$4n - 1$	Add 7
$7n + 1$	Add 4
$3n - 1$	Add 6
$6n + 1$	Add 5
$5n - 1$	Add 3

What do you notice?

10 Which of the following statements are true and which are false?

a 396 is the 44th term of the sequence with nth term $9n$.

b 95 is the 17th term in the sequence with nth term $6n - 7$

c 89 is a term in the sequence with nth term $14n - 3$

d 323 is a term in the sequence with nth term $40n + 3$

e 137 is a term in the sequence with nth term $27n + 3$

f 26 is a term in the sequence with nth term $100 - 13n$.

g -12 is a term in the sequence with nth term $78 - 15n$.

h -126 is a term in the sequence with nth term $130 - 16n$.

Sequences with a *constant difference* between consecutive terms:

■ have a term-to-term rule of the form   + constant difference

■ have a position-to-term rule or nth term of the form nth term = $an + b$

where a is the constant difference and b is a positive or negative integer.

For example,
the sequence 5, 11, 17, 23, 29, ... has a constant difference of **6**

	5	11	17	23	29

Differences   +**6**   +**6**   +**6**   +**6**

The constant difference is **6**, so the term-to-term rule is   add 6

The nth term rule is   **$6n - 1$**

Some sequences do **not** have a constant difference between consecutive terms.

For example,
the first five terms of the sequence with nth term n^2 are 1, 4, 9, 16, 25, …

Term		1		4		9		16		25
Differences			**+3**		**+5**		**+7**		**+9**	
				+2		+2		+2		

All sequences that contain an n^2 term have a similar sort of difference pattern.

Example 4

A sequence has nth term $2(n - 3)^2$
a   Find the first five terms of this sequence.
b   Find the pattern of differences between consecutive terms of the sequence.
    What do you notice?

Solution 4

a   i nth term $2(n - 3)^2$

Term number	1st term	2nd term	3rd term	4th term	5th term
n	**1**	**2**	**3**	**4**	**5**
$n - 3$	**1** $- 3 = -2$	**2** $- 3 = -1$	**3** $- 3 = 0$	**4** $- 3 = 1$	**5** $- 3 = 2$
$(n - 3)^2$	$(-2)^2 = 4$	$(-1)^2 = 1$	$0^2 = 0$	$1^2 = 1$	$2^2 = 4$
$2(n - 3)^2$	$2 \times 4 = 8$	$2 \times 1 = 2$	$2 \times 0 = 0$	$2 \times 1 = 2$	$2 \times 4 = 8$
Sequence	8	2	0	2	8

The first five terms are 8, 2, 0, 2, 8

ii Sequence   8   2   0   2   8
    Differences   **−6**   **−2**   **+2**   **+6**
                   $+ 4$ $+ 4$ $+ 4$

The differences between the terms in the sequence follow a pattern with constant difference 4

Exercise B

1   The cards show the first five terms of some sequences with first term 2

Sequence 1	Sequence 2	Sequence 3	Sequence 4
2, 5, 8, 11, 14, …	2, 3, 5, 8, 12, …	2, 4, 8, 14, 22, …	2, 4, 8, 16, 32, …

Sequence 5	Sequence 6	Sequence 7	Sequence 8
2, 5, 11, 29, 83, …	2, 8, 14, 20, 26, …	2, 3, 6, 11, 18, …	2, 0, −2, −4, −6, …

Which of the sequences have a constant difference between consecutive terms?

2 a A sequence has nth term $4n + 7$
   What is the constant difference between consecutive terms of this sequence?
   b The constant difference between the terms of a linear sequence is 5
   Write down three possible nth terms for this sequence.

3 a A sequence has nth term $n^2 + 1$
   i Write down the first five terms of this sequence.
   ii Describe the pattern of differences between consecutive terms.
   b Repeat part **a** for the sequences with nth terms:
   i $n^2 + n$ **ii** $n(n + 1)$ **iii** $(n + 1)^2$
   iv $(n - 1)^2$ **v** $2n^2 + 1$ **vi** $(n + 2)(n - 3)$

4 A sequence has nth term $2n$.
   Explain why it is not possible for 1001 to be a term in this sequence.

5 Tom says that 503 is a term in the sequence with nth term $5n$.
   Explain why he is wrong.

6 a Explain why 122 is **not** a term in the sequence with nth term $4n$.
   b Explain why 151 is a term in the sequence with nth term $10n + 11$

7 a A linear sequence contains the term 101
   One possible nth term for such a sequence is $5n + 1$ because 101 is 1 more
   than a multiple of 5
   Write down five other possible nth terms for a linear sequence containing 101.
   Give a reason for each of the nth terms you choose.
   b Show that $n^2 + 1$ and $2n^2 + 3$ are both possible nth terms for a sequence that
   contains the term 101

8 The nth terms of some linear sequences are shown below.
   $2n + 1$ $3n + 2$ $4n - 3$ $5n + 2$ $6n - 3$ $10n + 15$
   a **i** In which of the sequences do multiples of 3 occur?
       ii Which of the sequences contain **only** multiples of 3?
   b **i** In which of the sequences do odd numbers occur?
       ii Which of the sequences contain **only** odd numbers?
   c **i** In which of the sequences do multiples of 5 occur?
       ii Which of the sequences contain **only** multiples of 5?
          Explain your answer.

9 a The number machine gives the nth term of a sequence.

Term number, n ⟶ [square] ⟶ [×2] ⟶ nth term

   Describe the pattern of differences between consecutive terms of this
   sequence.

b   Repeat for the sequences given by these number machines.

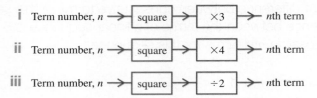

i   Term number, n → square → ×3 → nth term

ii   Term number, n → square → ×4 → nth term

iii   Term number, n → square → ÷2 → nth term

10 A sequence has nth term $2n^2 + 4n + 5$
Use trial and improvement to show that 75 is a term in this sequence.

36.2 Finding the nth term of a sequence

CAN YOU REMEMBER

- How to use the nth term of a sequence to generate terms in the sequence?

IN THIS SECTION YOU WILL

- Learn how to find the nth term of a sequence with a constant difference between consecutive terms.
- Work out the nth terms of sequences based on patterns of shapes and numbers.
- Connect nth term rules to the patterns of shapes upon which they are based.

Some sequences of multiples are shown below.

Multiples of **2**	2		4		6		8
Differences		+**2**		+**2**		+**2**	

Term-to-term rule
add 2
nth term $2n$

Multiples of **3**	3		6		9		12
Differences		+**3**		+**3**		+**3**	

Term-to-term rule
add 3
nth term $3n$

Multiples of **10**	10		20		30		40
		+**10**		+**10**		+**10**	

Term-to-term rule
add 10
nth term $10n$

This sequence is based on the multiples of 2

The multiples of 2	2		4		6		8
1 more than the multiples of 2	3		5		7		9
Differences		+**2**		+**2**		+**2**	

Term-to-term rule
add 2
nth term $2n + 1$

This sequence is based on the multiples of 3

The multiples of 3	3		6		9		12
4 more than the multiples of 3	7		10		13		16
Differences		+3		+3		+3	

> Term-to-term rule
> **add 3**
> *n*th term $3n + 4$

This sequence is based on the multiples of 10

The multiples of 10	10		20		30		40
2 less than the multiples of 10	8		18		28		38
Differences		+10		+10		+10	

> Term-to-term rule
> **add 10**
> *n*th term $10n - 2$

Example 1

a Find the *n*th term of each of the following linear sequences.

   i 1, 6, 11, 16, …   **ii** 5, 9, 13, 17, …

b Use the *n*th term to find the 250th term of each of the sequences.

Solution 1

a **i**   1   6   11   16

          +5   +5   +5

> Term-to-term rule **add 5**
> The sequence is based on the multiples of 5

Term number (*n*)	1	2	3	4	*n*
Multiple of **5** (**5** × *n*)	$5 \times 1 = 5$	$5 \times 2 = 10$	$5 \times 3 = 15$	$5 \times 4 = 20$	$5n$
Term	1	6	11	16	
Term − **5***n*	$1 - 5 = -4$	$6 - 10 = -4$	$11 - 15 = -4$	$16 - 20 = -4$	-4

Term − **5***n* = −4
The *n*th term is **5***n* − 4

> So each term is 4 less than a multiple of 5

  ii   5   9   13   17

          +4   +4   +4

> Term-to-term rule **add 4**
> The sequence is based on the multiples of 4

Term number (*n*)	1	2	3	4	*n*
Multiple of **4** (**4** × *n*)	$4 \times 1 = 4$	$4 \times 2 = 8$	$4 \times 3 = 12$	$4 \times 4 = 16$	$4n$
Term	5	9	13	17	
Term − **4***n*	$5 - 4 = 1$	$9 - 8 = 1$	$13 - 12 = 1$	$17 - 16 = 1$	1

Term − **4***n* = 1
The *n*th term is **4***n* + 1

> So each term is 1 more than a multiple of 4

b **i** *n*th term $5n - 4$
When $n = 250$,
$5n - 4 = 5 \times 250 - 4 = 1246$
So the 250th term is 1246

  ii *n*th term $4n + 1$
When $n = 250$,
$4n + 1 = 4 \times 250 + 1 = 1001$
So the 250th term is 1001

Example 2

Matchsticks are used to make this pattern of shapes.

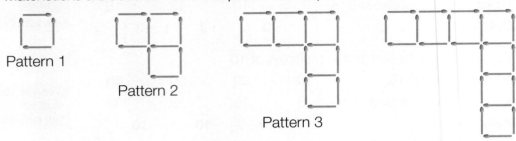

Pattern 1

Pattern 2

Pattern 3

Pattern 4

a Find an expression for the number of matchsticks needed to make Pattern n.
b Find the number of the pattern that uses 304 matchsticks.

Solution 2

a The number of matchsticks in each pattern is shown in the table

Pattern number	1	2	3	4
Number of matchsticks	4	10	16	22

The number of matchsticks forms the sequence 4, 10, 16, 22, …

Difference = **6**   Term-to-term rule **add 6**

This can be seen from the diagram, where 6 blue matchsticks are added each time to make the next pattern.
So the sequence is based on the multiples of **6**

Term number (n)	1	2	3	4	n
Multiple of **6** ($6 \times n$)	$6 \times 1 = 6$	$6 \times 2 = 12$	$6 \times 3 = 18$	$6 \times 4 = 24$	$6n$
Term	4	10	16	22	
Term $- 6n$	$4 - 6 = -2$	$10 - 12 = -2$	$16 - 18 = -2$	$22 - 24 = -2$	-2

So the number of matchsticks in Pattern n is $6n - 2$

b When there are 304 matchsticks
$$6n - 2 = 304 \qquad \text{Add 2 to both sides}$$
$$6n = 306 \qquad \text{Divide both sides by 6}$$
$$n = 51$$
So Pattern 51 uses 304 matchsticks.

Exercise A

1 The *n*th term of the sequence 5, 10, 15, 20, 25, … is $5n$.
Write down the *n*th term of the following sequences.

   a 6, 12, 18, 24, 30, …   **b** 12, 24, 36, 48, 60, …

   c 8, 16, 24, 32, 40, …   **d** $\frac{1}{2}$, 1, $1\frac{1}{2}$, 2, $2\frac{1}{2}$, …

   e $\frac{1}{4}$, $\frac{1}{2}$, $\frac{3}{4}$, 1, $1\frac{1}{4}$, …   **f** $-2, -4, -6, -8, -10, …$

   g $-5, -10, -15, -20, -25, …$ **h** $-\frac{1}{2}, -1, -1\frac{1}{2}, -2, -2\frac{1}{2}, …$

2 The sequence 5, 10, 15, 20, 25, … has *n*th term $5n$.
Write down the *n*th term of these sequences

   a 6, 11, 16, 21, 26, ….   **b** 4, 9, 14, 19, 24, …

   c 8, 13, 18, 23, 28, …   **d** 1, 6, 11, 16, 21, …

   e -4, 1, 6, 11, 16, …

3 **a** Write down the *n*th term of the sequence 3, 6, 9, 12, 15, …

   b Write down the *n*th term of these sequences

      i 4, 7, 10, 13, 16, …   **ii** 2, 5, 8, 11, 14, …   **iii** 8, 11, 14, 17, 20, …

      iv -2, 1, 4, 7, 10, …   **v** 13, 16, 19, 22, 25, …

4 For each of these sequences write down the term-to-term rule and find the *n*th term.

   a 5, 11, 17, 23, 29, …   **b** 7, 11, 15, 19, 23, …

   c 8, 14, 20, 26, 32, …   **d** 20, 17, 14, 11, 8, …

   e -2, 5, 12, 19, 26, …   **f** 5, $5\frac{1}{2}$, 6, $6\frac{1}{2}$, 7, …

   g 102, 105, 108, 111, 114, …   **h** 21, 29, 37, 45, 53, …

   i 4, $6\frac{1}{2}$, 9, $11\frac{1}{2}$, 14, …   **j** 100, 91, 82, 73, 64, …

5 These patterns are made from dots.

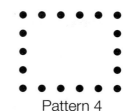

Pattern 1   Pattern 2   Pattern 3   Pattern 4

   a Find an expression for the number of dots in Pattern *n*.

   b How many dots form Pattern 100?

   c Which pattern in the sequence has 502 dots?

6 The diagrams show patterns made from matchsticks.

Pattern 1   Pattern 2   Pattern 3   Pattern 4

   a Find an expression for the number of matchsticks in Pattern *n*.

   b How many matchsticks will be needed to make pattern 50?

   c James has 300 matchsticks. Can he make Pattern 150?

7 The diagrams show hexagon patterns made from matchsticks.

  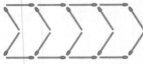

1 hexagon   2 hexagons   3 hexagons   4 hexagons

a   Find an expression for the number of matchsticks needed to make *n* hexagons.
b   How many hexagons can be made with 82 matchsticks?

8 These pentagon patterns are made from matchsticks.

1 pentagon   2 pentagons   3 pentagons

Copy and complete this table.

Number of pentagons	1	2	3	4	*n*		200
Number of matchsticks	5	9	13			101	

9 These diagrams show patterns made from orange and white squares.

 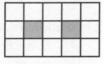 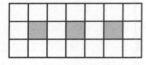

Diagram 1   Diagram 2   Diagram 3

a   Find an expression for the number of white squares in Diagram *n*.
b   In which diagram are there 328 white squares?

10 These diagrams are made from black square tiles.

Diagram 1   Diagram 2   Diagram 3

a   Find an expression for the number of tiles in Diagram *n*.
b   Helen has 100 black tiles. What is the biggest diagram she can make?

Some sequences involve the products of pairs of numbers.
To find the *n*th term of sequences like this:
■   find the *n*th term of each sequence of numbers separately
■   multiply these *n*th terms together to find the *n*th term for the sequence of products.

Do the same for a sequence involving one number divided by another.

Example 3

Find the *n*th term of each of these sequences.

a $1 \times 3, 3 \times 7, 5 \times 11, 7 \times 15, \ldots$ **b** $\frac{1}{5}, \frac{4}{8}, \frac{9}{11}, \frac{16}{14}, \frac{25}{17}, \ldots$

Solution 3

a Look at each of the numbers in the products separately.
The first numbers form the sequence 1, 3, 5, 7, …
This sequence has constant difference 2, so it is based on the multiples of **2**

Term number (*n*)	1	2	3	4	*n*
Multiple of **2** (**2** × *n*)	$2 \times 1 = 2$	$2 \times 2 = 4$	$2 \times 3 = 6$	$2 \times 4 = 8$	**2*n***
Term − **2*n***	$1 - 2 = -1$	$3 - 4 = -1$	$5 - 6 = -1$	$7 - 8 = -1$	−1

So the first number in the product has *n*th term $2n - 1$
The second numbers form the sequence 3, 7, 11, 15, …
This sequence has constant difference 4, so it is based on the multiples of **4**

Term number (*n*)	1	2	3	4	*n*
Multiple of **4** (**4** × *n*)	$4 \times 1 = 4$	$4 \times 2 = 8$	$4 \times 3 = 12$	$4 \times 4 = 16$	**4*n***
Term − **4*n***	$3 - 4 = -1$	$7 - 8 = -1$	$11 - 12 = -1$	$15 - 16 = -1$	−1

So the second number in the product has *n*th term $4n - 1$
So the *n*th term of the sequence $1 \times 3, 3 \times 7, 5 \times 11, 7 \times 15, \ldots$ is
$(2n - 1)(4n - 1)$.

b Look at each of the numbers in the fractions separately.
The numerators are the square numbers 1, 4, 9, 16, 25, … and have *n*th term n^2.
The denominators 5, 8, 11, 14, 17, … have constant difference 3
This sequence is 2 more than the multiples of 3 and has *n*th term $3n + 2$

So the *n*th term of the sequence $\frac{1}{5}, \frac{4}{8}, \frac{9}{11}, \frac{16}{14}, \frac{25}{17}, \ldots$ is $\dfrac{n^2}{3n + 2}$.

Sometimes the *n*th term can be found from looking at the way the patterns in a sequence grow.

Example 4

These patterns are made from square counters.

   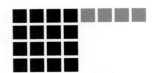

Pattern 1   Pattern 2   Pattern 3   Pattern 4

Explain why the number of counters in Pattern *n* is $n^2 + n$.

Solution 4

Pattern 1 has one black square + one red square
Pattern 2 has a 2 × 2 square of black squares + two red squares
Pattern 3 has a 3 × 3 square of black squares + three red squares
…

Pattern n has an $n \times n$ square of black squares + n red squares.
So the number of counters in Pattern n is $n \times n + n = n^2 + n$.

This expression can be obtained directly from the pattern.
The black squares form a square and the red squares form a line.
The side of the square and the line are both the same size as the pattern number.

Exercise B

1 Each of the sequences in the table has an nth term of the form an^2

Term number, n	1	2	3	4	5	nth term
Sequence 1	1	4	9	16	25	n^2
Sequence 2	2	8	18	32	50	$2n^2$
Sequence 3	10	40	90	160	250	
Sequence 4	0.5	2	4.5	8	12.5	
Sequence 5	5	20	45	80	125	

Find the nth terms of sequences 3, 4 and 5

2 Each of the sequences in the table has an nth term of the form $n^2 + b$.

Term number, n	1	2	3	4	5	nth term
Sequence 1	1	4	9	16	25	n^2
Sequence 2	3	6	11	18	27	$n^2 + 2$
Sequence 3	0	3	8	15	24	
Sequence 4	6	9	14	21	30	
Sequence 5	−4	−1	4	11	20	

Find the nth terms of sequences 3, 4 and 5

3 Write down the nth term of each of these sequences.
   a $2 \times 3, 3 \times 4, 4 \times 5, 5 \times 6, \ldots$ **b** $2 \times 3, 5 \times 5, 8 \times 7, 11 \times 9, \ldots$
   c $2 \times 3, 6 \times 7, 10 \times 11, 14 \times 15, \ldots$ **d** $2 \times 2, 4 \times 8, 6 \times 14, 8 \times 20, \ldots$

4 Write down the nth term of each of these sequences.
   a $\dfrac{2}{3}, \dfrac{3}{5}, \dfrac{4}{7}, \dfrac{5}{9}, \dfrac{6}{11}, \ldots$ **b** $\dfrac{1}{5}, \dfrac{4}{6}, \dfrac{9}{7}, \dfrac{16}{8}, \dfrac{25}{9}, \ldots$ **c** $\dfrac{4}{3}, \dfrac{7}{12}, \dfrac{10}{21}, \dfrac{13}{30}, \dfrac{16}{39}, \ldots$
   d $\dfrac{7}{7}, \dfrac{4}{17}, \dfrac{1}{27}, -\dfrac{2}{37}, -\dfrac{5}{47}, \ldots$ **e** $\dfrac{9}{7}, \dfrac{14}{12}, \dfrac{19}{17}, \dfrac{24}{22}, \dfrac{29}{27}, \ldots$

5 **a** The first five terms of a sequence are 2, 5, 8, 11, 14, …
  i What are the differences between terms?
  ii Explain why the sequence has *n*th term $3n - 1$

 b The first five terms of a sequence are 7, 9, 11, 13, 15, …
 Tom says that the *n*th term of this sequence is $5n + 2$
 Explain why Tom is wrong.

 c A sequence has *n*th term $(n - 5)^2 + 4$
 Explain why all the terms in this sequence are positive.

6 Sarah is trying to find the *n*th term of the
sequence 5, 12, 21, 32, 45, …
She starts by subtracting the square numbers
1, 4, 9, 16, 25, … from each term in the sequence.

| $5 - 1 = 4$ |
| $12 - 4 =$ |
| $21 -$ |

 a **i** Copy and complete Sarah's list.
  ii Write down the *n*th term of the linear sequence she obtains.
 b Explain why the *n*th term of the sequence 5, 12, 21, 32, 45, … is $n^2 + 4n$.

7 **a** **i** Show that the equation $5n - 6 = 3n + 2$ has the solution $n = 4$
  ii Explain why this shows that the fourth terms of the sequences with *n*th terms
    $5n - 6$ and $3n + 2$ are equal.
  iii Show that the equal fourth term has the value 14
 b Two sequences have *n*th terms $6n - 10$ and $3n + 14$
  i What term of these sequences is equal?
  ii What is its value?
 c Two sequences have *n*th terms $7n - 13$ and $5n + 16$
 Do these sequences have an equal term? Explain your answer.

8 This pattern is made from small square tiles.

      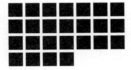

Pattern 1   Pattern 2   Pattern 3   Pattern 4

 a Billy says
  Use the patterns to explain why Billy is right.
 b Sasha looks at Pattern 3 like this.

    $2 \times 5 + 3 = 13$

> The number of small tiles in Pattern *n* is given by the expression $n^2 + (n-1)^2$

  i Explain why Sasha writes $3 \times 7 + 4 = 25$
    for Pattern 4
  ii Sasha says
   Use Sasha's work to explain why
   she is also right.

> The number of small tiles in Pattern *n* is given by the expression $(n-1)(2n-1) + n$

Chapter summary

- The *n*th term of a sequence is a *position-to-term* rule where *n* represents the position of a term in the sequence.
- The *n*th term can be used:
  - to work out the terms in a sequence
  - to check whether a given term is in a sequence
  - to find the position of a given term in a sequence.
- Sequences with *a constant difference* between consecutive terms:
  - have a term-to-term rule of the form   + constant difference
  - have a position-to-term rule or *n*th term of the form   *n*th term = *an* + *b*

    where *a* is the constant difference and *b* is a positive or negative integer.
- Some sequences involve the products of pairs of numbers.
  To find the *n*th term of sequences like this:
  - find the *n*th term of each sequence of numbers separately
  - multiply these *n*th terms together to find the *n*th term for the sequence of products.
  Do the same for a sequence involving one number divided by another.
- Sequences can be shown as patterns made, for example, from dots, squares or matchsticks. Sometimes the *n*th term can be found from looking at the way the patterns in a sequence grow.

Chapter review

1   **a**   The *n*th term of a sequence is 4*n* + 3
  - **i**   Write down the first three terms of the sequence.
  - **ii**   Is 82 a term in the sequence? Explain your answer.

    b   Tim builds fence patterns from matchsticks as shown below.

Pattern 1	Pattern 2	Pattern 3
4 matchsticks	7 matchsticks	10 matchsticks

       How many matchsticks are in Pattern *n*?

2   Matchsticks are used to make this pattern of pentagons.

Pattern 1	Pattern 2	Pattern 3
5 matchsticks	9 matchsticks	13 matchsticks

    a   How many matchsticks are needed for Pattern 5?
    b   Write down an expression for the number of matchsticks in Pattern *n*.
    c   Which pattern uses 101 matchsticks?

3 The nth term of a sequence is $5n - 1$
  a Write down the first and second terms of the sequence.
  b Which term of the sequence is equal to 54?
  c Explain why 100 is not a term in the sequence.

4 Patterns are made from green and white squares.

1st pattern   2nd pattern   3rd pattern   4th pattern
  a How many green squares are there in the nth pattern?
  b How many white squares are there in the nth pattern?

5 A sequence of numbers is shown: 5   8   11   14   17
  a Find an expression for the nth term of the sequence.
  b Explain why 99 will not be a term in this sequence.

6 a Stars are arranged to form a sequence of patterns as shown.

   ☆   ☆☆☆   ☆☆☆☆☆   ☆☆☆☆☆☆☆
Pattern 1   Pattern 2   Pattern 3   Pattern 4
  Write an expression for the number of stars in Pattern n.
  b Counters are arranged to form a sequence of patterns as shown.

  Write an expression for the number of counters in Pattern n.

7 a A sequence begins -2, -1,   0,   1,   2,   …
  Write an expression for the nth term of the sequence.
  b The nth term of a different sequence is $7n + 1$
  What is the difference between the first and second terms of this sequence?

8 Sticks are arranged to form a sequence of patterns as shown.

Pattern 1   Pattern 2   Pattern 3   Pattern 4
Write an expression for the number of sticks in Pattern n.

9 John and Sarah are each asked to continue a sequence that begins 2, 5, …
  a John writes 2, 5, 8, 11, 14, … Write down the nth term of John's sequence.
  b Sarah writes 2, 5, 8, 13, 20, … Write down the nth term of Sarah's sequence.

Common factors and common multiples

37.1 Products of prime factors

Here is a list of prime numbers starting with the smallest:

2, 3, 5, 7, 11, 13, 17, 19, ...

The factors of 20 are 1, 2, 4, 5, 10 and 20

2 and 5 are the *prime factors* of 20

The prime factors of a number are all its factors that are also prime numbers.

Every number can be written as a product of prime factors.

20 written as the product of its prime factors is $2 \times 2 \times 5$

There are two methods of writing a number as a product of prime factors – the *repeated division* method and the *factor tree* method.

Example 1

Write 18 as a product of prime factors.

Solution 1

Repeated division method

Start by dividing 18 by its smallest prime factor, 2

Dividing by 2	$18 \div \mathbf{2} = 9$	

9 is not divisible by 2, so divide by the next smallest prime factor.

This can be set out as:

$$\begin{array}{r} 2)\underline{18} \\ 3)\underline{9} \\ 3)\underline{3} \\ 1 \end{array}$$

Dividing by 3	$9 \div \mathbf{3} = 3$
Dividing by 3 again	$3 \div \mathbf{3} = 1$

Stop when you get to 1

18 written as a product of prime factors is $\mathbf{2 \times 3 \times 3}$

Example 2

Write 45 as a product of prime factors.

Solution 2

Factor tree method
Start with any multiplication that gives 45
$45 = 5 \times 9$
5 is prime so shade that branch to show it is complete.
9 is not a prime number, so find the factors of 9
$9 = 3 \times 3$
3 is a prime number so all the branches now end in primes.

45 written as a product of prime factors is $3 \times 3 \times 5$
The same method can be used without showing the products on a factor tree
$45 = 5 \times 9$
$45 = 5 \times 3 \times 3$

Exercise A

1 Work out these products of primes.

    a 5×7 **b** $2 \times 2 \times 3 \times 3$ **c** $3 \times 5 \times 5$

    d $3 \times 5 \times 7$ **e** $2 \times 2 \times 2 \times 3$ **f** $3 \times 3 \times 11$

    g $2 \times 2 \times 2 \times 5 \times 5$

2 For each of the following numbers, write them as a product of two factors, not including 1

    a 8   **b** 20   **c** 25   **d** 30

    e 32   **f** 35   **g** 36   **h** 42

    i 48   **j** 60   **k** 81   **l** 90

3 Write down the prime factors of each of the following numbers.

    a 8   **b** 14   **c** 15   **d** 25

    e 27   **f** 35   **g** 49   **h** 50

    i 81   **j** 100   **k** 121

4 Copy and complete to find the prime factors:

    a 2)16   **b** 2)54   **c** 3)39
       2) 8   3)___   )___
)___   )___   )___
)___   )___
)___   )___

5 Copy and complete the factor trees.

a   b   c

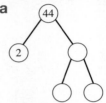 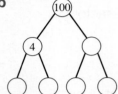 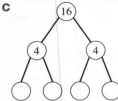

6 Write each of these numbers as a product of its prime factors.

a	10	**b**	15	**c**	24	**d**	28
e	30	**f**	36	**g**	42	**h**	45
i	50	**j**	60	**k**	81	**l**	90

7 Work out these products.

a	$5 \times 7 \times 7$	**b**	$2 \times 3 \times 3 \times 11$
c	$5 \times 5 \times 7 \times 11$	**d**	$5 \times 7 \times 11 \times 11$
e	$2 \times 2 \times 3 \times 13 \times 23$	**f**	$3 \times 17 \times 19$
g	$2 \times 2 \times 5 \times 5 \times 17 \times 23$	**h**	23×29

8 Use a calculator to find a prime factor greater than 10 for each of the following numbers.

a	184	**b**	153	**c**	116	**d**	275
e	369	**f**	124	**g**	620	**h**	5800

9 Write each of these numbers as a product of its prime factors.

a	112	**b**	125	**c**	144	**d**	150
e	180	**f**	184	**g**	200	**h**	500

A number can be written as a product of its prime factors using *index form* (or *power form*).

Example 3

Write 54 as a product of prime factors. Give your answer in index form.

Solution 3

Repeated division method

$$2\underline{)54}$$
$$3\underline{)27}$$
$$3\underline{)9}$$
$$3\underline{)3}$$
$$1$$

Factor tree method

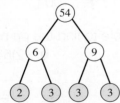

$54 = 2 \times 3 \times 3 \times 3 = 2 \times 3^3$ $54 = 2 \times 3 \times 3 \times 3 = 2 \times 3^3$

Exercise B

1 Write each product in index form.
   a $2 \times 2 \times 2 \times 3 \times 3$ **b** $2 \times 5 \times 5 \times 5 \times 5$
   c $3 \times 3 \times 5 \times 5 \times 7$ **d** $2 \times 3 \times 5 \times 7 \times 7 \times 7$
   e $3 \times 3 \times 5 \times 5 \times 5 \times 7 \times 11 \times 11$ **f** $2 \times 2 \times 2 \times 5 \times 11 \times 11 \times 13 \times 13 \times 13$

2 Write each product in index form by sorting the numbers into order first.
   a $3 \times 5 \times 2 \times 2 \times 3$ **b** $7 \times 2 \times 3 \times 2 \times 7$
   c $11 \times 11 \times 2 \times 11 \times 11$ **d** $5 \times 3 \times 5 \times 3 \times 5 \times 3$
   e $7 \times 5 \times 5 \times 5 \times 7 \times 7 \times 3 \times 2$ **f** $17 \times 13 \times 3 \times 5 \times 13 \times 7 \times 17 \times 13 \times 5$

3 Write each of these numbers as a product of its prime factors.
   Give your answer in index form.
   a 20   **b** 28   **c** 48   **d** 56
   e 72   **f** 162   **g** 90   **h** 100

4 **a** Write the numbers 48, 144 and 432 as a product of their prime factors.
        Give your answers in index form.
     b Comment on a pattern.
     c Write down the next number in the pattern, in index form.

5 **a** Here are two possible different factor
        trees for 40
        Find two more different factor trees for 40
        What do you notice?
     b Draw all possible factor trees for 18

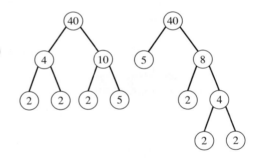

6 Write each of these numbers as a product of its prime factors.
   Give your answers in index form.
   a 132 **b** 156 **c** 250 **d** 400 **e** 480 **f** 620 **g** 720 **h** 900

7 Mark says that 2×6^3 is the same as 12^3
   Show that he is not correct.

8 Bev says that $(2 \times 3 \times 5)^2$ is the same as $2^2 \times 3^2 \times 5^2$
   Is she correct?
   Show your working.

9 Here are two numbers written as products of their prime factors.
   $2 \times 3 \times 5$ and $2 \times 3 \times 7$
   Is 6 a factor of both numbers? Explain your answer.

37.2 Highest common factor (HCF)

CAN YOU REMEMBER

- The meaning of 'factor', 'multiple', 'common factor', 'prime factor'?
- How to work out all the factors of a number?
- That every number has at least two factors, 1 and the number itself?
- How to write a number as a product of prime factors?

IN THIS SECTION YOU WILL

- Learn how to identify common factors of two numbers.
- Learn how to work out the highest common factor of two or more numbers.

Two numbers may have factors in common. The *highest common factor* (HCF) of two or more numbers is the *common factor* with the highest value.

To find the HCF of two or more numbers:

Method 1

- List all the factors of both numbers.
- Highlight the common factors.
- Find the common factor with the highest value.

Example 1

Work out the highest common factor (HCF) of 24 and 54

Solution 1

Work systematically to find the factors of both numbers.
Start with 1 and the number itself.

The factors of 24	The factors of 54
$1 \times 24 = 24$	$1 \times 54 = 54$
$2 \times 12 = 24$	$2 \times 27 = 54$
$3 \times 8 = 24$	$3 \times 18 = 54$
$4 \times 6 = 24$	$6 \times 9 = 54$

The factors of 24 are **1, 2, 3**, 4, ⑥, 8, 12, 24

The factors of 54 are **1, 2, 3**, ⑥, 9, 18, 27, 54

The highest common factor of 24 and 54 is 6

Exercise A

1 **i** Write down the factors of each number.

   ii Underline the common factors.

   iii Draw a circle around the highest common factor.

   a 8 and 12   **b** 15 and 25   **c** 12 and 24

   d 25 and 40   **e** 14 and 20   **f** 12 and 18

2 Find the highest common factor (HCF) of each of the following pairs of numbers.

   a 12 and 16   **b** 20 and 25   **c** 24 and 36

   d 18 and 32   **e** 16 and 28   **f** 14 and 42

   g 25 and 35   **h** 36 and 48

3 Find the highest common factor (HCF) of each of the following sets of numbers.

   a 10, 15 and 40   **b** 8, 12 and 20   **c** 9, 15 and 18

   d 8, 16 and 32   **e** 12, 18 and 22   **f** 18, 24 and 42

   g 25, 35 and 55   **h** 24, 36 and 48

4 Find the highest common factor (HCF) of each of the following pairs of numbers.

   a 48 and 54   **b** 36 and 72   **c** 24 and 84

   d 28 and 42   **e** 30 and 65   **f** 36 and 108

   g 40 and 88   **h** 56 and 108

5 Find the highest common factor (HCF) of each of the following sets of numbers.

   a 36, 42 and 54   **b** 16, 24 and 60   **c** 15, 24 and 39

   d 24, 60 and 72   **e** 15, 36 and 48   **f** 32, 42 and 56

   g 36, 48 and 90   **h** 25, 75 and 100

For very large numbers, it can take a long time to work out all the factor pairs.
Another method for finding the highest common factor of two or more numbers is:

Method 2

- Write each number as a product of its prime factors.
- Highlight any prime factors that are common to both numbers.
- Work out the product of the common prime factors – this is the HCF.

To simplify a fraction fully, divide both numbers by their highest common factor.
To factorise an expression completely, write the HCF of the terms outside the bracket.

Example 2

a Work out the highest common factor (HCF) of 16 and 24

b Use the highest common factor of 16 and 24 to simplify

   i $\dfrac{16}{24}$ **ii** $16x + 24$

Solution 2

a Write each number as a product of its prime factors.

$16 = \mathbf{2} \times \mathbf{2} \times \mathbf{2} \times 2$

$24 = \mathbf{2} \times \mathbf{2} \times \mathbf{2} \times 3$

Work out the product of the common factors:

$2 \times 2 \times 2 = 8$

The highest common factor (HCF) of 16 and 24 is 8

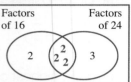

Show the factors on a diagram.

b **i** $\dfrac{16}{24} = \dfrac{16 \div 8}{24 \div 8} = \dfrac{2}{3}$ **ii** $16x = 8 \times 2x \quad 24 = 8 \times 3$

$16x + 24 = 8(2x + 3)$

Exercise B

1 **a** Work out the highest common factor of 32 and 48

  b Use the highest common factor of 32 and 48 to simplify $\frac{32}{48}$

2 Work out the highest common factor (HCF) of 30 and 25. Use the answer to factorise $30x + 25$

3 John says that the highest common factor of two numbers cannot be 1
Give an example to show that he is **not** correct.

4 Mary says that the highest common factor of two numbers cannot be one of the two numbers.
Give an example to show that she is **not** correct.

5 **a** Here are the first five multiples of 12

   12   24   36   48   60

  i What is the highest common factor (HCF) of all these multiples of 12?
  ii What is the highest common factor (HCF) of all multiples of 12?

  b Here are the first five multiples of 8

   8   16   24   32   40

  What is the highest common factor (HCF) of all multiples of 8?

  c Here are the first five multiples of x.

   x $2x$ $3x$ $4x$ $5x$

  What is the highest common factor (HCF) of all multiples of x?

6 **a** The HCF of 32 and another number is 16
The other number is between 40 and 50
What is it?

  b The HCF of 72 and another number is 24
The other number is between 90 and 100
What is it?

7 The highest common factor of two expressions is $2x$.
One of the two expressions is $6x$.
The other expression is larger than $6x$.
Write down one possibility for the other expression.

8 The highest common factor of two expressions is $5y$.
One of the two expressions is $20y$.
The other expression is smaller than $20y$.
Write down all the possibilities for the other expression.

37.3 Least common multiple (LCM)

CAN YOU REMEMBER

- The meaning of 'multiple'?
- The difference between a multiple and a factor?

IN THIS SECTION YOU WILL

- Find common multiples of two or more numbers.
- Learn how to work out the least common multiple of two or more numbers.
- Solve problems using least common multiples.

The *least common multiple* (LCM) of two or more numbers is the *common multiple* with the least (lowest) value.

For example,

3 has multiples 3, 6, 9, ⑫, 15, 18, 21, **24**, 27, 30, 33, **36**, ...

4 has multiples 4, 8, ⑫, 16, 20, **24**, 28, 32, **36**, ...

12, 24, 36, ... are common multiples of 3 and 4
The *least common multiple* of 3 and 4 is 12

To find the LCM of two or more numbers:

Method 1
- List the first few multiples of both numbers.
- Highlight the common multiples.
- Find the common multiple with the least value.

Example 1

Work out the least common multiple (LCM) of 8 and 12

Solution 1

The multiples of 8 are: 8, 16, ㉔, 32, 40, **48**, 56, 64, **72**, 80, ...

The multiples of 12 are: 12, ㉔, 36, **48**, 60, **72**, 84, ...

The common multiples of 8 and 12 are: 24, 48, 72, ... The LCM of 8 and 12 is 24

Exercise A

1 Write down the first ten multiples of each number.
Find the least common multiple of each pair of numbers.
a 3 and 4   **b** 5 and 6   **c** 3 and 9   **d** 6 and 8
e 8 and 10   **f** 6 and 9   **g** 10 and 15   **h** 6 and 7

2 Find the least common multiple (LCM) of each of the following sets of numbers.
a 3, 5 and 6   **b** 4, 5 and 10   **c** 3, 6 and 8
d 2, 4 and 7   **e** 5, 6 and 10   **f** 4, 5 and 6
g 2, 7 and 9   **h** 5, 8 and 10

3 Sausages are sold in packets of 10. Bread rolls are sold in packets of 12
Mrs Pate wants exactly the same number of each. She can only buy whole packets.
a Write down the first six multiples of 10 and 12
b What is the smallest number of sausages and bread rolls she can buy?
c Use the answer to **b** to work out the least number of packets of each she
should buy.

4 Arnold bangs his drum once every 4 seconds.
Fretwell bangs his drum once every 5 seconds.
Boswell bangs his drum once every 6 seconds.
They all start together.
How long is it before they again bang the drums at the same time?

5 Find the least common multiple (LCM) of each of the following pairs of numbers.
a 12 and 16   **b** 10 and 12   **c** 15 and 18   **d** 9 and 11
e 11 and 14   **f** 15 and 20   **g** 8 and 18   **h** 7 and 16

6 Find the least common multiple (LCM) of each of the following sets of numbers.
a 10, 12 and 15   **b** 8, 12 and 18   **c** 9, 12 and 15
d 8, 11 and 16   **e** 7, 8 and 12   **f** 7, 9 and 15
g 6, 15 and 20   **h** 8, 12 and 20

7 Rosie runs around a track in 54 seconds. Charlie runs around the same track in
72 seconds. They start together. How long is it before Rosie overtakes Charlie?

8 Trevor buys beans costing 28p per tin.
Belinda buys spaghetti costing 32p per tin.
They both spend the same amount.
What is the least amount that each could have spent?

The lowest common multiple (LCM) can be found without writing out lists of multiples.
Another method for finding the LCM of two or more numbers is:

Method 2
- Write each number as a product of its prime factors.
- Show all the factors of both numbers in a diagram.
- Work out the product of **all** these factors – this is the LCM.

Example 2

Work out the least common multiple (LCM) of 18 and 24

Solution 2

Write each number as a product of prime factors:

$18 = 2 \times 3 \times 3$

$24 = 2 \times 2 \times 2 \times 3$

The least common multiple is the product of **all** the factors of 18 and 24

So the LCM of 18 and 24 is $2 \times 2 \times 2 \times 3 \times 3 = 72$

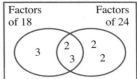

Show the factors on a diagram.

Exercise B

1 Write each number as a product of its prime factors and use a diagram to work out the least common multiple of

    a 15 and 40   **b** 14 and 35

2 Dietrich says that the least common multiple of two numbers cannot be one of the two numbers.

Give an example to show that he is **not** correct.

3 Polly says that the least common multiple of two numbers cannot be the product of the two numbers.

Give an example to show that she is **not** correct.

4 **a** Here are the factors of 12:   1   2   3   4   6   12

        What is the least common multiple (LCM) of all the factors of 12?

    b Here are the factors of 15:   1   3   5   15

        What is the least common multiple (LCM) of all the factors of 15?

    c What is the least common multiple (LCM) of all the factors of 80?

5 **a** Find the least common multiple (LCM) of the denominators of these two fractions: $\frac{1}{6}$ and $\frac{3}{10}$

    b Write each fraction as an equivalent fraction with the LCM of 6 and 10 as the denominator.

    c Add the two fractions. Write the answer in its simplest form.

    d Use the method from **a–c** to work out $\frac{2}{5} + \frac{3}{8}$

6 **a** The least common multiple (LCM) of 16 and one other number is 48

        The other number is between 20 and 30

        What is it?

    b The least common multiple (LCM) of two numbers is 180

        One of the numbers is between 40 and 50

        The other number is between 30 and 40

        What are the numbers?

7 x and y are both prime numbers.
Write down the least common multiple (LCM) of x and y.

8 x is even and y is odd.
Which statement is true?
A: The least common multiple (LCM) of x and y is even.
B: The least common multiple (LCM) of x and y is odd.
C: The least common multiple (LCM) of x and y could be odd or even.

Chapter summary

- The prime factors of a number are all its factors that are also prime numbers.
- Every number can be written as a product of prime factors.
- There are two methods of writing a number as a product of prime factors – the *repeated division* method and the *factor tree* method.
- A number can be written as a product of its prime factors using *index form*.
  For example, $36 = 2 \times 2 \times 3 \times 3 = 2^2 \times 3^2$
- The *highest common factor* (HCF) of two or more numbers is the common factor with the highest value.
- To find the HCF of two or more numbers:
  Method 1
  - List all the factors of both numbers.
  - Highlight the common factors.
  - Find the common factor with the highest value.
  Method 2
  - Write each number as a product of its prime factors.
  - Highlight any prime factors that are common to both numbers.
  - Work out the product of these common factors – this is the HCF.
- To simplify a fraction fully, divide the numerator and denominator by their highest common factor.
- To factorise an expression completely, write the HCF of the terms outside the bracket.
- The *least common multiple* (LCM) of two or more numbers is the common multiple with the least value.
- To find the LCM of two or more numbers:
  Method 1
  - List the first few multiples of both numbers.
  - Highlight the common multiples.
  - Find the common multiple with the least value.
  Method 2
  - Write each number as a product of its prime factors.
  - Show all the factors of both numbers in a diagram.
  - Work out the product of **all** these factors – this is the LCM.

Chapter review

1 a Express 24 as a product of its prime factors.
b Find the least common multiple (LCM) of 24 and 30

2 a Write 28 as a product of its prime factors.
b Find the least common multiple (LCM) of 28 and 35

3 a Write 18 as a product of its prime factors.
b What is the least common multiple (LCM) of 18 and 30

4 a Express 48 as a product of its prime factors.
Give your answer in index form.
b Find the highest common factor (HCF) of 18 and 48

5 a x and y are prime numbers.
$xy^2 = 50$
Find the values of x and y.
b Find the highest common factor of 50 and 75

6 a Express 54 as a product of its prime factors.
Give your answer in index form.
b Find the highest common factor (HCF) of 54 and 36

7 45 expressed as a product of prime factors in index form is $3^2 \times 5$
a Express 36 as a product of its prime factors.
Give your answer in index form.
b What is the highest common factor (HCF) of 45 and 36

8 Drinks are in packs of 24
Sandwiches are in packs of 18
A café wants the same number of drinks and sandwiches.
What is the lowest number of packs of drinks and sandwiches they could have?

9 What is the lowest number that is a multiple of both 14 and 15?

10 Cereal is sold in 500 gram boxes and costs £1.60 per box.
Coffee is sold in 300 gram jars and costs £4.20 per jar.
Harriet buys the same number of grams of cereal and coffee.
What is the least that she could have spent?

Averages for large data sets

38.1 Mean for grouped data

IN THIS SECTION YOU WILL

- Learn how to write data in groups.
- Learn how to find the midpoint of a group.
- Learn how to find an estimate of the mean for a grouped frequency distribution.
- Understand why the value found is only an estimate.

A large set of data should be put into groups.

For example, data on the heights, in metres, of 40 sunflower plants has been grouped in this table.

A frequency distribution where the data is in groups is called a *grouped frequency distribution.*

The group $0.8 \leqslant h < 1.0$ includes all the plants with heights from 0.8 m up to but

Height (h) metres	Frequency (f)
$0.8 \leqslant h < 1.0$	1
$1.0 \leqslant h < 1.2$	5
$1.2 \leqslant h < 1.4$	12
$1.4 \leqslant h < 1.6$	16
$1.6 \leqslant h < 1.8$	4
$1.8 \leqslant h < 2.0$	2

not including 1.0 m. A plant with height 1.0 m would be recorded in the next group.

In grouped data, the groups are sometimes called *class intervals.*

A grouped frequency distribution does not show the exact values of the original data, so an exact mean cannot be calculated.
Instead, the *midpoints* or *mid values* of the groups are used to

calculate an estimate of the mean, using the formula $\dfrac{\Sigma fx}{\Sigma f}$, where f is

the frequency for each group and x is the midpoint for each group.

Always check that the mean calculated is sensible. For most data sets it will be close to the 'middle' of the data values.

Example 1

a Calculate an estimate of the mean height of the sunflower plants from the previous table.

b Explain why the value in part **a** is only an estimate.

Solution 1

a Add two extra columns to the table, one for the midpoints x and one for the calculation of fx.

Add an extra row to the table for the totals of f and fh.

Calculate the midpoint for each group. For the group $0.8 \leqslant h \leqslant 1.0$, the midpoint is $\dfrac{0.8 + 1.0}{2} = 0.9$ and so on.

Height (h) metres	Frequency (f)	Midpoint (h)	fh
$0.8 \leqslant h < 1.0$	1	0.9	0.9
$1.0 \leqslant h < 1.2$	5	1.1	5.5
$1.2 \leqslant h < 1.4$	12	1.3	15.6
$1.4 \leqslant h < 1.6$	16	1.5	24.0
$1.6 \leqslant h < 1.8$	4	1.7	6.8
$1.8 \leqslant h < 2.0$	2	1.9	3.8
	$\Sigma f = 40$		$\Sigma fh = 56.6$

An estimate for the mean is $\dfrac{\Sigma fh}{\Sigma f} = \dfrac{56.6}{40} = 1.415$ metres

Check: the range of data values is from 0.8 to 2.0, so the middle of this range is 1.4   The value calculated is close to this middle value.

b This value is only an estimate because the exact values of each of the 40 heights are not known. The midpoints are estimates for the mean value for each group.

Exercise A

1 The grouped frequency distribution represents the lengths of 20 phone calls Natasha made.

Length of call (l minutes)	Frequency (f)	Midpoint (l)	fl
$0 \leqslant l < 6$	4	3	12
$6 \leqslant l < 12$	7		
$12 \leqslant l < 18$	9		
	$\Sigma f =$		$\Sigma fl =$

   a   Explain why the midpoint of the first group is 3
   b   Copy the table and complete the midpoint column.
   c   Complete the fl column.
   d   Calculate Σfl and Σf.
   e   Find an estimate of the mean length of Natasha's phone calls.

2   The grouped frequency distribution shows the length of ten worms (in cm) that Zoë dug up in her garden.

Length of worm, l (cm)	Frequency (f)	Midpoint (l)	fl
$2 \leqslant l < 6$	4		
$6 \leqslant l < 10$	5		
$10 \leqslant l < 14$	1		
	$\Sigma f =$		$\Sigma fl =$

   a   Copy and complete the table.
   b   Find an estimate of the mean length of worm dug up.

3   Jarnail collects information from a police officer about the speeds of the first 30 cars going past his school. The data is in the form of the grouped frequency distribution here.

Speed, s (mph)	Frequency (f)
$20 \leqslant s < 30$	21
$30 \leqslant s < 40$	6
$40 \leqslant s < 50$	3

   a   Copy the table.
       Add extra columns for the midpoint of each group and the value of fs.
       Complete these columns.
   b   Hence find an estimate of the average speed of these 30 cars.

4   For each part, calculate an estimate of the mean of the grouped frequency distributions.
   a   The table shows the heights of 50 men (in cm).

Height, h (cm)	Frequency (f)
$120 \leqslant h < 140$	4
$140 \leqslant h < 160$	17
$160 \leqslant h < 180$	21
$180 \leqslant h < 200$	8

   b   The table shows the length (in seconds) of 117 hit records.

Length of time, t (secs)	Frequency (f)
$120 \leqslant t < 150$	1
$150 \leqslant t < 180$	7
$180 \leqslant t < 210$	34
$210 \leqslant t < 240$	54
$240 \leqslant t < 270$	19
$270 \leqslant t < 300$	2

c The table shows the weight (in grams) of 59 apples.

Weight of apple, w (g)	Frequency (f)
$20 \leqslant w < 40$	5
$40 \leqslant w < 50$	16
$50 \leqslant w < 55$	13
$55 \leqslant w < 60$	22
$60 \leqslant w < 100$	3

When grouping data:
- Use equal-sized groups or class intervals where possible
- Use the lowest value in the data to decide where to start the first group
- Use the highest value in the data to decide where to end the last group
- Choose class intervals that give between four and ten class intervals in total.

Example 2

The data shows the time taken (in seconds) for 30 teachers to complete an obstacle course. The data has been rounded to one decimal place.

57.6	45.2	87.3	64.0	55.6	59.1	40.6	60.0	49.8	63.7
78.5	46.2	72.7	96.0	78.9	67.3	66.1	64.5	50.3	47.2
66.8	44.4	99.3	50.2	64.7	71.5	84.3	88.8	67.1	53.4

a Calculate the mean of this data.
b Construct a grouped frequency distribution using groups of width 10
c Calculate an estimate of the mean of the grouped frequency distribution.
d **i** Use your answers to **a** and **c** to calculate the percentage error generated by grouping the data and calculating an estimate of the mean.
   ii Comment on your answer.
e Thirty sixth-form students also completed the obstacle course. The students' fastest time was 37.5 seconds, their slowest time was 116.7 seconds, and their mean was 62.8 seconds.
Compare the students' and teachers' times.

Solution 2

a the mean $= \dfrac{\text{total of all the values}}{\text{total number of values}}$

$= \dfrac{1941.1}{30} = 64.703... = 64.7$ seconds (one decimal place)

b Lowest $= 40.6$ so the first group should start at 40
Highest $= 99.3$ so the final group should end at 100
The groups have width 10, so are $40 \leqslant x < 50$ and so on.

Time taken, t (seconds)	Tally	Frequency
$40 \leqslant t < 50$	卌		6
$50 \leqslant t < 60$	卌		6
$60 \leqslant t < 70$	卌 ||||	9
$70 \leqslant t < 80$	||||	4
$80 \leqslant t < 90$	|||	3
$90 \leqslant t < 100$	||	2

c Add two extra columns for the midpoints, t, and for ft, and an extra row for totalling.

Time taken, t (seconds)	Frequency (f)	Midpoint (t)	ft
$40 \leqslant t < 50$	6	45	270
$50 \leqslant t < 60$	6	55	330
$60 \leqslant t < 70$	9	65	585
$70 \leqslant t < 80$	4	75	300
$80 \leqslant t < 90$	3	85	255
$90 \leqslant t < 100$	2	95	190
	$\Sigma f = 30$		$\Sigma ft = 1930$

$$\text{An estimate for the mean} = \frac{\Sigma ft}{\Sigma f} = \frac{1930}{30} = 64.333\ldots = 64.3 \text{ seconds (1 d.p.)}$$

d **i** Error $= 64.333 - 64.703 = -0.37$

$$\text{Percentage error} = \frac{\text{actual error}}{\text{correct value}} \times 100$$

$$= \frac{-0.37}{64.703} \times 100 = -0.57184\ldots = -0.57\% \text{ (two decimal places)}$$

   ii The error value is negative, which means that the estimate for the mean is lower than the true value. The percentage error is very small, because the estimate is close to the true value.

e The range for the teachers' times is $99.3 - 40.6 = 58.7$ seconds.
The students had a larger range of times (79.2 seconds).
The mean time for the teachers (64.7 seconds) is greater than the mean time for the students (62.8 seconds). So on average, the teachers took longer than the students.

Exercise B

1 The lengths of 40 bananas are measured. The smallest banana is 14.6 cm. The largest banana is 29.4 cm. The data is grouped into class intervals of length 5 cm.

The first group is labelled $10 \leqslant l < 15$
Write down the labels for the rest of the groups.

2 Lawrence looks up the lengths of some motorways in a road atlas.
The shortest motorway is 3.2 miles. The longest motorway is 204.6 miles.
Lawrence groups the data into groups of 50 miles.
List the group labels Lawrence should have in his table.

3 Louise says that it is not possible for the estimated mean of a grouped frequency
distribution to be exactly the same as the true mean for the original data.
Is Louise correct? Explain your answer.

4 The times taken for 40 Year-11 pupils to complete a set of maths questions are
recorded below (to the nearest 0.1 minutes).

15.2	21.0	14.9	8.6	7.2	16.3	20.5	16.6	19.2	18.1
9.1	26.3	24.1	15.8	17.3	6.4	12.5	20.8	14.6	22.2
15.5	15.0	7.8	16.2	14.6	21.6	29.4	10.4	21.6	15.5
10.0	21.5	14.7	17.4	13.5	23.4	16.6	11.1	28.0	16.7

a Find the range of the times taken.
b Copy and complete the grouped frequency distribution table.

Time taken, t (minutes)	Tally	Frequency (f)
$5 \leqslant t < 10$		
$10 \leqslant t < 10$		

c Add extra columns to the table for the midpoints and ft.
d Add an extra row for the totals Σf and Σft. Hence find an estimate for the mean
time taken by the Year-11 pupils to complete the set of questions.
e The same questions were attempted by 40 Year-9 pupils. The mean time was
21.7 seconds and the range was 32.5 seconds.
Compare the performances of the Year-9 and Year-11 pupils on these maths
questions.

5 Terry has spilt water on his book.
The first label in his grouped frequency
table is now missing but he suspects
it is $10 \leqslant x < 20$
The estimated mean based on this
table is 37
Show that Terry is correct.

Length, x (metres)	Frequency
	5
$20 \leqslant x < 30$	12
$30 \leqslant x < 40$	24
$40 \leqslant x < 50$	22
$50 \leqslant x < 60$	7

6 20 snails were raced over a course of 25 centimetres. The times for each snail to complete the course are given below, in seconds, to one decimal place.

| 39.6 | 45.1 | 76.4 | 54.7 | 30.2 | 70.0 | 54.7 | 33.3 | 63.6 | 54.1 |
| 58.4 | 62.7 | 44.7 | 75.8 | 51.9 | 64.3 | 40.7 | 52.3 | 60.8 | 37.8 |

a Calculate the mean time for the snails to complete the course.
b Hence calculate the mean time for a snail to travel 1 metre.
c Put the data in groups of length 10. Make the first group $30 \leqslant t < 40$ and the final group $70 \leqslant t < 80$
  Draw up a grouped frequency distribution table and fill in the frequencies.
d Hence calculate an estimate of the mean for this grouped frequency distribution.
e Explain why the value calculated in **d** is an estimate.
f What is the percentage error caused by grouping the data and finding the estimate? Comment on your answer.

38.2 Finding the median for frequency distributions

CAN YOU REMEMBER

- How to find the median for a list of numbers?

IN THIS SECTION YOU WILL

- Find the median for a discrete frequency distribution.
- Find the group containing the median for a grouped frequency distribution.

When discrete data has been collected in a frequency table, the data is already ordered.

To find the median:

Step 1 Work out the total frequency $n = \Sigma f$.

Step 2 Work out $\dfrac{n + 1}{2}$ to find the position of the median in the data.

Step 3 Count along the frequencies until the class containing the median is reached.

If n is 50 or more, $\dfrac{n}{2}$ can be used to calculate the position of the median.

Example 1

A fair 4-sided die is rolled several times. The discrete frequency distribution shows the number of times each score occurs.

Find the median score on the die.

Die score	Number of times
1	8
2	7
3	10
4	5

Solution 1

Step 1 $n = 8 + 7 + 10 + 5 = 30$

Step 2 The position of the median is the $\dfrac{30 + 1}{2}$th = 15.5th value.

Add a third column showing the running total of the frequencies. This makes it easier to find the position of the median.
So the median is the mean of the 15th and 16th values

Die score	Number of times	Running total
1	8	8
2	7	8 + 7 = 15
3	10	15 + 10 = 25
4	5	25 + 5 = 30

Step 3 The 15th value is a 2 and the 16th value is a 3
So the median is $\dfrac{2 + 3}{2} = 2.5$

Exercise A

1 The number of fish caught by some anglers one morning is shown in the table.

Number of fish caught	Frequency
0	3
1	12
2	21
3	10
4	4

Find the median number of fish caught.

2 The number of times the children in a class of 25 are going on holiday in the next year is recorded in the table.

Number of holidays (x)	Frequency (f)
0	6
1	14
2	4
3	1

Find the median number of holidays.

3 The table shows the number of days' rain each week for 10 weeks.

Find the median number of days of rain per week.

Days of rain (x)	Number of times (f)
0	1
1	0
2	2
3	3
4	1
5	1
6	2
7	0

4 The table shows the number of
weddings held per week at a large
hotel over a long period of time.

Find the median number of
weddings held per week.

Number of weddings (x)	Frequency (f)
3	21
4	63
5	57
6	14
7	7

5 The number of red sweets in
50 mixed bags of the sweets
was counted.
The table shows the results.

Find the median number of
red sweets per bag.

Number of red sweets	Frequency
3	21
4	15
5	10
6	2
7	1
8	1

6 The frequency distribution shows some
of the number of times Oliver went
fishing per week over one year.

Find the median number of times
Oliver went fishing during the year.

Number of times Oliver went fishing	Frequency
1	7
2	19
3	13
4	10
5	3

A grouped frequency distribution does not give the original data values.

For a grouped frequency distribution:
- The median value cannot be found (instead, find the group that contains the median)
- The range cannot be found, as the exact highest and lowest values are not known
- The modal class (the class with the highest frequency) can be identified.

Example 2

The frequency distribution on page 720 shows the heights, h, of 40 sunflower plants in
metres.
a Find the group that contains the median.
b Find the modal class.

Solution 2

a **Step 1** $n = 40$

Step 2 The position of the median is the $\dfrac{40 + 1}{2}$th = 20.5th value.

This is the average of the 20th and 21st values.

Step 3 Add a running total column to the table.

Height, h metres	Frequency	Running total
$0.8 \leqslant h < 1.0$	1	1
$1.0 \leqslant h < 1.2$	5	6
$1.2 \leqslant h < 1.4$	12	18
$1.4 \leqslant h < 1.6$	16	34
$1.6 \leqslant h < 1.8$	4	38
$1.8 \leqslant h < 2.0$	2	40

The 20th and 21st values both lie in the group $1.4 \leqslant h < 1.6$

Step 4 The median is in the group $1.4 \leqslant h < 1.6$

b The modal class is also $1.4 \leqslant h < 1.6$

Exercise B

1 The grouped frequency distribution represents the lengths of 20 internet sessions

Find the group which contains the median.

Length of session, t (minutes)	Frequency (f)
$1 \leqslant t < 7$	4
$7 \leqslant t < 13$	7
$13 \leqslant t < 19$	9

2 The grouped frequency distribution shows the widths of 10 toy cars (w cm).

Find the group which contains the median width of toy car.

Width of toy car, w (cm)	Frequency (f)
$2 \leqslant w < 8$	4
$8 \leqslant w < 14$	5
$14 \leqslant w < 20$	1

3 A speed trap records the following information about the speeds of 30 cars. The data is in the form of the grouped frequency distribution.
   a Find the group which contains the median speed.
   b Which is the modal group?

Speed, s (mph)	Frequency (f)
$20 \leqslant s < 30$	14
$30 \leqslant s < 40$	13
$40 \leqslant s < 50$	3

4 The table shows the heights of 50 athletes (h, in cm)
   a Find the group that contains the median height.
   b Which is the modal group?

Height, h (cm)	Frequency (f)
$120 \leqslant h < 140$	4
$140 \leqslant h < 160$	22
$160 \leqslant h < 180$	16
$180 \leqslant h < 200$	8

5 The table shows the lengths (in seconds) of 100 speeches in the House of Commons.

Length of speech, t (seconds)	Frequency (f)
$120 \leqslant t < 150$	2
$150 \leqslant t < 180$	7
$180 \leqslant t < 210$	31
$210 \leqslant t < 240$	50
$240 \leqslant t < 270$	8
$270 \leqslant t < 300$	2

Find the group that contains the median length of speech.

6 The table shows the weight (w, in grams) of 59 oranges.

Weight of orange, w (g)	Frequency (f)
$10 \leqslant w < 40$	5
$40 \leqslant w < 70$	16
$70 \leqslant w < 95$	13
$95 \leqslant w < 130$	22
$130 \leqslant w < 160$	3

Find the group within which the median weight of orange lies.

7 20 snails were raced over a course of 25 centimetres. The times for each snail to complete the course are given below in seconds to one decimal place.

| 39.6 | 45.1 | 76.4 | 54.7 | 30.2 | 70.0 | 54.7 | 33.3 | 63.6 | 54.1 |
| 58.4 | 62.7 | 44.7 | 75.8 | 51.9 | 64.3 | 40.7 | 52.3 | 60.8 | 37.8 |

   a Write the data in order. Find the median length of snail.
   b Write the data in a frequency distribution table, with groups $30 \leqslant x < 40$, $40 \leqslant x < 50$, etc.
   c Find the group within which the median length lies.
   d Comment on your answers to **a** and **c**.

8 The grouped frequency table shows the time taken, t, for a group of Year-11 students to complete some maths problems.

Time taken, t (minutes)	Frequency
$5 \leqslant t < 10$	6
$10 \leqslant t < 15$	13
$15 \leqslant t < 20$	10
$20 \leqslant t < 25$	9
$25 \leqslant t < 30$	2

   a Show that the median lies in the group $15 \leqslant t < 20$

   b Three absent pupils who completed the test at a later date, all took under 15 minutes to complete the test. Does this change which group contains the median?

9 The incomplete frequency distribution table shows the weights of 37 cookies (in g).

The median lies in the group $30 \leqslant w < 35$ Copy and complete the table to show one possible set of frequencies.

Weight, w (g)	Frequency
$15 \leqslant w < 20$	3
$20 \leqslant w < 25$	
$25 \leqslant w < 30$	
$30 \leqslant w < 35$	
$35 \leqslant w < 40$	17

38.3 Frequency polygons

CAN YOU REMEMBER

- How to collect data into a grouped frequency distribution?
- How to find the midpoint of a group?

IN THIS SECTION YOU WILL

- Learn how to draw a frequency polygon for a grouped frequency distribution.

A *frequency polygon* is a line graph that shows the shape of a grouped frequency distribution.
It is constructed by plotting the frequency against the midpoint for each class interval.

Example 1

The frequency distribution shows the heights of 40 sunflower plants in metres measured to the nearest centimetre.

Draw a frequency polygon for this frequency distribution.

Height (x)	Frequency (f)
$0.8 \leqslant x < 1.0$	1
$1.0 \leqslant x < 1.2$	5
$1.2 \leqslant x < 1.4$	12
$1.4 \leqslant x < 1.6$	16
$1.6 \leqslant x < 1.8$	4
$1.8 \leqslant x < 2.0$	2

Solution 1

Work out the midpoint for each group, then plot it against the frequency for that group.

Height (x)	Midpoint	Frequency (f)	Coordinates
$0.8 \leqslant x < 1.0$	0.9	1	(0.9, 1)
$1.0 \leqslant x < 1.2$	1.1	5	(1.1, 5)
$1.2 \leqslant x < 1.4$	1.3	12	(1.3, 12)
$1.4 \leqslant x < 1.6$	1.5	16	(1.5, 16)
$1.6 \leqslant x < 1.8$	1.7	4	(1.7, 4)
$1.8 \leqslant x < 2.0$	1.9	2	(1.9, 2)

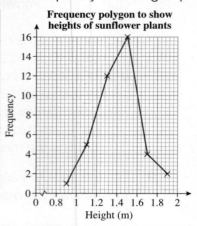

Frequency polygon to show heights of sunflower plants

Join the points with straight lines.

Exercise A

1 The frequency distribution shows the heights of 50 horses (in cm).

Height, h (cm)	Midpoints	Frequency (f)	Coordinates
$120 \leqslant h < 140$		4	
$140 \leqslant h < 160$		17	
$160 \leqslant h < 180$		21	
$180 \leqslant h < 200$		8	

a Copy the table and complete the midpoints column.
b Complete the coordinates column.
c Draw the frequency polygon.
  Use a horizontal scale of 1 cm to 10 cm, starting at 100 cm.

2 The table shows the lengths of time of 117 theatre shows (in minutes).

Length of time, l (min)	Frequency (f)
$120 \leqslant l < 150$	1
$150 \leqslant l < 180$	7
$180 \leqslant l < 210$	34
$210 \leqslant l < 240$	54
$240 \leqslant l < 270$	19
$270 \leqslant l < 300$	2

Draw the frequency polygon.

3 The frequency table shows the time taken (in minutes) for 30 people to complete a fun run.

Time taken, t (minutes)	Frequency (f)
$45 \leqslant t < 55$	6
$55 \leqslant t < 65$	6
$65 \leqslant t < 75$	9
$75 \leqslant t < 85$	4
$85 \leqslant t < 95$	3
$95 \leqslant t < 105$	2

Draw the frequency polygon.

4 The time taken for 40 Year-7 pupils to complete a set of science questions is recorded in the grouped frequency distribution.

Time taken, t (minutes)	Frequency (f)
$5 \leqslant t < 10$	5
$10 \leqslant t < 15$	9
$15 \leqslant t < 20$	14
$20 \leqslant t < 25$	9
$25 \leqslant t < 30$	3

Draw the frequency polygon.

5 The table shows the weight (in grams) of 53 pears.

Weight of pear, w (g)	Frequency (f)
$20 \leqslant w < 40$	5
$40 \leqslant w < 50$	16
$50 \leqslant w < 55$	13
$55 \leqslant w < 60$	16
$60 \leqslant w < 100$	3

Draw the frequency polygon.

6 The data represents the weights of 30 babies (in kg) born during the same week at a maternity hospital.

3.4	2.1	4.7	3.5	4.4	2.5	2.6	3.0	4.5	5.2
3.4	3.6	2.0	4.9	1.8	3.3	3.6	3.7	3.4	4.5
4.8	1.5	3.8	2.7	2.2	3.6	4.2	4.0	4.9	3.4

Collect the data into a copy of the table below.
Draw a frequency polygon to illustrate the data.

Weight of baby, w (kg)	Tally	Frequency (f)
$1 \leqslant w < 2$		
$2 \leqslant w < 3$		
$3 \leqslant w < 4$		
$4 \leqslant w < 5$		
$5 \leqslant w < 6$		

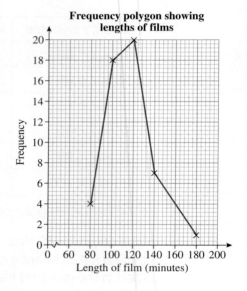

Frequency polygon showing
lengths of films

Example 2

Scarlett drew the following frequency polygon for the lengths of 50 films.
Construct the grouped frequency table from which the frequency polygon was drawn.

Solution 2

The points are plotted at the midpoints of the groups.
So the midpoints are
80, 100, 120, 140, 180
These are mostly 20 minutes apart, so the width of most groups is 20 minutes.
The 20 minute group with midpoint 80 is $70 \leqslant x < 90$
The next group is $90 \leqslant x < 110$ and so on.

The last group is $150 \leqslant x < 210$

The frequency for each group can be read off the graph.
The grouped frequency table is:

Length of film (x, minutes)	Frequency
$70 \leqslant x < 90$	4
$90 \leqslant x < 110$	18
$110 \leqslant x < 130$	20
$130 \leqslant x < 150$	7
$150 \leqslant x < 210$	1

Exercise B

1 The frequency polygon below represents the time before the Terriers football team concede their first goal in each game. (Assume that they always concede at least one goal.)

Construct the grouped frequency table that corresponds to this frequency polygon.

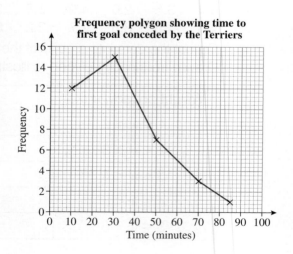

Frequency polygon showing time to
first goal conceded by the Terriers

2 The grouped frequency distribution below shows the weights of 40 steaks served in a restaurant.

Ishmail drew the following frequency polygon to illustrate this data.

Weight of steak (ounces)	Frequency
$6 \leqslant w < 8$	4
$8 \leqslant w < 10$	11
$10 \leqslant w < 12$	13
$12 \leqslant w < 16$	9
$16 \leqslant w < 24$	3

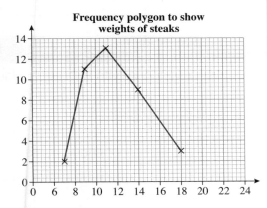

There are four errors in Ishmail's graph. Make a list of his errors.

3 The frequency polygon below shows the heights of some primary school students in cm.

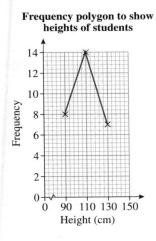

Use the frequency polygon to calculate an estimate of the mean height of the students.

> You may want to construct the grouped frequency distribution and add an fx column

4 The frequency distribution shows the times achieved by couples in the UK standing-still championships.
100 couples took part in the championships.
Draw a frequency polygon for the data. Use graph paper.

Time standing still, t (minutes)	Frequency
$0 \leqslant t < 100$	$4t$
$100 \leqslant t < 200$	$3t$
$200 \leqslant t < 300$	$2t$
$300 \leqslant t < 400$	t

38.4 Histograms for continuous data with equal class widths

■   How to draw bar charts for discrete data?

IN THIS SECTION YOU WILL

■   Learn how to draw a histogram for grouped continuous data with equal class widths.
■   Understand the differences between a histogram and a bar chart.

A *histogram* is a frequency diagram drawn to show grouped continuous data.

A histogram looks similar to a bar chart but with some very important differences.

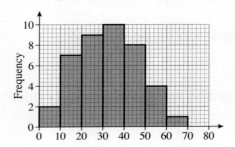

On a histogram:
■   There are no gaps between the bars
■   The x-axis is labelled as a continuous scale, in the same way as a graph axis
■   The **area** of each bar represents the frequency. In this section, all the groups are of equal width, so the height also represents the frequency.

Example 1

The frequency distribution shows the lengths of 20 roads in one town in kilometres.

Draw a histogram for this grouped frequency distribution.

Length (x) kilometres	Frequency (f)
$0.8 \leqslant x < 1.0$	0
$1.0 \leqslant x < 1.2$	3
$1.2 \leqslant x < 1.4$	6
$1.4 \leqslant x < 1.6$	8
$1.6 \leqslant x < 1.8$	2
$1.8 \leqslant x < 2.0$	1

Solution 1

The widths of the bars are given by the class intervals. The bars are all the same width, so the heights of the bars are given by the frequency.

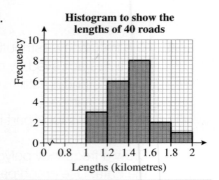

Exercise A

1 The table shows the weights of 50 cows (in kg)

Weight, x (kg)	Frequency (f)
$220 \leqslant x < 240$	4
$240 \leqslant x < 260$	17
$260 \leqslant x < 280$	21
$280 \leqslant x < 300$	8

Draw a histogram for this data.
Begin the horizontal axis at 200 kg.
Use a scale of 1 cm to 20 kg.
Use a scale of 1 cm to 2 cows for the vertical axis.

2 The table shows the length, in seconds, of 100 records by a famous group.

Length of time, t (secs)	Frequency (f)
$120 \leqslant t < 150$	1
$150 \leqslant t < 180$	7
$180 \leqslant t < 210$	26
$210 \leqslant t < 240$	45
$240 \leqslant t < 270$	19
$270 \leqslant t < 300$	2

Draw a histogram to show this data.

3 The frequency table shows the time taken (in seconds) for 30 teachers to complete an obstacle course.

Use this information to draw a histogram.

Time taken, t (seconds)	Frequency (f)
$40 \leqslant t < 50$	6
$50 \leqslant t < 60$	6
$60 \leqslant t < 70$	9
$70 \leqslant t < 80$	4
$80 \leqslant t < 90$	3
$90 \leqslant t < 100$	2

4 The time taken for 50 pupils to complete a questionnaire on homework is recorded in the grouped frequency distribution.

Draw a histogram.

Time taken, t (minutes)	Frequency (f)
$15 \leqslant t < 20$	5
$20 \leqslant t < 25$	9
$25 \leqslant t < 30$	24
$30 \leqslant t < 35$	9
$35 \leqslant t < 40$	3

5 The table shows the weight (in grams) of 60 apples.

Draw a histogram to show this data.

Weight of apple, w (g)	Frequency (f)
$20 \leqslant w < 30$	5
$30 \leqslant w < 40$	16
$40 \leqslant w < 50$	13
$50 \leqslant w < 60$	22
$60 \leqslant w < 70$	4

Example 2

The histogram shows the weights of 30 baskets
of strawberries.
a   What is the modal group?
b   Use the histogram to find an estimate of the mean
    weight of a basket of strawberries.
c   Ayeisha says, 'The range of the weights of the
    baskets is 4 kg.'
    Is Ayeisha correct? Explain your answer.

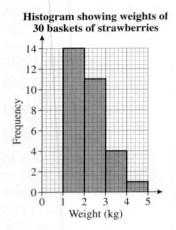

**Histogram showing weights of
30 baskets of strawberries**

Solution 2

a   Modal group is $1 \leqslant w < 2$

b

Weight, w (kg)	Frequency (f)	Midpoint (w)	fw
$1 \leqslant w < 2$	14	1.5	21
$2 \leqslant w < 3$	11	2.5	27.5
$3 \leqslant w < 4$	4	3.5	14
$4 \leqslant w < 5$	1	4.5	4.5
	$\Sigma f = 30$		$\Sigma fx = 67$

$$\text{Mean} = \frac{\Sigma fw}{\Sigma f} = \frac{67}{30} = 2.233\ldots \text{ kg}$$

c   Since the data is grouped, the actual weights are not known, so it is not possible
    to calculate the range.

Exercise B

1   The histogram shows the ages of 40 tourists
    on a visit to London.
    a   What is the modal age group?
    b   Calculate an estimate of the mean age of
        the tourists.
    c   In which group does the median age lie?
    d   Jack says, 'There are more tourists in their 20s
        than in their 40s.' Jill says that you cannot tell.
        Who is correct?
        Explain your answer.

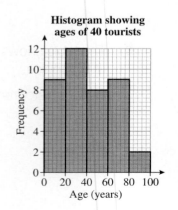

**Histogram showing
ages of 40 tourists**

2 The frequency polygon shows the lengths of 49 films.

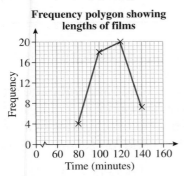

Construct the histogram for this data.

> You may wish to construct the grouped frequency distribution first.

3 Data is collected for the length of time, t, that 40 people can hold their breath.
The data is put into 20-second groups. The first group is $20 \leqslant t < 40$
The longest any of the people could hold their breath was 1 minute 52 seconds.
   a How many groups of data are there?
   b The frequency for the first group is 14. The frequencies for the remaining groups decrease in equal 'steps' finishing at 2 for the last group.
   Draw a histogram to show the data.

4 The times taken, t minutes, for customers' meals to arrive in a restaurant are recorded.
The results are:

8	12	16	9	18	19	24	7	16	24	11	29
14	10	18	9	12	24	22	16	23	20	10	7
16	17	25	13	6	18	15	16	24	20	16	17

Draw a histogram for this data. Use equal-sized groups starting with $5 \leqslant t < 10$

5 The histogram shows the lengths of a number of fossils dug up on an archaeological site.
   a Explain why the median fossil length could not be 31 mm.
   b If the fossils were measured in centimetres, in what way would the histogram change?
   c More fossils are found. It **is** possible now that the median is 31 mm.
   Draw a histogram which could represent **all** the fossils.

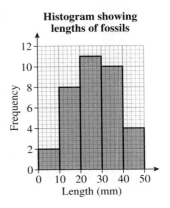

Chapter summary

- A large set of data should be put into groups.
- A frequency distribution where the data is in groups is called a *grouped frequency distribution*.
- In grouped data, the groups are sometimes called *class intervals*. The group $0.8 \leqslant x < 1.0$ includes all the values from 0.8 up to but not including 1.0
- A grouped frequency distribution does not show the exact values of the original data, so an exact mean cannot be calculated. Instead, an estimate of the mean is calculated, using the formula $\frac{\Sigma fx}{\Sigma f}$, where f is the frequency for each group and x is the midpoint for each group.
- Always check that the mean calculated is sensible. For most data sets it will be close to the 'middle' of the data values.
- When grouping data:
  - Use equal-sized groups or class intervals
  - Use the lowest value in the data to decide where to start the first group
  - Use the highest value in the data to decide where to end the last group
  - Choose class intervals that give between four and ten class intervals in total.
- To find the median for a set of discrete data in a frequency table:

  Step 1 Work out the total frequency $n = \Sigma f$.

  Step 2 Work out $\frac{n+1}{2}$ to find the position of the median in the data.

  Step 3 Count along the frequencies until the class containing the median is reached.

- If n is 50 or more, $\frac{n}{2}$ can be used to calculate the position of the median.
- For a grouped frequency distribution:
  - The median value cannot be found (instead find the group that contains the median)
  - The range cannot be found, as the exact highest and lowest values are not known
  - The modal class (the class with the highest frequency) can be identified.

- A *frequency polygon* is a line graph that shows the shape of a grouped frequency distribution. It is constructed by plotting the frequency against the midpoint for each class interval.
- A *histogram* is a frequency diagram drawn to show grouped continuous data.
- On a histogram:
  - There are no gaps between the bars
  - The x-axis is labelled as a continuous scale, in the same way as a graph axis
  - The **area** of each bar represents the frequency. When the groups are of equal width, the height also represents the frequency.

Chapter review

1 The frequency polygon shows the height of 45 male pole-vaulters.

  a From the frequency polygon, what is the modal height for a male pole-vaulter?

  b Construct the grouped frequency distribution of pole-vaulter heights.

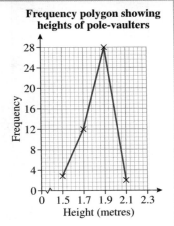

Frequency polygon showing heights of pole-vaulters

2 Five more pole-vaulters were added to the data for Question 2
Their heights were 1.57 m, 2.00 m, 1.88 m, 2.24 m and 2.13 m.
Construct a histogram to represent all 50 pole-vaulters' heights.

3 Victoria keeps a record of the time it takes the school bus to take her from her home to school. Her record for last month is shown in the table.

Time, t minutes	Frequency	Midpoint
$10 < t \leqslant 12$	5	
$12 < t \leqslant 14$	10	
$14 < t \leqslant 16$	4	
$16 < t \leqslant 18$	1	

  a Complete the midpoint column and use it to calculate an estimate of the mean time.

  b There are 200 school days in the year. Use the information in the table to estimate the number of days in a year on which Victoria's bus journey takes more than 14 minutes. (Victoria never misses a day of school!)

  c What is the probability that, on a randomly chosen day, the journey takes less than or equal to 12 minutes?

4 For this frequency distribution the estimated mean was calculated to be 10
The total frequency is 40

  a Find the missing frequency *.

  b Hence show the estimated mean was calculated correctly.

Length (cm)	Frequency
$0 \leqslant x < 4$	4
$4 \leqslant x < 8$	8
$8 \leqslant x < 12$	16
$12 \leqslant x < 16$	8
$16 \leqslant x < 20$	*

5

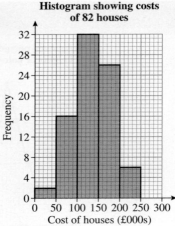

Histogram showing costs of 82 houses

Cost of houses (£000s)

The histogram shows the cost of 82 different houses sold in one city.

a   What is the modal group?

b   In which group does the median lie?

c   Calculate an estimate of the mean house price.

6   The grouped frequency distribution shows the length, x, in minutes of 100 tracks on rock CDs.

a   In which group does the median length of track lie?

b   Calculate an estimate of the mean length of track.

c   Draw a frequency polygon to display this data.

Length	Frequency
$0 \leqslant x < 2$	3
$2 \leqslant x < 4$	24
$4 \leqslant x < 6$	60
$6 \leqslant x < 8$	8
$8 \leqslant x < 10$	3
$10 \leqslant x < 12$	1
$12 \leqslant x < 14$	1

7

Height, h cm	Number of plants
$5 \leqslant h < 7$	8
$7 \leqslant h < 9$	15
$9 \leqslant h < 11$	12
$11 \leqslant h < 13$	5

The table shows the heights of 40 plants.

Number of plants

Height of plants, h cm

a   Draw a frequency diagram.

b   Calculate an estimate of the mean height of these 40 plants.

8   The grouped frequency table shows the speeds of cars measured by a police speed trap.

a   Calculate an estimate of the mean of this frequency table.

It was later found that the trap was recording a speed 3 miles per hour lower than it should have been.

Speed (miles per hour)	Frequency
$25 \leqslant x < 30$	65
$30 \leqslant x < 35$	17
$35 \leqslant x < 40$	12
$40 \leqslant x < 45$	5

b   Estimate the mean actual speed of the cars represented by the frequency table.

9 The amount of rain (measured in millimetres) was recorded for 60 days.

The grouped frequency table shows the results.

a Calculate an estimate of the mean rainfall per day.

b Give a reason why the estimate might be higher than the actual mean.

c Suggest another method for obtaining a more reliable average.

Rain (mm)	Frequency
$0 \leqslant x < 4$	41
$4 \leqslant x < 8$	6
$8 \leqslant x < 12$	7
$12 \leqslant x < 16$	3
$16 \leqslant x < 20$	2
$20 \leqslant x < 24$	0
$24 \leqslant x < 28$	0
$28 \leqslant x < 32$	0
$32 \leqslant x < 36$	1

Graphs

39.1 Linear graphs

CAN YOU REMEMBER

- How to substitute values into an expression or a formula?
- How to use a table of values to draw a linear graph?
- How to draw and identify straight lines with equations like $x = 2$, $y = -3$, $y = x$ and $y = -x$?

IN THIS SECTION YOU WILL

- Learn the meaning of the term 'linear function'.
- Increase skills in drawing the graphs of linear functions.
- Use graphs to solve linear *equations.*
- Learn the meaning of the term 'gradient' and work out the gradients of simple linear graphs.

In algebra a function is a special formula that connects values of **one** letter symbol with values of **one** other letter symbol.

For example $y = x + 2$, $y = 2x$, $x + 2y = 3$ and $y = x^2 + 2x$ are all functions.

Functions can be shown on a graph. Functions that give a straight-line graph are called *linear functions.* Linear functions involve only an x term and a y term and possibly a number term. They do not include squares, cubes or other powers.

The *gradient* measures the slope of a line.

It can be worked out from the formula

$$\text{Gradient} = \frac{\text{distance up}}{\text{distance along}}$$

For example

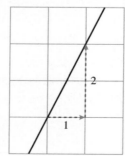

$$\text{Gradient} = \frac{2}{1}$$

$$= 2$$

Example 1

a   Draw the graph of $y = 3x - 1$ for values of x from -1 to 3
b   Find the gradient of the graph.

Solution 1

a   **Step 1:**   Choose three values of x from -1 to 3 (if possible include $x = 0$).
$x = 0$, $x = 1$ and $x = 2$

Step 2:   Substitute these values of x into $y = 3x - 1$
and obtain the corresponding values of y.

x	0	1	2
y	-1	2	5

When $x = 0$, $y = 3 \times 0 - 1 = 0 - 1 = -1$
When $x = 1$, $y = 3 \times 1 - 1 = 3 - 1 = 2$
When $x = 2$, $y = 3 \times 2 - 1 = 6 - 1 = 5$

Write the pairs of values of x and y as coordinates.

So the points with coordinates $(0, -1)$, $(1, 2)$ and
$(2, 5)$ lie on the graph of $y = 3x - 1$

Step 3:   Plot the coordinates on the grid and
draw a straight line through them.

Check   Only two points are needed to draw a
straight line. The third point acts as a check.

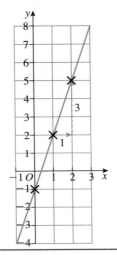

b   From the graph,   gradient $= \dfrac{\text{distance up}}{\text{distance along}} = \dfrac{3}{1} = 3$

To draw the graph of a linear function written in the form $2x + y = 8$, find coordinates on
the x-axis and the y-axis by substituting the values $y = 0$ and $x = 0$ into the function.

Example 2

Draw the graph of $2x + y = 8$ from $x = 0$ to $x = 5$

Solution 2

Find coordinates of points on $2x + y = 8$ at $x = 0$ and at $y = 0$

When $x = 0$ $2 \times 0 + y = 8$ $y = 8$
When $y = 0$ $2x + 0 = 8$ $x = 4$

x	0	4
y	8	0

So the points with coordinates $(0, 8)$
and $(4, 0)$ lie on the graph of $2x + y = 8$

Check   Choose a point on the line, say $(3, 2)$.
Substitute the x-coordinate and y-coordinate
into $2x + y$ and check that it gives the value 8
$2 \times 3 + 2 = 6 + 2 = 8$ ✓

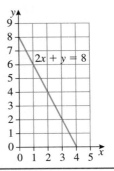

Exercise A

1 a Draw and label a grid with the x-axis from -4 to 4 and the y-axis from -10 to 10
  b Find the coordinates of points that lie on the graph of $y = x + 5$ at $x = -2$,
    $x = 0$ and $x = 2$
  c On the grid draw and label the graph of $y = x + 5$
  d Repeat parts **b** and **c** for the graphs of:
    i $y = x + 3$　　　　**ii** $y = x + 1$　　　　**iii** $y = x - 1$
    iv $y = x - 3$　　　　**v** $y = x - 5$
  e Work out the gradient of each graph drawn in this question. What do you notice?

2 a Draw and label a grid with the x-axis from -3 to 3 and the y-axis from -9 to 9
  b Find the coordinates of points that lie on the graph of $y = 3x$ at $x = -2$,
    $x = 0$ and $x = 2$
  c On the grid draw and label the graph of $y = 3x$
  d Repeat parts **b** and **c** for the graph
  e Work out the gradients of the graphs of $y = 3x$ and $y = 4x$.
  f On a new copy of the grid, draw the graphs of
    i $y = 3x$　　　　**ii** $y = -4x$　　　　　　　　What do you notice?

3 a Draw and label a grid with the x-axis from -3 to 3 and the y-axis from -8 to 10
  b Find the coordinates of points that lie on the graph of $y = 2x + 5$ at $x = -2$,
    $x = 0$ and $x = 2$
  c On the grid draw and label the graph of $y = 2x + 5$
  d Repeat parts **b** and **c** for the graphs of:
    i $y = 2x + 3$　　**ii** $y = 2x + 1$　　**iii** $y = 2x - 1$　　**iv** $y = 2x - 3$
  e Work out the gradient of each graph drawn in this question. What do you notice?

4 a Draw and label a grid with the x-axis from -3 to 3 and the y-axis from -10 to 10
  b On the grid draw and label the graphs of:
    i $y = 3x + 2$　　　　**ii** $y = 4x + 1$　　　　**iii** $y = 5x - 2$
  c Work out the gradient of each graph in part **b**
  d On a new grid draw the graphs of:
    i $y = 3x - 2x$　　　　**ii** $y = 5 - 3x$　　　　　　What do you notice?

5 a Draw and label a grid with both the x-axis and y-axis from -8 to 8
  b On the grid draw and label the graphs of:
    i $x + y = 8$　　　　**ii** $x + y = 4$　　　　**iii** $x + y = 0$
    iv $x + y = -4$　　　**v** $x + y = -8$

6 In this question use a new grid for each pair of graphs. Draw both the
  x-axis and the y-axis from 0 to 16
    a **i** Find the value of y when $x = 0$ in $x + 3y = 15$ and complete the coordinate
        $(0, ...)$.
      ii Find the value of x when $y = 0$ in $x + 3y = 15$ and complete the coordinate
        $(..., 0)$.
      iii On the grid draw and label the graph of $x + 3y = 15$
      iv Repeat parts **i**, **ii** and **iii** for $3x + y = 15$

b Repeat part **a** for each of these pairs of graphs.

   i $4x + y = 16$ and $x + 4y = 16$ **ii** $3x + 5y = 30$ and $5x + 3y = 30$

   iii $3x + 4y = 24$ and $4x + 3y = 24$ **iv** $2x + 5y = 20$ and $5x + 2y = 20$

7 a Draw and label a grid with the x-axis from -2 to 5 and the y-axis from -11 to 9

  b On the grid draw and label the graph of $y = 3x - 4$ from $x = -2$ to $x = 4$

  c Write down the coordinates of the point where the graph of $y = 3x - 4$ crosses each of these lines.

    i $y = -7$ **ii** $y = x$ **iii** $y = -x$ **iv** $x + y = 2$

8 a Draw and label a grid with both the x-axis and the y-axis from 0 to 8

  b On the grid draw and label the graph of $x + 2y = 6$

  c Write down the coordinates of the point where the graph of $x + 2y = 6$ crosses the line $y = x$.

    Check that the coordinates of this point fit $x + 2y = 6$

9 Graphs **A** to **E** are shown on the grid.
Match each equation to its graph.

  a $y = 6x - 5$ E

  b $y = x$ C

  c $y = 1$ A

  d $y = 5 - 4x$ D

  e $x + y = 1$ B

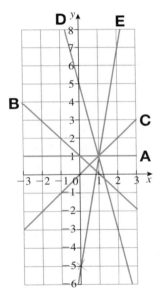

10 a Each of the coordinates **A** to **D** lies on the graph of one of functions **1** to **4**
Match the functions and coordinates.

Function 1	Function 2	Function 3	Function 4
$y = 2x - 5$	$y = 5 - 2x$	$y = 3x - 7$	$y = 7 - 3x$

Coordinate A	Coordinate B	Coordinate C	Coordinate D
$(3, -1)$	$(1, 4)$	$(1, -3)$	$(-1, -10)$

  b Draw graphs of functions **1** and **3** on the same grid.
Find the coordinates of the point where they cross.

  c Draw graphs of functions **2** and **4** on the same grid.
Find the coordinates of the point where they cross.

Linear graphs can be used to solve equations.

For example the solution of the equation
$3x + 4 = 2$ is the x-coordinate of the point
where the line $y = 3x + 4$ crosses the line $y = 2$

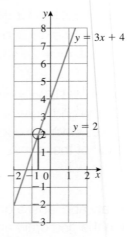

Linear graphs can be drawn to represent situations in real life.

Example 3

The distance, d kilometres, that Ben walks in t minutes is given by $d = \dfrac{t}{10}$.

a   Draw the graph of $d = \dfrac{t}{10}$.

b   Use the graph to find the time it takes Ben to walk 4 km.

t	0	30	60
d	0	3	6

Solution 3

a   When $t = 0$ minutes, $d = 0 \ \div 10 = 0$ km
    When $t = 30$ minutes, $d = 30 \div 10 = 3$ km
    When $t = 60$ minutes, $d = 60 \div 10 = 6$ km
    So the points with coordinates (**0**, **0**), (**30**, **3**)
    and (**60**, **6**) lie on the graph of $d = \dfrac{t}{10}$.

   Check   All three points lie on a straight line. ✓

b   The line passes through the point (**40**, 4).
    Ben takes **40** minutes to walk 4 km.

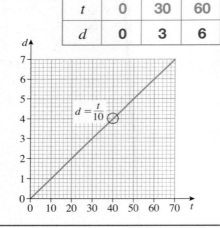

Exercise B

1   a   Match each graph with its gradient. The first one has been done for you.

Graph	Gradient
$y = 2x + 3$	
$y = 3x - 4$	1
$y = 5x + 2$	2
$y = 2x - 5$	3
$y = x + 4$	4
$y = 3x + 5$	5
$y = 4x + 1$	

   b   Which of the graphs in **a** are parallel?

2 **a** Draw and label a grid with the x-axis from -3 to 3 and the y-axis from -2 to 12

   b On the grid draw and label the graphs:

      i $y = 2x + 6$ **ii** $y = 2x + 2$ **iii** $y + 2x = 8$ **iv** $y + 2x = 4$

   c Write down the coordinates of the points where:

      i the graph of $y = 2x + 6$ crosses the graph of $y + 2x = 8$

      ii the graph of $y = 2x + 4$ crosses the graph of $y + 2x = 2$

3 The diagram shows the graph of $y = 4x + 1$

Copy the diagram.

Use the diagram to solve the equations below.

   a $4x + 1 = 5$

   b $4x + 1 = -2$

Show your method.

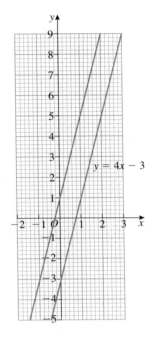

4 **a** Draw and label a grid with the x-axis from -2 to 3 and the y-axis from -9 to 8

   b On the grid draw and label the graph of $y = 5x - 3$

   c Use your graph to solve the following equations.

      i $5x - 3 = -8$ **ii** $5x - 3 = 7$

Show your method.

5 **a** Draw and label a grid with the x-axis from -4 to 3 and the y-axis from -3 to 13

   b On the grid draw and label the graph of $y = 2x + 6$

   c Use your graph to solve the following equations.

      i $2x + 6 = 9$ **ii** $2x + 6 = -1$

6 The points $A(2, 1)$, $B(2, 5)$, $C(4, 3)$, $D(4, 5)$ and $E(4, 7)$ are shown on the grid.

Find which of the points lie on the following lines

   a $x = 2$

   b $y = 5$

   c $x + y = 7$

   d $y = x - 1$

   e $y = 2x - 5$

   f $y = 3x - 5$

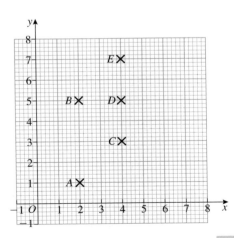

7 The points on the grid show John's attempt
at drawing the line $y = 5 - 3x$
   a How does John know he has made a mistake?
   b Which point is wrong? Explain your answer.
   c Draw the correct graph and use it to solve the
   equation $5 - 3x = 8$

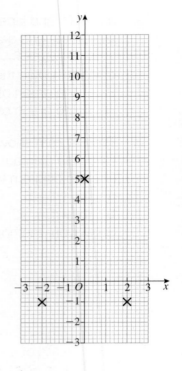

8 Use a graphical method to solve each of
these equations.
   a $5x - 2 = 4$
   b $2x + 3 = -2$

9 To convert the mark in a test, m, to a percentage, p,
a teacher uses the graph of $p = 5m$.
   a Copy these axes and extend the vertical
   axis to 100. Draw the graph
   of $p = 5m$ from $m = 0$ to 20

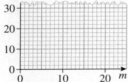

   b Bill scored 12 marks. Use the graph to find his percentage.
   c Betty's percentage is 85%. What mark did Betty score in the test?

10 The time it takes to cook a joint of meat is given by $T = 30W + 20$
T is the time in minutes. W is the weight in pounds.

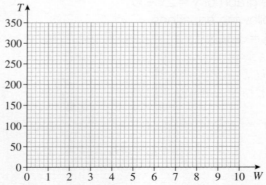

   a On a copy of the grid, draw the graph of $T = 30W + 20$
   b A joint of meat weighs 4 pounds.
   Use the graph to find how long it takes to cook this joint.
   c To cook a joint of meat it takes 1 hour 20 minutes.
   Use the graph to find the weight of this joint.

39.2 Quadratic graphs

Quadratic functions have an x^2 term. They can also have an x term and/or a number term. For example $y = x^2 - 1$, $y = x^2 + 5x$ and $y = x^2 + 3x - 5$ are quadratic functions.

The graph of a quadratic function has:
- a smooth U-shaped curve
- a vertical line of symmetry
- a maximum or a minimum point.

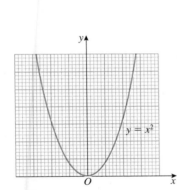
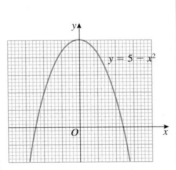
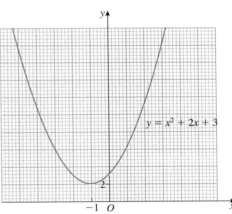

vertical line of symmetry is the y-axis minimum point is at (0, 0) U-shape

vertical line of symmetry is the y-axis maximum point is at (0, 5) $-x^2$ gives an inverted U-shape

vertical line of symmetry is the line $x = -1$ minimum point is at (−1, 2) U-shape

A quadratic curve may touch the x-axis, cross it twice or lie completely above or below it.

Example 1

a Complete the table and draw the graph of $y = 3 - x^2$.

x	−3	−2	−1	0	1	2	3
y			2	3	2	−1	−6

b Write down the coordinates of the maximum point on the graph.

Solution 1

Step 1: Complete the table of values.

a When $x = -3$ $y = 3 - (-3)^2 = 3 - 9 = -6$

When $x = -2$ $y = 3 - (-2)^2 = 3 - 4 = -1$

x	-3	-2	-1	0	1	2	3
y	-6	-1	2	3	2	-1	-6

Step 2: Write a list of coordinates from the table.

$(-3, -6), (-2, -1), (-1, 2), (0, 3), (1, 2), (2, -1) (3, -6)$

Step 3: Plot the points on a grid and join them with a smooth curve.

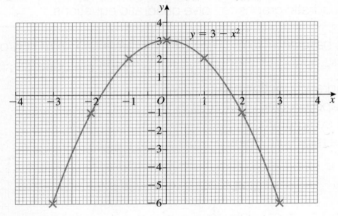

Check Maximum point ✓

Vertical line of symmetry ✓

Inverted smooth U-shaped curve ✓

b The maximum point has coordinates (0, 3)

Exercise A

1 Draw all the graphs in this question on a grid with the x-axis from -4 to 4 and the y-axis from -10 to 14

    a Complete the table of values for $y = x^2 - 3$

x	-3	-2	-1	0	1	2	3
y							

    b On the grid draw and label the graph of $y = x^2 - 3$ from $x = -3$ to 3

    c Repeat parts **a** and **b** for:

      i $y = x^2 + 4$

      ii $y = x^2 - 9$

      iii $y = x^2 + 2$

      iv $y = x^2 - 6$

    d At what point does the graph of $y = x^2 + 50$ cross the x-axis?

2 Draw all the graphs in this question on a grid with the x-axis from -4 to 4 and the y-axis from -30 to 30
Use a scale on the x-axis of 2 cm to 1 unit and a scale on the y-axis of 1 cm to 5 units.
  a Complete the table of values for $y = 2x^2$.

x	-3	-2	-1	0	1	2	3
y							

  b On the grid draw and label the graph of $y = 2x^2$ from $x = -3$ to 3
  c Repeat parts **a** and **b** for:
    i $y = x^2$ **ii** $y = -x^2$ **iii** $y = -2x^2$ **iv** $y = 3x^2$ **v** $y = -3x^2$

3 Draw all the graphs in this question on a grid with the x-axis from -4 to 4 and the y-axis from -15 to 10
  a Complete the table of values for $y = 5 - x^2$.

x	-3	-2	-1	0	1	2	3
y							

  b On the grid draw and label the graph of $y = 5 - x^2$ from $x = -3$ to 3
  c Repeat parts **a** and **b** for:
    i $y = 8 - x^2$ **ii** $y = -2 - x^2$
    iii $y = 1 - x^2$ **iv** $y = -5 - x^2$
  d At what point does the graph of $y = 50 - x^2$ cross the x-axis?

4 a Complete the table of values for $y = x^2 - x + 3$

x	-2	-1	0	1	2	3
y						

  b Draw the graph of $y = x^2 - x + 3$ from $x = -2$ to 3

5 a Complete the table of values for $y = x^2 - 2x - 4$

x	-2	-1	0	1	2	3	4
y							

  b Draw the graph of $y = x^2 - 2x - 4$ from $x = -2$ to 4
  c Write down the coordinates of the points where the graph of $y = x^2 - 2x - 4$ crosses the x-axis.

6 a Complete the table and draw the graph of $y = x^2 + 3x - 3$

x	-5	-4	-3	-2	-1	0	1	2
y								

  b On the same grid draw the line $y = 2x + 3$
  c Write down the coordinates of the points where the line $y = 2x + 3$ crosses the curve $y = x^2 + 3x - 3$

7 Make a table of values and draw a graph using a suitable grid for each of the following quadratic functions.

   a $y = 2x^2 - 5$ from $x = -3$ to 3

   b $y = x^2 + x - 3$ from $x = -4$ to 3

   c $y = x^2 - 4x + 2$ from $x = -1$ to 5

   d $y = x^2 + 4x - 1$ from $x = -5$ to 1

8 Match each graph to a function.

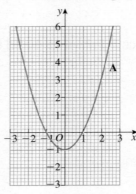 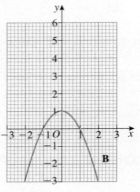 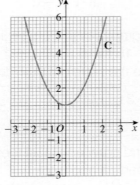 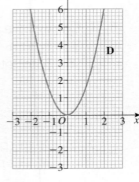

   a $y = x^2 + 1$ **b** $y = x^2 + x$ **c** $y = 1 - x^2$ **d** $y = x^2 - 1$

9 a Complete the table for $y = x^2 - 4x - 3$

x	−2	−1	0	1	2	3	4	5	6
y									

   b Complete the table for $y = 9 - x^2$

x	−4	−3	−2	−1	0	1	2	3	4
y									

   c Draw a grid with the x-axis from −5 to 7 and the y-axis from −8 to 10. Draw the graphs of $y = x^2 - 4x - 3$ and $y = 9 - x^2$ on the grid.

   d Write down the coordinates of the points where the graph of $y = 9 - x^2$ crosses the graph of $y = x^2 - 4x - 3$

10 a Make a table of values for the following quadratic functions.

      i $y = x^2 + x - 7$ for $x = -4$ to 3   **ii** $y = 8 - x^2$ for $x = -4$ to 4

   b On a grid with the x-axis going from −4 to 5 and the y-axis going from −9 to 14, draw the graphs of $y = x^2 + x - 7$ and $y = 8 - x^2$.

   c Write down the coordinates of the points where the graph of $y = x^2 + x - 7$ crosses the graph of $y = 8 - x^2$.

Using graphs to solve quadratic equations

A quadratic equation is normally written x^2 term $\pm$ x term $\pm$ number $= 0$

For example $x^2 - 5x - 4 = 0$

$(x + 2)(x + 5) = 0$ is also a quadratic equation.

Expanding, $(x + 2)(x + 5)$

$\qquad = x^2 + 2x + 5x + 10$

$\qquad = x^2 + 7x + 10$

$\times$	x	5
x	x^2	$5x$
2	$2x$	10

So the equation $(x + 2)(x + 5) = 0$ can be written $x^2 + 7x + 10 = 0$

Quadratic graphs can be used to solve quadratic equations.

Example 2

The graph of $y = x^2 + 3x - 3$ for values of x from -5 to 2 is shown on the grid.

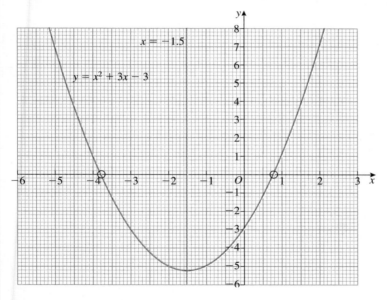

Use the graph to find the solutions of the equation $x^2 + 3x - 3 = 0$

Solution 2

To solve the equation $x^2 + 3x - 3 = 0$, find the x-coordinates of the points where the graph of $y = x^2 + 3x + 3$ crosses the line $y = 0$ (the x-axis).

The graph of $y = x^2 + 3x - 3$ crosses the line $y = 0$ (the x-axis) at the points $(-\mathbf{3.8}, 0)$ and $(\mathbf{0.8}, 0)$.

The solutions of the quadratic equation $x^2 + 3x - 3 = 0$ are $x = -\mathbf{3.8}$ and $x = \mathbf{0.8}$

Example 3

a   Complete the table and draw the graph of $y = (x - 2)(x + 1)$.

x	-3	-2	-1	0	1	2	3	4
y	10	4		-2		0	4	10

b   Use your graph to solve the equation $(x - 2)(x + 1) = 0$

Solution 3

a   When $x = -1$
    $y = (-1 - 2)(-1 + 1) = -3 \times 0 = 0$
    When $x = 1$
    $y = (1 - 2)(1 + 1) = -1 \times 2 = -2$

x	-3	-2	-1	0	1	2	3	4
y	10	4	0	-2	-2	0	4	10

b   The graph of $y = (x - 2)(x + 1)$ crosses
    the line $y = 0$ (the x-axis) at the points
    (**−1**, 0) and (**2**, 0)
    The solutions of the quadratic equation
    $(x - 2)(x + 1) = 0$ are $x = $ **−1** and $x = $ **2**

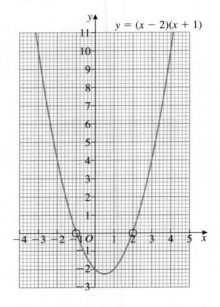

Exercise B

1   The graph of
    $y = x^2 + x - 2$ for
    values of x from -4
    to 3 is shown on
    the grid.
    Explain how the
    graph shows that
    the solutions of the
    equation
    $x^2 + x - 2 = 0$ are
    $x = -2$ and $x = 1$

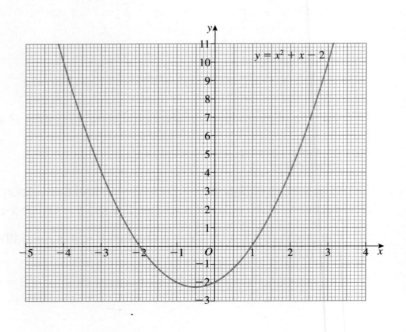

2 The diagrams show the graphs of $y = x^2 + 3$, $y = x^2 + 2x + 1$ and $y = x^2 - 3$

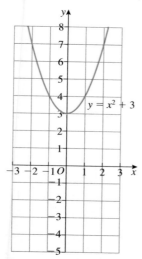 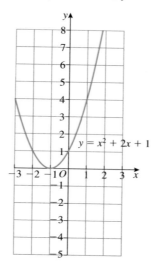 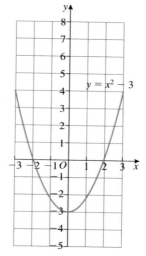

Are the following statements true or false? Use the graphs to explain each answer.

a The equation $x^2 + 3 = 0$ has two solutions.

b The equation $x^2 + 2x + 1 = 0$ has only one solution.

c The equation $x^2 - 3 = 0$ has two solutions.

d The minimum point of the graph of $y = x^2 + 2x + 1$ lies on the y-axis.

e The graph of $y = x^2 + 3$ has a maximum point at $(0, 3)$.

3 **a** Complete the table for values of $y = x^2 + 3x + 1$

x	-5	-4	-3	-2	-1	0	1	2
y								

b Draw the graph of $y = x^2 + 3x + 1$ for values of x from -5 to 2

c Use your graph to solve the equation $x^2 + 3x + 1 = 0$

4 Here is the graph of $y = x^2 - 6x + 3$

a Write down the coordinates of the minimum point on the graph.

b Use the graph to solve the equation $x^2 - 6x + 3 = 0$

Explain how you obtained your answer.

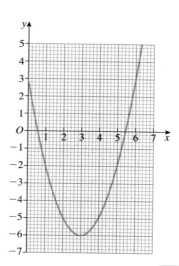

5 **a** Complete the table for $y = 15 - 2x^2$.

x	-3	-2	-1	0	1	2	3
y							

b Draw the graph of $y = 15 - 2x^2$ for values of x from -3 to 3

c Use the graph to solve the equation $15 - 2x^2 = 0$

6 **a** Complete the table and draw the graph of $y = (x - 4)(x - 1)$.

x	-1	0	1	2	3	4	5	6
y								

b Find the coordinates of the point where the graph of $y = (x - 4)(x - 1)$ crosses its line of symmetry.

c Use the graph to solve the equation $(x - 4)(x - 1) = 0$

7 **a** Complete the table and draw the graph for $y = (x - 3)(x + 2)$.

x	-4	-3	-2	-1	0	1	2	3	4	5
y										

b Use your graph to solve the equation $(x - 3)(x + 2) = 0$

8 Amy is trying to draw the graph of $y = x^2 - 3x - 2$
Here is her work.

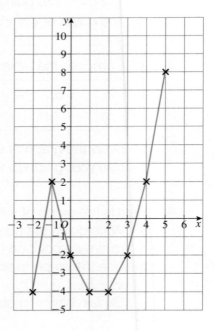

x	-2	-1	0	1	2	3	4	5
y	-4	2	-2	-4	-4	-2	2	8

Amy's teacher says she has made two mistakes.
a What mistakes has Amy made?
b Correct Amy's mistakes and draw the correct graph of $y = x^2 - 3x - 2$
c Use the graph to solve the equation $x^2 - 3x - 2 = 0$

9 **a** Complete the table for $y = 4x - x^2$.

x	-1	0	1	2	3	4	5
y							

b On a suitable grid draw the graph of $y = 4x - x^2$ from $x = -1$ to 5

c Use your graph to solve the equation $4x - x^2 = 0$

10 a Complete the table for $y = (x + 1)(3 - x)$.

x	-2	-1	0	1	2	3	4
y							

  b On a suitable grid draw the graph of $y = (x + 1)(3 - x)$ from $x = -2$ to 4

  c Use your graph to solve the equation $(x + 1)(3 - x) = 0$

Chapter summary

- In algebra a function is a special formula that connects values of **one** letter symbol with values of **one** other letter symbol.

- Functions that give a straight-line graph are called *linear functions*. Linear functions involve only an x term and a y term and possibly a number term. They do not include squares, cubes or other powers.

- To draw the graph of a linear function:

  Step 1 Choose three values of x that span the grid for the graph.

  Step 2 Substitute these values of x into the function and work out the values of y. This can be done using a table of values.
  Write the values of x and y as coordinates (x, y).

  Step 3 Plot the coordinates on the grid and draw a straight line through them.
  Check that the three points lie on a straight line.

- To draw the graph of a linear function written in the form $2x + y = 8$, find coordinates on the x-axis and the y-axis by substituting the values $y = 0$ and $x = 0$ into the function.

- Linear graphs can be used to solve equations. For example, the solution of the equation $3x + 4 = 2$ is the x-coordinate of the point where the line $y = 3x + 4$ crosses the line $y = 2$

- Linear graphs can be drawn to represent situations in real life.

- Quadratic functions have an x^2 term. They can also have an x term and/or a number term. For example $y = x^2 - 1$ and $y = x^2 + 3x - 5$ are quadratic functions.

- The graph of a quadratic function has:
  - a smooth U-shaped curve
  - a vertical line of symmetry
  - a maximum or minimum point.

- To draw the graph of a quadratic function using a table of values:

  Step 1 Complete the table of values of x and y.

  Step 2 Write a list of coordinates from the table.

  Step 3 Plot the points on a grid and join them with a smooth curve.

  Check that the graph:
  - has a maximum or minimum point
  - has a vertical line of symmetry
  - is a smooth U-shaped curve (inverted if the function includes $-x^2$).

Quadratic graphs can be used to solve quadratic equations.
For example, the solutions of the equation $x^2 + 2x - 1 = 0$ are the x-coordinates of the points where the line $y = x^2 + 2x - 1$ crosses the line $y = 0$ (the x-axis).

Chapter review

1 **a** On a copy of the grid, draw the graph of
$y = x - 1$
   b The line $y = -4$ crosses the line $y = x - 1$
at the point P.
What are the coordinates of P?

2 **a** On a copy of the grid from question **1**, draw
and label the lines $y = -1$ and $y = 2x + 3$
   b Write down the coordinates of the point
where the lines $y = -1$ and
$y = 2x + 3$ cross.

3 **a** On a copy of the grid from question **1**, draw
the graph of $y = 3x - 2$ for values of x from
-2 to 3
   b The line $y = -5$ crosses $y = 3x - 2$ at P. Write
down the coordinates of P.
   c Use the graph to solve the equation $3x - 2 = -8$

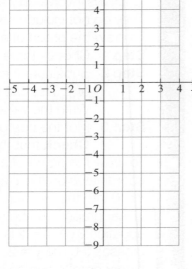

4 **a** Copy this grid and draw the graph
of $x + y = 6$
   b P is a point on the line $x + y = 6$
Peter says, 'The x-coordinate of P is one
less than the y-coordinate of P.'
Write down the coordinates of P.

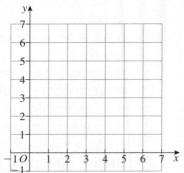

5 The line $y = 3x - 1$ goes through
the point $P(-5, a)$.
What is the value of a?

6 **a** Copy the grid from question **4**. Draw the graph of $2x + 5y = 10$
   b Show that the point $(-5, 4)$ lies on this line.

7 **a** Show that the graphs of $y = x + 2$ and $y = 6 - x$ cross at the point $(2, 4)$.
   b Find the coordinates of the point where the graphs of $y = 3x - 4$ and $y = -x$ cross.

8 An electrician charges £C for a repair depending on t, the time taken in minutes, according to the relationship $C = 0.6t + 40$

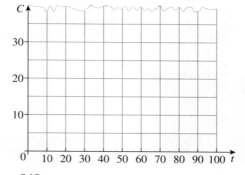

a Copy the grid. Make the C-axis go up to 100. Draw the graph of
$C = 0.6t + 40$

b Use the graph to find:

i how much the electrician charges for a repair lasting 20 minutes

ii the length of a repair costing £76

c Explain why a repair cannot cost less than £40

9 a Complete the table of values for $y = x^2 - 4$

x	−3	−2	−1	0	1	2	3
y	5	0			−3	0	

b Copy the grid from question **1**. Draw the graph of $y = x^2 - 4$ for values of x from −3 to 3

c Write down the values of x at the point where the line $y = 2$ crosses the graph.

10 a Complete the table of values for $y = x^2 - 2x - 1$

x	−2	−1	0	1	2	3	4
y		2	−1		−1	2	7

b Copy the grid from question **1**. Draw the graph of $y = x^2 - 2x - 1$ for values of x from −2 to 4

c Use the graph to solve the equation $x^2 - 2x - 1 = 0$

11 a Complete the table of values for $y = (2 + x)(3 - x)$.

x	−2	−1	0	1	2	3	4
y		4	6	6	4	0	

b Copy the grid from question **1**. Draw the graph of $y = (2 + x)(3 - x)$ for values of x from −2 to 4

Coordinates and loci

40.1 2D and 3D coordinates

CAN YOU REMEMBER

- How to plot (x, y) coordinates in all four quadrants on a grid?
- The properties of two-dimensional shapes such as rectangles and parallelograms?

IN THIS SECTION YOU WILL

- Use 2D coordinates to draw and complete shapes.
- Find the coordinates of the midpoint of a line.
- Describe points in space using 3D coordinates.

Two-dimensional shapes can be drawn on a grid by plotting the coordinates of the vertices. A missing *vertex* can be found by using the properties of the shape, for example knowing that the sides are of equal length.

Example 1

a On a square grid plot the points $A(3, 2)$, $B(5, 2)$ and $C(5, 6)$.

b Plot the point D such that $ABCD$ is a rectangle.

c Write down the coordinates of point D.

Solution 1

a, b

c The coordinates of D are $(3, 6)$

Example 2

Find the coordinates of the midpoint of AB.

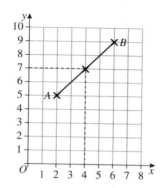

Solution 2

By measuring the line AB or counting the squares, mark the midpoint.
The coordinates of the midpoint are (4, 7).

The midpoint of a line can be found without drawing.
The midpoint of a line joining two points has coordinates
(mean of the two x-coordinates, mean of the two y-coordinates).

Example 3

Find the midpoint of the line AB joining the points $A(2, 5)$ and $B(6, 9)$ without drawing the line.

Solution 3

x-coordinate is the mean of 2 and $6 = \dfrac{2 + 6}{2} = 4$

y-coordinate is the mean of 5 and $9 = \dfrac{5 + 9}{2} = 7$

The midpoint is (4, 7).

A and B are the same points as in Example 2. This method gives the same answer.

Exercise A

For questions **1–3** draw a grid with x and y values from -4 to 8

1 $EFGH$ is a square. The coordinates of E, F and G are (4, 5), (7, 5) and (7, 2).
   a Plot E, F and G on a grid.
   b Plot the point H on the grid to complete the square.
   c Write down the coordinates of H.

2 $ABCD$ is a rectangle.

   $A = (2, -3)$ $B = (-3, -3)$ $C = (-3, 5)$
   a Plot A, B and C on a grid.   **b** Work out the coordinates of D.

3 $PQRS$ is a parallelogram.
   $P = (-2, 3)$ $Q = (3, 3)$ $R = (5, -1)$
   a Plot P, Q and R on a grid.   **b** Work out the coordinates of S.

4 The diagram shows four lines.
Write down the midpoint of:

a *AB*

b *CD*

c *EF*

d *GH*

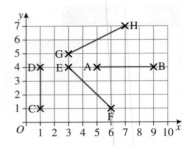

5 *ABCD* is a parallelogram.
Write down the coordinates of the midpoint of:

a *AB*

b *BC*

c *CD*

d *AD*

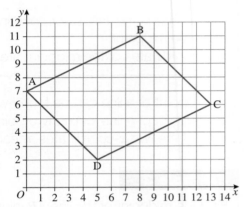

6 Work out the midpoint of each of the following pairs of points:

a *A* (3, 4) and *B* (5, 8)

b *C* (−3, 2) and *D* (1, 6)

c *E* (0, −1) and *F* (5, 3)

d *G* (−2, −6) and *H* (−4, −4)

7 Triangle *ABC* has vertices *A*(−2, 1), *B*(3, 4) and *C*(1, −1).
Work out the coordinates of the midpoint of each side of the triangle.

8 The midpoint of a line *PQ* is (9.5, 3).
P is the point (7, −2).
Work out the coordinates of *Q*.

9 *EFGH* is a rectangle.
E = (−2, 2)   *F* = (1, 2)   *G* = (1, −2)

a Work out the coordinates of H.

b Work out the coordinates of the midpoint of:

i FG   **ii** GH

10 *S* is the point (−5, 1).
The midpoint of the line *ST* is (−1, −2).
Work out the coordinates of *T*.

Three-dimensional coordinates can be used to represent points in space.

The diagram shows a cuboid drawn on a three-dimensional grid with *x*, *y* and *z* axes.

Each vertex has three coordinates (*x*, *y*, *z*) representing the distances along the *x*, *y* and *z* axes.

A has coordinates (4, 0, 0).

E has coordinates (4, 3, 0).

F has coordinates (4, 3, 6).

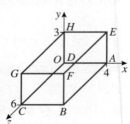

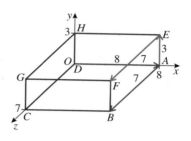

Example 4

The diagram shows a cuboid drawn on a three-dimensional grid.

Point A has coordinates (8, 0, 0).

Point H has coordinates (0, 3, 0).

Point C has coordinates (0, 0, 7).

Write down the 3D coordinates of points B and F.

Solution 4

Point B is 8 units in the x direction, 0 units in the y-direction and 7 units in the z-direction.

The coordinates of B are (8, 0, 7).

Point F is 8 units in the x-direction, 3 units in the y-direction and 7 units in the z-direction.

The coordinates of F are (8, 3, 7).

Exercise B

1 The diagram shows a cuboid drawn on a 3D grid.
A is the point (0, 0, 0).
B is the point (5, 0, 0).
D is the point (0, 0, 10).
E is the point (0, 3, 0).
Write down the 3D coordinates of:
  a C **b** F **c** G **d** H

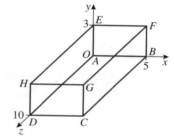

2 The diagram shows a cuboid drawn on a 3D grid.
B is the point (9, 0, 0).
G is the point (9, 3, 8).
Write down the 3D coordinates of:
  a E **b** F **c** H

3 Which of the following 3D coordinates are for vertex G in the diagram?
  a (9, 2, 7)
  b (7, 2, 9)
  c (7, 9, 2)
  d (2, 7, 9)

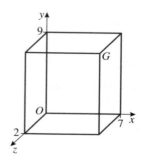

4

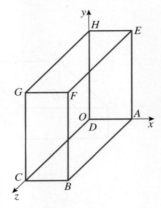

This 3D diagram shows
a cuboid.
F has 3D coordinates
(4, 11, 6).

Write down the coordinates of the other vertices
of the cuboid.

5   The 3D diagram shows a cube.
A is the point (5, 0, 0).
B is the point (5, 0, 3).
Write down the coordinates of:
a   *C*
b   *E*
c   *G*

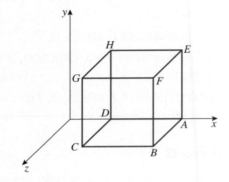

40.2 Constructions and loci

CAN YOU REMEMBER

- How to use a pair of compasses to draw a circle accurately?
- How to construct a triangle using ruler and compasses?
- How to use and draw scale diagrams?

IN THIS SECTION YOU WILL

- Learn how to construct the perpendicular bisector of a straight line.
- Learn how to construct the bisector of an angle.
- Understand the meaning of the words *locus* and *loci*.
- Learn how to draw the locus of points with given rules.

The *perpendicular bisector* of a line *bisects* the line
(divides it into two equal sections) at an angle of 90°

The perpendicular bisector of the line *AB* is shown. All the
points on the perpendicular bisector of *AB* are *equidistant*
from *A* and *B* (an equal distance from *A* and from *B*).

The perpendicular bisector of a line can be constructed accurately using a ruler and
compasses.

Draw a line AB of length 7 cm.
Using ruler and compasses only, construct the perpendicular bisector of AB.

Solution 1

Step 1: Draw line AB accurately.

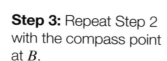

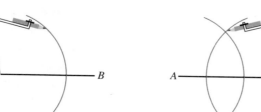

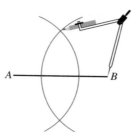

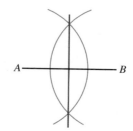

Step 2: Open the compasses to a radius greater than half the length of AB.
Keep the compasses at this setting throughout the construction.
Put the compass point at A and draw an arc through the line AB.

Step 3: Repeat Step 2 with the compass point at B.

Step 4: Join the points of intersection of the two arcs with a straight line. Leave in all the arcs to show how the construction was drawn. This line is the perpendicular bisector of AB.

Other lines can be constructed perpendicular to a given line.

Use ruler and compasses to construct the perpendicular from point P to the line shown.

$\times P$

Solution 2

Step 1: Open the compasses to a radius greater than the distance between point P and the line.

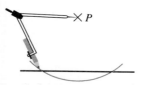

Put the compass point on P and draw an arc cutting the line in two places.

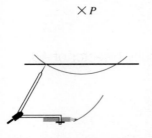

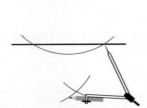

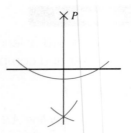

Step 2: Put the compass point at the first point of intersection and draw another arc below the line.

Step 3: Keeping the compasses at the same radius, repeat step 2 from the other point of intersection. Make sure the arcs cross as shown.

Step 4: Join the intersection of these two arcs to point P with a straight line. This line is perpendicular to the original line.

Example 3

Draw a line perpendicular to AB such that angle A is 90°.

Solution 3

The perpendicular line must cut AB at A.

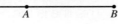

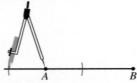

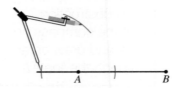

Step 1: Extend the line past point A.

Step 2: Put the compass point on A and draw arcs to intersect the line on either side of A.

Step 3: Open your compasses wider. Put the compass point on the first point of intersection of the line and draw an arc above (or below) the line.

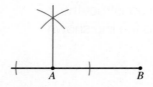

Step 4: Keeping the compasses at the same radius repeat step 3 from the other point of intersection. The two arcs should intersect.

Step 5: Join point A to the point where the arcs intersect. This line is perpendicular to AB and forms a 90° angle at A.

This construction can also be used to draw a right-angled triangle.

An *angle bisector* is a line that bisects an angle.

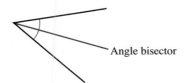

Angle bisector

Any point on the angle bisector is equidistant from the lines that form the angle.

The angle bisector can be constructed accurately using ruler and compasses.

Example 4

Using ruler and compasses only, construct the bisector of angle A.

A

Solution 4

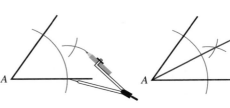

Step 1: Put the point of the compasses on A. Draw an arc to cut both lines.

Step 2: Put the compass point on the intersection of the arc and one line. Draw an arc inside the angle.

Step 3: Repeat Step 2 with compasses on the intersection of the arc and the other line. The two new arcs should intersect.

Step 4: Join the point of intersection of these two arcs to point A. Leave in all the arcs. This line is the angle bisector of angle A.

Exercise A

1 Draw each line, leaving space for the construction. Using ruler and compasses only, construct the perpendicular bisector of each line.

a 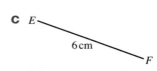 A————B
5 cm

b C
4 cm
D

c E——— 6 cm ———F

d G———H
3 cm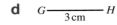

2   Copy the following diagrams.
Using a ruler and compasses only, construct the angle bisector.

a   Angle $ABC = 60°$
Check that each new angle
measures 30°

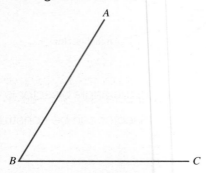

b   Angle $DEF = 40°$

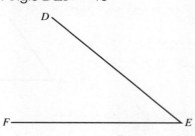

Check that each new angle
measures 20°

c   Angle $LMN = 130°$

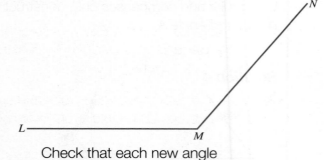

Check that each new angle
measures 65°

d   Angle $PQR = 150°$

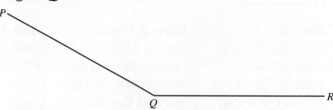

Check that each new angle measures 75°.

3   Copy the following diagrams.
Using a ruler and compasses only, construct the perpendicular from the point to the line.

a

b

4   Draw a line AB 8 cm long. Using ruler and compasses only, construct the perpendicular bisector of AB.
Use compasses to mark a point 10 cm from A on the perpendicular bisector.

5 Use a protractor to draw an angle of 70°. Using ruler and compasses only, construct the bisector of the angle.
Mark the point on the bisector which is 3 cm from the angle.

6 Using ruler and compasses only:
   a construct an equilateral triangle ABC of side 7 cm
   b construct the bisector of angle A. Draw it long enough to intersect BC
   c measure and write down the distance from angle A to the intersection with BC.

7 Using ruler and compasses only:
   a construct triangle PQR with $PQ = 8$ cm, $QR = 7$ cm and $PR = 4.5$ cm
   b construct the perpendicular bisector of QR
   c mark the point, S, where the perpendicular bisector cuts PQ
   d measure and write down the distance from the midpoint of QR to S.

8 The diagram shows a sketch of a right-angled triangle. Using ruler and compasses only, construct an accurate drawing of the triangle.

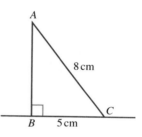

9 Draw a large triangle. Using ruler and compasses only, construct the perpendicular bisectors of each side of your triangle.
These bisectors should meet at a point. Mark the point Y.

A *locus* (plural *loci*) is the path of a point which moves according to a rule.

The locus of a point which moves so that it is always 1 cm away from a fixed point C is a circle of radius 2 cm with centre C.

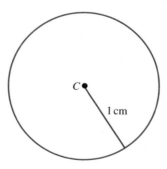

Every point on the path of the circle is 1 cm from C.

The locus of all the points that are equidistant from two fixed points is the perpendicular bisector of the line joining the points.

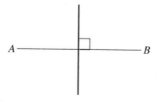

Every point on the perpendicular bisector is equidistant from A and B.

The locus of all the points that are equidistant from two straight lines that meet at an angle is the angle bisector.

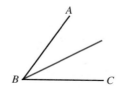

Every point on the angle bisector is equidistant from AB and BC.

Example 5

The diagram shows a triangle ABC.
Draw the triangle accurately.
Draw the locus of points that are 3 cm from B.
Shade the region inside the triangle which is
less than 3 cm from B.

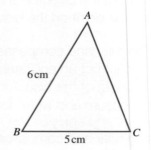

Solution 5

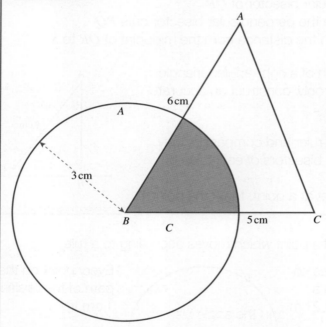

The locus of points that are 3 cm
from B is a circle, centre B and
radius 3 cm.
The shaded region shows the area
within the circle which is less than
3 cm from B.

Example 6

Draw the locus of points that are exactly 2 cm from the line ST.

Solution 6

The locus has two straight edges and two semicircular ends. All points on the locus
are 2 cm from the line ST.

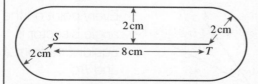

Example 7

The diagram shows a
triangular cornfield.

A scarecrow stands in the field.
It is equidistant from BC and
AC and 6 m from A.

Using ruler and compasses
find the position of the
scarecrow.

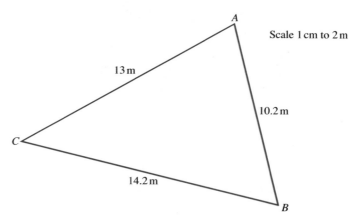

Scale 1 cm to 2 m

13 m

10.2 m

14.2 m

Solution 7

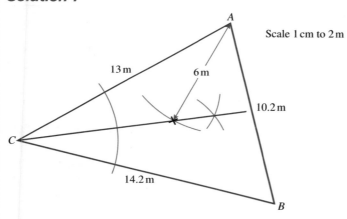

Scale 1 cm to 2 m

All points equidistant from BC
and AC lie on the angle
bisector of C.

The points 6 m from A lie on a
circle with centre A and radius
6 m.

6 m is represented by 3 cm on
the diagram.

Draw the arc of the circle of
radius 3 cm and centre A
which is inside the triangle.

The scarecrow stands where the arc and the angle bisector intersect (marked
with a cross).

Exercise B

1 A, B and C are three points on a straight line.

Draw the locus of points that are:
a 3 cm from A **b** 4.5 cm from B **c** 2 cm from C

2 Draw a line AB 6 cm long.
Construct the locus of points that are exactly 3 cm from AB.

3 Draw a rectangle with length 4 cm and width 3 cm.
Draw the locus of points outside the rectangle that are 3 cm from the rectangle.

4 The diagram shows an equilateral triangle of side 9 cm.
   a   i Sketch the triangle.
      ii Sketch the locus of points outside the triangle that
         are 1 cm from the triangle.
   b   Draw the equilateral triangle using a ruler and protractor.
      (Remember the angles of an equilateral triangle = 60°)
      Using ruler and compasses only, show all the points inside
      the triangle that are more than 4 cm from each vertex.

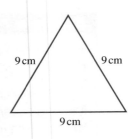

5 The diagram shows a rectangle *PQRS*.
   Copy the diagram. Using ruler and compasses only, construct
   the locus of points inside the rectangle that are equidistant from
   RQ and *RS*.

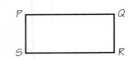

6 A dog is tied to the corner of a shed by a rope of
   length 4 m.
   Copy the diagram and construct the locus of points that
   show the boundary of where the dog can go.

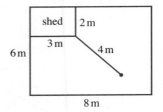

7 A radio transmitter is designed to give good reception in an area greater than 50 km
   but less than 150 km from the transmitter.
   Using a scale of 1 cm to 25 km, draw a scale diagram to show the area within
   which there is good reception.

8 The diagram shows a sketch of a field.
   a   Make a scale drawing of the field using a scale of
      1 cm to 50 m.
   b   A well is 200m from corner *A* and 325m from corner *B*.
      Mark the position of the well on the scale drawing.

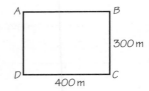

9 Two boats *X* and *Y* are 30 km apart. *Y* is due east of *X*.
   a   Use a scale of 1 cm to 5 km to make a scale drawing
      showing the position of the two boats.
   b   Shade the region which is less than 15 km from boat *X* and less than 25 km
      from boat *Y*.

10 A rectangular plot of land *PQRS* measures 10 m by 7 m.
   A gold coin is buried on the plot of land. The coin is
   equidistant from *PQ* and *QR* and equidistant from *R* and *S*.
   a   Using a scale of 1 cm to 1 m draw the plot of land.
   b   Using ruler and compasses only, find and mark the
      position of the gold coin.

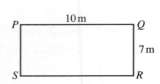

Chapter summary

- The midpoint of a line joining two points has coordinates (mean of the two x-coordinates, mean of the two y-coordinates).
- Three-dimensional coordinates can be used to represent points in space. For example, F is the point (6, 5, 8).

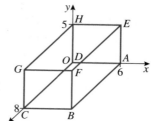

- The *perpendicular bisector* of a line bisects the line at an angle of 90°
- An *angle bisector* is a line that bisects an angle.

Diagram of angle bisector

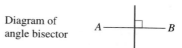

- A *locus* (plural *loci*) is the path of a point which moves according to a rule.
- The locus of all the points that are equidistant from two fixed points is the perpendicular bisector of the line joining the two points.
- The locus of all the points that are equidistant from two straight lines that form an angle is the angle bisector.

Chapter review

1 A rectangle *ABCD* has vertices at A (−2, 6) B (−2, 1) and C (4, 1).
 a Plot these points on a grid.
 b Work out the coordinates of D.

2 The diagram shows the line *PQ* which joins points P (−1, −3) and Q (5, 2).
Find the coordinates of the midpoint of *PQ*.

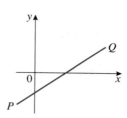

3 Draw a line ST 10 cm long.
 a Use ruler and compasses to construct the perpendicular bisector of *ST*. You **must** show clearly all your construction arcs.
 b Mark a point on the perpendicular bisector which is 6 cm from *T*.

4 The diagram shows a triangle *ABC*.

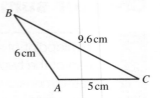

   a   On a copy of the diagram draw accurately the locus of points that are 3 cm from *C*.

   b   Shade the region inside the triangle which is more than 3 cm from *C*.

5 Draw an angle of 110°. Label it angle *A*.

Use ruler and compasses to construct the bisector of the angle *A*.

You **must** show clearly all your construction arcs.

6 The diagram shows a cuboid drawn on a 3D grid.

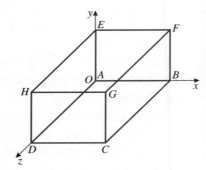

A is the point (0, 0, 0).

B is the point (7, 0, 0).

E is the point (0, 5, 0).

D is the point (0, 0, 9).

Write down the 3D coordinates of:

   a   *C*   **b**   *F*

   c   *G*   **d**   *H*

7 *A* is the point (2, 9).

The midpoint of the line *AC* is the point *B* with coordinates (7, 13).

Work out the coordinates of *C*.

8 Draw a line *AB* 6 cm long. Using a ruler and compasses only, construct a line perpendicular to *AB* which goes through point *B*.

9   **a**   Draw a square of side 4 cm.

     b   Draw the locus of points outside the square that are 2 cm from the square.

10 *ABC* is an equilateral triangle of side 6 cm.

   a   Using ruler and compasses only, construct the triangle.

   b   A point *T* is inside the triangle.

       T is nearer to *AB* than to *AC*.

       T is more than 5 cm from *C*.

       T is more than 3 cm from *B*.

       Shade the region in which *T* could lie.

Index

Published by: Pearson Education Limited, Edinburgh Gate, Harlow, Essex CM20 2JE, England
www.longman.co.uk

First published 2006
ISBN-10: 1-405-81628-7
ISBN-13: 978-1-405-81628-1

Concept design by Mick Harris. Cover design by Juice Creative Ltd. Index by John Holmes.

Typeset by Tech-Set, Gateshead

Printed in the U.K. by CPI

The publisher's policy is to use paper manufactured from sustainable forests.

Live Learning, Live Authoring and Live Player are all trademarks of Live Learning Ltd.

The Publisher wishes to draw attention to the Single-User Licence Agreement below. Please read this agreement carefully before installing and using the CD-ROM.

We are grateful to the following for permission to reproduce photographs:
Alamy Images: pg140 (©Image Source), pg275 (©Action Plus), Pg402 (©FAN travelstock); **Corbis:** pg187 (Royalty-Free); **Education Photos:** pg657 (educationphotos.co.uk/walmsley); **Getty Images:** pg20 (b) (The Image Bank) (Karen Beard), pg138 (The Image Bank) (Serge Kroughlikoff, pg141 (Taxi) (Ian McKinnell), pg430 (Time Life Pictures); **Punchstock Royalty-Free Images:** pg20 (t) (digitalvision), pg442 (digitalvision); **Royalty-Free Images:** pg651 (PhotoDisc Vol.44 – Nature, Wildlife & the Environment 2)

Picture Research by Karen Jones. Figurative illustration by Joanne Kerr.

Every effort has been made to trace the copyright holders and we apologise in advance for any unintentional omissions. We would be pleased to insert the appropriate acknowledgement in any subsequent edition of this publication.

Crown copyright material is reproduced with permission of the Controller of HMSO.